A.K. Colter.
11033-108 Street
Edmonton.
Phone. 21480

~~H.C. White~~
~~7204 105th St.~~
~~Edmonton, Alberta.~~

"Dagmarr" Colter.
"The Fiend"

FUNDAMENTALS OF

Electricity

and

Electromagnetism

By

VERNON ANDREW SUYDAM, Ph.D.

PROFESSOR OF PHYSICS, BELOIT COLLEGE
BELOIT, WISCONSIN

THIRD PRINTING

NEW YORK
D. VAN NOSTRAND COMPANY, Inc.
250 FOURTH AVENUE

First Published June 1940
Reprinted February 1945, August 1946

PRINTED IN U. S. A.

this book from the beginning to the end; the old and the new view-points are compared and contrasted.

The complex-number treatment of alternating current problems is so universally used that it seems very desirable for students to master this method by systematic study rather than to come upon it more or less by chance. To this end, a short chapter is devoted to the algebra of complex numbers and this is followed by a chapter on the use of complex numbers in alternating current circuit calculations and a further chapter on the complex number derivations of alternating current bridge formulae. The author has given this material to his students for many years and has found that they have little difficulty in acquiring a working knowledge of the method.

It is assumed that the student has completed a course in the calculus. Differential equations are used throughout the book, but the methods of solution are developed as occasion arises so that a previous course in differential equations is not required, although, of course, it is an advantage. One idea has been kept in mind throughout the entire development of the text; to lead students by easy progressive stages from the simple to the more complex. Therefore, practically all of the mathematical expressions are introduced and developed from fundamental principles. With few exceptions, formulae are not given without formal proof.

The author has drawn heavily on many previous publications in this field in the preparation of this book. His obligations in this respect are too numerous for individual mention, yet as far as has been possible references to sources are given. The author wishes to take this occasion to acknowledge his indebtedness to those who have aided in the preparation of this book by reading the manuscript and offering constructive criticisms; and to his wife and daughter, Eleanor, for valuable aid in the preparation of the manuscript and in proof-reading.

V.A.S.

BELOIT, WISCONSIN
  April, 1940

CONTENTS

GLOSSARY OF SYMBOLS

ϵ	Dielectric coefficient—Kinetic energy of a gas molecule or electron.
κ	Specific inductive capacity.
Q, q	Electric charge.
σ	Electric surface density—Magnetic surface density—Conductivity—Coefficient of Thomson effect.
E	Electric field intensity.
D	Electric flux density.
V	Electric potential—Magnetic potential—Volume.
U, W	Energy.
e	Electronic charge—Base of Naperian logarithms.
C	Capacitance.
L	Inductance—Moment of force.
R	Resistance.
i	Current density.
I, i	Any electric current.
P	Electric polarization—Power.
η	Electric susceptibility.
α	Molecular polarizability.
m	Magnetic pole strength—mass.
μ	Permeability.
$\mathcal{P}$	Permeance.
$\mathcal{R}$	Reluctance.
ν	Reluctivity.
H	Magnetic field intensity.
B	Magnetic flux density.
$I = \sigma$	Intensity of magnetization (magnetic moment/unit volume)
M	Magnetic moment—Mutual inductance—Magnetomotive force.
k	Magnetic susceptibility—The Boltzmann constant.
I	Moment of inertia.
ρ	Resistivity—Volume density.
$\mathcal{E}, \varepsilon$	Electromotive force or potential difference.

xviii

G, g Conductance.

j $\sqrt{-1}$.

f, ν Frequency.

λ Wavelength.

ω Angular velocity—Solid angle—Ohmic resistance.

Z, z Impedance.

x Reactance.

Y, y Admittance.

g Conductance in complex form.

b Susceptance in complex form.

Φ, ϕ Magnetic Flux.

A Area—Vector quantity in complex numbers.

θ, ϕ Any angle—Phase angle.

θ Phase defect.

c Speed of light.

s Any speed.

v Velocity—Ratio between cgse. and cgsm. units.

X, Y, Z Components of E in x, y, and z directions.

α, β, γ Components of H in x, y, and z directions.

τ Time constant.

Q The Faraday electrolytic constant—Thermoelectric power.

N The Avogadro constant—Number of windings.

emf.   Electromotive force.

mmf.   Magnetomotive force—micromicrofarad.

f.   Farad.

mf.   Microfarad.

ϕ Strength of Magnetic shell—Work function.

π Peltier coefficient.

h Planck's constant.

cgs.   Centimeter-gram-second.

cgse.   Centimeter-gram-second-electrostatic.

cgsm.   Centimeter-gram-second-electromagnetic.

mks.   Meter-kilogram-second.

FUNDAMENTALS OF ELECTRICITY
AND ELECTROMAGNETISM

HISTORICAL INTRODUCTION

WHAT IS ELECTRICITY ?

THE BEGINNINGS OF OUR KNOWLEDGE OF ELECTRICITY are lost in the mists of antiquity. What is known is excellently told by Park Benjamin in his history entitled, "The Intellectual Rise in Electricity." Magnetism was first recognized in connection with the iron ore magnetite (Fe_3O_4) which was widely distributed on the islands in the Aegean sea and along its shores, and in Asia Minor. An electric effect was first observed when amber—a mineralized yellowish resin—if rubbed, attracted light bodies. Thales of Miletus (640–546 B.C.), one of the "seven wise men" of early Greece, is credited with this knowledge, as well as with the knowledge that magnetite or lodestone possesses the property of attracting iron. Because of the association of electric attraction with amber this phenomenon came to be known as the "amber attraction." From the earliest observations down to the middle of the 16th century magnetic and electric attraction were held by the world in general to be of the same nature and consequently the same mystic beliefs were held for both. Cardan (1551 A.D.) drew a clear distinction between them and contrasted their behaviors. With these facts William Gilbert (1600) was familiar. He recognized that magnetite and amber are alike in attractive power, but that they are not so in orientation relative to the earth (verticity), and, therefore, presumably they have not the same kind of primordial fluid, since the field of force which determines the orientation of lodestone is absent in case of amber. In "De Magnete" Gilbert goes to some length to prove that magnetism is different from electricity. Gilbert divided substances into two classes, *electrics* and *non-electrics*, the former possessing the property of amber and the latter neutral so far as this quality is concerned. He invented an instrument which he called a "versorium"—in modern terminology an electroscope—which was a light rod mounted on a pivot so as to turn freely as does a compass needle. With this instrument he tested many substances for the amber effect. Many of Gilbert's experiments resulted in genuine discoveries. However, when he philosophized to account for the differences between magnetic effects and electric effects, his reasoning was as vague and fantastic as was that of the Chinese centuries before. In his own mind though his theories were sufficient for the differences he sought.

Amber was used for ornamental purposes, and was much prized, at a very early period, long before the founding of Rome and Carthage. It was found along the shores of the Baltic sea and was brought to the Mediterranean region by the Phoenicians, the maritime people of the time, or overland by caravans. Amber ornaments and beads have been found in the tombs of Mycenae and at various places throughout Sardinia and ancient Etruria, along the caravan routes from the Baltic to the Mediterranean, and among the ruins of the Lake Dwellers of Europe. The yellow color of amber reminded the imaginative Greeks of virgin gold, and recalled to them the yellow sunshine. All substances having a yellowish color were children of the sun "Elector." Thus in Hellenic speech amber came to be called "electron," and hence the name electricity.

There is no recorded evidence that these early peoples who used amber for ornamental purposes or otherwise were acquainted with its electric properties, yet it may be presumed that they were, since this mysterious substance was woven into their fables, myths, and poems. "Amber is gathered," so ran one fable, "by the maiden guardians of the golden Hesperides as it falls from the poplars into Lake Electrum." Pliny (23 A.D. to 79 A.D.), however, records that the Syrian women called amber "harpaga" or "the clutcher." Amber distaffs were used by the Syrian women in spinning yarn, and they noticed that the yarn would cling to the distaff as would dust or bits of leaves or chaff, hence the name, "the clutcher." Benjamin says that this was probably the first intelligent observation of an electric effect.

For the earliest beliefs as to the nature of this mysterious quality that amber possesses, the "amber attraction," we must look to the religion and mythology of Greece. The Hellenes lived in a world of their own imaginative creation, a world peopled by their own fancy with deities who, they imagined, entered into and controlled every act of their lives. Every phenomenon of nature was likewise controlled by and was the work of some anthropomorphic deity. Earthquakes were the struggles of imprisoned giants against the bonds of higher gods. Zeus, the supreme deity, wept in the rain drops, and the tears of Niobe fell in the snow flakes. The wind was the breath of Aeolus. The waves of the sea were excited by the wrathful stroke of Neptune's (Poseidon) trident. Lightning was the thunderbolt of Zeus. All nature was evidence of the actions of deities, and, naturally, electric and magnetic phenomena were due to the acts of deities.

Living at this time there was a brilliant young man, Thales of Miletus (640 B.C.), one of those "souls born out of time extraordinary prophetic, who are rather related to the system of the world than to their particular age and locality." In Thales's mind was commingled the conceptions of the spirit god of the Egyptians, the anthropomorphic deities of the Greeks, the mists and shadows of the human mind, and the beginnings of philosophy. He for the first time in the history of man insisted on finding the explanation of physical phenomena in the things themselves, and not through the agency of some deity, which was a figment of the imagination. "Thus speculation disengaged itself from theological guidance, the effects of nature became no longer the sport of unseen beings and the causes of all changes were sought in the conditions of the things themselves." Now the natural effect which Thales sought to explain by a theory, physical in that it was connected with the thing itself, and not supernatural, was the attractive power of the lodestone. And thus the mystery of magnetism gave impetus to the first philosophy. Thales's sayings are only legendary, as he left no writings of his own. All that we know of him is through hearsay, since his teachings were recorded several centuries after his time. Aristotle (384–322 B.C.) says of him, "Thales too, as is related, seems to regard the soul as somehow producing motion, for he said that the stone has a soul since it moves iron." Thus Thales discarded supernatural interposition in natural phenomena, and in its place assumed a soul or spirit inherent in the magnet itself whereby it was able to draw unto itself iron or magnetite. Herein he perceived a first principle, common to all nature, a soul in an otherwise lifeless substance. There is some doubt as to the authenticity of this animistic conception of nature which is attributed to Thales. However, most writers on the history of electricity ascribe to Thales the conception of a soul in amber as well as in magnetite. The origin of animism is usually attributed to Pythagoras and Plato. There is but a single reference extant to Thales's amber soul, and that occurs in the "Lives and Opinions of Eminent Philosophers," by Diogenes Laertius, 2nd century A.D. The sentence is: "But Aristotle and Hippias say that he attributed souls also to lifeless things, forming his conceptions from the nature of the magnet and the amber."

That the conception of a soul or spirit residing in the substance and causing the mysterious behavior of lodestone and amber was not universally held by ancient philosophers is attested by the writings of Theophrastus (372–287 B.C.) who succeeded Aristotle and carried on his teachings. Aristotle possessed a large collection of stones. The gathering of these stones was quite largely the work of the armies of Alexander the Great. Theophrastus classified them, and in his writings we find definite information concerning the "amber attraction." He says, "Amber is a stone. It is dug out of the earth in Liguria, and has a power of attraction." Theophrastus nowhere makes any mention of a soul animating amber. He says, on the contrary, of its qualities: Its "concretion" is due to heat or cold. Thus he takes only a scientific or material view of this strange attraction, although his explanation is vague and erroneous.

In general both magnetism and electricity were conceived of as souls residing in the substances magnetite and amber from the time of Thales down to the middle of the 16th century. In 1501 in Milan, Italy there was "born out of time extraordinary" another person, one Jerome Cardan, who in 1551 took the next step in answering the question, "What is electricity?" Cardan was educated as a physician, although he wrote a treatise on mathematics, and was undoubtedly the most famous physician of his age. Both lodestone and amber were much sought and used by physicians of Cardan's time and earlier. These substances were supposed to have remarkable curative values owing to the occult and superstitious mysteries surrounding them. Doses of powdered lodestone were administered in cases of marital troubles. It was obvious, according to prevailing belief of that day, that the patients lacked some spiritual element which the lodestone could supply, a belief following quite as naturally as our belief in the efficacy of codliver oil because of its vitamin content. Legend relates that the priests of Samothrace sold magnet rings, the samothracian rings, for the cure of rheumatism and gout. Amber when burned was supposed to be a sure preventative of plagues, and when such terrible scourges ravaged Europe the demand for the resin was great. In the form of pills it was a specific for checking hemorrhages, nausea, and catarrh. It was also carved into rings, beads, and rosaries and worn as an amulet.

Being a physician, Cardan had much to do with both magnetite and amber, as did all physicians of his day and age. He turned from his medical practice, as did Gilbert nearly three centuries later, to experiment with and to theorize about the cause of the strange behaviors of these substances. As a result of his investigations he, for the first time in history, distinguished sharply between magnetism and electricity, or between the inherent nature of magnetite and amber, and points out their differences. Moreover, he originated the fluid theory of electricity, for he says, speaking of amber, that "It has a fatty and glutinous humor which, being emitted, the dry object desiring to absorb it moves towards the source, that is, the amber. For every dry thing, as soon as it begins to absorb moisture, is moved towards the moist source, like fire to its pasture; and since the amber is strongly rubbed, it draws the more because of its heat." Here we have a fluid theory of electricity which later was applied to magnetism, heat and combustion. Cardan took the soul out of amber and substituted therefor a "fatty and glutinous humor," that is, a fluid. The fact that this fluid was intangible and invisible seems not to have caused Cardan embarrassment. Cardan thought of this fluid as material, and not as the subtle, imponderable fluid of a later period. The year 1551, in which Cardan published his theory, may be taken as marking the end of the soul or spirit concept of both electricity and magnetism and the beginning of the fluid theories. It marked the transition from the supernatural to the natural theories of electricity and magnetism.

Substances, like amber, which contained this fluid were called by Gilbert (1600) electrics, and those that did not contain it were called non-electrics. However, the full development of the fluid theory did not come until the middle of the 18th century. We must go back to an earlier age than that of Cardan for the earliest notions of an electric fluid. Undoubtedly he derived his ideas from the fanciful "virtues" of an earlier date. A "virtue" was thought of as something, a primordial element, which entered into the constitution of all bodies. "They were effluvia, sometimes corporal, such as air, sometimes incorporal, or more properly highly diffuse, such as those which emanated from a body, and surrounding it, form its orb or sphere of virtue." Gilbert speaks of an "orb of virtue" (*orbis virtutis*) surrounding a magnet. Thus we have the early ideas of a field of influence surrounding a magnet, an electrified substance, or the earth, which today is called a field of force. Neckam of England in the 12th century says that attraction takes place "as by the power of heat, or by a *virtue*, or by the natural quality of similitude, or by the law of vacuity." Again William the Clerk, a bard of the 12th century, in an attempt to account for the fact that the compass needle points to the north after being rubbed with magnetite, says it receives a *virtue* from the stone. But whence does the stone get its virtue? Clearly from the pole star, else why should the needle point to that star in preference to any other object in the universe, as, for example, the moon. In the same century the Italian poet, Guido Guinicelle, writes:

> In what strange regions 'neath the polar star
> May the great hills of massy lodestone rise,
> Virtue imparting to the ambient air
> To draw the stubborn iron; while afar
> From that same stone, the hidden virtue flies
> To turn the quivering needle to the Bear,
> In splendor blazing in the northern skies.

Note that the virtue is imparted "to the ambient air to draw the stubborn iron." Here we have the conception of a fanciful influence emanating from a magnetic substance and acting at a distance upon other magnetic substances, which took the form of a field of force at a later period. Of course, a poet merely reflects the prevailing opinions of the age in which he lives; he is a mirror of the times.

The idea of a "virtue" in and surrounding everything and accounting for natural phenomena was carried to the extreme by Otto von Guericke of Germany in the 17th century. Of the incorporal virtues he says, not all are perceptible because of the limitations of our senses, but those that are perceptible come from the earth or the sun. From the earth arise "impulsive virtues," "directive virtues," "turning virtues," "sound virtues," etc., from the sun "light and color virtues," and from the moon "frost-making virtues." All these virtues are alike in that they enter into the constitution of all bodies and can act at a distance. Thus von Guericke extended the fluid or virtue theory to all substances. He invented the first electrostatic machine (1672), a sulfur sphere which could be revolved about an axis and so develop a charge by friction. With this machine he electrified substances; he exhibited electric attraction and repulsion and also discovered electric conduction, as well as the electric spark. He conceived of the earth as "a vast electric machine rotated by the hand of the Almighty and excited by the friction of the solar rays." Thus he sought an explanation of the electric charge upon the earth.

The fluid theory of electricity was further developed in the 18th century due to the researches of Charles Francois Du Fay (France) and Benjamin Franklin (U. S.), each typifying a different trend in the theory. Du Fay's researches followed closely upon those of Gray (1730) in England who investigated primarily electric conductivity. Du Fay found that bits of gold leaf were attracted by electrified glass or rock crystal, but that when contact was made they were then repelled. However, when in this condition the gold leaf was found to be attracted by electrified gumcopal, amber, and Spanish wax. He says of this discovery, "I cannot doubt that glass and crystal operate in exactly the opposite way to gumcopal and amber; so that a leaf repelled by the former because of the electricity which it contracted will be drawn to the latter. And this leads me to conclude that there are perhaps *two kinds of different electricities.*" Although Du Fay thought of electricity as a fluid he here calls it simply electricity. To the kind of electricity obtained on glass when rubbed with silk he gave the name "vitreous," and to the kind obtained on amber or wax when rubbed with fur he gave the name "resinous." This is a statement of Du Fay's two-fluid theory of electricity (1733). Du Fay made the further discovery that a substance may be electrified by direct contact or by induction, and that Gilbert's classification of substances into electrics and non-electrics was in error. He found that all substances may be electrified if insulated. Gilbert's electrics were found to be poor conductors or insulators and his non-electrics were found to be good conductors, which explains Gilbert's classification, since Gilbert neither dried substances nor insulated them before attempting to electrify them. It may be noted, also, in this connection, that after Peregrinus (1265) made the discovery that a magnet has two poles, one at either end, there was advanced at a later date the theory that there are two magnetic fluids which reside only in the opposite ends of the magnet. This may be called the two-fluid theory of magnetism.

Franklin (1747) sought to explain the phenomena observed by Du Fay by postulating a single electric fluid which just filled a substance when in the electrically neutral state. If a substance contained more than the normal amount he said that it was positively electrified (vitreous), and if less than the normal amount he said it was negatively electrified (resinous). In Franklin's theory there were two entities, electricity and ordinary matter, whereas in the Du Fay theory there were three entities, vitreous and resinous electricity and ordinary matter. Had Franklin postulated that an excess of electric fluid gave negative electrification he would have been essentially in accord with present-day theory so far as the signs of the charges are concerned. Franklin's theory had simplicity in its favor, which, according to a principle advanced by Newton, was more in accord with nature, since, "Nature," so says Newton, "is pleas'd with simplicity and affects not the pomp of superfluous causes." In this statement Newton reveals that animism has not completely vanished, since he assigns spirit or soul attributes to nature. However, Franklin's hypothesis ran into difficulties which more than compensated for the advantage it seemed to have, because of simplicity, over the Du Fay two-fluid theory. Since, on the one-fluid theory, a deficiency of electric fluid means a negative charge, there must be a limiting value for a negative charge, namely, when a substance is devoid of electric fluid. But two such electrified substances, i.e., substances having no electric fluid would repel each other, and with the greatest possible force. The one-fluid advocates were hesitant to push this argument to the limit. However, the German physicist, Aepinus (1759), went the whole distance and asserted that matter devoid of electric fluid is self-repellant. However, there was no experimental evidence as to the behavior of substances possessing their maximum negative charges, i.e., matter itself. Therefore, the one-fluid theory fell into disrepute, and was finally completely replaced by the two-fluid theory.

During the closing years of the 18th century and the early years of the 19th century mathematical physicists developed an elaborate and entirely satisfactory mathematical theory of electrostatic phenomena built upon the two-fluid hypothesis, so that by 1830 the two-fluid theory was thoroughly entrenched. But, as has happened so often in science, as soon as one theory seems established and is universally accepted new experimental evidence renders its claim to finality untenable, and so it was with the two-fluid theory of electricity. In 1798 Volta developed an electric current by chemical action in the voltaic cell, and from 1800 to 1802 Davy and Ritter produced chemical decomposition by means of the electric current. In 1820 Oersted discovered that an electric current is surrounded by a magnetic field of force, thus showing that electric phenomena and magnetic phenomena are not entirely unrelated, but rather are different aspects of the same phenomenon. In 1822 Seebeck showed that an electric current can be generated directly from heat, and in 1834 Peltier developed heat directly from an electric current. Also, in the Joule effect heat is developed directly from an electric current. These experiments pointed to the electric current as "a mode of motion" or a form of energy. In 1831 Faraday obtained the reverse Oersted effect when he developed an electric current (induced current) by varying the magnetic flux linked with a closed electric circuit. In 1845 Faraday discovered that a transparent, isotropic substance, when placed in a powerful magnetic field, acquires the property of rotating the plane of polarization when plane, polarized light traverses the medium in the direction of the lines of flux (Faraday effect). In 1865 Maxwell published his electromagnetic theory in which he showed that electromagnetic waves have the velocity of light, and in 1887 Hertz produced electromagnetic waves experimentally and measured their velocity and found it to be the velocity of light. Thus the domain of optics was annexed to that of electricity. Thus apparently isolated domains of physics were shown to have something in common, a unification of isolated phenomena was in progress.

Along with this development came a change in thought as regards the nature of electricity, so that by 1865 electricity was not thought of as a material fluid confined to a substance, but as something less material, more elusive and subtle, and exerting an influence far beyond the confines of the substance. Maxwell's merger of optics and electricity suggested to Sir Oliver Lodge that electricity is in some inexplicable manner a phenomenon of the ether. He explained electrostatic and magnetic phenomena as due to ether stresses, electric currents as ether flow, and magnetism as ether vortices, after the ideas of Descartes. Thought at that time was focused quite largely upon the field of force (*orbis virtutis*), and so gave rise to what may be called the *ether theory* of electricity, which regarded electricity as an imponderable, immaterial fluid in and surrounding the electrified body or conductor bearing a current.

However, the ether theory was no sooner established than it began to die. It was immediately succeeded by the present *quantum theory* of electricity. In fact, the genesis of the quantum theory antedated the fully established ether theory. Faraday's experiments in electrolysis pointed unmistakably towards a quantum of electricity, or a natural unit of electricity. In Wilhelm Weber's theory of magnetism (1871) there was postulated an atom having a light positive charge rotating around a heavy, negative charge, the positive charge in cir-

cuital motion acting as a solenoidal current and so developing a magnetic field of force. This was Weber's elementary magnet, which, as
we see, was due to an elementary electric charge in orbital motion.
Our present theory of magnetism merely reverses the signs of the
charges in the Weber theory. In 1874 Johnston Stoney in his paper
entitled, "The Physical Units of Nature," definitely asserted the
atomic nature of electricity, and made a rough calculation of the elementary charge on the basis of Faraday's experiments in electrolysis. He was the first to use the term "electron" for this elementary
charge. In 1881 Helmholtz, in his Faraday lecture, says:

> Now the most startling result of Faraday's law is perhaps
> this. If we accept the hypothesis that the elementary substances
> are composed of atoms, we cannot avoid concluding that elec-
> tricity also, positive as well as negative, is divided into definite
> elementary portions, which behave like atoms of electricity.

Thus Helmholtz definitely recognized the atomic nature of electricity.
However, Maxwell's electromagnetic theory of electricity was based
essentially upon a continuous electric fluid, and therefore was continuous in nature. In his "Treatise on Electricity and Magnetism,"
in discussing electrolysis, he says: "It is extremely improbable that
when we come to understand the true nature of electrolysis we shall
retain in any form the theory of molecular charges." Helmholtz, however, saw in electrolysis incontrovertible evidence of the atomic
nature of electricity. He visualized electricity as a specific chemical
element whose atoms combine with those of other elements to form
ions. Moreover, the electric element seemed to be monovalent, since in
electrolysis the charge carried by an ion is proportional to its valence.
In 1891 Lorentz began the reconciliation of these contradictory
theories of electricity in his electron theory of electricity. He postulated that all electric effects taking place within a substance are due to
discrete electric charges called electrons, and all electrostatic and
electromagnetic effects taking place at a distance are due to the intervention of the ether. He assumed that each electron was in some
manner bound to the ether of space so that any change in the relative positions of the electrons developed ether disturbances which
were propagated outward with the velocity of light, thus producing an
apparent "action-at-a-distance."

It was during this time that attention was being directed to the
electric discharge in a vacuum tube, called a Crookes tube, since
Crookes brought this class of phenomena prominently to the attention

of scientists by a display before the British Association in 1879. Crookes thought the effects were due to electrified molecules of the residual gas in the tube. In 1897 J. J. Thomson, using a Crookes tube, showed that the electrified particles emanating from the cathode are in reality negatively charged and have a mass about 1/1,840 of the mass of the hydrogen ion, and the same charge as is carried by the hydrogen ion in electrolysis. Townsend, Wilson, and Millikan extended and confirmed the findings of Thomson. Stoney had used the term "electron" to signify either a positive or negative charge, but beginning with Thomson's researches the term "electron" was reserved for the cathode particles, and like particles wherever found. Then followed the isolation of the positive unit charge or proton which is an hydrogen ion, the neutron (Chadwick, 1932) which has the same mass as the proton but is electrically neutral, and the positive electron or positron (Anderson, 1932) which has the same mass as the electron but bears an equal positive charge. Other particles are appearing on the scientific horizon. One of these is the neutrino, which was predicted from theoretical considerations by Fermi and gained a semblance of physical reality as the result of experiments performed by K. T. Bainbridge at Harvard University in 1935. However, the neutrino is at present a hypothetical particle which is supposed to have about the mass of an electron and to be electrically neutral. It has not as yet been isolated. Its existence is demanded by theory in order to explain the transformation of a neutron while still in the nucleus of an atom into a proton, which remains, and an electron and neutrino which escape.

In 1927 Davisson and Germer found that an electron beam when reflected from a crystal formed a diffraction pattern as does a light beam, and G. P. Thomson obtained diffraction rings when a beam of electrons was passed through a thin film of metal. Thus the electron behaves as light and therefore has a wave aspect. Also, since it is deflected in a magnetic field and an electric field, it behaves as a particle of electricity. Thus the electron has a dual nature. To account for this dual behavior of the electron J. J. Thomson finds that it behaves as though it possesses a nucleus of negative electricity concentrated in a small sphere which is surrounded by a wave structure of much larger dimensions, perhaps 10,000 times the diameter formerly assigned to the electron. "On this view the electron is associated with and accompanied by a group of waves which guide and direct its motion."

With the advent of the theory of relativity and the quantum theory of radiation there seems to be no place for the ether of space as formerly conceived. The Lorentz idea of an electron being inseparably bound up with the ether of space may be modified by postulating that the electron carries its own ether with it, so to speak, i.e., the "orb of virtue" surrounding and extending out from it may be thought of as a part of the electron, and not a separate entity. Most electric effects are due to electrons. An excess of electrons on a body produces negative electrification, and a dearth of electrons produces positive electrification owing to ionized atoms. The electric current is a drift of electrons which develops a magnetic field through the relative motion of electric fields. Magnetism is due to electrons in orbital motions about the positive atomic nuclei. The photoelectric effect is due to the impacts of photons on electrons.

But what of the view that is held quite generally today that electricity, whatever it may be, is the sole world stuff? Is matter a mere manifestation of electricity, or is there something apart from electricity which we may call matter as in the one-fluid and two-fluid theories of electricity? Beginning with the theoretical discussion by J. J. Thomson (1893), which showed that a charged sphere in motion through the ether would encounter a resistance which to all intents and purposes would appear as an increase in inertia or mass, the idea that mass is an electric effect gained ground until electricity became the sole entity. This idea was confirmed in a measure by Kaufmann's experiments with swift moving electrons which showed that there was an increase in mass with velocity when the velocity is high. If the neutron and neutrino (if the neutrino is found to have a real existence) are eventually found to be independent entities devoid of electric charge they must represent what has been called ordinary matter. However, present-day electric theory leads to the conclusion that the neutron is a proton and an electron is close union, so close that their fields of force annul each other. In modern physical theory electricity occupies a dominant position. In the nineteenth century matter and electricity were thought of as two separate and independent entities. Today electricity is the fundamental entity of which matter is merely an aspect that electricity may exhibit to a greater or less extent according to circumstances. But theories have a predilection for changing, and, while today physics points to an electric theory of matter, tomorrow may bring their complete separation.

We have now a discursive picture of the attempts man has made down through the ages to understand and to formulate theories as to the nature of electricity and magnetism. We have not reached the end of the journey; perhaps we shall never reach the end of the journey. The ultimate nature of electricity and magnetism is still beyond our ken. We formulate theories and construct mental images in our endeavor to understand the ultimate realities of nature, but we are not at all sure that our subjective pictures coincide with objective reality. The game, however, is a fascinating one, and it has intrigued man from the time of the earliest philosophers down to present-day physicists. What *is* electricity? What *is* matter? These questions are still unanswered. However, the laws and principles governing these unknown entities are definite, and, for the most part, well known. It is with these laws and principles that we are now directly concerned. They will be unfolded, so far as space permits, in the following pages.

CHAPTER I

ELECTROSTATICS

1. The phenomenon of electrification by friction (*triboelectrification*) finds a ready explanation in the present-day electron theory. According to this theory, the atoms of matter are composed of negative corpuscles (electrons), positive corpuscles (protons), and neutral corpuscles (neutrons). There is today the possibility that there are a number of other elementary particles. Electrons and protons are presumably discrete units of negative and positive electricity. Of their physical existence we are certain, but their configurations are purely hypothetical. The heavy protons and neutrons constitute the center or nucleus of the atom, which contains practically all of its mass and does not suffer disintegration except under special and very unusual conditions. In the case of all of the elements, excepting hydrogen, the nucleus, together with the completed shells of electrons, is called the kernel. The electrons in uncompleted outer shells of the atoms (valence electrons) are in a more or less unstable condition and may be detached from the atoms. The kernel is relatively stable. However, the electrons composing the kernel are sometimes displaced, as, for example, in the generation of X-rays. The valence electrons, being relatively loosely held, may wander from atom to atom under excitation, or may exist free from the atom for a time. The kernel, which we may call the atom proper, remains relatively fixed in position in all solids. When two substances are rubbed together many of the valence electrons of one of the substances may be transferred to the other in some way that is little understood. The substance that acquires an excess of electrons is negatively electrified; the other substance is positively electrified, because upon its surface there is a dearth of electrons.

Du Fay called the kind of charge which glass takes when rubbed with silk "vitreous," and the kind of charge which sealing wax takes when rubbed with fur "resinous." Benjamin Franklin suggested the terms positive (vitreous) and negative (resinous) to distinguish the

14

two kinds of charges, and this nomenclature is now in general use. It was later discovered that the kind of charge obtained upon any given substance when rubbed with another depends upon the substance used as rubber. Thus, when glass is rubbed with silk its charge is positive, but when rubbed with fur its charge is negative. Substances can be arranged in a table (triboelectric series) such that a substance will be electrified positively on being rubbed with another if that substance occurs below it in the table, and it will be electrified negatively if that substance occurs above it. Electrification is influenced by temperature, humidity, and purity of the substances, and, therefore, a triboelectric series is at best only approximate. Such a table is the following, taken from the Smithsonian Tables:

> Rabbit's fur
> Glass
> Mica
> Wool
> Cat's fur
> Silk
> Cotton
> Wood
> Amber
> Resin
> Metals (Cu, Ni, Co, Ag, etc.)
> Sulphur
> Metals (Pt, Au)
> Celluloid

By connecting an uncharged gold-leaf electroscope to the outside of a metal ice pail and insulating the ice pail Faraday established several important facts pertaining to electrostatic phenomena. These experiments have been termed "Faraday's ice-pail experiments." They are fully explained in any text book on general physics. On lowering a charged metal ball, suspended by a silk thread, into the pail the leaves of the electroscope will diverge until the charge is well within the pail when no further divergence takes place, even though the charge is moved about within the pail without making contact with it. If the charge is removed without touching the pail the leaves of the electroscope collapse completely. If the charge while within the pail touches it there is no further divergence of the leaves, but the metal ball is completely discharged. This shows that the induced charge on the outside of the pail is equal to the induced charge on the inside of the pail, and that each is equal to the charge on the metal ball.

It was further established that equal charges of either kind produce equal divergence of the leaves. If equal charges on two separate metal balls are lowered simultaneously into the pail no divergence of the leaves of the electroscope takes place, whether the metal balls touch each other or not, thus showing that two equal but opposite charges completely neutralize each other. If two insulators are rubbed together, and thus charged by friction, and then lowered separately into the pail the same divergence of the leaves takes place in each case, but when the charged bodies are lowered together into the pail there is no divergence of the leaves, which shows that when charges are produced by friction they are equal in magnitude.

While a charge is transferred completely from one conductor to another if the latter is hollow and the former is placed inside and contact is made, the charge is not transferred completely if contact is made on the outside of the hollow conductor. The amount of transfer of electricity that takes place when a charged conductor is brought in contact with an uncharged conductor externally depends upon the relative sizes and shapes of the two conductors.

The electron has a rest mass of $9.12(10)^{-28}$ gm. and a diameter of about $3.8(10)^{-13}$ cm. The proton has a mass which is about 1,840 times that of the electron, and its diameter is less in approximately an inverse ratio to its mass. Of course, the size of either an electron or a proton is indefinite, as either the calculated or measured size has a large element of uncertainty. These units of electricity are undoubtedly tenuous structures of some physical reality, unknown to science, which merge imperceptibly into their accompanying auras, which are called electric fields of force. In metals the mean distance between adjacent nuclei is of the order of $4(10)^{-8}$ cm., which is roughly the diameter of an atom. Assuming these figures to be approximately correct, and further assuming electrons and atomic nuclei to be spherical, and that an electron is magnified to the size of a golf ball, then the atom of hydrogen, say, would have a diameter of about two and a half miles. The nuclei of even the heaviest atoms do not appear to be very much larger than in the lighter atoms, and, therefore, any atom is a very open structure, consisting mostly of free space, or rather of the overlapping fields which are integral parts of the atomic constituents. The material universe contains at least 92 such aggregations, each having a positive nuclear charge equal to the *atomic number*, or ordinal number in the periodic table of the elements. In a normal or neutral atom the number of electrons outside the nucleus is equal to the positive charge in the nucleus. This is also the number of protons in the nucleus, according to present-day theory. The individual atoms of a given element do not in general all have the same mass, though having the same chemical properties, and hence the same place in the periodic table of the elements. Such are called *isotopes*. The variation in the masses of isotopes is due to a variation in the number of neutrons in the nucleus.

When one or more electrons are removed from an atom, by friction or otherwise, the residue of the atom is known as a *positive ion*. It requires work to remove an electron from an atom, and this work can be measured. It is found that certain electrons of the configuration are more loosely bound to the positive nucleus than others in a given element, and that the binding force varies among the elements. In solids the atoms are held in relatively fixed positions by forces between them, and this fixed spacial structure possesses sufficient rigidity to give permanence of shape. In certain types of solids the space lattice formed by the atoms is such that the more loosely bound electrons associated with the atoms are so influenced by contiguous atomic charges as to be able to move about among the atoms with comparative freedom. These comparatively free electrons are called *conduction electrons*, and substances possessing these characteristics are known as conductors. The electrons are, however, retained by the physical boundaries of the solid and so prevented from escaping from the substance, except under very special conditions such as at high temperatures or under the influence of light. Metals belong to this class of substances. However, the degree of conductivity, or degree of freedom of conduction electrons, varies among the substances called conductors. If, on the other hand, the electronic binding forces and the relative positions of atoms forming the solid lattice structure are such as to make relative motions of electrons very difficult we have a class of substances known as *insulators*. With these substances, when a charge (positive or negative) is produced by friction, or imparted to the substance in any manner, it remains localized and does not distribute itself over the surface of the body as is the case with conductors. To a first approximation this is a qualitative picture of the physical problem. If there were perfect freedom of motion of conduction electrons there would be perfect conductors, i.e., substances having infinite conductivity. The nearest approach to ideal perfect conductors is to be found in the case of some metals close to the absolute zero of temperature, the phenomenon being known as *super-*

conductivity. If there were absolutely no freedom of motion of electrons in a substance we would have perfect insulators. No such insulators exist. As a matter of fact, the degree of conductivity varies markedly from conductor to conductor, and the insulating quality of insulators varies from insulator to insulator, and in each class of substances temperature changes and purity have a marked effect.

Since like charges repel one another and unlike charges attract one another, a negative charge on a conductor will be on the surface of the body. If there is a dearth of electrons in a conductor the interior positive ions attract the relatively free mobile electrons from the surface, thus leaving the surface positive, unless indeed all of the atoms of a conductor were ionized, in which case there would be a positive charge throughout the substance of the conductor, a condition which never obtains under ordinary conditions.

Machines have been built for the separation of charge, which are known as electrostatic generators. They usually employ a combination of friction and induction. The electrophorus and Wimshurst electrostatic generators (described in books on general physics) are examples of such machines. The van de Graaff generator is a very superior type of electrostatic generator of recent design. For a description of this generator, see "Atomic Physics," by Physics Staff of Univ. of Pittsburgh, p. 271.

2. The Inverse Square Law. Coulomb's Law. — This law was first discovered by Priestley in 1767 and rediscovered by Coulomb in 1785. Du Fay made the discovery that charges of the same sign repel each other and charges of opposite signs attract each other. The mechanism whereby this attraction or repulsion is brought about was unknown to Du Fay, nor is it now known. Investigators of that age explained electric attraction and repulsion by the "action-at-a-distance" of one charge upon the other as they explained gravitational attraction. Action at a distance without an intervening medium of some sort was repugnant to Faraday. Consequently he introduced the hypothesis that the so-called ether of space is caused to be in a state of strain owing to the presence of charges of electricity. Stresses existing in the strained ether were conceived to be accountable for forces of attraction or repulsion acting between charges of electricity, the stresses being modified by the presence of material media. Following this line of reasoning Faraday introduced the artifice of lines and tubes of force, which were thought to extend from a positively charged body to a negatively charged body. The lines and tubes of force were adjudged to be under tension longitudinally and under pressure laterally. In this manner Faraday sought to supply a mechanism for electrostatic forces of attraction and repulsion. However, we are totally unacquainted with the structure, nature, and even the existence of this postulated universal medium, the so-called ether of space. We are driven, therefore, to interpret electrostatic forces in terms of the charges giving rise to them, which is essentially "action at a distance" coupled with the conception that in some inexplicable manner these forces act through space itself. In the absence of knowledge of the true nature of the physical mechanism Faraday's figment of lines and tubes of force has served a useful purpose in supplying a concrete picture upon which we may focus attention and base calculations. That electric disturbances are propagated through space with a finite velocity is in support of a medium theory as against the action-at-distance theory. Considerations of this nature led Maxwell to his electromagnetic theory. Later experiments verified Maxwell's abstract deductions and thus gave support to the view that free space possesses physical properties.

Having established that electric forces exist, the next inquiry is as to the manner in which these forces vary with the magnitudes of the charges, the distance between them, and the intervening medium. Coulomb established the law of electric forces. This he did by means of his torsion balance (described in books on general physics). He balanced the torque produced by charges on two gilt pith balls against the torsional couple of a fine silver wire. Knowing the distance between the charges, their magnitudes, and the torsional constant of the wire he was able to arrive at the law, which is as follows: *The mutual force existing between two point charges varies directly as the product of the charges and inversely as the square of the distance between them.* Expressed mathematically the law is:

$$F = \frac{qq'}{\epsilon d^2}. \tag{2.1}$$

Coulomb performed his experiments in air and so was unaware of the fact, discovered later, that the intervening medium affects the magnitude of the force between the charges. ϵ was not included in

Coulomb's original equation.[1] It is a coefficient which depends upon the units adopted and the intervening medium. The unit of charge was arbitrarily chosen so as to make $\epsilon = 1$ in free space when F is measured in dynes and d in cms. This unit of charge is called the cgse.[2] unit. Thus, *the cgse. unit of charge is that charge which will repel an equal and like charge with a force of one dyne when separated by a distance of one cm. in free space.* It should be noted that ϵ is unity for free space in this equation *only* when the charges are measured in cgse. units, since the unit cgse. charge was so chosen as to make $\epsilon = 1$. However, if q, d, and F are expressed in any other units, ϵ is not equal to 1 for free space. Thus if q is expressed in cgsm. units, $\epsilon = c^{-2}$, where $c = 2.998(10)^{10}$, the ratio between the magnitudes of the units of charge in the two systems.

At a later period experiments with different dielectrics between the plates of condensers led to the discovery that the force between the charged plates varies with the nature of the medium between them, where the term medium is taken to include free space as a limiting case. Franklin, Cavendish, and Faraday performed these experiments and found that ϵ has a value greater than unity in the cgse. system of units for all media other than free space. ϵ has the value 1.00059 for air and 1.000246 for hydrogen under standard conditions. For most purposes ϵ is taken equal to 1 for air in the cgse. system of units.

If the minus sign be given to a negative charge and the plus sign to a positive charge, then when F is positive the charges are like, and when F is negative the charges are unlike. Faraday gave the name *specific inductive capacity* to ϵ. Owing to the fact that insulators alone can support electric stresses, Faraday called such media *dielectrics*. Therefore, since ϵ depends upon the dielectric between the charges, the term *dielectric constant* is now quite generally used for ϵ. ϵ is a constant for any given dielectric under unvarying physical conditions, but varies from dielectric to dielectric. Since the physical conditions

---

[1] It is a moot question among physicists as to whether ϵ should be introduced into the discussion at this point or held in abeyance until the discussion of dielectrics is taken up. The author prefers to introduce ϵ at the start of the discussion, since in reality it belongs in the equation. The only reason it does not appear in Coulomb's equation for free space is because the cgse. unit charge was so selected as to make it unity.

[2] For the sake of brevity, following the International Critical Tables, the abbreviations cgs., cgse., and cgsm. will be used for centimeter-gram-second, centimeter-gram-second-electrostatic, and centimeter-gram-second-electromagnetic, respectively.

affecting a dielectric are seldom constant, ϵ varies considerably for any given dielectric, as will be seen in Chapter III, and, therefore, the term *dielectric coefficient* is probably a better term to characterize the effect of the dielectric.

Superficial or Surface Density. — When a body receives an electric charge the charge is usually upon the surface. On an insulator the charge is in general localized, as insulators do not permit the free flow of electrons either over the surface or through the substance. On a conductor, however, the charge distributes itself over the surface, and is wholly on the surface, as conductors permit a free flow of electrons. Since static charges are usually upon the surfaces of bodies it is convenient in many instances to express the quantity of charge upon unit area. This is called the *surface* or *superficial density* and will be designated σ units per cm.^{2} If a charge q is uniformly distributed over a surface, then

$$\sigma = \frac{q}{a} \text{ units per cm.}^2 \qquad (2.2)$$

If the distribution is not uniform over the surface we can only speak of the surface density at a point. The expression for the surface density at a point is

$$\sigma = \frac{dq}{da} \text{ units per cm.}^2 \qquad (2.3)$$

The surface density on an insulator is not, in general, uniform nor does it necessarily bear any relationship to the curvature of the surface. In the case of conductors, however, since the charge is free to flow, the surface density varies in such wise as to be directly proportional to the curvature of the surface at a given place. Thus at a point of large curvature the surface density may become very great, so great in fact that a flow of electrons to or from the conductor may take place. Hence sharp points on a conductor facilitate electric discharge, whereas flat surfaces or surfaces of small curvature retard electric discharge.

3. The Electrostatic Field of Force. — An electrostatic field of force is the region surrounding an electric charge in which a force acts on another charge. This force usually varies from point to point in the field both in intensity and direction. If it does not the field is said to be uniform. Faraday imagined an electric charge to be surrounded by a medium, the so-called ether, which became strained owing to the

presence of the charge, and the lines of strain he thought of as lines of force. Maxwell endowed the Faraday lines of force with something akin to physical reality and gave to them a quantitative value. By assuming a longitudinal tension he sought to account for attraction between unlike charges, and by assuming a lateral pressure between the lines he sought to account for repulsion between like charges. This was the postulated mechanism whereby he attempted to account for the observed phenomena.

In view of the fact that the physical properties of the ether are unknown to us, and even its very existence unproved, present-day physicists think of a *line of force* merely as the trajectory of a hypothetical small positive charge possessing no inertia, if free to move in the field. The tangent to a trajectory at any point in the field is the direction of the electric force at that point. A line of force, in current thought, is merely a convenient fiction which serves to clarify thinking and to aid in calculations. With this understanding as to the status of lines of force we may proceed to treat them in the real sense in which Faraday and Maxwell treated them. They supply a mechanism which, in the absence of knowledge of the actual mechanism, will account for many known observations.

Since lines of force or lines of flux are purely arbitrary, it is clear that they may be of any arbitrarily assigned density whatsoever. A *tube of flux* is a bundle of a large number of lines of flux, arbitrarily chosen. *Electric intensity E* is the force in dynes acting on a unit cgse. charge of electricity, when in a field of force, assuming that the field is not distorted by the presence of the unit charge and the intensity thereby changed. Tubes of flux are drawn in such density that the number of tubes of flux per cm.^{2} of cross section is everywhere equal in magnitude to the electric intensity in free space, the field assumed to be uniform over a square centimeter. If the field is not uniform we can speak only of the flux density at a point in the field, meaning by this the number of tubes of flux which would pass through a cm.^{2} if the field had a constant strength equal to its value at the point in question. A field of force of unit strength is one in which a unit charge of electricity experiences a force of one dyne. Therefore, a field of unit strength in a vacuum contains one tube of flux per cm.^{2} of cross section. When flux density D is defined in this manner it follows, as we shall see in Section 5, that 4π tubes of flux are associated with a unit cgse. charge of electricity.

Some writers assign one line of flux to each tube of flux as here defined, the single line of flux being imagined to extend along the axis of the tube of flux. In that case there would be 4π lines of flux associated with each unit cgse. charge of electricity. Some physicists object to the concept of discrete lines of flux and prefer the more satisfying concept of tubes of flux filling all of the space where a field of force exists. There is another tube of flux sometimes used, called a unit or Faraday tube of flux, which is associated with a unit cgse. charge of electricity. In this usage the bundle of lines of flux associated with each tube of flux is taken as 4π, and so each unit cgse. charge of electricity has associated with it one tube of flux or 4π lines of flux.

4. Relationship between Flux Density D and Intensity E in a Dielectric. — As will be shown in Section 5, 4π tubes of flux diverge from a unit cgse. charge of positive electricity or converge to a unit cgse. charge of negative electricity in free space (vacuum) as here used. Therefore it may be reasonably assumed that the same number of tubes of flux will still be associated with a unit charge of electricity when immersed in a material dielectric of dielectric coefficient ϵ. But now the number of tubes of flux no longer yields the same intensity E owing to the presence of polarization charges induced in the dielectric. The intensity E we know from experimental evidence depends upon the medium in which the charge is immersed; it is a function of the dielectric coefficient ϵ and varies inversely with it, as may be seen from Coulomb's equation. By application of Coulomb's equation it is easy to see that $E_0 = \epsilon E$, where E_0 is the intensity in free space and E the intensity in a medium of dielectric coefficient ϵ. Since in the cgse. system of units the flux density is taken numerically equal to the intensity in free space, i.e., $D = E_0$, it follows that

$$D = \epsilon E. \tag{4.1}$$

Since a force of E dynes acts on a unit charge of electricity, a force of $F = qE$ dynes will act on a charge of q units. Also, since 4π tubes of flux are associated with each unit cgse. charge of electricity, $4\pi q$ tubes of flux are associated with a charge of q units. D and E are vector quantities. The sense is taken as the direction in which a free positive charge would move.

5. Number of Tubes of Flux Associated with Unit cgse. Charge. — Let a "point" charge of q units be surrounded with a sphere of radius r

cms. with q at the center.   At any point P on the surface of this sphere in free space

$$D = E = \frac{q}{r^2} \text{ numerically.}$$

If the "point" charge is isolated in free space the tubes of flux are radial and uniformly distributed and the flux density over the surface of the sphere will be constant.   Since there are $4\pi r^2$ $cm.^2$ on the surface of a sphere, the total number N of tubes of flux passing through the surface is

$$N = \frac{4\pi r^2 q}{r^2} = 4\pi q. \tag{5.1}$$

Therefore, there are 4π tubes of flux associated with each unit cgse. charge, when flux density is defined in the manner indicated.

6. Gauss's Law. — Gauss's law, which is useful in the solution of many problems, states that the total normal flux N taken over any closed surface surrounding a charge q is equal to $4\pi q$, where q is the total charge within the enclosure. This may be proved as follows: If

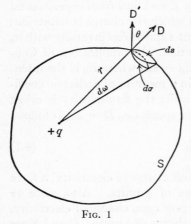

any closed surface whatsoever is taken in the electric field having a charge q within and D' is the component of the flux density in the direction of the normal to the surface, we are to prove that

$$N = \int_s D' ds = 4\pi q, \tag{6.1}$$

where the integration is taken over the whole surface. If q is positive the flux is directed outward, if negative it is directed inward.

FIG. 1

If the enclosed space is a vacuum the intensity E is numerically equal to the flux density D. However, in general, $D = \epsilon E$. Therefore, in terms of intensity, (6.1) becomes

$$N = \epsilon \int_s E' ds = 4\pi q. \tag{6.2}$$

In order to prove that this expression is true let us select an element of surface ds on the closed surface s surrounding q, Fig. 1. Join each point of the periphery of ds to the point at which q is located. The cone thus formed will cut out an element of area $d\sigma = ds \cos \theta$ on the surface of a sphere of radius r passing through ds. Now $E' = E \cos \theta$, and since

$$E = \frac{q}{\epsilon r^2}, \qquad E' = \frac{q}{\epsilon r^2} \cos \theta.$$

Hence, (6.2) becomes

$$N = \int_s \frac{q}{r^2} \cos \theta \, ds = q \int_s \frac{d\sigma}{r^2} = q \int_s d\omega = 4\pi q, \qquad (6.3)$$

where $d\sigma/r^2 = d\omega$ is the solid angle subtended at q by the element of area.

Gauss's law is equivalent to saying that 4π tubes of flux emanate from a unit positive charge or converge to a unit negative charge. This will be true, as here used, no matter what medium surrounds the charge, since the intensity and not the flux is influenced by the medium.

If a number of point charges $q_1, q_2, q_3, \ldots$ are within the surface the same argument obtains for each, and, therefore, the total normal flux through the surface is

$$N = 4\pi(q_1 + q_2 + q_3 \ldots) = 4\pi\Sigma q. \quad (6.4)$$

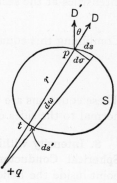

FIG. 2

The charges within the surface may be both positive and negative. In the special case where $\Sigma q = 0$, $N = 0$. If the charge is a continuous distribution of volume density ρ within an enclosure of volume V, we have

$$N = 4\pi \int_v \rho dv \qquad (6.5)$$

Charge Outside the Surface. — Any charge outside the surface S contributes nothing to the total normal flux over the surface. In order to show this let a point charge $+q$ be located outside the surface, Fig. 2. Draw any cone, with apex at $+q$, which intersects the surface.

Then at p

$$E' = \frac{q}{\epsilon r^2} \cos \theta. \text{ Thus } D'ds = \epsilon\, E'ds = \epsilon \frac{q}{\epsilon r^2} \cos \theta\, ds = q\, dw, \quad (6.6)$$

since $\cos \theta\, ds/r^2 = dw$, the solid angle subtended by the surface ds at q. At t the normal flux over the surface $ds' = -\, q\, dw$, the negative sign indicating that the tubes of flux are drawn inward. Therefore,

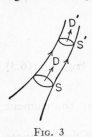

these two elements which subtend the same solid angle dw contribute nothing to the total normal flux over the surface S. All other cones drawn with $+q$ as apex and cutting the surface S also contribute nothing to the total normal flux. Thus a charge located outside the surface S contributes nothing to the normal flux over the surface.

Fig. 3

7. In any Tube of Flux the Intensity and Flux Density Are both Inversely as the Cross Section taken Normal to the Tube. Let S and S' be the cross sectional areas of a tube of flux, D and D' the flux densities, and E and E' the intensities at the sections, Fig. 3. Then, by Gauss's law

$$S'D' - SD = 0. \quad (7.1)$$

Combining this equation with the equation $D = \epsilon E$, we have

$$\frac{D}{D'} = \frac{E}{E'} = \frac{S}{S'}. \quad (7.2)$$

These equations are true since there is no component of the intensity normal to the sides of the tube.

8. Intensity within a Charged Hollow Spherical Conductor. — Let P be any point inside the hollow charged spherical conductor. Draw cones with apices at P, as indicated in Fig. 4. Then

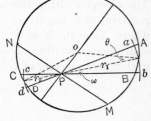

$$\text{area } ab = \text{area } AB \cos \theta$$

$$\text{area } cd = \text{area } CD \cos \theta. \quad (8.1)$$

Fig. 4

Also, by solid geometry, $ab/r_1^2 = cd/r_2^2 = w$, the solid angle of the pair of cones. ab and cd are the spherical caps. Therefore,

$$ab = r_1^2 w, \quad \text{and} \quad cd = r_2^2 w.$$

Hence

$$\text{area } AB = \frac{ab}{\cos \theta} = \frac{r_1^2 \, w}{\cos \theta}$$

$$\text{area } CD = \frac{cd}{\cos \theta} = \frac{r_2^2 \, w}{\cos \theta}. \tag{8.2}$$

The charges on AB and CD are $(AB)\sigma$ and $(CD)\sigma$ respectively. Let us assume that the force between electric charges varies as the inverse nth power of the distance between them. Then the intensity at P due to the charge on AB is

$$E' = \frac{(AB)\sigma}{\epsilon \, r_1^n} = \frac{w r_1^2 \sigma}{\epsilon \, r_1^n} \cos \theta,$$

and due to the charge on CD,

$$E'' = \frac{w r_2^2 \, \sigma}{\epsilon r_2^n} \cos \theta. \tag{8.3}$$

E' and E'' will be directed away from the point P in opposite directions along the common axis of the pair of cones.

In the particular case where $n = 2$, the intensities E' and E'' are equal, each being equal to $w\sigma/\epsilon \cos \theta$, and since they are oppositely directed they annul each other. The whole sphere may be divided up into pairs of cones, and with each pair the resultant force at P is zero. Therefore, if the electric force between charges of electricity varies inversely as the square of the distance, as required by Coulomb's law, the space within a charged hollow spherical conductor is a region of zero intensity. This gives a means of verifying Coulomb's law experimentally.

Let us investigate the condition inside a charged hollow spherical conductor assuming that the force between charges of electricity does not vary as the inverse square of the distance between them, but as the inverse nth power of the distance. Equations (8.3) will then obtain. If $n > 2$ and $r_1 > r_2$, the component of the intensity due to the charge on the element of surface CD is greater than the component of the intensity due to the charge on the element of surface AB, since

$$\frac{1}{r_2^{n-2}} > \frac{1}{r_1^{n-2}}.$$

This will be true at P for all elements of surface to the lower left of the plane NPM, since all elements to the left of this plane are nearer to P than the corresponding elements to the upper right of this plane. If the charge on the surface of the spherical conductor is positive there will be a resultant force on a positive charge at P which will by symmetry be directed towards the center of the sphere. If the charge on the sphere is negative, the resultant intensity at P is directed out from the center along the radius passing through P. On the other hand, if $n < 2$ it can be shown by the same process of reasoning that there will be a resultant intensity at any point P, not at the center of the sphere, but of opposite sense to the former.

That n is equal to 2 within the limits of experimental error was shown experimentally by Cavendish, and at a later date by both Faraday and Maxwell. The common plan of these experiments was as follows: A conducting sphere A was supported concentrically

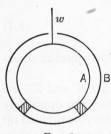

Fig. 5

inside a conducting sphere B and insulated therefrom, Fig. 5. A small orifice in B permitted a fine wire w connected with A to be brought out through the sphere B. B is given a positive charge, say. A and B are then brought into conducting communication by means of the wire w, and the connection is then broken so that A and B are again insulated from each other. B is then discharged and A is tested for charge by connecting the wire w to an electroscope or a quadrant electrometer. From the foregoing reasoning it is seen that A should show a positive charge if $n > 2$ and a negative charge if $n < 2$.

Cavendish used a pith-ball electroscope as a detector of charge but could detect no charge on A. He, therefore, concluded that n is equal to 2 within the accuracy of the experiment, which he estimated as under 1% error. Faraday used a gold-leaf electroscope but failed to detect any charge on A. Maxwell used a quadrant electrometer as a detector and also failed to detect a charge on A. Maxwell determined the smallest charge on A that could be detected and from that calculated that n differs from 2 by less than 1 part in 21,600. Recently, Plimton and Lawton,[1] using improved equipment, have established that the exponent in the Coulomb law is equal to 2 to within 1 part in 10^9.

[1] Plimton and Lawton, Phys. Rev., 50, 1066, 1936.

9. Electric Intensity in the Neighborhood of a Charged Spherical Conductor. — Let A be a spherical conductor in free space charged with $+q$ cgse. units, Fig. 6. It is assumed that the sphere is sufficiently isolated so that the field is regular and radial. We will consider the effect of the whole charge $+q$ at any external point P. Draw a concentric sphere about the charged sphere such that P is on the surface of this sphere. It is postulated that the electric flux is uniformly distributed over the surface of this sphere. Applying Gauss's law, we have

$$4\pi r^2 D = 4\pi r^2 \epsilon E = 4\pi q, \quad \text{or} \quad E = \frac{q}{\epsilon r^2}. \tag{9.1}$$

This expression shows that the effect of the charge on the surface of a sphere at any external point is the same as though the whole charge were concentrated at the center of the sphere.   A parallel case is that of gravitational attraction, which also varies inversely as the square of the distance. The earth, for example, attracts masses external to itself as though its whole mass were concentrated at its centroid. In this case, however, the mass is distributed throughout the volume and is not confined to the surface, as is a charge of electricity on a conducting sphere. The effect is the same, though, and the proof follows the same line as in the elec-

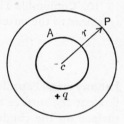

FIG. 6

tric case, since the earth may be imagined to be made up of a very great number of very thin spherical shells for each of which the argument holds. If the earth were a spherical shell there would be no gravitational force acting on a mass within the shell. This is the analogue of zero intensity within a charged spherical conductor which was developed in Section 8, and follows because of the inverse square law.

An interesting speculation, which, however, has little if any actual application in electric problems, is the variation of the electric intensity within a spherical uniform distribution of charge of volume density ρ. One of the early atom models, advanced by J. J. Thomson, was a uniform distribution of positive electricity in spherical form within which the electrons were conceived to be embedded. We may think of the sphere as composed of a very great number of concentric spherical shells. Take any point P within the sphere. The effect of each shell outside of P is to produce zero intensity at P. The effect at P of all the shells inside is as though their total charge were concentrated at the center. The whole charge inside of P, which alone contributes to the intensity, is $\frac{4}{3}\pi r^3\rho$. The intensity at P is, therefore,

$$E = \frac{\frac{4}{3}\pi r^3\rho}{r^2} = \frac{4}{3}\pi\rho r = Cr. \qquad (9.2)$$

The intensity is, therefore, a maximum at the surface and varies for all points within the uniformly distributed volume charge directly as the radius r to the point, being zero at the center. For points outside the spherical distribution, however, the intensity varies inversely as the square of the distance from the center. The proof for this is the same as for surface distribution.

10. Coulomb's Theorem. — This theorem states that the intensity *very near* to the outer surface of a charged conductor is equal to

$$E = \frac{4\pi\sigma}{\epsilon}.$$

Let any small capsule with its geometrical axis parallel to the tubes of flux cut the surface as shown in section in Fig. 7. Let the element of surface on the conductor cut out by the capsule be da, and let the normal sections of the capsule immediately above and below the surface be ds and ds'. The charge within the capsule is σda. There is no flux inside the conductor, nor through the sides of the capsule. Therefore, by Gauss's law,

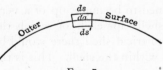

Fig. 7

$$D\,ds = 4\pi\,\sigma\,da. \qquad (10.1)$$

If ds is very near the surface of the conductor, it is essentially equal to da. This is more nearly true the less the curvature of the surface. Hence, with negligible error, we may write

$$D = \epsilon E = 4\pi\sigma, \quad \text{or} \quad E = \frac{4\pi\sigma}{\epsilon}. \qquad (10.2)$$

For the special case of a sphere Coulomb's theorem may be proved very simply as follows: It has already been shown that for external points the intensity due to a charge on a sphere is as though the whole charge were concentrated at the center of the sphere. For a point immediately outside the surface of the sphere, at distance r_1 cms. from the center of the sphere, the intensity is

$$E = \frac{q}{\epsilon\, r_1^2}.$$

Also, $q = 4\pi r^2 \sigma$, where r is the radius of the sphere. Therefore,

$$E = \frac{4\pi r^2 \sigma}{\epsilon\, r_1^2}.$$

If the point is very close to the surface of the sphere r_1 may be taken equal to r with negligible error. We have then, as before,

$$E = \frac{4\pi\sigma}{\epsilon}.$$

Of course the larger r is the greater may be the absolute difference between r_1 and r with the same percentage error in E. In the special case of an infinite plane surface E is constant for all distances from the surface.

11. Mechanical Force Acting upon a Unit Area of a Charged Conductor. Electrostatic Pressure. — We will follow the derivation given by Page and Adams,[1] as it seems to be the most direct. The charge on a conductor is not confined to its material geometrical surface, but, rather, it may be said to occupy a thin layer of indefinite thickness extending below and above the surface. Imagine this thin layer of electricity to be made up of a large number of surfaces parallel to the surface of the conductor, and so spaced that the charge $d\sigma'$ per unit area between each pair of adjacent surfaces is the same. Then, since each and every natural unit of electricity is accompanied by its own field of force, the intensity will increase by a constant amount in passing from surface to surface, being zero at the innermost surface. Let σ' be the charge per unit area included between the nth surface and the innermost, then the intensity at this nth surface will be

$$E' = \frac{4\pi\sigma'}{\epsilon}. \tag{11.1}$$

[1] Principles of Electricity by Page and Adams, p. 32.

Therefore, the stress (tension) on the surface of the conductor per cm.^{2} is given by

$$F = \frac{4\pi}{\epsilon} \int_0^\sigma \sigma' d\sigma' = \frac{2\pi\sigma^2}{\epsilon}. \tag{11.2}$$

Eliminating σ by combining (10.2) and (11.2), there results

$$F = \frac{\epsilon E^2}{8\pi} \text{ dynes/cm.}^2, \tag{11.3}$$

in which the mechanical force is expressed in terms of the intensity E at a point in the field immediately outside the geometrical surface of the conductor. Since both σ and E appear as squares the force on the surface is always a tension, and, therefore, independent of the sign of the charge on the surface. The force on unit charge on the surface of the conductor is given by

$$f = \frac{F}{\sigma} = \frac{2\pi\sigma}{\epsilon} = \frac{E}{2} \text{ dynes.} \tag{11.4}$$

Force of Attraction between the Plates of a Charged Condenser. Since the plates of a condenser are conductors the charge is distributed uniformly over the surface, except at the edges. Therefore, the surface density is constant. Consequently the intensity of the electric field between the plates of a parallel-plate condenser is constant, except at the edges. The tubes of flux are straight, of constant cross-sectional area, and equally spaced. They extend from the positive plate to the negative plate. At the edges of the plates the field fades out gradually, and therefore in this region the tubes of flux are curved outward. They are not of constant cross-sectional area, nor are they equally spaced. We may assume however that the tubes of flux are uniform throughout, which would be the case if the condenser plates were surrounded by a guard ring (see Section 34). The field between the plates of a charged condenser is therefore equivalent to the field of an infinite charged conducting plane, which was treated in Section 10. Therefore equation (10.2) holds for all points between the plates of a charged condenser of the guard-ring type. If there are no other charges in the neighborhood the intensity is zero outside the plates.

The mechanical force on each cm.^{2} of the inside surface of each plate is

$$F = \frac{2\pi\sigma^2}{\epsilon} = \frac{2\pi q^2}{\epsilon A^2} \text{ dynes/cm.}^2, \tag{11.6}$$

where q is the charge on one of the plates and A is the area of one plate. For the whole plate the mechanical force is

$$F = \frac{2\pi q^2}{\epsilon A} \text{ dynes.} \tag{11.7}$$

By combining with expressions already derived (11.6) may be expressed in the following forms:

$$F = \frac{\epsilon E^2}{8\pi} = \frac{D^2}{\epsilon 8\pi} \text{ dynes/cm.}^2 \tag{11.8}$$

Since the potential difference V between the plates is the quantity which is usually measured rather than the charge, this expression is more useful when stated in terms of the potential difference. The cgse. potential difference between the plates is given by $V = Ed$ ergs/cgse. unit charge, where d is the distance between the plates in cms. This follows since potential difference, in the cgse. system of units, is the work done in transporting a unit cgse. charge from the negative to the positive plate. Thus the intensity of the field between the plates is $E = V/d$, or the potential gradient in ergs/cgse. unit charge/cm. or dynes/cgse. unit charge. Introducing this expression for E, we obtain

$$F = \frac{\epsilon V^2}{8\pi d^2} \text{ dynes/cm.}^2 \tag{11.9}$$

12. Energy in the Electrostatic Field. — We are now in a position to consider the question of the energy in the electrostatic field of force and to evaluate it. If, as Faraday and Maxwell postulated, there is an imponderable medium of some sort, the so-called ether, surrounding a charged body and the medium is in a strained condition because of the presence of the charge there must be distributed energy throughout the medium so far as strain exists. This follows after the analogy with elastic bodies. In setting up strain in a medium, initially unstrained, work must be done and the work thus done must be stored in the medium as potential energy of deformation, exactly as energy of deformation is stored in the spring of a watch when wound. We might expect this energy to be some function of ϵ and E.

If there is no medium in free space in the ordinary meaning of that term, i.e., if the so-called ether is without form or substance, a mere property of space, there can be no strain and hence no stress as

in ponderable media. However, although the phenomena taking
place in space are beyond our purview, we know that there is energy
in free space, and that in setting up a field of force about a charged
body energy is added to space. Therefore, however abstract and ill-
defined a field of force may be, we can, nevertheless, derive an expression for the energy in the field and feel sure that the expression represents the energy due to the field. Let us think of the two plates of a
charged condenser, one plate bearing a charge of $+q$ cgse. units and
the other a charge of $-q$ cgse. units. Let us assume that the condenser
is surrounded by a guard ring, after the manner of Lord Kelvin's
guard-ring condenser (Section 34), so that the field is uniform everywhere between the plates. There is no field outside the plates if the
condenser is isolated electrically. As we have seen, there is a force of
attraction between the plates, and this force can be accurately measured. In order to separate the plates a distance dl work must be
done, and the work so expended must exist somewhere as potential
energy. The charges on the plates have remained unaltered during
the separation. The field between the plates has remained constant
in strength, but there has been an increase in the volume of the field.
Therefore, we may conclude that the work done in separating the
plates is stored in the increment of volume as potential energy. This
energy per unit volume of field may be calculated as follows:

The mechanical force acting on each sq. cm. of the inside surface
of one of the plates has been found to be

$$F = \frac{\epsilon E^2}{8\pi} \text{ dynes/cm}^2.$$

Therefore, the work done in moving one sq. cm. of surface a distance
of one cm. in a direction opposite to the electric pull is

$$U = \frac{\epsilon E^2}{8\pi} \text{ ergs/cm.}^3 \tag{12.1}$$

This expression may be put in the following alternate forms:

$$U = \frac{D^2}{\epsilon 8\pi} = \frac{\epsilon V^2}{8\pi d^2} = \frac{DE}{8\pi} \text{ ergs/cm.}^3 \tag{12.2}$$

While E is constant at all points between the plates of a guard-ring
condenser it is not constant for fields in general. E usually varies
from point to point in the field. This, however, in no wise vitiates

the argument. We can always take two essentially parallel, equipotential planes, in any given field, of areas da and distance dl apart. The field of force between these two equipotential planes is the same as though the areas da were charged conductors having surface densities which would produce the identical field of intensity E actually existing between the equipotential planes. Thus the conditions under which E was derived are satisfied and the expression for the energy in the field becomes universally true. E is the intensity at a point, and, therefore, U is the energy density at the point. Since both ϵ and E may vary from point to point, the energy content W of a volume V in a field is indicated as follows:

$$W = \int_v \frac{\epsilon E^2}{8\pi} \, dv \text{ ergs.} \tag{12.3}$$

13. Electrostatic Potential. — Strictly speaking, electrostatic potential difference exists *in* an electrostatic field of force, and because of the field, and is determined by the positions and magnitudes of electric charges. The sense of an electrostatic field has been defined as the direction in which a free positive charge would move. A free negative charge would move in the reverse direction. The point a in an electrostatic field from which a free positive charge may move to a point b has been said to be at the higher potential because of the meanings of the terms plus and minus, and because it was formerly

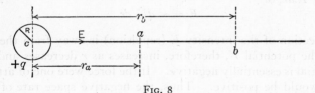

Fig. 8

assumed that a plus charge alone moved. A free positive charge moves *down* a potential gradient and a free negative charge moves *up* a potential gradient because of the manner of defining terms.

The cgse. difference of potential between two points a and b, Fig. 8, is defined as the work in ergs required to move a unit positive charge from b to a against the electric forces in the field. In order to calculate the difference of potential between points a and b we may proceed as follows: Let us say that a charge $+q$ is distributed uniformly over the surface of a conducting sphere isolated electrically, or in effect is concentrated at the center c. Let the points be distant r_a and r_b respectively from the center c. Let unit positive charge be moved from b to a. The force acting on a unit charge is

$$E = \frac{1 \times q}{\epsilon r^2} \text{ dynes.}$$

Therefore, the work done in moving the unit charge from b to a is

$$V_a - V_b = -\int_{r_b}^{r_a} \frac{q}{\epsilon r^2}\, dr = \frac{q}{\epsilon}\left(\frac{1}{r_a} - \frac{1}{r_b}\right) \text{ ergs/unit charge.} \quad (13.1)$$

To obtain the potential at the point a we have only to set r_b equal to ∞. We then have

$$V_a = \frac{q}{\epsilon r_a} \text{ ergs/unit charge.} \quad (13.2)$$

Thus the potential at a is the work required to move a unit positive cgse. charge from infinity to a, or from a point of zero potential to a. For the potential at a point on the surface of the sphere we set r_a equal to R, the radius of the sphere. We then have

$$V = \frac{q}{\epsilon R} \text{ ergs/unit charge.} \quad (13.3)$$

If the points a and b are at a distance dr apart we may write $dV = - E\, dr$, or

$$E = - dV/dr. \quad (13.4)$$

The direction of the intensity E (repulsion) is away from the charge $+q$. The potential V, therefore, increases as r decreases and so the differential is essentially negative. If the force were one of attraction dV/dr would be positive. Thus, the negative space rate of change of potential is the intensity E.

At a point where $E = 0$, as within a charged spherical conductor, we have $dV/dr = 0$, and on integrating, $V =$ constant. Thus for all points inside a charged spherical conductor the potential is constant and equal to the potential at the surface when the charge is confined to the surface; the region within is an equipotential region.

The potential at any point in an electric field is a function of the coordinates of the point only, *point function*, the distribution of charge remaining unaltered. Thus, the work done in moving a charge from one point to another is independent of the path. A system such as this is called a *conservative system*. If the electric force acts from *a* to *b* work is done on a positive charge *by an external agent* in moving it from *b* to *a*. Therefore, *a* is said to be at a *higher* potential than *b*. If a charge is moved from *b* to *a* by any path whatsoever the work done is $q(V_a - V_b)$ ergs. Since potential is measured in terms of work it is a scalar quantity. If a positive charge is free to move in an electric field it will move in the direction of the electric force, or from a point of *high* to a point of *low* potential. In this case work is done *on* the charge *by the electric field*. A free negative charge will move from a point of *low* to a point of *high* potential, or *up* a potential gradient.

The expressions high and low potentials, up and down potential gradients came into use at a time when it was supposed that a current of electricity was a flow of positive charge, the flow of electricity being likened to the flow of a liquid under gravity. These terms should be reversed if it is the negative charge which moves, otherwise flow is *up* a potential gradient, which does violence to our conception of flow. In the case of currents of electricity in metallic circuits the current consists of a stream of negative electrons flowing from low to high potential. As it is the negative charge which generally moves, it is unfortunate that these terms were first used and still are used as though it were a positive charge which moves. One must keep in mind that *up* and *down*, *high* and *low* are not necessarily related to direction of flow. These terms are for the most part archaic so far as they relate to electric phenomena.

14. Potential Due to Several Point Charges. — Let q_1, q_2, q_3, . . . be point charges. Then, since potential is a scalar quantity, the potential at any point P distant r_1, r_2, r_3, . . . respectively from the point charges is

$$V_P = \frac{q_1}{\epsilon r_1} + \frac{q_2}{\epsilon r_2} + \frac{q_3}{\epsilon r_3} + \cdots = \sum \frac{q}{\epsilon r} \text{ ergs/unit charge,} \quad (14.1)$$

assuming ϵ to be constant throughout the region. In the case of a continuous distribution of charge of volume density ρ occupying a volume V, and a surface density σ over the surface S, we have

$$V_P = \int_v \frac{\rho \, dv}{\epsilon r} + \int_s \frac{\sigma \, ds}{\epsilon r}.$$

Rectangular Components of E. — Suppose a point charge $+q$ to be located at the origin of coordinates, Fig. 9. Then the point a is at a higher potential than the point b, since a is nearer to q than b. Hence

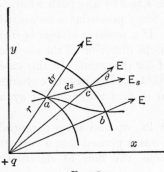

work must be done in moving a unit charge from b to a. Since all paths are equivalent, the charge might be moved along the path ba, or by the path bca. Let us say it is moved by the path bca. From b to c no work is done, since b and c are at the same distance from q. In moving the unit charge from c to a an amount of work

Fig. 9

$$dV = -\frac{q}{\epsilon r^2} ds \cos \theta = -\frac{q}{\epsilon r^2} dr$$

is done. Therefore, the component of E in the direction of the displacement ds is

$$\frac{\partial V}{\partial s} = -\frac{q}{\epsilon r^2} \cos \theta = -E_s, \quad \text{or} \quad E_s = -\frac{\partial V}{\partial s}. \tag{14.2}$$

If ds is parallel to the x axis, we have $E_x = -\partial V/\partial x$. Similar expressions obtain for the y and z directions. Therefore, we have

$$E_x = -\frac{\partial V}{\partial x}, \quad E_y = -\frac{\partial V}{\partial y}, \quad E_z = -\frac{\partial V}{\partial_z}. \tag{14.3}$$

These expressions are very useful in the solutions of many problems.

Equipotential Surfaces. — An equipotential surface is any surface in an electrostatic field such that no work is done in moving a charge from point to point upon it. Thus there can be no component of electric force tangent to the surface. Hence tubes of flux cut equipotential surfaces orthogonally. Therefore, along any equipotential surface

$$\frac{dV}{dr} = 0, \quad \text{and} \quad V = \text{constant.}$$

The surface of a charged conductor is an equipotential surface and the space within is an equipotential region. If this were not so a transfer of electricity would take place and there would be a component of electric force tangent to the surface which would cause a flow. But no flow takes place. The earth, being a conductor, is essentially at the same potential throughout and is, therefore, taken to be at zero potential. Since a charged conductor is an equipotential surface the tubes of flux are normal to the surface.

15. Potential and Intensity within any Conductor. — We will first show that there is no resultant charge at a point which is occupied by conducting material, unless the point is on the surface of the conductor. If the point is within the conducting material it is possible to surround it by a sphere of infinitesimal radius such that every point on the surface of the sphere is within the conducting material. But the intensity within conducting material is zero, $E = 0$, and, therefore, $D = 0$, since $D = \epsilon E$. Therefore,

$$N = \int_s D \, ds = 0,$$

and, consequently, there can be no resultant charge within the conducting material itself.

We have seen in Section 8 that the intensity anywhere within a hollow charged conducting sphere is zero and, therefore, the potential is constant, provided, of course, there are no free charges inside the sphere. We are now in a position to inquire into the more general case, i.e., what are the conditions as regards intensity and potential inside *any* conducting body whatsoever, be it solid or hollow? Let B, Fig. 10, be any charged conductor of any size or shape whatsoever. As we have seen, any charge it may have resides wholly on the surface, which is an equipotential surface. Now, if the space within the equipotential surface B is not an equipotential region and at the same potential as the surface, an equipotential surface A can be drawn within B. If so, the potential of B is at every point either above or below that of A. If above, there is a field of force between B and A and the tubes of flux are everywhere directed inward, and if below, the tubes of flux are directed outward. If there is a field of either sense we have by Gauss's law

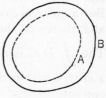

FIG. 10

$$\int_s D \, ds = 4\pi q,$$

where q is the resultant charge within the surface A. But there is no charge within the surface A, and therefore, $\int_s D\,ds = 0$. That is, there is no field over the surface A. The $\int D\,ds$ might conceivably be zero owing to the summation of equal positive and negative values. This we see cannot obtain since the intensity E must have the same sign all over the surface A because the potential of A is everywhere either above or below that of B. Therefore, the intensity must be zero at every point on the surface of A. The same argument holds for all surfaces that may be drawn within B, and holds whether the space be wholly filled with conducting material or not. Thus the region within B is an equipotential region and the intensity is everywhere equal to zero.

It follows from the foregoing that there cannot be a charge on the inner surface of a hollow conducting body unless there is a charge within the hollow space. If there were we could draw the surface A within the conducting material between the inner and outer surfaces. We should then have

$$\int_s D\,ds = 4\pi q,$$

and there would be a field of force and hence a difference of potential. But a difference of potential cannot exist within conducting material, and, therefore, the intensity at every point on the surface of A is zero. The $\int_s D\,ds$ is zero, and therefore, q is zero. If, however, there *is* a charge within the hollow space then there must be an equal and opposite charge on the inner surface of the hollow conductor. This follows since the surface A, if drawn *in* the conducting material between the inner and outer surfaces, has zero intensity everywhere over its surface. Therefore,

$$\int_s D\,ds = 0,$$

and the resultant charge within A is zero.

This discussion makes general the special case treated in Section 8. This has a very important practical application in electric screening. Any closed conductor constitutes a screen for electric fields outside of it. Whatever electric fields may exist outside a closed conducting surface the intensity within the surface will remain zero since the region within a closed conducting surface is always an equipotential region.

16. Flux Density and Intensity outside a very long Charged Cylindrical Conductor. — Let the charge per unit length be λ cgse. units. Enclose a unit length of the cylinder with a concentric Gaussian surface, Fig. 11. The ends, a and b, of this short cylinder will contribute nothing to the total flux, as the tubes of flux, being radial, are parallel to the ends. Therefore, applying Gauss's law to this cylindrical enclosure, we have

$$2\pi r D = 4\pi\lambda, \quad \text{or} \quad D = \frac{2\lambda}{r}, \quad \text{and} \quad E = \frac{2\lambda}{\epsilon r}, \qquad (16.1)$$

where λ is the linear density. r is measured from the axis of the cylinder, and, therefore, the radius of the cylinder does not affect E. It is assumed that the cylinder is so long that the tubes of flux are radial and normal to the surface for some distance from it. However, for great distances this expression is not exact unless the cylindrical conductor is infinite in length. Thus the accuracy with which this formula gives the value of E for large values of r will depend upon the length of the cylinder.

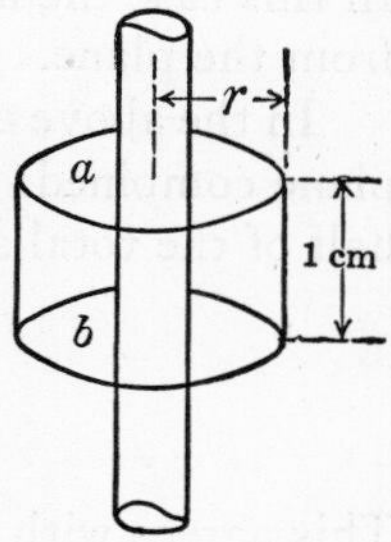

FIG. 11

Potential. — Since $E = -\dfrac{\partial V}{\partial r}$, we may obtain an expression for the potential difference as follows:

$$\frac{\partial V}{\partial r} = -\frac{2\lambda}{\epsilon r}, \quad \text{and} \quad V = -\int_{r_2}^{r_1} \frac{2\lambda}{\epsilon r} \, dr = \frac{2\lambda}{\epsilon} \log_e \frac{r_2}{r_1}, \qquad (16.2)$$

where $r_2 > r_1$. This expression suffers the same limitations as does the expression for intensity. Treating the above integral as an indefinite integral, we have

$$V = C - \frac{2\lambda}{\epsilon} \log_e r, \qquad (16.3)$$

where C is a constant of integration which can be evaluated only when the boundary conditions are known.

17. Intensity Due to a thin Charged Lamina of Infinite Extent. —

Suppose we have an infinite plane distribution of electricity of uniform

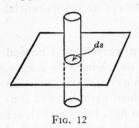

FIG. 12

surface density σ. It is obvious that the tubes of flux are everywhere normal to the surface of the plane on either side. Let us take a cylindrical Gaussian enclosure with sides parallel to the tubes of flux which cuts the plane as shown in Fig. 12. Let ds be the area of the surface cut out on the plane, and hence also the areas of the ends of the Gaussian cylinder. The contribution of each end of the cylinder to Gauss's integral is $D\,ds = \epsilon E\,ds$. Therefore, for both ends of the cylinder, we have

$$2\epsilon E\,ds = 4\pi\sigma\,ds, \text{ whence } E = \frac{2\pi\sigma}{\epsilon}. \qquad (17.1)$$

In this case the intensity is constant and independent of the distance from the plane.

In the above expression σ is the surface density on both sides of the plane combined. Let the surface density on one side of the plane be half of the total surface density or σ_1. Then

$$E = \frac{4\pi\sigma_1}{\epsilon}. \qquad (17.2)$$

This agrees with the expression obtained in Section 10.

18. Measurement of the Fundamental Electronic Charge. — As

has been stated, electricity is not continuous, but, on the contrary, occurs in extremely small discrete elementary units. This was the important discovery that was made at the very end of the last century. It is very essential for any quantitative discussion of atomic phenomena in electricity to know the magnitude of the fundamental natural unit of electricity. One of the most accurate methods for the measurement of this elementary unit of electricity was devised by R. A. Millikan. The observations were made on minute charged drops of oil, and, therefore, the experiment is known as the *Millikan oil-drop experiment*.[1]

[1] See, Electons (+ and −), Protons, Photons, Neutrons, and Cosmic Rays by R. A. Millikan, p. 118.

Millikan's oil-drop layout is indicated diagrammatically in Fig. 13. Of course, the actual experimental setup was very complicated. Two brass plates, *a* and *b*, are placed horizontally, one above the other, accurately parallel and separated by about 0.5 cm. The plates, as indicated, are held in place by a bakelite frame, which serves, also, as an insulator. A battery B of potential *V* is connected to the brass plates through a reversing switch, the potential difference between the plates being controlled by a potentiometer resistor *r*. The upper plate is ordinarily positive and the lower negative, so that a negatively charged drop will move upward. The top plate has several very fine holes, one of which *h* is shown, so as to admit oil drops to the observation chamber *C* from the spray chamber above. Oil is sprayed into the spray chamber through the orifice *O* by means of an atomizer. Oil was used so as to prevent loss of weight by evaporation. Many of the very small oil drops will find their way through the holes in the upper plate to the chamber *C* below. Some of these oil drops will be charged in the process of formation. However, in order that there may be a plentiful supply of electrons present, the air in the observation chamber *C* may be ionized by X-rays or radium. The oil drops in chamber *C* are

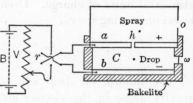

FIG. 13

bound to pick up or lose ions, either positive or negative. After passing through the opening *h* a charged oil drop will settle to the plate *b* in the absence of an electric field. Falling in the viscous air a drop acquires a certain constant terminal velocity. When the electric field is applied, with polarity as shown in the Figure, negatively charged drops will be retarded, arrested in flight, or caused to move upward depending upon the strength of the field. If charged positively a drop will move downward with a greater velocity than when acted upon by gravity alone. The oil drops are observed with a long-focus microscope through the glass window ω, being illuminated by a flash light through another window not shown. The illuminated drops appear as tiny bright spots of light. In the eyepiece of the microscope there is a calibrated scale, each division corresponding to a definite distance that an oil drop may move in the field of view. A single drop, if negatively charged, may be held in the field of view for a half hour or longer.

Let w be the weight in gms. of an oil drop which is under observation. Then, since the terminal velocity is always proportional to the force acting upon the drop, we will have, when the electric field is zero,

$$wg = Kv_1, \tag{18.1}$$

where K is a factor of proportionality.

Now, let the electric field be applied, with polarity as shown, and strong enough so that the negatively charged drops move upward. We will then have for the particular drop under observation

$$Ee_n - wg = Kv_2, \tag{18.2}$$

where $E = V/300d$ cgse. units, V being the difference in potential between the plates expressed in volts (1 volt $= 1/300$ cgse. p.d.), and d the distance between the plates in cms. e_n is the charge on the drop expressed in cgse. units, the subscript n indicating the number of elemental units of charge. Dividing one equation by the other, we have, on solving for e_n,

$$e_n = \frac{wg}{Ev_1}(v_1 + v_2). \tag{18.3}$$

The minute oil drop will settle down under the influence of gravity alone in the viscous air with a limiting velocity given by Sir George Stokes's law.

$$v = \frac{2}{9}\frac{gdr^2}{\eta}, \tag{18.4}$$

where g is the acceleration due to gravity in cgs. units, d the difference in density between the drop and the surrounding atmosphere expressed in gms./cm.^{3}, r the radius of the drop in cms., and η the viscosity of the air in cgs. units. The velocity v_1 was measured by timing the fall. Thus r is obtained, and then the weight w of the drop is found from the equation

$$w = \tfrac{4}{3}\pi dr^3. \tag{18.5}$$

By combining equation (18.3) with equation (18.4) and (18.5), there results

$$e_n = \frac{9\pi}{E}\sqrt{\frac{2\eta^3 v_1}{gd}}(v_1 + v_2) = C(v_1 + v_2), \tag{18.6}$$

where C is a constant for a particular drop in a constant electric field.

Let us say that the charge on the drop changes to a new value e_m by gaining or losing charge. The terminal velocity will change to a new value v_3, say. We will then have, by subtraction,

$$e_n - e_m = C(v_2 - v_3), \quad \text{or} \quad \Delta e = C\Delta v. \tag{18.7}$$

When many values of Δv are obtained for a given drop and electric field it is found that Δv is always an integral multiple of some smallest value. It follows, therefore, that Δe is, also, always an integral multiple of some smallest or basic value, which must be the elemental charge e which is sought.

The value of e_n in every case was found by Millikan to be an integral multiple of

$$e = 4.770(10)^{-10} \text{ cgse. unit} = 1.590(10)^{-19} \text{ coulomb.}$$

It was found that Stokes's law did not hold accurately for these small oil drops. Stokes derived his law on the assumption that the size of the falling body is very large as compared with the size of a molecule of air, or the mean free path in the air. Some of the very small oil drops do not conform to this assumption. Some of the drops are so small that they will, so to speak, drop through "holes in the atmosphere" between the molecules at times. Millikan made a correction to Stokes's law to meet this contingency, and the above value of e was obtained after this correction had been made. This value of e was accepted for many years as the most accurate obtainable. Later an X-ray method for measuring e, to be described in Section 223, was developed, and the value obtained was higher than Millikan's value. In fact, the discrepancy was too great to be attributed to experimental errors. Many attempts have been made to account for this discrepancy, but it is not yet fully cleared up. One cause of the discrepancy was found in the value of the coefficient of viscosity η for air which had been used by Millikan. A redetermination of η gave the value 0.0001835 at 23° C. instead of the value 0.000182 which was used by Millikan. With this new value of η the oil-drop experiment gives the value

$$e = 4.818(10)^{-10} \text{ cgse. unit.}$$

The X-ray value is $e = 4.8029(10)^{-10}$ cgse. unit. Bond found η to be 0.0001834 at 23° C. Ishida repeated the oil-drop experiment using the old value of η and obtained

$$e = 4.806(10)^{-10} \text{ cgse. unit.}$$

As a result of the exhaustive researches that have been carried out in this field it seems that the most accurate value obtained for the electronic charge e at the present time is

$$e = 4.8029(10)^{-10} \text{ cgse. unit,}$$

$$e = 1.6022(10)^{-20} \text{ cgsm. unit,}$$

$$e = 1.6022(10)^{-19} \text{ coulomb.}$$

The following conversion table is appended for reference:

Quantity	Absolute-practical units	cgsm. units	cgse. units
Charge	1 coulomb	10^{-1}	$3(10)^9$
Current	1 ampere	10^{-1}	$3(10)^9$
Resistance	1 ohm	10^9	$\dfrac{1}{9(10)^{11}}$
Emf. or p.d.	1 volt	10^8	$\dfrac{1}{300}$
Capacitance	1 farad	10^{-9}	$9(10)^{11}$
Inductance	1 henry	10^9	$\dfrac{1}{9(10)^{11}}$

PROBLEMS

1. Derive an expression for the intensity at a point outside a spherical distribution of charge of radius a and volume density ρ, ρ being a function of the radius vector only.

What is the intensity at a point P inside the sphere when the volume density ρ is proportional to the distance from the center? Take $\rho = 0$ at the center and $\rho = \rho_1$ at the surface.

2. (a) Two pith balls, each having a mass of m gms., are suspended in a vacuum from a point by two strings each of length l cm. When each pith ball is given a charge of q units each of the strings makes an angle ϕ with the vertical. Derive an expression for the magnitude of q.

(b) Derive an expression for the magnitude of q when the pith balls are suspended in a medium of dielectric coefficient ϵ.

3. Given two horizontal parallel conducting plates of very large area on one of which there is a positive charge of surface density σ and on the other an equal negative charge. Between the plates there is a dielectric of dielectric coefficient ϵ. Derive an expression for the intensity at a point P between the plates. What is the intensity at any point above or below the plates?

4. (a) Given an infinitely long conducting cylinder of radius a having a surface density σ. What is the intensity at a point outside the cylinder? (b) At a point inside the cylinder? (c) If the charge is distributed uniformly throughout the volume of the cylinder and has a volume density ρ, what is the intensity at a point outside the cylinder? At a point inside the cylinder? (d) If the volume density varies directly as the distance from the axis of the cylinder, what is the intensity at a point outside the cylinder? At a point inside the cylinder? Take the volume density 0 at the center and ρ_1 at the surface.

5. If V is expressed in spherical or polar coordinates show that

$$E_r = -\frac{\partial V}{\partial r}, \quad E_\theta = -\frac{\partial V}{r\partial\theta}, \quad E_\phi = -\frac{\partial V}{r\sin\theta\partial\phi},$$

where r, θ, and ϕ are the polar coordinates, r the radius vector, θ the polar angle, and ϕ the azimuth angle.

6. A charge of 500 cgse. units is at the point $(0,0)$ and a charge of -300 cgse. units is at the point $(10,0)$ in the xy plane. Calculate the intensity at the points $(30,0)$, $(0,30)$, and $(10,20)$. The coordinate distances are in cms. At what point in the xy plane is the intensity zero?

7. Using the data of Problem 6, derive the general expression for the potential and then calculate the potential at the given points. Calculate the intensity at the given points. To do so evaluate

$$E_x = -\frac{\partial V}{\partial x} \quad \text{and} \quad E_y = -\frac{\partial V}{\partial y}$$

Then $E = \sqrt{E_x^2 + E_y^2}$. Compare these values with those obtained in Problem 6. Investigate the potential at the point where $E = 0$.

8. A fine wire of length l cms. has distributed uniformly over its surface a charge of $+q$ cgse. units. Derive an expression for the potential at a point on the axis of the wire at a distance h beyond its end. Obtain an expression for the intensity by differentiating the expression for the potential. If the wire is 20 cms. long and bears a charge of 200 cgse. units, calculate the potential and the intensity at a point on the axis of the wire extended and 20 cms. from the proximal end.

9. A very thin circular conducting disc of radius R cms. is in the yz plane with its center at the origin of coordinates. The disc has a charge of surface density σ. Derive expressions for the potential and intensity at a point on the x axis distant h cms. from the origin. Also find the intensity when $h = 0$.

10. Derive the expression for the potential at a point outside a uniformly charged spherical shell by finding the potential for the charge on an element of the surface and integrating over the surface of the sphere. In this case evaluate the integral

$$V = \int \frac{\sigma da}{r}.$$

Then find the intensity by differentiating the expression for the potential. Also by this same method find the potential and intensity for an inside point.

11. In an atom of hydrogen there is one electron and one proton separated on the average by a distance of $1(10)^{-8}$ cm. The electron is a charge of $-4.8029(10)^{-10}$ cgse. unit and the proton has an equal positive charge. Assuming that the inverse square law holds within the atom, calculate the force between the electron and the proton. If the mass of the electron is $9.1154(10)^{-28}$ gm., calculate the frequency of the electron in its orbital motion.

12. If in an X-ray tube the potential difference between anode and cathode is 120,000 volts, calculate the energy in ergs which a cathode particle (electron) acquires in falling through this voltage. What velocity will the electron have when it strikes the target? What energy will an electron acquire in falling through one volt (electron volt)?

13. Given two isolated conducting spheres of radii a and b cms. One of the spheres is given a charge q. The spheres are then connected by a long, fine wire of negligible capacitance. In what manner will the charge distribute itself over the surfaces of the spheres? How are the surface densities on the two spheres related?

14. Given a charged conductor having a surface such that the curvature varies from point to point. Prove that the surface density varies inversely as the radius of curvature at a given point.

15. The center of a conducting sphere of radius one cm. is at the origin of coordinates in a rectangular frame of reference. The sphere is given a charge of $+200$ cgse. units. What is the potential at the surface of the sphere? At the point (50,0)? A second conducting sphere of radius 1.2 cms. is placed with its center at (30,0). A fine wire then connects the two spheres. Calculate the potential at the surface of the system. Calculate the potential at the point (50,0) after the spheres are connected. Calculate the intensity at the point (50,0) in the two cases.

16. The conditions are as in Problem 15, except that the sphere at (30,0) is given a charge of -300 cgse. units. Repeat all of the calculations as in Problem 15.

17. A parallel-plate condenser with vacuum dielectric has plates each 15 cms. square and 0.5 cm. apart. The condenser is charged until the surface densities are $+8$ and -8 cgse. units. (a) Calculate the mechanical force between the plates due to the charges. (b) Calculate the difference of potential between the plates. (c) Calculate the potential energy in the field between the plates. Assume that there is no fringing at the edges of the plates.

18. One cgsm. unit of charge is equivalent to c cgse. units of charge. What is the dielectric coefficient for a vacuum when charges are measured in cgsm. units?

19. A parallel-plate condenser has plates each 20 cms. square. The dielectric coefficient of the medium between the plates is 2. Electric charges of $+2000$ and -2000 cgse. units are placed upon the plates. (a) What is the cgse. difference of potential between the plates when 0.5 cm. apart? What is the difference of potential in volts? (b) How much work is required to move the plates 0.5 cm. farther apart? (c) What has become of this work?

20. Two equal and like point charges are at a distance of $2d$ cms. apart. Erect a plane midway between them and normal to the line joining the charges. Find in this plane the locus of points which have the maximum intensity.

21. A slender ring having a radius of r cms. is uniformly charged with q cgse. units of electricity. Derive an expression for the intensity at any point P distant x cms. from the center of the ring along the axis of the ring.

22. Suppose a particle of mass m gms. carrying a charge of e cgse. units is projected with an initial velocity u cms./sec. in a uniform electric field of intensity E cgse. units. The particle is projected against the field and parallel to the lines of flux (x axis). (a) Set up the differential equation for the motion. (b) Obtain the velocity-time equation and the time t' taken for the velocity to be reduced to zero. (c) Obtain the space-time equation and the distance passed over in time t'. The boundary conditions are: When $t = 0$, $x = 0$, $v = u$.

23. The conditions are as in Problem 22 except that the direction of projection has the same sense as the field. (a) Obtain the velocity-time equation. (b) Obtain the space-time equation. The boundary conditions are as in Problem 22.

24. The conditions are as in Problem 22 except that the direction of projection is normal to the field. Set up the differential equations for the motion in the x direction and in the y direction. Solve these equations and obtain the equation of the trajectory in rectangular coordinates. The boundary conditions are: When $t = 0$, $x = 0$, $v = u_x$, $y = 0$, $v_y = 0$.

25. Given a fine, straight wire l cms. long and having an electric charge of linear density $-\lambda$ cgse. units per cm. of length, and located in a medium of dielectric coefficient ϵ. Derive the expression for the potential at a point P located h cms. away from one end of the wire on a perpendicular from that end.

Derive also the expressions for the x and y components of the intensity at the point P, the resultant intensity, and the angle the resultant intensity makes with the perpendicular from the end of the wire (x axis).

CHAPTER II

CAPACITANCE, ELECTROSTATIC ENERGY, AND IMAGES

19. General Relations. — When a quantity Q cgse. units of electricity is imparted to several conducting bodies which are connected by long, fine wires their potentials are the same, but the quantity of charge which each will take is not, in general, the same. The quantity of charge which each will take will depend upon its size and shape when electrically isolated. Thus different conductors when in conducting communication, though at the same potential, have different capacities for holding a charge of electricity.

Let us first consider a single, isolated sphere. The cgse. potential is given by

$$V = \frac{Q}{\epsilon R}.$$

Multiplying or dividing Q by any number multiplies or divides V by the same number. Therefore, V is always proportional to Q, and so we have

$$Q = \epsilon R V = CV, \tag{19.1}$$

in which C is a constant of proportionality, and equal to ϵR in the special case of a sphere. The constant C is called the *electrostatic* capacitance of the sphere. The same argument holds for a conductor of any shape, for in general,

$$V = \int_s \frac{\sigma \, ds}{\epsilon r}. \tag{19.2}$$

In this summation multiplying or dividing every elementary charge by any number multiplies or divides V by the same number, and hence V is always proportional to Q no matter what the shape of the conductor may be, and, therefore, we may write in all cases $Q = CV$. Thus, *the capacitance of a conductor is defined as the quantity of electricity placed on the conductor which is required to produce unit potential*. This defining equation is true in any system of units.

Since the capacitance of a conductor is expressed in terms of potential, we shall expect it to be affected by the dielectric surrounding the conductor. When a charged conductor is surrounded by a dielectric the intensity E' at every point in the field of force is one ϵth of the intensity E which would obtain were the conductor in free space and bearing the same charge. Therefore, since potential is $\int E\, dr$, we see that the potential V' of a charged conductor surrounded by an infinite dielectric is one ϵth of its potential in free space. That is,

$$V' = V/\epsilon. \tag{19.3}$$

Combining this equation with the defining equation for capacitance (19.1), we have

$$C' = \frac{Q}{V'} = \frac{\epsilon Q}{V} = \epsilon C. \tag{19.4}$$

Since Q/V is the capacitance in vacuo, we see that *the capacitance of an isolated conductor in a medium of dielectric coefficient ϵ is ϵ times its capacitance in vacuo*, where ϵ is defined by equation (1.1) in the cgse. system of units.

In equation (19.4) the charge Q is the same on both sides of the equation. If, however, we put $V' = V$, the charges are not equal, but, on the contrary, we shall have

$$Q' = \epsilon Q. \tag{19.5}$$

That is, *the same isolated conductor when surrounded by a dielectric of dielectric coefficient ϵ will take ϵ times the charge it would take if at the same potential in vacuo.*

In the special case of a sphere we have $Q = \epsilon RV = CV$. Thus we see that the capacitance of an isolated sphere is ϵR, i.e., its capacitance is ϵ times its radius expressed in cms. From this relationship *the cgse. unit of capacitance has been defined as the capacitance of an isolated sphere of one cm. radius when in vacuo*, i.e., when ϵ is unity. Electrostatic capacitance is, therefore, expressed in cms.

The unit of capacitance in the practical system of units, *the farad* (f.), is $9(10)^{11}$ cgse. units. Also, by equation (19.1), *a conductor has a capacitance of one farad when its potential is one volt and its charge one coulomb.* Therefore, a sphere having a radius of $9(10)^{11}$ cms. has a capacitance of one farad. A microfarad (mf.) is 10^{-6} f., or $9(10)^5$ cgse. units; it is the capacitance of an isolated sphere having a radius

$1\,\mu f = 10^{-6} f$

of $9(10)^5$ cms. A micromicrofarad (mmf.) is 10^{-12} f., or 0.9 cgse. unit; it is the capacitance of an isolated sphere having a radius of 0.9 cm.

20. The Condenser. — The capacitance of an isolated conductor depends upon its dimensions and the surrounding dielectric only. When, however, it is in the neighborhood of other charged bodies its capacitance is altered. A simple experiment will serve to show this.

Let an isolated metal disc a, Fig. 14, be connected to the knob of a gold-leaf electroscope and given a charge $+q$ units of electricity. The leaves of the electroscope will diverge, the amount of divergence being a measure of the potential. The capacitance is given by the equation $q = CV$. Now bring up another and like metal disc b which is earth connected. The disc b will take an equal negative charge by induction. The leaves of the electroscope will move closer

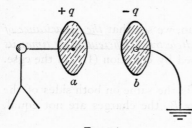

+q −q

a b

FIG. 14

together because of the proximity of the negative charge, thus showing that the potential has decreased, charge remaining constant, and, therefore, that the capacitance has increased. Move b closer to a and the leaves of the electroscope move closer together, showing that the nearer b is to a the less is its potential and, therefore, the greater its capacitance. If we insert between a and b a slab of dielectric, as for example a plate of glass, the leaves of the electroscope move still closer together, showing that the capacitance has increased because of the presence in the field of force of a dielectric of larger dielectric coefficient than that of air. This sort of an arrangement constitutes a *condenser*. Of course, disc b need not be grounded. The only requirement is that it bear an equal and opposite charge. Therefore, *a condenser consists of conductors in close proximity which may be charged oppositely, the space separating the conductors being occupied by a gaseous, solid, or liquid dielectric.* Free space is also a dielectric. It is the dielectric which is taken as the standard with dielectric coefficient equal to 1 in the cgse. system of units.

There are various types and forms of condensers, some of which will be described in the following pages. A common capacitance effect was observed in the early days of radio when in tuning an unshielded radio receiving set the volume of the received signal

changed when the hand was used in tuning. The strength of the
signal changed again when the hand was removed. The hand is an
earth-connected conductor, and, when in close proximity to the condensers and wiring of an unshielded set, changes slightly the effective
capacitance. Again, when one comes close to the oscillating circuit
of an unshielded radio transmitter, common in the early days of
radio, the capacitance is changed slightly and hence also the transmitter frequency. This effect is called *body capacitance*. The wires
in any network of conductors possess capacitance with respect to each
other. This effect is called *distributed capacitance*. The antenna of a
broadcasting transmitter forms with the ground or counterpoise a
condenser which has a definite capacitance. It is the fixed capacitance
in the antenna system. Any change in distance between antenna and
ground or counterpoise changes the capacitance and hence the fundamental frequency of the transmitted signal. This is why the Government requires that the antenna of a broadcasting transmitter be kept
tight enough so as not to sway in the wind. Many other examples of
capacitance effects will occur to the reader.

21. Energy of a Charged Conductor or Condenser. — We have as
the defining equation for the capacitance of *any* charged conductor or
condenser,

$$Q = CV.$$

In the case of a parallel-plate condenser V is the difference of potential
between the plates, and Q is the charge on one plate. V is the work
in ergs done in moving one cgse. unit of positive electricity from a
point of zero potential up to an isolated conductor or in moving one
cgse. unit of positive electricity from the negative to the positive
plate of a condenser. Therefore, the work required to move a charge
dq into its final position will be, in any case,

$$dU = V\,dq = \frac{q}{C}\,dq \text{ ergs.}$$

The total work done in raising the charge from 0 to Q is, therefore,

$$U = \int_0^Q \frac{q}{C}\,dq = \frac{Q^2}{2C} \text{ ergs.} \tag{21.1}$$

Combining this equation with the defining equation for capacitance, we have the following expressions for the energy of a charged conductor or condenser:

$$U = \frac{Q^2}{2C} = \tfrac{1}{2}CV^2 = \tfrac{1}{2}QV \text{ ergs.} \qquad (21.2)$$

In the special case of a charged sphere

$$U = \int_0^Q \frac{q \, dq}{\epsilon R} = \frac{Q^2}{2\epsilon R} \text{ ergs.} \qquad (21.3)$$

Equation (21.3) shows that the energy of a charged sphere is the energy in vacuo divided by the dielectric coefficient. This is true of a condenser as well, since, as we have seen, $V' = V/\epsilon$. Thus, if a condenser having a dielectric of coefficient ϵ has a charge Q its energy is one ϵth of what it would be were it to have a vacuum as dielectric and the same charge.

If, however, we have two condensers having the same dimensions and charged to the same potential, one containing a dielectric of coefficient ϵ and the other having a vacuum dielectric, the condenser having the dielectric of coefficient ϵ will possess ϵ times the energy of the vacuum condenser. This follows from relation (19.5), which holds for condensers as well as isolated conductors. Thus, by equation (21.2), we have

$$U = \tfrac{1}{2}Q'V = \tfrac{1}{2}\epsilon \, QV, \qquad (21.4)$$

where Q' is the charge taken by the condenser having a dielectric of coefficient ϵ and Q is the charge taken by a vacuum condenser at the same potential. Therefore, *when charged to the same potential, other things being equal, the charges and energies of condensers are directly proportional to their dielectric coefficients*.

If all quantities are measured in practical units, the energy will be expressed in *joules*, a joule being 10^7 ergs = a newton-meter. The *newton* is defined in the mks. system of units as that force which will impart to a kilogram an acceleration of one meter/sec.^{2} Therefore, a newton is 10^5 dynes.

22. Condensers Connected in Parallel and in Series. — There are two distinct ways of connecting condensers, as with all other electric

units, i.e., *parallel and series*. A parallel connection is shown in Fig. 15. When so connected the difference of potential between the plates of all of the condensers is the same, i.e., V = constant. The charge which each condenser will take however will depend upon its dimen-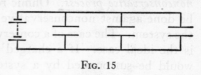

Fig. 15

sions and the nature of its dielectric, i.e., upon its capacitance. The total charge taken by the combination will be, therefore,

$$Q = q_1 + q_2 + q_3 + \cdots q_n. \tag{22.1}$$

For the total capacitance we have $Q = CV$, and for the individual capacitances, $q_1 = c_1V$, $q_2 = c_2V$, $q_3 = c_3V$, $\ldots q_n = c_nV$. Therefore by substituting in (22.1), there results

$$CV = c_1V + c_2V + c_3V + \cdots c_nV,$$

or

$$C = c_1 + c_2 + c_3 + \cdots c_n. \tag{22.2}$$

That is, when condensers are connected in parallel, the total equivalent capacitance is the algebraic sum of the capacitances of the individual condensers.

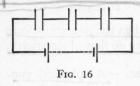

Fig. 16

A series grouping of condensers is shown in Fig. 16. When so connected the charge q taken by each condenser is the same, i.e., q = const. This follows since the same quantity of electricity is displaced across each section of the circuit in the same time interval. Hence in this case the total potential difference over all is the sum of the potential differences over the individual condensers. That is,

$$V = v_1 + v_2 + v_3 + \cdots v_n. \tag{22.3}$$

Therefore,

$$1/C = 1/c_1 + 1/c_2 + 1/c_3 + \cdots 1/c_n. \tag{22.4}$$

Thus, when condensers are connected in series, the reciprocal of the total or equivalent capacitance is the algebraic sum of the reciprocals of the individual capacitances. Equations (22.2) and (22.4) may be used with any system of units.

23. Dissipation of Energy on Transfer of Charge. — Whenever a charge of electricity is transferred from one point to another by conducting material there is dissipation of energy. Such a transfer is a *nonconservative process.* Ohmic resistance is present and work must be done against nonconservative forces which cannot be returned to the system. The case of a conservative system discussed in Section 13 is the ideal case. If a charged body were isolated in free space it would be surrounded by a system of equipotential surfaces and a transfer of charge from one equipotential surface to another would be independent of the path. However, if the transfer is made by means of conducting material, as in actual cases, there is always a transformation of electric energy into heat energy.

This is evident when a charged conductor or condenser is connected in parallel with another charged conductor or condenser and a transfer of electricity takes place. Let the charges be Q_1 and Q_2, the capacitances C_1 and C_2. Before connection is made the combined energy of the two condensers is

$$U_1 = Q_1^2/2C_1 + Q_2^2/2C_2,$$

and after joining the total energy is $U_2 = \dfrac{(Q_1 + Q_2)^2}{2(C_1 + C_2)}$. Therefore, the loss of energy is

$$u = U_1 - U_2 = \frac{Q_1^2}{2C_1} + \frac{Q_2^2}{2C_2} - \frac{(Q_1 + Q_2)^2}{2(C_1 + C_2)} = \frac{(Q_1 C_2 - Q_2 C_1)^2}{2C_1 C_2 (C_1 + C_2)}.$$

The loss is zero only when $Q_1 C_2 = Q_2 C_1$, i.e., when the potentials were the same before connection was made, and hence no flow of electricity.

24. Capacitance of a Spherical Condenser. — A spherical condenser consists of two concentric spheres separated by a dielectric.

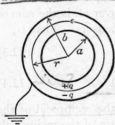

FIG. 17

Let b be the radius of the outer sphere and a the radius of the inner sphere, Fig. 17. Give to the inner sphere a charge of $+q$ cgse. units of electricity, and ground the outer sphere. The charge is given to the inner sphere by means of a fine wire passing through a small hole in the outer sphere and insulated therefrom. Because of symmetry it is seen that the tubes of flux between the inner and outer spheres are uniformly distributed and radial, converging to the common center of the two spheres. The field of force is restricted to the space between the spheres, which is occupied by a dielectric of coefficient ϵ, let us say. Imagine a spherical surface of radius r in the dielectric between the spheres and concentric with them. The intensity is constant over the surface of this sphere, which constitutes a Gaussian surface. We therefore have

$$4\pi r^2 \epsilon E = 4\pi q, \quad \text{and hence} \quad E = \frac{q}{\epsilon r^2}. \tag{24.1}$$

also,

$$\frac{dV}{dr} = -E = -\frac{q}{\epsilon r^2}.$$

Therefore,

$$V = -\int_b^a \frac{q}{\epsilon r^2}\, dr = \frac{q}{\epsilon}\left(\frac{1}{a} - \frac{1}{b}\right) = \frac{q}{\epsilon}\left(\frac{b-a}{ab}\right). \tag{24.2}$$

On combining this equation with the defining equation for capacitance we have

$$C = \frac{\epsilon\, ab}{b - a}. \tag{24.3}$$

If a and b are expressed in cms., C is in cgse. units. This formula may also be written

$$C = \frac{\epsilon\,\sqrt{A_1 A_2}}{4\pi\, d}, \tag{24.4}$$

where A_1 and A_2 are the areas of the surfaces of the spheres and d is the radial distance between them. Capacitance in cgse. units may be changed to practical units by means of the conversion table given in Section 18.

In the case just considered the inner sphere was given a charge and the outer sphere was grounded. The outer sphere then took a negative charge by induction. Thus the proximity of the earth and other earth-connected objects in no wise affected the capacitance of the condenser. The grounded outer sphere acts as a screen.

The conditions are somewhat different, however, if the outer sphere is given a charge and the inner sphere is grounded. If the potential difference between inner and outer spheres is the same as in the first case, the charge on the outer sphere will not be the same as before, since an added charge is required because the outer sphere forms a condenser with the earth and surrounding grounded objects.

If the outer sphere is given a positive charge, the part of this charge which is concerned in the capacitance effect with the inner sphere is

$$q_1 = \frac{\epsilon \, ab \, V}{b - a}.$$

Let C' be the capacitance between the outer sphere and earth and grounded objects. Then the charge concerned in this capacitance effect is

$$q_2 = C'V.$$

Hence the total charge on the outer sphere is

$$q = q_1 + q_2 = \frac{\epsilon \, ab \, V}{b - a} + C'V.$$

The total capacitance is

$$C = \frac{q}{V} = \frac{\epsilon \, ab}{b - a} + C'. \tag{24.5}$$

C' will vary with conditions, and besides cannot be measured with any degree of accuracy. Therefore, it is preferable to ground the outer sphere and give a charge to the inner sphere.

25. Capacitance of a Parallel-Plate Condenser. — A parallel-plate condenser consists of two parallel metal plates of any form whatsoever separated by a dielectric, Fig. 18. Different forms are given to the plates for one purpose or another, but the shape of the plates in no wise alters the nature of the problem. Let one plate be given a charge of $+ q$ units and the other a charge of $- q$ units by connecting the plates to the terminals of a battery or d.c. dynamo. The field of force is wholly between the plates, neglecting fringing at the edges, and the tubes of flux are straight and uniformly spaced. Except at the edges the field of force is constant. Its intensity is

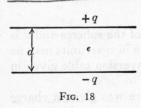

FIG. 18

$$E = \frac{4\pi \, \sigma}{\epsilon} = \frac{4\pi \, q}{\epsilon \, A}.$$

Therefore, by the definition of potential, we have

$$V = Ed = \frac{4\pi \, qd}{\epsilon \, A} \text{ ergs unit charge.} \tag{25.1}$$

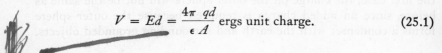

Combining with the defining equation for capacitance we have

$$C = \frac{\epsilon A}{4\pi d} \text{ cgse. units.} \qquad (25.2)$$

d is in cms. and A in cms.^{2} Changing to practical units, we have

$$C = 8.85(10)^{-14}\frac{\epsilon A}{d} \text{ farads} = 8.85(10)^{-8}\frac{\epsilon A}{d} \text{ mf.}$$

$$= 8.85(10)^{-2}\frac{\epsilon A}{d} \text{ mmf.}$$

In these formulae no correction has been made for the curvature of the field at the edges of the plates. If the areas of the plates are large compared with the distance d the error introduced may be neglected. For more exact formulae and formulae for other types of condensers the reader is referred to Circular 74, U. S. Bureau of Standards, and to Formulae and Tables for the Calculation of A.C. Problems by Louis Cohen (1913), Chapter III.

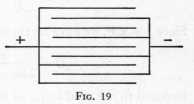

FIG. 19

If instead of two plates there are n similar plates equally spaced, alternating plates being connected together forming a parallel grouping, Fig. 19, the formula is

$$C = \frac{\epsilon(n-1)A}{4\pi d} \text{ cgse. units} = 8.85(10)^{-8}\frac{\epsilon(n-1)A}{d} \text{ mf.} \qquad (25.3)$$

26. Capacitance of Coaxial Cylinders. — When a metal cylinder is placed coaxially inside a hollow metal cylinder of larger radius, the space between the cylinders being occupied by a dielectric, we have what is called a cylindrical condenser. A submarine cable is a practical example of a cylindrical condenser. The cable itself is the inner cylinder, the salt water of the ocean is the outer cylinder, and the insulation enclosing the cable is the dielectric. A cross section of such a cable is represented diagrammatically in Fig. 20. If we consider the cable to be of great length it

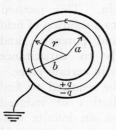

FIG. 20

can be seen that the tubes of flux are normal to the common axis of the cylinders, equally distributed and radial.

Let the charge on the inner cylinder be $+q$ cgse. units per cm. of length. Imagine a Gaussian cylindrical surface of radius r between the inner and outer cylinder such that $a < r < b$, where a is the radius of the inner cylinder and b that of the outer. We then have

$$2\pi r \epsilon E = 4\pi q, \quad \text{and hence} \quad E = \frac{2q}{\epsilon r}. \tag{26.1}$$

But

$$\frac{dV}{dr} = -E = -\frac{2q}{\epsilon r}. \tag{26.2}$$

And therefore,

$$V = -\int_b^a \frac{2q}{\epsilon r} dr = \frac{2q}{\epsilon} \log_e \frac{b}{a}. \tag{26.3}$$

Since $q = CV$, we have for the capacitance per unit length of cable,

$$C = \frac{\epsilon}{2 \log_e (b/a)} \quad \text{cgse. units.} \tag{26.4}$$

Reduced to mfs. and $\log_{10}$, we have

$$C = \frac{2.416(10)^{-7}\epsilon}{\log_{10}(b/a)} \quad \text{mfs.} \tag{26.5}$$

27. Electric Images. — The distribution of induced charges upon conducting surfaces may be found very simply in many cases by the method of electric images which was devised by Lord Kelvin. This method leads also to a solution of field intensity and potential, and consequently to capacitance calculations in certain cases.

Let it be required to find the distribution of induced charge upon an infinite conducting plane nm, maintained at zero potential, due to a point charge $+q$ distant h from the plane. Fig. 21 shows the distri-

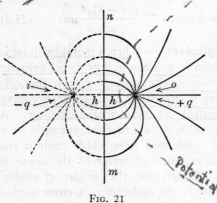

FIG. 21

bution of electric flux. It can be shown that the intensity at all points upon the plane and to the right of the plane will be the same if the plane is removed and a point charge $-q$ is placed at i, such that $ic = co$, the line oi being normal to the plane nm, Fig. 22. Thus the scheme is to find an electric charge such that a certain surface, ultimately to coincide with the conducting surface upon which there is an induced charge due to the point charge $+q$, shall be the equipotential surface $V = 0$. The charge $-q$ is called the *electric image* of the charge $+q$, after the optical analogy.

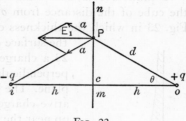

FIG. 22

At any point on the plane the potential is zero. That is,

$$\frac{q}{oP} - \frac{q}{iP} = 0, \tag{27.1}$$

when we consider the point charge $+q$ at o and the point charge $-q$ at i and the plane nm removed. It is required to find the distribution of the surface density of the induced charge upon nm which will produce the same field as the charge $-q$ at i with the plane nm removed. Considering $-q$ and $+q$, we have at P

$$a = \frac{q}{\epsilon d^2}, \quad \text{and} \quad E_1 = \frac{2q}{\epsilon d^2} \cos \theta = \frac{2qh}{\epsilon d^3}.$$

Also from Coulomb's theorem, if there is a surface density $-\sigma$ at P upon the plane nm due to $+q$ at o,

$$E_2 = \frac{4\pi \sigma}{\epsilon}.$$

If the intensities E_1 and E_2 are to be the same, we must have

$$-\frac{4\pi \sigma}{\epsilon} = \frac{2qh}{\epsilon d^3}, \quad \text{or} \quad \sigma = -\frac{qh}{2\pi d^3}. \tag{27.2}$$

This expression determines the value of σ at all points upon the plane nm which will produce the same field intensity at all points to the right of *nm* as would be produced by a charge $-q$ at i with the plane removed.

Equation (27.2) shows that the surface density varies inversely as the cube of the distance from o. This is represented graphically in Fig. 23 in which the thickness of the shaded area is proportional to the surface density. In the calculations for Fig. 23 a charge of 100 cgse. units was taken at a perpendicular distance $h = 10$ cms. from the plane. The Figure shows that the induced, negative charge on the conducting plane is heaped up near the charge $+q$, i.e., there is an excess of free electrons on the plane *nm* distributed as indicated by the shaded area in the Figure. If there were a charge $-q$ at o there would be a dearth of free electrons near o, which might be represented graphically by the image of the shaded area in Fig. 23. It can be shown that the fields of force to the right of the plane *nm* are identical when we have the charges $-q$ and $+q$, on the one hand, and the charge $+q$ and the induced charge of variable density $-\sigma$ on the plane *nm*, on the other hand. Thus there is one and only one distribution of $-\sigma$ which will fulfill the conditions, and that is expressed by equation (27.2).

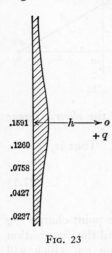

.1591

.1260

.0758

.0427

.0237

FIG. 23

The force between the charge $+q$ and the induced charge upon the plane is the same as the force between $+q$ and $-q$, or

$$F = -\frac{q^2}{\epsilon(io)^2} = -\frac{q^2}{\epsilon\, 4h^2} \text{ dynes.}$$

The total induced charge upon the plane is

$$q' = -\int_0^\infty 2\pi\, r\, \sigma\, dr = -q \int_0^{\frac{\pi}{2}} \sin\theta\, d\theta = -q. \qquad (27.3)$$

Thus the charge $-q$ to the left of the plane *nm* may be considered removed and distributed over the equipotential plane *nm*, in the manner found, and the field of force to the left of *nm* obliterated.

The potential and intensity at any point P in the field of force due to the charges $+q$ and $-q$, and hence also in the field of force due to

$+q$ and the negative distributed induced charge on the plane nm, are obtained as follows, Fig. 24:

$$V = \frac{q}{\epsilon r} - \frac{q}{\epsilon s} = \frac{q}{\epsilon r} - \frac{q}{\epsilon \sqrt{r^2 + 4h^2 + 4rh \cos \theta}}$$

$$E_r = -\frac{\partial V}{\partial r} = \frac{q}{\epsilon r^2} - \frac{q(r + 2h \cos \theta)}{\epsilon(r^2 + 4h^2 + 4rh \cos \theta)^{\frac{3}{2}}} \qquad (27.4)$$

$$E_\theta = -\frac{\partial V}{r \, \partial \theta} = \frac{2qh \sin \theta}{\epsilon(r^2 + 4h^2 + 4rh \cos \theta)^{\frac{3}{2}}}. \qquad (27.5)$$

28. Electric Image in Case of a Sphere. — We may take as one other example under electric images that of a charge induced upon a grounded spherical conductor. We are to find a point i within the sphere and a charge e which when placed at i will make all points upon the surface of the sphere at zero potential when the sphere is removed, Fig. 25.

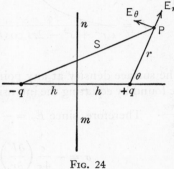

Fig. 24

A charge $+q$ at o will induce a negative charge upon the sphere of distributed density $-\sigma$. To obtain the position of i take

$$(co)(ci) = a^2. \qquad (28.1)$$

Then

$$a/co = ci/a.$$

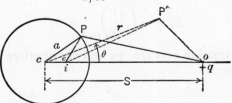

Fig. 25

Thus triangles coP and ciP are similar, and hence $iP/oP = a/co$ for all points upon the surface of the sphere. If we take

$$e = -\frac{a}{s} q = -\frac{iP}{oP} q, \qquad (28.2)$$

then all points upon the surface of the sphere will be at zero potential due to a charge $-e$ at i and a charge $+q$ at o. Thus,

$$V = \frac{q}{\epsilon(oP)} - \frac{e}{\epsilon(iP)} = \frac{q}{\epsilon(oP)} - \frac{iP}{\epsilon(oP)} \times \frac{q}{iP} = 0. \quad (28.3)$$

In calculating potential and intensity it will be convenient to use polar coordinates with c as origin and r, θ as variables, the line co being $\theta = 0$. At any point P' in the field of force outside the sphere the potential due to $+q$ and ϱ and $-e$ at i is

$$V = \frac{q}{\epsilon(oP')} - \frac{qa}{\epsilon s(iP')} ,$$

or

$$V = \frac{q}{\epsilon(r^2 + s^2 - 2rs \cos \theta)^{1/2}} - \frac{aq}{\epsilon s \left(r^2 + \dfrac{a^4}{s^2} - 2r \dfrac{a^2}{s} \cos \theta \right)^{1/2}}.$$

The surface density at any point P on the surface of the sphere may be found by equating the intensity at P (due to $-e$ at i and $+q$ at o) to $\dfrac{4\pi\sigma}{\epsilon}$. Therefore, since $E_r = -\left(\dfrac{\partial V}{\partial r}\right)_{r=a}$,

$$\sigma = -\frac{\epsilon}{4\pi}\left(\frac{\partial V}{\partial r}\right)_{r=a} = -\frac{q}{4\pi}\frac{s^2 - a^2}{a(oP)^3}. \quad (28.4)$$

Thus the surface density varies inversely as the cube of the distance from o.

Further,

$$E_\theta = -\left(\frac{\partial V}{r\, \partial \theta}\right)_{r=a} = 0.$$

The force of attraction between $+q$ and the negative induced charge upon the sphere is

$$F = -\frac{eq}{\epsilon(oi)^2} = -\frac{aq^2}{\epsilon s(oi)^2} = -\frac{aq^2}{\epsilon s(oc-ci)^2} = -\frac{asq^2}{\epsilon(s^2-a^2)^2} \text{ dynes. } (28.5)$$

The total induced charge upon the sphere is $e = -aq/s$.

The foregoing discussion is based upon the requirement that the surface of the sphere be at zero potential. If the surface of the sphere is at any other potential than zero, a uniformly distributed charge Q over its surface, in addition to the induced charge, will give a potential $Q/\epsilon a$ at the surface of the sphere. Thus the surface of the sphere remains an equipotential surface.

If the sphere is insulated and uncharged to begin with in free space, say, the total charge on the sphere must be maintained at zero when in the presence of a charge $+q$ at a distance s from the center of the sphere. In order that this may be true, there must be the equivalent of a charge $+e = +aq/s$ at the center in addition to the charge $-e$ at i. Since, with a charge $-e$ at i alone, the potential at the surface of the sphere is zero, the potential at the surface of the insulated sphere must be $+e/a = + q/s$. Then, the attraction between the sphere and charge $+q$ at o is that due to a charge $+aq/s$ at c, a charge $-aq/s$ at i, and a charge $+q$ at o, or approximately

$$-\frac{2a^3q^2}{s^5},$$

if s is large as compared with a. If the insulated sphere is now given a charge $\pm Q$, the potential at the surface of the sphere is $+ q/s \pm Q/a$, and the force between the charge $+q$ at o and the charged sphere is that due to charges $+aq/s$ and $\pm Q$ at c, a charge $-aq/s$ at i, on the one hand, and a charge $+q$ at o, on the other hand.

A lower limit to the force acting on an uncharged spherical conductor when in an electric field of force may be obtained by applying the condition that the space rate of change of energy is a force. We have already found the correct expression for this force by the method of images. Let us consider an uncharged spherical conductor of radius a, with center distant s from a point charge q. The potential energy in the field in free space is $U = E^2/8\pi$ ergs/cm.^{3} But E at a distance s from the charge q is q/s^2. Therefore, $U = q^2/8\pi s^4$. $F = - dU/ds = q^2/2\pi s^5$ dynes/cm.^{3} The force acting on a sphere of volume $v = \frac{4}{3}\pi a^3$ would be $2a^3q^2/3s^5$ dynes. This is $\frac{1}{3}$ of the value obtained above. The result here obtained is too small owing to the fact that the presence of the conductor in the field distorts it. That is, the tubes of flux, instead of being radial from the charge q in the neighborhood of the sphere, bend in all around the sphere so as to meet its surface normally, since it is an equipotential surface.

29. Capacitance of a Telegraph Wire. — The capacitance of a single horizontal telegraph wire may be calculated by means of its electric image. Such a wire is a cylindrical conductor at a distance h

above the surface of the earth, which may be taken as an infinite plane at zero potential, Fig. 26.

Let the charge on the wire be $+q$ cgse. units per cm. of length.

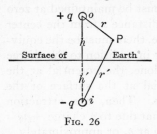

FIG. 26

This will induce a negative charge upon the surface of the earth beneath the wire. In order to find the field intensity and the surface density $-\sigma$ upon the surface of the earth, let us take the image of $+q$ at o as $-q$ at i a distance h beneath the surface of the earth. In order to obtain the potential at a distance r from a uniformly charged cylindrical conductor, we draw a Gaussian surface around the wire, concentric with it, and of radius r. Then

$$2\pi r \epsilon E = 4\pi q, \quad \text{and} \quad E = \frac{2q}{\epsilon r}.$$

Hence

$$V = -\int \frac{2q}{\epsilon r} dr + C' = C' - \frac{2q}{\epsilon} \log_e r.$$

Therefore, the potential at a point P distant r and r' respectively from the wire and its image is

$$V = C'' - \frac{2q}{\epsilon} \log_e r + \frac{2q}{\epsilon} \log_e r'.$$

If the potential is to vanish at the surface of the earth $C'' = 0$. Therefore,

$$V = \frac{2q}{\epsilon} \log_e \frac{r'}{r}.$$

Let a be the radius of the wire. At the surface of the wire $r = a$, and $r' = 2h$, very nearly. Hence, at the surface of the wire the potential is

$$V = \frac{2q}{\epsilon} \log_e \frac{2h}{a}.$$

And, since $q = CV$, we have for the capacitance

$$C = \frac{\epsilon}{2 \log_e \dfrac{2h}{a}} \text{ cgse. units/cm.} \tag{29.1}$$

The expression just derived is not quite accurate. A more accurate expression is obtained by first deriving an expression for the capacitance of two infinitely long parallel wires. Let o and b be the sections of two infinitely long charged filaments l cms. apart, Fig. 27.

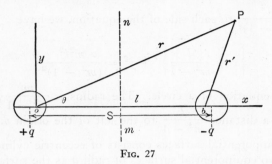

FIG. 27

Let the charges per cm. of length be $+q$ and $-q$ cgse. units. Since the sections of the filaments are points, the potential at P, distant r and r' respectively from the filaments, is given by

$$V = \frac{2q}{\epsilon} \log_e r' - \frac{2q}{\epsilon} \log_e r = \frac{q}{\epsilon} \log_e \frac{r'^2}{r^2}.$$

This equation satisfies the requirement that the potential shall be zero at every point on the median plane nm. The condition to be satisfied at all points on any equipotential surface is that r'^2/r^2 shall be constant. Therefore, since

$$r'^2 = r^2 + l^2 - 2rl \cos \theta,$$

we have

$$\frac{r'^2}{r^2} = \frac{r^2 + l^2 - 2rl \cos \theta}{r^2} = m^2,$$

where m is a particular constant for each equipotential surface. Thus

$$m^2 r^2 - r^2 + 2rl \cos \theta = l^2.$$

Dividing by $m^2 - 1$, we have

$$r^2 + 2r \cos \theta \left(\frac{l}{m^2 - 1} \right) = \frac{l^2}{m^2 - 1}.$$

Transforming to rectangular coordinates by use of $x = r \cos \theta$ and $y = r \sin \theta$, there results

$$x^2 + 2x \left(\frac{l}{m^2 - 1} \right) + y^2 = \frac{l^2}{m^2 - 1}.$$

Adding $\dfrac{l^2}{(m^2 - 1)^2}$ to each side of the equation, we have

$$\left\{ x + \frac{l}{m^2 - 1} \right\}^2 + y^2 = \frac{m^2 l^2}{(m^2 - 1)^2}.$$

This is the equation of a circle. The radius is $\dfrac{ml}{m^2 - 1}$, and the center is at a distance $\dfrac{l}{m^2 - 1}$ to the left of the origin o. Thus, a family of equipotential surfaces consists of eccentric cylinders. We may take two equipotential surfaces of radii a as the surfaces of the wires considered, and let the charge on each filament be distributed over the surface of the wire. The intensity inside of each wire will be zero. The radius of each wire is given by

$$a = \frac{ml}{m^2 - 1}. \tag{29.2}$$

The distance between the axes of the wires is

$$s = l + \frac{2l}{m^2 - 1} = \frac{m^2 + 1}{m^2 - 1} l. \tag{29.3}$$

Eliminating l between (29.2) and (29.3), we have

$$m^2 - \frac{s}{a} m + 1 = 0.$$

The roots are

$$m = \frac{s \pm \sqrt{s^2 - 4a^2}}{2a}.$$

The positive root of m refers to the positive wire, and the negative root refers to the negative wire. Thus the potential of the positive wire is

$$V = \frac{2q}{\epsilon} \log_e m = \frac{2q}{\epsilon} \log_e \frac{s + \sqrt{s^2 - 4a^2}}{2a}, \tag{29.4}$$

and of the negative wire

$$V' = \frac{2q}{\epsilon} \log_e \frac{s - \sqrt{s^2 - 4a^2}}{2a}.$$

The difference of potential between the wires is

$$V - V' = \frac{2q}{\epsilon} \log_e \frac{s + \sqrt{s^2 - 4a^2}}{s - \sqrt{s^2 - 4a^2}}.$$

Therefore, the capacitance per unit length is

$$C = \frac{q}{V - V'} = \frac{\epsilon}{2 \log_e \dfrac{s + \sqrt{s^2 - 4a^2}}{s - \sqrt{s^2 - 4a^2}}}. \tag{29.5}$$

Now to obtain the exact expression for the capacitance of a single wire relative to the earth, at a distance h above its surface, we have only to consider the median plane nm to be replaced by the surface of the earth at $V = 0$, and the charge $-q$ an induced charge distributed over it. The field between the median plane and the positive wire has not been changed. The field on the other side of the wire has vanished. Thus, the potential of the single, horizontal wire relative to the earth is obtained by setting $s = 2h$ in (29.4). Therefore,

$$V = \frac{2q}{\epsilon} \log_e \frac{h + \sqrt{h^2 - a^2}}{a}.$$

Then the capacitance per unit length is

$$C = \frac{q}{V} = \frac{\epsilon}{2 \log_e \dfrac{h + \sqrt{h^2 - a^2}}{a}} \text{ cgse. units.} \tag{29.6}$$

Putting $a = 0$ under the radical this expression reduces to (29.1).[1]

The force between two parallel conductors charged equally and oppositely is the same as the force between the filaments within the wires. The intensity due to an infinitely long filament bearing a charge of q units per cm. of length is, at perpendicular distance l, by (16.1)

$$E = \frac{2q}{\epsilon l}.$$

[1] See Principles of Electricity by Page and Adams, page 106; The Theory of Electricity and Magnetism by Webster, page 312.

The second filament is in the field of the first, and therefore the force on a charge q per unit length is

$$F = Eq = -\frac{2q^2}{\epsilon l} \text{ dynes.} \tag{29.7}$$

The distance l, of course, approaches more nearly to the distance between the wires the smaller the wires.

omit most of.

30. Parallel-Plate Condenser with Compound Dielectric. — We

FIG. 28

may take an ordinary parallel-plate, air condenser with distance d between the plates and area A, and insert a slab of dielectric of coefficient ϵ, thickness t, and area greater than A, as shown in Fig. 28.

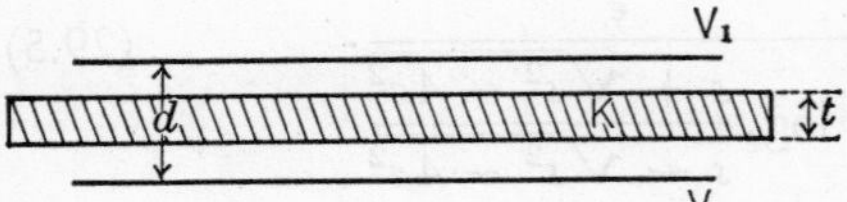

The intensity between the plates of a parallel-plate condenser is

$$E = \frac{4\pi q}{\epsilon A},$$

except where fringing occurs at the edges of the plates. Therefore,

$$V_1 - V_0 = V = \frac{4\pi q}{A}(d - t) + \frac{4\pi qt}{\epsilon A},$$

or

$$V = \frac{4\pi q}{A}\{(d - t) + t/\epsilon\}.$$

And, since $q = CV$,

$$C = \frac{A}{4\pi\{(d-t) + t/\epsilon\}} \text{ cgse. units.} \tag{30.1}$$

A condenser with a compound dielectric may be used to measure the dielectric coefficient ϵ. The dielectric coefficients of several dielectrics were measured by Boltzmann in 1837 by this method. The method is as follows: With air only between the plates, which are d' cms. apart, give to one of the plates a charge q, and ground the other plate. Then

$$C' = \frac{A}{4\pi d'}.$$

Next insert a slab of the dielectric, whose dielectric coefficient is to be measured, of thickness t and area greater than A. Measure the potential of the insulated plate with a gold-leaf electroscope or quadrant electrometer. The presence of the inserted dielectric will cause the potential to be less than it was before. Now separate the plates until the same potential is indicated as before. Let the distance between the plates now be d'' cms. We then have

$$C'' = \frac{A}{4\pi \left\{(d'' - t) + t/\epsilon\right\}} \quad \text{cgse. units.} \qquad (30.2)$$

But, since the charge and the potential are the same as in the air condenser, the capacitances are the same in the two cases, and therefore,

$$d' = (d'' - t) + t/\epsilon,$$

from which we obtain

$$\epsilon = \frac{t}{t - (d'' - d')}. \qquad (30.3)$$

The denominator of equation (30.1) may be written

$$4\pi \left\{d - (1 - 1/\epsilon)t\right\}.$$

Before the introduction of the slab it was $4\pi d$. Thus the slab has had the same effect as would be produced by moving the plates a distance $(1 - 1/\epsilon)t$ nearer together.

Suppose the slab to be partly between the plates of the condenser and partly outside. Let the area of the slab that is between the plates be B. Then the part occupied by the air alone is $A - B$. The tubes of flux will be straight, except at the edges of the plates and the slab. Neglecting the small error introduced because of this distortion of the field, we have

$$C = \frac{B}{4\pi \left\{d - (1 - 1/\epsilon)t\right\}} + \frac{A - B}{4\pi d},$$

or

$$C = \frac{A}{4\pi d} + \frac{B(1 - 1/\epsilon)t}{4\pi d(d - (1 - 1/\epsilon)t)}. \qquad (30.4)$$

Thus C decreases as B decreases, or the difference of potential increases. The stored energy in the condenser is

$$U = \frac{1}{2}\frac{q^2}{C} = \tfrac{1}{2}CV^2.$$

Since the charge q is maintained constant, the energy of the condenser increases as the slab is withdrawn. There must be, therefore, a mechanical force acting on the slab which opposes its withdrawal, i.e., the slab is being drawn into the space between the plates where the field of force is the strongest, and the potential energy of the condenser is a minimum. This is a particular case of a general rule to the effect that a dielectric having a coefficient greater than that of the surrounding medium is acted on by a force which tends to draw it into the strongest part of the electric field. This electric case is only a special case of a still more general law of nature, which is that *any system when left to itself will assume such a configuration as to make its potential energy a minimum.*

That there is a force on an uncharged body of dielectric coefficient ϵ, greater than the dielectric coefficient of the surrounding medium, tending to draw it into the strongest part of the field, may be seen from a consideration of the energy in the field. In any electric field of force the energy in a volume v is given by

$$U = \int_v \frac{\epsilon E^2}{8\pi}\, dv = \int_v \frac{D^2}{8\pi\,\epsilon}\, dv.$$

Consider a body of dielectric coefficient $\epsilon > 1$ in an electric field of force in air, ϵ for air being taken equal to 1. That part of the field occupied by the body has less energy than when occupied by air alone. Thus, when the body is in the field the energy of the whole system is less than when the body is not in the field. If the field is not uniform, the energy of the whole system is least when the body occupies the strongest part of the field. Thus, when a body is situated in a non-uniform field of force there is a force acting on it tending to move it in a direction from a weaker to a stronger field. To move it in the reverse direction would be to increase the total energy of the system, and therefore to do work on the body. But the only way work can be done on a body is against an opposing force. In a uniform field there is no force acting on the body, since the total energy of the system does not change with change in position of the body.

31. Standard Condensers. — The capacitance of a condenser in absolute measure must be obtained from its dimensions. This is its *geometrical capacitance*. The unknown capacitance of a condenser is then determined experimentally by comparison with the standard condenser. Three such standard condensers will be described, two of which are due to Lord Kelvin.

(a) *The Guard Ring Standard Condenser*. — This was the first satisfactory standard condenser. As has been stated, the capacitance of an ordinary parallel-plate condenser is not accurately given by the expression

$$C = \frac{\epsilon A}{4\pi d},$$

owing to the fact that the field of force at the edges of the plates is distorted and nonuniform, and so the intensity is not constant in this region.

Lord Kelvin obviated this difficulty by making the insulated plate m circular and surrounding it with a guard ring g, thus making the field uniform out to the edge of the plate, the nonuniform field being at the outer edge of the guard ring, Fig. 29. There is still a slight irregularity in the field at the gap between m and g. Kelvin used as the effective area A of the plate m the arithmetical

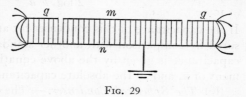

FIG. 29

mean between the area of the plate itself and that of the circular opening in the guard ring. The distance d between the plates was measured by means of a micrometer screw which moved the plate n. In using the condenser, n is grounded and m and g are connected together and given a charge. g is then grounded, after being disconnected from m. A charge q remains on m, the value of which is given by the relation

$$q = CV = \frac{\epsilon V A}{4\pi d}, \quad \text{or} \quad C = \frac{\epsilon A}{4\pi d}.$$

This value for the capacitance in cgse. units then may be used in the measurement of an unknown capacitance by some comparison method. C may be changed to practical units by means of the conversion table given in Section 18.

(b) *The Cylindrical Standard Condenser*. — This condenser is a variable standard condenser of the coaxial cylinder type, Fig. 30.

m and c are coaxial cylinders of the same diameter, with a small air gap separating their ends. The inner cylinder n is also coaxial with the other two, and it is provided with a micrometer screw so that it

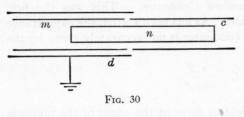

may be moved axially in or out of m, thus permitting the length within m to be accurately measured. m is surrounded by a grounded, metallic cylinder d to prevent its capacitance from being affected by outside

FIG. 30

influences. In use, both n and c are grounded, and m is insulated and given a charge. Then, if n is moved into m by a measured amount Δl, the change in capacitance is

$$C = \frac{\epsilon \, \Delta l}{2 \log_e b/a} \text{ cgse. units.}$$

If the capacitance of this condenser for any particular setting is measured by comparison with another standard condenser, its change in capacitance is given by the above equation for any measured movement of n, and so the absolute capacitance is known.

(c) *The Spherical Condenser.* — The capacitance of a spherical condenser is given by equation (24.3). A spherical condenser does not suffer from fringe effects, which is the common ill of both the parallel-plate and cylindrical condensers. It has other defects, however, when put to practical use. The inner sphere must be accurately concentric with the outer sphere, and therefore supported in some manner. Corrections must be made for the supports, the hole in the outer sphere, and connecting wire by means of which a charge is imparted to the inner sphere. The dimensions must be known to a high degree of accuracy, and corrections must be made for any temperature variations. The dielectric coefficient must be accurately known, and the dielectric must be free from dielectric losses and absorption. Air is the only dielectric which is sufficiently perfect to satisfy the requirements, and so has been used in all primary standard condensers. Hence errors due to extraneous effects introduce a comparatively large error, and so cannot be neglected.

32. Ratio between cgse. and cgsm. Units. — The ratio between an electric quantity when measured in cgse. units and when measured in cgsm. units comes out to be the velocity of light in free space, or a power of that velocity, according to the theoretical deductions of Maxwell. Therefore, this ratio is of very great theoretical importance, and its accurate determination has been attempted by many investigators. In the measurement of this ratio, the spherical condenser was used by Rowland (1870), by Rosa (1889), and by Rosa and Dorsey (1905).[1] Later and more refined measurements of the ratio between the cgse. and cgsm. units and the velocity of light have brought these two quantities into very close agreement. The latest and most accurate value for the velocity of light in free space is $2.99774(10)^{10}$ cms. sec.[2]

The cylindrical condenser was also used by Rosa and Dorsey. In their use of this type of primary standard condenser, it was used to measure absolute capacitance and not change in capacitance. The cylinders of the Rosa and Dorsey condenser were of fixed and definite length, the field distortion at the ends of the cylinders being corrected by a coaxial guard cylinder at either end, after the plan of the Kelvin guard-ring, parallel-plate condenser.

33. Electrostatic Potential Measuring Instruments. — In the comparison of the capacitances of condensers, as in many other experiments with static charges, some means of accurately measuring potentials and potential variations is required. In measuring electrostatic potential the measurement must be made in such a manner as not to change the magnitude of the charge, or, if a slight change is made, to be able to make proper corrections. The reading of the instrument must not depend on drawing charge continuously from the source. In fact, in all experiments with electrostatic charges, good insulation is absolutely essential, and therefore we must not add to the difficulty of insulation by providing an escape for the charge through the measuring instrument. Voltmeters, potentiometers, and galvanometers of the type used in current circuits cannot be used.

The gold-leaf electroscope was used by Faraday and other scientists of his day and later as an instrument for the detection of a charge and its identification. The electroscope was also used as a static potential measuring instrument. Faraday used it in this manner in

---

[1] See, A New Determination of the Ratio of the Electromagnetic to the Electrostatic Unit of Electricity, by E. B. Rosa and N. E. Dorsey, Bulletin, Bureau of Standards, Vol. 3, 1907.

[2] Michelson, Pease and Pearson. Astro. Phys. Jr. 82, 26 (1935).

his investigations of the dielectric coefficients of dielectrics. The magnitude of the divergence of the leaves of an electroscope is a measure of the potential of a charged body to which it is electrically connected, and a change in the divergence of the leaves is a measure of the change in potential. In many experiments the absolute value of the potential is not required; all that is required is deflections that are proportional to potential differences. In this respect the electroscope serves the purpose of a potential differences indicating instrument. However, the low sensitivity of an electroscope, and the uncertainty of the values of its readings, have restricted its usefulness until quite recently. The electroscope has been so perfected of late as to make it a much more sensitive instrument, and its readings have been made surer and more accurate by taking observations of deflections by means of a telescope provided with a scale. This instrument is now being used for a detector of static charges, more particularly in radioactive and ionization investigations.

The capacitance of a modern electroscope is very small, of the order of 10^{-12} farad, and hence it may be used in measuring a very minute charge. As an example, let us say that the sensitivity of the electroscope is 100 scale divisions per volt. Then, by use of the defining equation for capacitance, we obtain 10^{-14} coulomb per division for its charge sensitivity. These instruments are used extensively in measuring very small electric currents due to ionization produced in a gas by some ionization agent, such as a radioactive substance. In order to measure a current the rate of fall of the leaf of the electroscope must be observed. If, with the above mentioned instrument, the leaf is observed to fall 1 division in 100 seconds, say, this corresponds to the aquisition of charge at the rate of 10^{-16} coulomb per second. Since the ampere is the rate of change of charge of 1 coulomb per second ($i = dq/dt$), this corresponds to a current of 10^{-16} ampere. Thus it may be seen that a modern electroscope is a very sensitive instrument.

34. Kelvin's Absolute Electrometer. — Many attempts were made by the early investigators of electrostatic phenomena to develop an electrometer which would give a satisfactory absolute measure of electrostatic potential. Lord Kelvin finally perfected his *absolute*, or *attracted-disc electrometer*, which, in addition to being a potential indicating instrument, was an absolute instrument, in that difference of potential was measured in terms of force, length, and area. In Fig.

31 is shown schematically a modified form of Kelvin's absolute electrometer.

This electrometer is essentially a guard-ring, air condenser.
P is the circular disc of the guard-ring condenser of area A cm^2. In
this form of the instrument
the electrostatic attraction
between the charged plates
P and N is measured directly,
as shown. In use the plates
are all grounded at first, and
masses are placed in the scale
pan until the plate P is
exactly in the plane of the
guard-ring G. The condenser
is then charged to a poten-

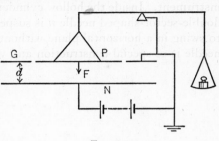

Fig. 31

tial difference V. The plate P will then be attracted, and an
additional mass m must be placed in the scale pan to balance the
electrostatic force of attraction, and bring the plate P again exactly
into the plane of the guard-ring G. We then have

$$mg = \frac{AE^2}{8\pi}.$$

Therefore,

$$V = Ed = d\sqrt{\frac{8\pi\, mg}{A}} \text{ ergs/cgse. unit charge.} \quad (34.1)$$

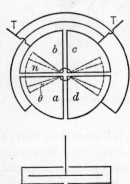

Fig. 32

35. The Quadrant Electrometer. — The
quadrant electrometer is more sensitive than
the attracted-disc electrometer, but on the
other hand, measures potential differences
only after calibration; it is not an absolute
instrument. It is a very useful instrument;
it possesses high sensitivity and precision,
and may be used in a great variety of ways.

The instrument consists of a pair of
quadrants with a vane, or needle as it is
called, suspended between them, as shown
in plan and section in Fig. 32. Its construction is shown in Fig. 33, the case having
been removed to show the working parts. The quadrants are
formed out of a short, hollow, metal cylinder of length small as

compared with its radius, i.e., it is shaped like a pill box. The cylinder is cut into quadrants, the quadrants being separately insulated. Let the quadrants be *a*, *b*, *c*, *d*. The opposite quadrants, *a-c* and *b-d*, are electrically connected and brought out to the terminals *T* of the instrument. Inside the hollow cylinder, or quadrant box, the metallic, double-sector-shaped needle *n* is suspended by a fiber so as to be free to swing in a horizontal plane without touching the quadrants. The needle is of special construction and very light.

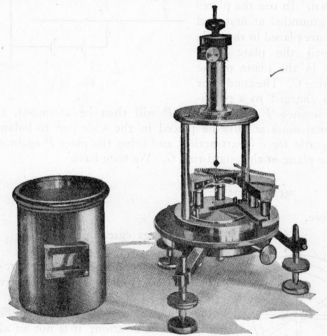

Courtesy Gaertner Scientific Corp.

FIG. 33

The needle is charged to a potential *V* which is higher than that of either pair of quadrants. If the suspension is a conductor the needle is charged through it, but if the suspension is a nonconductor a special charging wire is required. The deflections are observed with a telescope and scale, or lamp and scale, after the manner of the mirror galvanometer. With the quadrants and needle discharged, the suspension is adjusted so that the needle is in a symmetrical position with respect to the two pairs of quadrants, as shown. However, when the terminals T are connected to the points whose difference of potential $(V_2 - V_1)$ is required, and the needle is given a high potential charge, it will be deflected. The charged needle, situated as it is between the two charged plates separated by air, constitutes a condenser arrangement. The area of the needle that is between one pair of quadrants a-c forms with that pair a parallel-plate condenser, and the area that is between the other pair of quadrants b-d forms another parallel-plate condenser. Of course, the quadrants have capacitance relative to ground and to each other, which will be small and constant. The deflection of the needle is very approximately proportional to the difference of potential between the quadrants, and takes place in a direction from positive to negative. In turning, the needle twists the suspension, coming to rest when the opposing torques are equal.

The complete theory of the quadrant electrometer is somewhat involved. However, an approximate solution may be obtained as follows: Let V be the high potential of the needle, V_1 the potential of one pair of quadrants, and V_2 the potential of the other pair of quadrants. Let c_1 be the capacitance of the needle and one pair of quadrants, and c_2 the capacitance of the needle and the other pair of quadrants. The total energy of the charged condensers in any position of the needle is

$$U = \tfrac{1}{2}c_1(V - V_1)^2 + \tfrac{1}{2}c_2(V - V_2)^2 + U', \qquad (35.1)$$

where U' is the constant energy due to capacitance to ground and to one set of quadrants relative to the other. The work done by a couple L in producing an angular twist $d\theta$ is $dU = L\,d\theta$, or $L = dU/d\theta$. c_1 and c_2 will depend upon the position of the needle, and hence will be functions of θ, and the only variables in the energy equation, since the potentials are maintained constant. Therefore,

$$L = \frac{1}{2}\frac{dc_1}{d\theta}(V - V_1)^2 + \frac{1}{2}\frac{dc_2}{d\theta}(V - V_2)^2. \qquad (35.2)$$

This torque is balanced by that due to the twisted fiber, which, for small angular displacements, is proportional to θ, or $L = k\theta$, where k is the torsional constant of the suspension. Since the needle turns out of one pair of quadrants and into the other pair of quadrants, we will have

$$\frac{dc_1}{d\theta} = -\frac{dc_2}{d\theta} = k',$$

where k' is essentially constant. Therefore,

$$k\theta = \tfrac{1}{2}k'\left\{(V - V_1)^2 - (V - V_2)^2\right\},$$

or
$$\theta = \tfrac{1}{2}K\left\{(2V - (V_1 + V_2)\right\}(V_2 - V_1). \tag{35.3}$$

If V is large as compared with V_1 and V_2, we may write

$$\theta = KV(V_2 - V_1), \quad \text{or} \quad V_2 - V_1 = \frac{1}{KV}\theta = K'\theta. \tag{35.4}$$

Thus the difference of potential, $V_2 - V_1$, is proportional to the deflection θ. K' is determined experimentally by taking $V_2 - V_1$ as a known difference of potential. The quadrant electrometer when used in this manner is said to be *heterostatically* connected.

In case the difference of potential to be measured is large, the needle may be electrically connected to one pair of quadrants, say the pair of quadrants at potential V_2. The quadrant electrometer is then said to be used *idiostatically*. Putting $V = V_2$, we have

$$k\theta = \tfrac{1}{2}k'(V_2 - V_1)^2. \tag{35.5}$$

Thus we have the equations:

$$\theta = KV(V_2 - V_1) \text{ heterostatic}, \tag{35.6}$$

and

$$\theta = K'(V_2 - V_1)^2 \text{ idiostatic}. \tag{35.7}$$

It will be noticed that when the connection is heterostatic the deflections are proportional to the first power of $(V_2 - V_1)$, and that, therefore, a reversal of potential will produce a reversal of deflection, whereas when the connection is idiostatic the deflections are proportional to $(V_2 - V_1)^2$, and that, therefore, the deflection is always in the same direction whether the potential is positive or negative. Therefore, the electrometer when idiostatically connected will give deflections on alternating potentials. It is used in this manner as an alternating- as well as a direct-potential indicator, or, when calibrated, as a voltmeter.

While in use the potential V must be maintained constant. This may be accomplished by connecting the needle to a B battery of the kind used in radio sets. The needle is usually made of thin sheet aluminum. If high sensitivity is not required a phosphor bronze suspension serves the purpose well as it is conducting. When high sensitivity is required a quartz suspension is used. Quartz is an insulator, but the fiber may be made conducting by dipping it in a strong solution of calcium chloride. Calcium chloride is strongly hygroscopic and will, therefore, keep the surface of the quartz sufficiently moist to render it conducting. If the instrument is to be used to give potential values the scale must be calibrated by observing deflections produced by known potential differences.

Electrostatic Voltmeters. — A calibrated electrometer becomes an electrostatic voltmeter. When used as a voltmeter the connection is idiostatic. In fact, since the needle is connected to one pair of quadrants, this pair of quadrants produces no effect, and is, therefore, omitted. The equation of the instrument is then

$$\theta = K'V^2,$$

where V is the difference of potential being measured. On alternating potentials

$$\theta = \frac{K'}{T} \int_0^T V^2 \, dt.$$

A special type of electrostatic voltmeter calibrated for voltages up to 130 volts has been developed by Ayrton and Mathers. For low voltages the needle is in the form of a closed rectangle suspended by a fiber, and the quadrants are simply half cylinders, the parallel sides of the rectangular needle being concentric with the cylinders. The needle is drawn into the cylinders by electrostatic attraction. When the voltage is high, above about 800 volts, the needle is pivoted on jewelled bearings as with the ordinary voltmeters of the D'Arsonval or electrodynamometer types.

For high voltages the electrostatic voltmeter is a multicellular quadrant electrometer idiostatically connected. The needle is made of a number of blades so mounted as to move into the spaces between the segments of the quadrants after the manner of a variable air condenser, such as is used in radio work. The needle is attached to a pointer which moves over a scale, which is calibrated to read in volts by connecting to known potential differences.

Electrostatic voltmeters possess several advantages over other types of voltmeters. They absorb no energy, and, at low frequencies, they do not disturb the potential difference being measured. There are no induction effects, or magnetic disturbances. At low voltages, however, they are very delicate if sensitive, and hence cannot be made robust enough to be portable in the usual sense. When measuring low potential differences on d. c. circuits contact potentials must be eliminated by reversals.[1]

36. The Dielectric Coefficient and Specific Inductive Capacity. —

One of the earliest observations relative to dielectrics, other than that of their insulating quality, was that the capacitance of a condenser is altered when the dielectric is changed. Coulomb failed to detect a variation of the force between charged bodies owing to a change in the dielectric because he worked only in air. The variation in the force between charged bodies, owing to a change in the nature of the surrounding medium, was deduced from experiments with condensers, and later tested directly. The capacitance of a given condenser is a minimum with a vacuum as dielectric; it is greater with all other dielectrics, the amount by which the capacitance is increased depending upon the nature of the dielectric. The constant of proportionality ϵ between the capacitance of a given condenser with a vacuum dielectric and with any other dielectric has been called, as we have seen, the dielectric coefficient. Thus, equation (19.4) gives

$$\epsilon = \frac{C'}{C}. \qquad (36.1)$$

From this equation, we may define the dielectric coefficient of a dielectric (strictly only in the cgse. system of units) as *the ratio of the capacitance of a condenser with the substance as dielectric to that of the same condenser with a vacuum dielectric.* Naturally the earliest investigations of the properties of dielectrics pertained to the measurement of dielectric coefficients. One such investigation, made by Boltzmann, we have described in Section 30. A vast amount of work has been done in making measurements of dielectric coefficients, the method being, for the most part, the comparison of capacitances by some scheme or other.

Specific Inductive Capacity.—We have from electrostatics

$$F = \frac{qq'}{\epsilon d^2}, \qquad (36.2)$$

which is the defining equation for the force between electric charges in a dielectric of coefficient ϵ. ϵ will depend upon the units in which

[1] See Electrical Measurements by Frank A. Laws, pp. 253–259.

q, F, and d are expressed. If the charges are in free space, we may write, in general,

$$F_0 = \frac{qq'}{\epsilon_0 d^2}$$

(36.3)

On dividing (36.3) by (36.2), we have

$$\frac{F_0}{F} = \frac{\epsilon}{\epsilon_0} = \kappa.$$

(36.4)

κ is now called the *specific inductive capacity* of the medium, a restricted use of the term. κ will be the same numerically in all systems of units and is to be distinguished, as here used, from ϵ, the dielectric coefficient, which depends on the system of units in which the charges are expressed. In the cgse. system of units ϵ_0 was arbitrarily taken equal to unity, and so in that system of units ϵ is numerically equal to κ, and there is no distinction between them, but this is not true in any other system of units. Since the capacitances of condensers of the same dimensions are directly proportional to the dielectric coefficients, equation (36.1), in reality, gives the *specific inductive capacity*, when cgse. units are used. From this point of view, ϵ and κ are related much as are density and specific gravity. In the metric system of units density and specific gravity are numerically equal, but not in any other system of units. Since specific inductive capacity (κ) is the more general term, has the same value in all systems of units, and is what we usually mean when using the terms *dielectric constant* or *dielectric coefficient*, we will use it, except where Coulomb's equation is involved. *κ is a factor which compares the dielectric properties of material media with free space as a standard.*

37. Faraday's Method of Measuring κ. — Faraday, the first to measure κ, compared the capacitances of two spherical condensers, which were exactly of the same dimensions, when air was the dielectric in one of them and the dielectric under test was in the other. Each condenser possessed a brass knob making contact with the inner sphere for the purpose of communicating charge to it. The potential was measured by touching the knob with a proof plane and determining the charge removed by means of a gold-leaf electroscope, the quantity of charge removed being proportional to the potential. Obviously this was not a very accurate method of measuring potential, but it was the best at Faraday's disposal. When the outer spheres were grounded and both condensers were filled with air, and one of the condensers was charged and tested for potential, and then joined to the uncharged condenser and again tested for potential, it was found that the potential was one half of its former value, as it should be if the condensers were identical. The lower half of one of the condensers was then filled with a substance, shellac let us say, while air was the dielectric in the other. It was found, on carrying out the tests as before, that the common potential after joining the condensers was less than half of its former value, thus showing that the total capacitance was more than double its former value. The derivation of the necessary equations will not be given here, as this method is outmoded.

The modern method of measuring capacitance is usually a comparison method, and some form of alternating-current bridge is used. These bridges will be fully explained in Chapter XXII.

Omit

38. Many of the variations in the measurements of κ have consisted in the types of condensers used. Special types of condensers have been used in the researches by the many investigators in this field, the types depending upon the facilities and materials at hand and the specific nature of the problem. There seems to be no standard type of condenser for this purpose. However, the General Radio Company has designed a special condenser for the measurement of specific inductive capacities and power factors of liquid dielectrics.

There are certain precautions that must be observed in all capacitance measurements. All parts of the electric circuit should be shielded and well insulated, and all materials and surfaces should be thoroughly clean and dry. Wires, when run through the air, should be by the most direct routes and with as few supports as possible. In measuring very small capacitances the distributed capacitance of the circuit outside the fixed condensers may be comparatively large, and so introduce a large percentage error. If the distributed capacitance cannot be measured, some method must be used that will eliminate it. It can usually be eliminated by a substitution method, whereby the circuit remains fixed in position and the known and unknown capacitances inserted and measured alternately. There are other factors that affect the specific inductive capacity. These will be considered in the following pages.

39. Variations of κ. — Different investigators have measured κ, and by a variety of methods. For pure substances the results are fairly concordant. However, the dielectrics that have been used

Read lightly

most, mica, glass, and ebonite, are of variable and uncertain composition, and therefore definite values for κ cannot be given. There are other factors such as temperature, frequency, and moisture which affect the value of κ for a given material.

(a) *Temperature.* — In the case of most substances κ varies with the temperature. A few substances are very constant. Thus, Mattenklodt found that mica was constant to within 1 part in 10,000 for a change of 30° C., and the capacitance of a mica condenser was constant for a voltage range of 0 to 600,000 volts. Most of the commonly used dielectrics show small variations except for very low temperatures.

The temperature coefficient α of a dielectric is defined as the percent variation in κ per degree C. Pellat and Sacerdote found the following values for α for paraffine wax and ebonite: [1]

		Range
Paraffine wax....................	−0·036	11° to 32° C.
Paraffine wax....................	−0·056	11° to 83° C.
Ebonite.......................	−0·088	10° to 20° C.

Schmidt [2] found α = 0.1 for sulfur. Many liquids have large temperature coefficients, such as aniline (−0.35), benzol (−0.07), carbon disulphide (−0.09), ethyl ether (−0.46), ethylene chloride (−0.5), ammonia (−0.4). Dewar and Fleming investigated some common liquids in the frozen state down to −185° C.[3] They found that liquids, such as water and ethyl alcohol, which have abnormally high specific inductive capacities at ordinary temperatures, give low values at these very low temperatures. Thus, ice which has a value of κ = 94 at −2° C. gave κ = 2.4 to 2.9 at −185° C. Nitrobenzol gave κ = 32 at 15° C. and κ = 2.6 at −185° C. These values were obtained at a frequency of 100 cycles per sec. For very low frequencies, i.e., below 1 cycle per sec., the effect of change in temperature is very pronounced.

(b) *Frequency* — Many substances, both solids and liquids, show little variation in κ over a range of frequency from 100 cycles per sec. up to $3(10)^7$ cycles per sec. For very low frequencies, however, κ increases markedly as the frequency decreases. Thus, Thomas found in the case of paraffine paper, celluloid, and ice that κ increased

[1] Comptes Rendus, CXXVII, 544, 1898.
[2] Ann. der Physik, XLIV, 329, 1914.
[3] Roy. Soc. Proc., LXI, 2, 299, 316, 358, 368, 1897.

markedly, as the frequency decreased, for frequencies below 50 cycles per sec.[1]

(c) *Pressure.* — The specific inductive capacities of liquids and gases undergo changes with pressure, which are comparatively large. Ortvay[2] examined a number of liquids at varying pressures, and found that they obeyed the relation

$$\kappa_p = \kappa_1(1 + \alpha p - \beta p^2), \tag{39.1}$$

where p is the pressure and α and β are positive constants. κ increases as p increases.

The following variations in κ with p for air are typical of gases:[3]

P	1	149	334 atmos.
κ	1.000585	1.0839	1.1691

These data follow closely the Clausius-Mosotti relation (Sec. 49)

$$Kd = \frac{\kappa - 1}{\kappa + 2}, \tag{39.2}$$

where d is the density and K is a constant to be determined from experimental data. Another formula, which fits the data more closely, often given for the variation of κ with p is

$$\kappa_p = 1 + \frac{mp}{76}, \tag{39.3}$$

where m is a constant to be determined from experimental data, and p is the pressure in cms. of Hg.

(d) *Moisture.* — All dielectrics which absorb moisture suffer large variations in κ. In general, variations with temperature and frequency increase with increase in moisture content. Many insulating materials used in electric engineering absorb moisture very appreciably. This not only changes κ, but decreases the resistivity and dielectric strength.

(e) *Dielectric Coefficient and Index of Refraction.* — The velocity c with which an electromagnetic wave travels is given by the equation

$$c = \frac{v}{\sqrt{\epsilon\mu}}.$$

---

[1] Phillips Thomas, Journ. Franklin Inst., CLXXVI, p. 283, 1913.
[2] R. Ortvay, Ann. der Physik, XXXIX, 1, 1911.
[3] A. Occhialini and E. Bodareu, Nuovo Cimento, VI, 15, 1913; and K. Tangl, Ann. der Physik, XXIII, 559, 1907.

ϵ is the dielectric coefficient of the medium in cgse. units, μ is the permeability of the medium in cgsm. units, and v is the ratio between the electromagnetic and electrostatic units of charge. (See Section 333, Chap. XXIV.) Since the index of refraction n of light is

$$n = u_1/u_2,$$

where u_1 is the velocity in the first medium and u_2 is the velocity in the second medium, we have

$$n = \sqrt{\frac{\epsilon_2}{\epsilon_1}}, \tag{39.4}$$

since $\mu = 1$ very nearly for all diamagnetic and weakly paramagnetic substances. If radiation is passed from a vacuum to a dielectric of coefficient ϵ the above equation reduces to

$$\epsilon_2 = \epsilon = n^2, \tag{39.5}$$

since $\epsilon_1 = 1$ for a vacuum. For gases this relation holds remarkably well, as will be seen by the following comparison between experimental values of ϵ and the squares of the indices of refraction.

	ϵ	n^2
Air	1.000586	1.0005854
Hydrogen	1.000264	1.0002774
CO	1.000984	1.0008088
Nitrogen	1.000606	1.0005441

For most other substances this relationship does not hold, as will be seen from the following values:

	ϵ	n^2
Water	78.00	1.77
Paraffine	2.14	2.02
Sulfur	2.40	4.47
Crown Glass	3.24	2.38
Acetone	21.00	1.84
Amyl Alcohol	16.00	1.98
Ethyl Alcohol	26.80	1.58

In some of these cases the agreement, while not good, is not so bad but that the law may be considered to be reasonably well fulfilled. The discrepancies are undoubtedly due to the fact that ϵ and n were not measured at the same frequency. Recent investigations go to

Red Light

show that equation (39.5) holds whenever ϵ and n are measured at the same frequency, no matter how high or low. Thus, the refractive index of water when measured with electric waves at a million cycles per sec. is slightly less than 9, the square of which agrees very well with the value of $\epsilon = 78$.

PROBLEMS

1. An isolated sphere in free space has a radius of 10 cms., and is charged to a potential of 12,000 volts. What is its capacitance in mmfs.? What is its energy in ergs? In joules? What is its charge? It is then connected by a fine wire to a distant sphere of the same size. Calculate the potential of the system, and the amount of energy dissipated. What has become of the dissipated energy? 1 joule = 10^7 ergs.

2. A condenser has a capacitance of 10 mfs. and is charged to a potential of 900 volts. Calculate the charge in cgse. units and in coulombs. Also calculate the energy in ergs and in joules. A second condenser has a capacitance of 2 mfs. and is charged to a potential of 1,200 volts. Calculate the charge and the energy. These two condensers are now connected in parallel. What is the final voltage, and what is the energy dissipation?

3. A point charge q' is 3 cms. from an infinite conducting plane. Calculate the total induced charge on that portion of the plane within a circle of 4 cms. radius whose center is at the foot of the normal to the plane from the charge q'.

4. What must be the total charge upon the surface of a soap bubble of radius 1 cm. and surface tension 30 dynes per cm. in order that the air pressure on the inside of the bubble shall be the same as on the outside?

5. Three condensers are connected in parallel and charged to a potential difference of 1,000 volts. The charges taken by the three condensers are $3(10)^{-3}$, $5(10)^{-3}$, $7(10)^{-3}$, coulomb respectively. What are the respective capacitances? What is the total equivalent capacitance? How much energy is stored in each condenser? In all three when connected?

6. The three condensers of Problem 5 are connected in series and charged to a potential of 1,000 volts over all. What charge does each take? What is the difference of potential across each condenser? What amount of energy is stored in each condenser? What is the total equivalent capacitance?

7. Calculate the capacitance per meter of two ⚡ 14 parallel wires separated in air so that their centers are 0.5 cm. apart. Diameter of ⚡ 14 wire is 0.167 cm.

8. A ⚡ 14 wire is parallel to the surface of the earth, its axis being one meter from the ground. What is its capacitance per meter of length relative to the ground?

9. If the wire in Problem 8 is charged to a potential of 1,200 volts, what charge is induced on the ground per meter of length of wire?

10. Following the argument of Section 29, show that when a parallel-plate condenser is charged to a potential difference of V with a vacuum dielectric, and then again charged to the same potential difference with a dielectric of specific inductive capacity κ separating the plates, the charge taken in the latter case is κ times the charge taken in the former case.

11. A parallel-plate condenser is maintained at the same potential difference, first with a vacuum dielectric and second with a dielectric of specific inductive capacity κ. Find the ratio of the force of attraction between the plates in the second case to the force in the first case.

12. As in Problem 11, find the ratio between the forces when the charges are maintained constant in the two cases.

13. Calculate the capacitance of a guard-ring condenser having a plate 16 cms. in diameter when the distance between the plates is 12 mms., first when the space between the plates is occupied by air only, and second when 8 mms. of the space is a dielectric of specific inductive capacity 6 and 4 mms. is air.

14. The inside radius of a spherical condenser is 10 cms. and the outside radius is 11 cms. Calculate the capacitance when the inner sphere is given a charge and the outside sphere is grounded. Take $\kappa = 1$.

15. Calculate the capacitance of the spherical condenser of Problem 14 when the inner sphere is grounded and the outer sphere is given a charge, assuming that the capacitance effect of the outer sphere relative to earth is the same as that of an isolated sphere of the same radius.

16. A wire 8.6 mms. in diameter has a gutta-percha insulating sheathing which is 7 mms. in radial thickness. The specific inductive capacity of the gutta-percha is 4. Calculate the capacitance per mile when laid in the salt water of the ocean.

17. Derive a general equation for the energy dissipated when a charged condenser shares its charge with an uncharged condenser.

18. Derive an expression for the energy dissipated when a charged sphere of radius R shares its charge with an uncharged sphere of radius R'.

19. A point charge of $+30$ cgse. units of electricity is 5 cms. in vacuo above a large horizontal metal plate, earth connected. Calculate the electric attraction between the charge and metal plate. Calculate the surface density of the induced charge at a point P on the plate immediately beneath the charge. Calculate the surface density at a point 5 cms. from P.

20. A charge of $+60$ cgse. units of electricity is placed 15 cms. from the center of a grounded conducting sphere of 7 cms. radius. What is the induced charge upon the sphere? What is the force between the charge and the induced charge upon the sphere? At what point is the electric image?

21. In Problem 20 assume the sphere to be insulated and uncharged to begin with. Calculate the potential at the surface of the sphere, and the force between the charge $+60$ and the sphere.

22. What charge would need to be placed upon the sphere in Problem 21 in order to make the force between the sphere and the charge $+60$ equal to zero? What would be the potential of the sphere then be?

23. A condenser is made of two parallel plates separated by 0.75 cm. in air. The plates are maintained at a constant difference of potential. What effect will be produced on the attraction between the plates when a slab of glass, specific inductive capacity 8 and thickness 0.5 cm., is inserted between them, the faces of the slab of glass being parallel to the plates.

24. What would be the effect of inserting the slab of glass in Problem 23 after the battery has been disconnected from the condenser, i.e., when the charge remains constant?

25. With data as in Problem 19, calculate the potential and intensity (in magnitude and direction) at a point 5 cms. from the charge $+30$ on a line drawn horizontally through the charge.

26. Derive the expression for σ (28.4) by equating the sum of the normal components of the intensity at P (due to $-e$ at i and $+q$ at o) to $4\pi\sigma$. Obtain the intensities by a direct application of Coulomb's law for the force between charges.

27. What change in the potential energy is brought about in Problem 23 and 24 by inserting the slab of dielectric?

28. A charge of $q = +100$ cgse. units is at a perpendicular distance of 10 cms. from an infinite, earth-connected, conducting plane. Derive an expression for the surface density of the induced charge upon the plane, and calculate its value at a point n upon the plane 5 cms. from the base b of the perpendicular from the charge q to the plane. Let a line in the plane, perpendicular to bq and passing through b, be taken as the y axis, and the line bq extended the x axis. Then calculate the potential at the point 13, 4. Also, calculate the intensity, in magnitude and direction, at the point 13, 4. The specific inductive capacity is unity.

29. Reduce the capacitance given by (29.1) to mfs. per cm. and also to mfs. per mile.

CHAPTER III

DIELECTRIC THEORY AND BEHAVIOR

40. Dielectrics versus Conductors. — Insulating media or dielectrics are media that are capable of supporting electric stresses. Conductors are media which are incapable of supporting electric stresses, and, therefore, do not possess dielectric strength. The distinction between dielectrics and conductors may be explained on the electron theory by the assumption that the electrons are quite rigidly bound to the atoms composing dielectrics, and, therefore, do not move appreciably under the application of electric stresses, i.e., the protons and electrons within the atoms, while suffering relative displacements, do not part company, unless the electric stress exceeds the elastic limit of the atom and electrons are torn loose. In conductors, according to the best evidence at hand, there are always, at all temperatures, and under all conditions free electrons (conduction electrons) in the interatomic and intermolecular spaces that are unattached to atoms and are, therefore, free to move under the slightest electric stress. Or, if the electrons are not actually free from the atoms, they are held with such weak bonds as to make it possible for them to move from atom to atom with comparative freedom. In conductors, it was at one time assumed in the solution of some problems, that innumerable electrons are entirely detached from the atoms, that they fill the intermolecular spaces and there partake of the properties of a gas and are amenable to the gas laws. This was the classical Drude-Lorentz theory of metallic conduction, which postulated an electron gas obeying the well-known Maxwell distribution law of the kinetic theory of gases, and sharing in the thermal energy of the molecules and atoms of the conductor. However, in 1928 Sommerfeld showed that this conception is untenable, and, further, introduced a new electron theory of metals based upon the Fermi-Dirac distribution which was proposed in 1927. This will be explained more fully under metallic conduction.

In insulators there are, apparently, few if any free electrons, since the electrons are more or less rigidly bound to the atoms. Of course, the rigidity with which the electrons are bound to the atoms must vary among the dielectrics, as also among the conductors, being influenced by temperature and alloying. The boundary line between the two classes of substances, conductors and dielectrics, is not sharp, and in any case temperature has a marked effect. There is a relationship between the values of resistivity and specific inductive capacity of the various substances such that if these values be written in parallel columns the one increases as the other decreases. This relationship is shown in the Table below.[1] Substances having a resistivity of about 10^6 ohm-cm. mark the boundary line between substances classified as conductors and those classified as dielectrics. Dielectrics may be classified as substances whose specific inductive capacity ranges from 1 to about 30. Substances such that κ lies between 30 and about 6 are semi-conductors, and those such that κ lies between 6 and 1 are insulators.

ρ	10^{-5}	1	10^5		10^{10}	10^{15}		10^{20}
κ		80			20	6	3	2
	Conductors				Semi-conductors	Dielectrics Insulators		

41. Displacement Currents.

— If a condenser be included in a d.c. electric circuit and the circuit be closed, then during a short interval of time subsequent to closing the circuit, each wire of the circuit is traversed by a current which rapidly decreases to zero. The dielectric between the plates of the condenser is now subjected to electric stresses and hence undergoes electrostatic strain. Clerk Maxwell, who had no knowledge of the modern electron theory, supposed that the electric stress produced an *electric displacement* within the dielectric which was proportional to the electric stress, and that there was a displacement or action of some kind across any section of the dielectric (whether merely ether or a material dielectric) which was equivalent to the displacement of electricity in the conductors of the circuit outside the condenser.

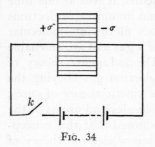

FIG. 34

[1] Liquid Dielectrics by A. Gemant, p. 4.

Consider the condenser, shown in Fig. 34, to be a part of an electric circuit. During charging and discharging there is at any instant a surface density of $+\sigma$ on one plate and $-\sigma$ on the other plate, and, after the conception of Faraday and Maxwell, the space between the plates is threaded by tubes of flux. Thus, at the instant the surface density is σ, there are $4\pi\sigma$ tubes of flux per sq. cm., or

$$4\pi\sigma = \kappa E, \quad \text{and} \quad \sigma = \frac{\kappa E}{4\pi} \text{ cgse. units/cm.}^2 \qquad (41.1)$$

Maxwell called σ the *electric displacement* in the dielectric separating the plates of the condenser, i.e., the equivalent quantity of electricity caused to cross each sq. cm. of area of the dielectric drawn normal to the tubes of flux. If there is an electric force acting through the dielectric from one plate to the other, then the electric charges within a material dielectric must move under its influence throughout the extent of the dielectric, positive electricity being displaced toward the negative plate and negative electricity toward the positive plate. In an isotropic dielectric this displacement is proportional to the electric force at every instant of time, as mechanical strain is proportional to stress in elastic bodies. Thus, in material dielectrics, there is a displacement of positive charge in one direction and negative charge in the other direction throughout the extent of the dielectric, the displacement taking place in the direction of the electric force in isotropic dielectrics.

Upon closing the circuit the displacement begins; it continues at first rapidly, and then more slowly until the elastic reactions within the atoms of the dielectric balance the electric force. The rate of displacement per sq. cm. is obtained by differentiating (41.1) with respect to time. Thus

$$\mathbf{i} = \frac{d\sigma}{dt} = \frac{\kappa}{4\pi}\frac{dE}{dt} \text{ cgse. units/cm.}^2 \qquad (41.2)$$

$\mathbf{i}$, the current density, ceases when E reaches a constant value, which is determined by the difference of potential between the plates. This current is thought of as continuous throughout the extent of the dielectric, and it is accompanied, while it lasts, by a magnetic field of force as is the conduction current in the conductors outside the condenser. That a charge of electricity in motion produces a magnetic field of force similar to that produced by a conduction current in a wire was proved by Rowland, who rotated a charged ebonite disc and tested its magnetic effects.[1] **i** is Maxwell's displacement current.

Such an electric displacement within the material of a dielectric may be explained on the electron theory if we imagine the atoms of the dielectric to undergo strain when subjected to an electric force. No matter what the arrangement of the protons and electrons within the atom may be, whether the electrons are in orbital motions about the nucleus or otherwise disposed, we may conceive of a relative displacement of the positive and negative charges taking place within the atom, the protons being displaced toward the negative plate and the electrons toward the positive plate. If a current of electricity in a conductor be a displacement of electricity along the conductor, then the displacement of electricity within a dielectric constitutes a *transient* electric current. When the atoms of the dielectric are thus strained under the influence of electric force, the medium is said to be *polarized internally*, as each atom has a positive side and a negative side analogous to a magnet. When the centroid of the electrons becomes separated from the centroid of the protons in an atom the atom constitutes what is called an *electric dipole* or *electric doublet*. As will be seen in Section 45 the displacement of charge in the dielectric per sq. cm. is not equal to σ.

When the plates of a condenser are separated by a perfect vacuum there are no material atoms, and consequently no electric charges between the plates. Therefore, we cannot speak of a displacement current in a vacuum in the same sense as with a material medium, nor can we say that the medium is polarized. However, the electric field in a perfect vacuum possesses physical properties, and these physical properties undergo changes with changes in the electric force. Therefore, during the time the intensity between the plates is changing, during charging or discharging, equation (41.2) represents a current in free space of value

$$\mathbf{i} = \frac{1}{4\pi} \frac{dE}{dt} \text{ cgse. units/cm.}^2 \qquad \varepsilon = 1 \qquad (41.3)$$

 However, this is not a current in quite the same sense as the current represented by equation (41.2). Equation (41.3) states that, if at any point in free space the intensity E is changing at the rate dE/dt the phenomena accompanying this change are identical with what

[1] H. A. Rowland, Ann. d. Phys. CLVIII (876).

would occur in the surrounding space if a current **i** per sq. cm. were actually flowing through the same space in the direction in which E is changing.

42. Dielectric Strength. — It is reasonable to suppose that if we continue to increase the electric force (called by Maxwell electromotive force), and the atomic strain or electric displacement within the atom is always proportional to the stress or intensity, a maximum strain will eventually be reached which the atoms of a given dielectric can sustain. Any increase of difference of potential across the condenser beyond this maximum will cause a breakdown of some of the atoms; electrons will be torn loose from the atoms and will begin to migrate toward the positive plate, thus constituting a true conduction current. These free electrons will gain speed under the influence of the potential gradient. They will collide with over-strained atoms and help to disrupt them. This will quickly mount to a great rush of electrons through the dielectric, thus causing a spark or arc discharge. The dielectric is broken down or punctured. *The difference of potential per unit length of dielectric normal to the plates when the electric strain has reached its maximum is called the dielectric strength of the material.* The value of the dielectric strength varies with different dielectrics, and with the same dielectric under different physical conditions. With gaseous dielectrics, and to a less extent with other dielectrics, any ionizing agent, such as ultraviolet radiation, X-rays, radium, will accelerate the breakdown of the dielectric.

43. Dielectric Behavior. — We have seen that if a condenser is given a charge with air as a dielectric, and then the same charge with some other dielectric, oil say, the capacitance has increased, which is equivalent to saying the difference of potential between the plates has decreased. This means, according to our definition of difference of potential, that the electric intensity between the plates has diminished. This was the first observed indication that the force between electric charges depends on the medium between and surrounding the charges as well as on the distance between them, and led to the modification of Coulomb's law as first stated by introducing ϵ into the denominator.

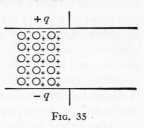

FIG. 35

We may explain tentatively the decrease in the intensity in a dielectric, other than a vacuum, when in the polarized condition as follows: Let us consider a parallel-plate condenser, Fig. 35, the space between the plates being impregnated with the polarized atoms of a dielectric. In calculating the intensity between the plates we must take into account the charges on the atoms as well as the charges on the plates. The Figure will show that the polarities of the atoms are in opposition to the polarity of the plates, and therefore have the effect of diminishing the intensity due to the charges on the plates. Therefore, the effect of the polarized dielectric is to impose a component of electric force in opposition to the electric force engendered by the charges on the plates. This accounts for the decrease in potential between the plates for a given charge, and hence the increase in capacitance.[1]

44. Electric Dipoles. — A satisfactory theory of dielectric behavior was first formulated by Lord Kelvin, following the line of argument of a corresponding theory of magnetism formulated by Poisson. While this theory was formulated prior to the advent of the electron theory, it is readily translated into the notation of the electron theory. When an atom of a dielectric is subjected to an electric force its protons shift in the direction of the field and its electrons shift in the reverse direction, the amount of shift in isotropic media being proportional to the strength of the field, and takes place in the direction in which the field acts. An atom so strained constitutes an electric dipole, or, except in the case of hydrogen, a collection of dipoles, since the elementary dipole is composed of one electron and one proton. If two equal but opposite point charges are at the same place their fields exactly overlap and neutralize each other at every point, and, consequently, there is no action on a third charge. If, however, the two point charges of opposite signs are in the electric field produced by other charges they will be slightly separated, and their fields will not annul each other at every point. They will then constitute an electric doublet (dipole), and there will be at every point in the surrounding space an intensity and a potential due to the doublet. A neutral atom has no field outside itself for points not too close to the atom. However, when in an electric field it behaves as an electric dipole and then develops a field of its own which has at exterior points an intensity and a potential.

[1] See Jeans's Electricity and Magnetism, pp. 127–128.

We may calculate the intensity and the potential at any point P in the field of force due to an electric dipole, such that the distance r measured from the center of the dipole is large in comparison with the distance separating the charges, Fig. 36. Let $+q$ and $-q$ be two point charges, and s the distance separating them. The potential at P is

$$V = \frac{q}{r_1} - \frac{q}{r_2} = \frac{q}{r - \frac{s}{2}\cos\theta} - \frac{q}{r + \frac{s}{2}\cos\theta} = \frac{qs\cos\theta}{r^2 - \frac{s^2}{4}\cos^2\theta},$$

very nearly if r is large as compared with s. Further, $(s^2/4)\cos^2\theta$ will be small in comparison with r^2, and so may be neglected. Therefore,

$$V = \frac{qs}{r^2}\cos\theta = \frac{m}{r^2}\cos\theta. \tag{44.1}$$

The product $sq = m$ is called the *electric moment* of the dipole. m is a *vector quantity* having as direction the line s and sense taken in the direction from $-q$ to $+q$. Thus the direction of the polarization of a dielectric is that of the resultant of its collective elementary dipoles.

The components of the electric intensity in the direction of increasing r and increasing θ are obtained by differentiating the expression for V. Thus,

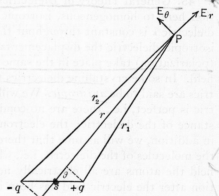

FIG. 36

$$E_r = -\frac{\partial V}{\partial r} = \frac{2m}{r^3}\cos\theta,$$
$$\left.\begin{array}{l} \end{array}\right\} \tag{44.2}$$
$$E_\theta = -\frac{\partial V}{r\partial\theta} = \frac{m}{r^3}\sin\theta.$$

When $\theta = 0$, $E_r = 2m/r^3$, and $E_\theta = 0$. When $\theta = \pi/2$, $E_r = 0$, and $E_\theta = m/r^3$. Also when $\theta = \pi/2$ the potential is zero for all values of r. Therefore the median plane bisecting s and normal to it is the equipotential plane $V = 0$. The electric dipole has its analogue in the magnetic dipole. The numerator in the expression for the potential due to a dipole is the component of the electric moment in the direction of the radius vector r.

If many electric dipoles are contained in a given small volume the potential at a point distant r from the center of the element of volume may be expressed by equation (44.1), in which m is the vector sum of the moments of all of the elementary dipoles in the element of volume, and θ is the angle which the resultant vector makes with the radius vector r. If the atoms of an isotropic dielectric are in an electric field, as between the plates of a charged condenser, the electric moments of the elementary dipoles of the polarized medium combine into a resultant moment which has the same direction as the impressed field.

45. General Theory of Dielectrics. — We will restrict our discussion here to homogeneous, isotropic dielectrics. In a homogeneous dielectric κ is constant throughout the extent of the dielectric. In an isotropic dielectric the displacements of charges within the dielectric (polarization) take place in the same direction as the applied electric field. In some crystalline dielectrics this is not the case. Such dielectrics are said to be *anistropic*. We will, further, assume that the dielectric is perfect, i.e., there are no conduction electrons within the substance of the dielectric; the electrons are all bound electrons. And, in addition, we will assume that there is no permanent polarization of the molecules of the dielectric, i.e., when there is no impressed electric field the atoms are all electrically neutral, and return to this condition after the electric field has been removed. These are ideal conditions, but they are essential to a simple discussion of a very complicated and somewhat obscure subject.

Let us now consider more closely an isotropic dielectric when in an impressed field, as between the plates of a charged condenser. We must now distinguish between two kinds of charges, i.e., bound charges which result from polarization in a dielectric, and are called *fictitious charges*, and free charges, called *real charges*, such as occur on the condenser plates. In the former case the charges are displaced within the atoms of the dielectric, but are bound to the atoms and are an integral part of them. In the latter case the charges are entirely free from atoms. In the case here considered the intensity arising from the charged plates of the condenser is constant, if the condenser is a guard-ring condenser. Therefore, all of the atoms of the dielectric are presumably polarized to the same extent and the polarization is constant throughout the extent of the dielectric. Hence the fictitious charges in its interior vanish, since the negative side of one polarized atom is adjacent to the positive side of the next polarized atom. At the surfaces of the dielectric facing the plates of the condenser there are fictitious charges which, though bound to the atoms of the dielectric, are, nevertheless, free to develop fields of force. The dielectric, if this theory be correct, develops a field of force in much the same manner as does a permanent magnet. Thus, facing the real charge on the positive plate there is a negative fictitious charge on that face of the dielectric, and facing the real charge on the negative plate there is a positive fictitious charge on that face of the dielectric. In a perfect dielectric there would be no free or real charges within the dielectric, and therefore the fictitious charges on the two faces of the dielectric are the only charges having their origin in the dielectric.

Let us now calculate the fictitious charge on the dielectric per sq. cm., thus obtaining its surface density. To do so, let us consider a bar of the dielectric extending from one plate of the condenser to the other, of area of cross section a and length l, the distance between the plates. Let the fictitious charges per sq. cm. on the ends of this bar be $+\sigma_P$ and $-\sigma_P$. Then the electric moment of the bar is $\sigma_P \, al$. But the volume of the bar is al, and therefore the electric moment per unit volume is σ_P. *The polarization P of a dielectric is, by definition, the electric moment per unit volume.* Therefore, the polarization P is equal to the surface density of the fictitious charge, or

$$\sigma_P = P. \quad = electric \; mom/unit \; volume \tag{45.1}$$

Now if there were no material dielectric between the plates of the condenser when charged to a potential V, there would be an intensity $E = 4\pi \sigma_E$ between the plates, or the surface density of that part of the real charge on the plates giving rise to E would be $\sigma_E = E/4\pi$. As we have seen, $E_0 = \kappa E$, where E_0 is the intensity that would obtain in absence of a material dielectric and E is the actual existing intensity within the material dielectric. However, with the material dielectric present, and *the potential the same as before*, there is a fictitious charge developed of amount $\sigma_P = P$ per sq. cm., and this charge *must be matched* by an equal but opposite charge (real) on the adjacent plate. Therefore, the *total real charge* on the plate per sq. cm. is

$$\sigma = \sigma_E + \sigma_P, \quad \text{or} \quad \sigma = \frac{E}{4\pi} + P. \tag{45.2}$$

Hence

$$D = 4\pi\,\sigma = E + 4\pi\,P,$$

or

$$D = E + 4\pi\,P. \tag{45.3}$$

P and E are both vector quantities, and therefore D is a vector quantity. Equation (45.3) states, in terms of flux density, that the real surface density σ on a plate gives rise to D tubes of flux. This flux is split up into two parts in the dielectric: E tubes of flux, due to σ_E, which have a real existence, and 4π P tubes of flux, arising from polarization, but annulled by the 4π σ_P tubes of flux arising from the real charge σ_P upon the plate. Thus the presence of the polarized dielectric enables the condenser plates to take an added charge at the same potential.

Fig. 37

In isotropic dielectrics P is proportional to and parallel to E, and we may therefore write $P = \eta\,E$, or $\eta = P/E$. η is called the *electric susceptibility*, and is analogous to *magnetic susceptibility*. Further, D is proportional to E, and therefore we may write $D = \kappa E$. Substituting these values in (45.3) we have

$$\kappa E = E + 4\pi\,\eta\,E = E(1 + 4\pi\,\eta),$$

or

$$\kappa = 1 + 4\pi\,\eta. \tag{45.4}$$

In anisotropic dielectrics, such as some crystalline substances, P and E do not have the same direction. Then D is the vector sum of E and $4\pi\,P$, as indicated in Fig. 37.

46. The Displacement Current. — We have from the foregoing Section, $D = 4\pi\,\sigma$, or $\sigma = D/4\pi$. Since a current is given by $i = dq/dt$, we see that the total displacement current density is given by

$$\mathbf{i} = \frac{1}{4\pi}\frac{dD}{dt}. \tag{46.1}$$

But, from equation (45.3), we have

$$\frac{D}{4\pi} = \frac{E}{4\pi} + P,$$

and, on differentiating,

$$i = \frac{1}{4\pi}\frac{dD}{dt} = \frac{1}{4\pi}\frac{dE}{dt} + \frac{dP}{dt}. \tag{46.2}$$

The right-hand side of equation (46.2) is made up of two parts, one arising from the variation of the resultant intensity E in the dielectric and the other arising from the variation of the polarization charges in the dielectric. These two terms represent the equivalent current in the space between the plates of a condenser. When there is no material dielectric present, $P = 0$, and hence $\frac{dP}{dt} = 0$. The displacement current is then simply $\frac{1}{4\pi}\frac{dE}{dt}$, which never vanishes so long as the conduction current in the circuit outside the condenser is varying.

Prior to the time of the appearance of Maxwell's electromagnetic theory (1862–1864) a circuit containing a condenser was considered as an "open circuit". In Maxwell's electromagnetic theory the speculative assumption was made that all electric circuits are closed. The originality of Maxwell's theory consisted in supposing that a circuit containing a condenser, say (even a vacuum condenser), though apparently open, is in reality closed by the generation of another kind of current flowing from the one plate of the condenser to the other through free space. This "etheral" current Maxwell called a displacement current, and he assumed that this type of current would produce the same magnetic effects as an ordinary conduction current. Of course, an "open circuit" need not be restricted to a circuit containing a vacuum condenser. For example, if we have two insulated charged metal spheres, one + the other −, and then connect them with a wire a transient current flows. According to Maxwell's assumption an equivalent current flows in the space surrounding the spheres during the time of the flow thus completing the circuit. Oersted discovered (1820) that a magnetic field accompanies a conduction current. Thus magnetic effects are associated with charges of electricity in relative motion. According to our modern picture of the atoms of matter there are circulating charges of electricity (electrons) within the atoms which produce magnetic effects, since they are equivalent to circulating currents. "These circulating currents are known generally as *amperian currents* and they resemble the persistent currents in superconductors rather than ordinary currents in that their flow involves no energy dissipation." They are responsible for the magnetic field of a permanent magnet. Thus magnetic effects are inseparably associated with an electric current of some kind.

The *direction* of a displacement current is considered as follows: If D is *increasing*, the displacement current is in the direction of fall of potential. If D is *decreasing*, the displacement current is in the reverse direction. These statements are consistent with the fact that whenever a current (conventional) flows down a potential gradient through an electric device energy is being absorbed. In our present case, energy is being stored in the electromagnetic field. The reverse current means energy being returned to the source, or electromagnetic energy decreasing.

47. Energy Relations. — The energy in the dielectric of a condenser is split up into two parts also. We have

$$D = E + 4\pi P.$$

Multiplying by E and dividing by 8π, we have

$$\frac{DE}{8\pi} = \frac{E^2}{8\pi} + \frac{1}{2} EP. \tag{47.1}$$

This, by (12.2), is the energy per cm.[3] $\dfrac{E^2}{8\pi}$ is the potential energy stored in the electric field, and $\frac{1}{2} EP$ is the potential energy stored in the dielectric proper due to strained atoms.

That this last term is the correct expression for the potential energy stored in strained atoms may be seen by an independent derivation. The work done in creating a dipole of moment $m = ql$ by a field E is $qEl = mE$. Therefore, the work done in increasing the electric moment from P to $P + dP$ per cm.[3] is $EdP = \eta EdE$, since $P = \epsilon E$. Therefore, the total energy per cm.[3] is

$$\eta \int_0^E E \, dE = \tfrac{1}{2}\eta E^2 = \tfrac{1}{2} EP. \tag{47.2}$$

When $P = 0$, i.e., when there is no material dielectric, the total energy is $\dfrac{E^2}{8\pi}$, which is the energy per cm.[3] in an electric field of intensity E in free space.

48. The Inner Field. — The actual intensity E' which is effective in polarizing an atom within the dielectric is not represented in (45.3). The force acting on an atom within the dielectric will be influenced by surrounding polarized atoms as well as by the charges on the plates of the condenser.

In obtaining an expression for E' we will follow the treatment given by Debye.[1]

The force E' may be thought of as made up of two components.

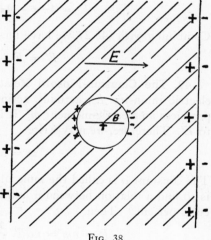

Thus,

$$E' = E_1 + E_2. \quad (48.1)$$

E_1 is due to the charge distributed uniformly over the plates of the condenser, and therefore,

$$E_1 = 4\pi\,\sigma. \quad (48.2)$$

Let us imagine a small sphere within the dielectric with a unit positive charge at its center, Fig. 38. It is required to calculate the force acting on

Fig. 38

this charge. The radius of the sphere r is taken large as compared with molecular dimensions, but small as compared with macroscopic magnitudes. The sphere is assumed to be empty. The force E_2 is due to the polarized dielectric surrounding the small sphere in question. E_2 is made up of two parts, first, the force due to the fictitious charges on the dielectric facing the plates of the condenser, and second, the charge on the surface of the small spherical cavity which is due to polarization. Thus, $E_2 = e_1 + e_2$. e_1 is due to the fictitious charges on the dielectric facing the plates of the condenser, and is $e_1 = -4\pi P$, since the surface charge $\sigma_P = P$. e_1 is negative

[1] P. Debye, Polar Molecules.

since E, acting to the right, is taken as positive. To calculate the component e_2 we may proceed as follows: Let da be a surface element of area on the surface of the small sphere, θ the angle between r and P, Fig. 38. The force on the interior unit positive charge is found by applying Coulomb's law. The magnitude of P_n (normal to the surface of the sphere) is $P \cos \theta$. But $da = 2\pi r^2 \sin \theta \, d\theta$, and therefore,

$$\int_s \frac{P_n da}{r^2} \cos \theta = 2 \int_0^{\frac{\pi}{2}} \frac{P \cos^2 \theta}{r^2} \cdot 2\pi r^2 \sin \theta \, d\theta = \frac{4}{3}\pi P. \quad (48.3)$$

Now substituting in (48.1), we have

$$E' = 4\pi \sigma - 4\pi P + \tfrac{4}{3}\pi P.$$

Combining with (45.2), we have finally

$$E' = E + \tfrac{4}{3}\pi P. \quad (48.4)$$

49. The Clausius-Mosotti Relation. — Let us assume that the electric intensity E', actually acting on a molecule of a dielectric, produces an electric moment m. It is assumed that m is proportional to E'. Therefore, we may write

$$m = \alpha E'. \quad (49.1)$$

The constant α is called the molecular *polarizability*, and our purpose is to find a relation between α and κ. Let n be the number of molecules per cm.[3] Then

$$P = nm = n\alpha E' = n\alpha (E + \tfrac{4}{3}\pi P). \quad (49.2)$$

Also,

$$D = E + 4\pi P, \quad \text{and} \quad D = \kappa E.$$

Eliminating E and P between these equations we find that

$$\frac{\kappa - 1}{\kappa + 2} = \frac{4\pi}{3} n\alpha. \quad (49.3)$$

Thus, if α is an invariable molecular constant, $\dfrac{\kappa - 1}{\kappa + 2}$ is proportional to the density, which is relation (39.2). The constant α has been shown to be approximately equal to the cube of the radius of the molecule. Consequently, the approximate size of a molecule may be calculated from measurements of specific inductive capacity. Thus, this derivation has a measure of heuristic value. For a more extended discussion of this subject the reader is referred to special treatises.[1]

50. Refraction of Tubes of Flux. — In many cases tubes of flux pass from one dielectric to another. It is necessary, therefore, to investigate the conditions at the boundary or interface separating two insulating media. We will divide the investigation into two parts: (a) Intensity parallel to the interface. (b) Intensity normal to the interface.

(a) Let κ' and κ'' be the specific inductive capacities of the two media, E' and E'' the intensities in the two media, Fig. 39. Draw two equipotential surfaces, a and b, normal to the interface nm, and

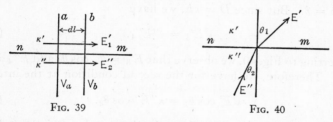

FIG. 39   FIG. 40

at a distance dl apart. The equipotential surfaces a and b are with reference to the intensities E'_1 and E''_2, which are components of the total intensities E' and E''. Very close to the interface on either side the distance between the two equipotential surfaces will be the same. Hence, very close to nm, we have

$$V_a - V_b = E'_1 \, dl = E''_2 \, dl. \tag{50.1}$$

Therefore, $E'_1 = E''_2$; and since $E'_1 = E' \sin \theta_1$, and $E''_2 = E'' \sin \theta_2$, Fig. 40, we have as the first equation to be satisfied at the interface

$$E'_1 \sin \theta_1 = E''_2 \sin \theta_2. \tag{50.2}$$

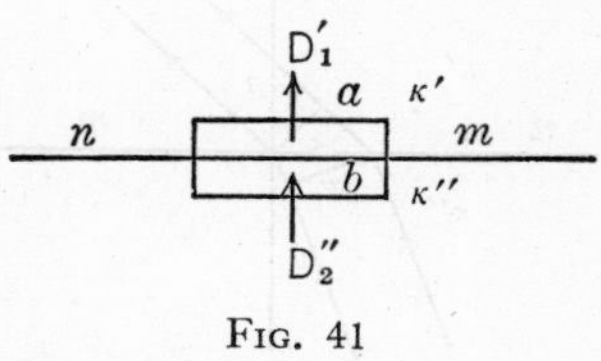

(b) Let us consider a very short cylinder with diameter large compared with its height, drawn as shown in Fig. 41 with one end of the cylinder just above and the other just below the interface. Applying Gauss's law to

FIG. 41

this cylinder, we have

$$\int_s \kappa E \, ds = 4\pi q = 0. \tag{50.3}$$

[1] Van Vleck, J. H., Electric and Magnetic Susceptibilities. Smyth, C. P., Dielectric Constant and Molecular Structure. Debye, P., Polar Molecules.

q is equal to zero since it is assumed that there are no free charges at any point within a dielectric or between the dielectrics. As a charge at the interface generally does not exist we may give no further consideration to it. Then we may say, with negligible error, that the total normal flux passing through the end a of the cylinder is equal to the total normal flux passing through the end b of the cylinder. The total normal flux over the end a of the cylinder is $D'_1 a$, and over the end b, $-D''_2 b$, outward directed flux being positive and inward directed flux being negative. Therefore,

$$D'_3\, a - D''_4\, b = 0, \quad \text{or} \quad D'_3 = D''_4,$$

since $a = b$. But since $D = \kappa E$, we have

$$\kappa' E'_3 = \kappa'' E''_4. \tag{50.4}$$

On referring to Fig. 40, we observe that $E'_3 = E' \cos \theta_1$ and $E''_4 = E'' \cos \theta_2$. Therefore, we have for the second condition at the interface

$$\kappa' E' \cos \theta_1 = \kappa'' E'' \cos \theta_2. \tag{50.5}$$

Since equation (50.2) and (50.5) are simultaneously and independently true, we obtain, by dividing one by the other

$$\frac{\kappa'}{\kappa''} = \frac{\tan \theta_1}{\tan \theta_2}. \tag{50.6}$$

Equation (50.6) is the law of refraction of tubes of flux as they pass from one dielectric to another. If $\kappa' = \kappa''$, $\theta_1 = \theta_2$, and there is no

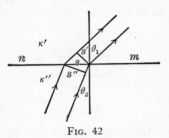

FIG. 42

bending of the tubes of flux at the interface. Also, if the tubes of flux are normal to the interface there is no bending. This law is very similar to Snell's law in optics.

We may extend the consideration of tubes of flux which pass from one dielectric to another. Let s' and s'' be the right sections respectively of a tube of flux on the two sides of a surface of separation, Fig. 42. We then have by geometry $s' = s \cos \theta_1$, $s'' = s \cos \theta_2$. On combining with (50.5), we obtain

$$\kappa' E' s' = \kappa'' E'' s''. \tag{50.7}$$

Thus we see that the proposition which was proved for a single dielectric in Section 7 is true also for tubes of flux as they pass from one dielectric to another.   That is, *throughout the length of a tube of flux the product κE and the right sectional area is a constant.*

51. Energy in the Electrostatic Field.—We may now derive again, using a different line of argument, the expression for the energy per cm.³ in an electrostatic field of force. Let us imagine a tube of flux to be divided into segments by a series of equipotential surfaces, Fig. 43. We have seen that any equipotential surface may be replaced by a charged conducting surface.

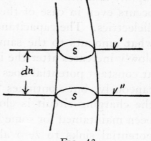

FIG. 43

Any two such surfaces distant dn apart constitute a parallel-plate condenser. The energy of a charged condenser is

$$dU = \tfrac{1}{2}q(V' - V'') = \tfrac{1}{2}q\,dV.$$

But $q = \sigma s$. Hence, $dU = \tfrac{1}{2}\sigma s\,dV = \tfrac{1}{2}\sigma s \dfrac{dV}{dn}\,dn.$

Now $dV/dn = E$, and $\sigma s = \kappa E s/4\pi$ by Coulomb's theorem.   On substituting these values in the above equation, we have

$$dU = \tfrac{1}{2}\frac{\kappa E s}{4\pi}\frac{dV}{dn}\,dn = \frac{\kappa E^2}{8\pi}\,s\,dn.$$

This is the energy in volume $s\,dn$. Putting $s = 1$ sq. cm. and $dn = 1$ cm., we have

$$U = \frac{\kappa E^2}{8\pi} \text{ ergs/cm.}^3 \tag{51.1}$$

52. Imperfect Dielectrics (*Actual Dielectrics*).—The foregoing discussion has been restricted to ideal dielectrics. While certain substances approach closely to the ideal conditions they can never be actually realized. Many of the physical characteristics of the dielectrics are associated with departures from their ideal prototypes. This is an extensive field and the literature is voluminous, but a few of the more prominent characteristics of actual dielectrics may be noted.

(a) Residual Charge and Absorption. — If a condenser having a solid or liquid dielectric is charged and then left to itself it is found that the potential between the plates gradually diminishes, at first rapidly and then more slowly, approaching a final steady state. This occurs even in case of the purest and most perfect solid and liquid dielectrics. The capacitance of the condenser appears to increase, or, what amounts to the same thing, the charge at constant potential slowly increases after the initial rush of charge. Thus the condenser at constant potential does not take its full charge at first and instantaneously, but continues to take charge for some little time after the charging circuit is closed. If, after the charging potential has been maintained for some little time, the condenser is discharged, the potential sinks to zero almost instantly. However, if after being initially discharged it is left insulated for a time it will exhibit a difference of potential of the same sign, and one or more subsequent discharges of diminishing magnitude may be obtained. The subsequent discharges are due to what is called *residual charge* and the process of taking residual charge is called *dielectric absorption*. The dielectric behaves on charge as though it could not at first take its full charge or full strain, and on discharge it behaves as though it could not instantly give up its full charge or recover instantly from strain. This slow recovery after electric strain resembles somewhat elastic fatigue in elastic bodies.

Dielectric absorption is characteristic of practically all insulating materials, but its cause is imperfectly understood. Its general character, however, is well known. Generally speaking, only solids show absorption effects at both charge and discharge. Liquids generally show absorption on charge, but give no residual discharge. Absorption decreases in general as the purity of the dielectric increases. Thus, very pure quartz, sulfur, paraffine, and mica absorb very little. Absorption generally increases with rise in temperature. Air condensers show practically no absorption.[1]

Since there is a gradual change in the capacitance of a condenser on charging owing to absorption, there is uncertainty in the measured value of the capacitance of a condenser in many cases. In order to avoid errors of this nature the charging time should not exceed a half second and the discharge should follow immediately. The smaller these time intervals are made the more accurate becomes the mea-

[1] See Lectures on Dielectric Theory and Insulation by Whitehead.

sured value. Consequently, *the capacitance of a condenser may be defined as the instantaneous charge required to produce unit difference of potential between its plates*. Capacitance measuring methods which employ high frequency potentials give the lowest values. The higher the frequency employed the nearer is the approach to the geometrical capacitance. Air condensers are used as standards as air is practically free from absorption effects. In the gaseous state the molecules are separated by distances large as compared with their dimensions, and are therefore relatively free and hence their mutual interactions are negligibly small. Gases possessing *nonpolar* molecules (not permanently polarized) are very nearly ideal dielectrics. However, gases always possess conduction electrons to a limited extent owing to ionizing agents such as ultraviolet light and cosmic rays. In the case of gases the intensity E' is very nearly equal to E. Absorption is associated with the time lag required for polarization to be completed under a given field intensity. This time lag affects the value of the molecular polarizability α, and the breakdown strength of a dielectric. There is, also, a relaxation time required for molecules to completely regain the nonpolar state. The internal molecular adjustments require a longer time in solid dielectrics than in liquid dielectrics, but they are practically negligible in gases.

(*b*) *Conduction*. — In addition to displacement currents in dielectrics, most dielectrics exhibit a true conduction or leakage current, which is usually very small. The absorption current is probably only the final dying away of the displacement current in the dielectric proper. If a dielectric has a conduction current, then by Ohm's law, it has ohmic resistance which is susceptible of measurement. If there were no conduction current the resistance would be infinite. The nature of the conduction current in dielectrics is obscure, and it is masked by absorption effects, but such evidence as we have points to a type of electrolytic conduction, or possibly such conduction as takes place in gases.

(*c*) *Power Factor and Phase Difference in Dielectrics.*[1]—A condenser having a perfect dielectric would consume no energy on alternating currents. The current would lead the applied emf. by exactly 90°. The only condensers which approach the ideal are those having gaseous dielectrics. All solid dielectrics have some conduction, and,

[1] See any book on general physics for the meaning of power factor and phase difference. Or (*c*) may be omitted until taken up later in this book. (Section 303).

even if free from absorption effects, consume some energy on alternating potentials since the current does not lead the applied emf. by exactly 90°; there is a component of the current i' in phase with the applied emf. which represents energy consumption. In Fig. 44 is shown the vector diagram of a condenser which has a conduction current, say, but no absorption. The angle ϕ is the phase angle and cos ϕ is the *power factor*. Since in condensers the angle ϕ is always very large, it is customary to take the angle 90° − ϕ, or θ, to express this condition or property of a dielectric. For this reason, and because θ is always small, θ is used to indicate the losses in dielectrics; it is called the *phase difference* or *phase defect*.

Condensers using the best dielectrics carefully prepared, with the exception of mica, show a phase difference much larger than can be accounted for because of conduction alone, and they possess capacitances in excess of their geometrical capacitances when measured in the usual manner. Since an increase in phase difference means an increase in the component of the current in phase with the applied emf., we see that a large phase difference signifies a large energy loss in the dielectric. This energy loss in the dielectric heats it, and the heating is usually in excess of that which can be accounted for by conduction alone. Therefore, there must be something more than conduction causing losses; there must be some other current component in phase with the applied potential. The conclusions from experiments seem to be that the alternating-current losses in solid dielectrics are due quite largely to absorption currents. The energy loss due to conduction alone is usually small as compared with that due to absorption, and there is no evidence of other losses such as hysteresis or viscosity losses. Since absorption causes a sustained current under a sustained potential it must cause a component of current to exist in phase with the applied potential. An increase in temperature usually results in an increase of phase difference, due quite largely to an increase in conduction. Thus, energy losses raise the temperature of the dielectric which in turn leads to further energy losses and still further rise in temperature. The presence of moisture in the dielectric also increases the conduction and hence the energy losses. This type of energy loss in a dielectric is called *dielectric loss*, and is due, for the most part, to the orientations and distortions of the molecules and molecular aggregations. It is not of the nature

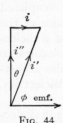

Fig. 44

of such losses as occur in magnetic materials which are classed under the name of hysteresis. Steinmetz used the term "dielectric hysteresis" to cover the energy losses in a dielectric, but Whitehead contends that this term is misleading and should not be used. In the case of gases dielectric losses are practically negligible.[1]

In addition to the losses due to absorption and leakage currents there is the *corona* loss at the edges of the plates of a condenser in case of high potentials. Dielectrics such as glass, rubber, paper, wax, etc., rapidly lose their insulating properties with rise in temperature. Above a certain critical potential most solid dielectrics soon break down under sustained alternating potentials. This is due to the cumulative losses which cause a rise in temperature; the higher the temperature the greater the losses, thus again causing a still further rise in temperature. Thus, paper condensers which can pass a puncture test of 4,000 volts d.c. will break down in a few minutes on a.c. potential of 2,000 volts at 60 cycles per sec. Mica condensers show the same effect. On high-frequency potentials the breakdown will come sooner and at lower potentials. Even quartz, one of the most perfect dielectrics, shows the same effect. A certain piece of quartz required 46,000 volts d.c. to puncture it, but broke down on 18,000 effective volts at 500 cycles per sec. in a few minutes (Morecroft).

53. Polar Molecules. — Experimental evidence goes to show that in the case of many gases (and liquids) the molecular polarizability given by the Clausius-Mosotti relation is too small, and that therefore the molecules of these gases have a permanent electric moment; the positive and negative charges in the molecule are normally slightly displaced resulting in permanent dipoles, although the molecule is electrically neutral. Molecules having a permanent electric moment are called *polar molecules*. Polar molecules are normally oriented at random and so have no net polarization, but under an impressed electric field they tend to line up with the field thus contributing to the net polarization. It can be shown that in the case of polar gases the molecular constant in (49.1) is represented by the relation

$$\alpha' = \alpha + \frac{\beta}{T}. \tag{53.1}$$

[1] For further information see: Dielectric Theory by J. H. Van Vleck and also by C. P. Smyth; Dielectric Phenomena in High Voltage Engineering by F. W. Peek.

α is the molecular polarizability as for nonpolar molecules. β is a constant depending upon the magnitude of the permanent polarization characteristic of the molecule, and T is the absolute temperature. The molecular constant α is independent of the temperature, since it is a measure of the polarizability of a nonpolar molecule in an electric field. Polar molecules, however, in the absence of an electric field have no net polarization since their orientations are random. In an electric field they tend to line up with the field and so will contribute to the resultant polarization. Thermal agitation of the molecules, however, will have the effect of disorientation, and so, as the temperature increases, the disorientating influence increases and the term β/T decreases. Some of the typical polar gases are HCl, HBr, HI, SO_2, H_2O, NH_3. It will be seen from (49.3) that if n is known α can be calculated from the measured specific inductive capacity. Then by (53.1) β may be obtained from temperature measurements. Thus it is possible to measure the displacement polarization due to an impressed field and also the permanent polarization of molecules. Each contributes to the specific inductive capacity κ. Thus, in NH_3, 16% of κ at room temperature is due to displacement polarization and 84% to permanent dipole moment. This study has enabled the chemist to learn a great deal about the structural shapes of molecules. It also throws light upon the failure of the relation $n^2 = \kappa$ (39.5). This relation holds best in the case of nonpolar molecules.

There are certain types of dielectrics in which the displacement polarization may be "frozen," and thus become in a measure permanent. For example, if carnauba wax is melted and allowed to solidify in a strong electric field, it is found to have retained a volume polarization and will orient itself if suspended in an electric field, as a magnet orients itself in a magnetic field. Such a substance in which the molecular polarization is "frozen" is called an *electret*.

54. Miscellaneous Dielectric Effects. — In some dielectrics there are free charges which are slightly mobile but cannot leave the dielectric. In the presence of an electric field these mobile charges migrate toward the electrodes, and, on reversing the field, there is a heavy initial current. These mobile charges affect the measured value of the specific inductive capacity and care must be exercised in measuring κ when this limited form of conduction is present. Heated pyrex glass between lead electrodes shows this effect.

Liquids, as a rule, are not as perfect dielectrics as gases and some solids. A small proportion of the molecules of even pure liquids are positive or negative ions and these ions migrate through the liquid in the presence of an electric field. Also, the presence of any solid material suspended in a liquid results in a larger conductivity and a lowered dielectric strength. The particles in a colloidal solution in general possess a certain net charge and their migration through the liquid due to an electric field is called *cataphoresis*.

Practically all dielectrics suffer a slight extension in the direction of an applied electrostatic field. This phenomenon is known as *electrostriction*. The electrostrictive force S, which is always a tension, is given by

$$S = \frac{\kappa - 1}{\kappa} \frac{E_0^2}{8\pi} \text{ dynes/cm.}^2 \text{ in cgse. units.}[1]$$

There are certain crystals, such as tourmaline, quartz, Rochelle salts, and tartaric acid that possess interesting electromechanical properties. If one of these crystals be placed between a pair of metal plates and mechanical stresses are applied a separation of charge takes place, certain regions becoming positively charged and others negatively charged, thus bringing about a difference of potential between these regions. This phenomenon is known as the *piezoelectric effect*. The polarity reverses with a change from a compressive to a tensile stress. Conversely, if a piezoelectric crystal is placed in an alternating electric field, the crystal either extends or contracts depending upon the sense of the field, the effect being most pronounced when the period of the electric oscillation is the same as the period of the free mechanical vibration of the crystal. Because of this characteristic such crystals are used as standards of frequency, and are used extensively in controlling the frequencies of broadcasting stations. The extension or contraction of the crystal is proportional to the first power of the impressed p.d. Rochelle salts have the largest piezoelectric effect, but these crystals are too fragile for commercial use and so the more robust quartz crystals are used in broadcasting transmitters. These crystals are also distorted with changes in temperature and positive charges are produced in certain regions and negative charges in other regions. This phenomenon is known as the *pyroelectric effect*.

Another interesting phenomenon is the valve action of certain metals (aluminum, magnesium, and tantalum) when in an electrolytic solution. An oxide type of film forms on the surface of the metal

[1] Page and Adams, Principles of Electricity, p. 53.

separating it from the electrolyte when the metal is the positive electrode in an electrolytic cell, but not when the metal is the negative electrode. Since this film offers a very high resistance to flow of current in one direction, it then acts as a dielectric, and consequently there are capacitance effects. For a film on an aluminum anode in a borate solution at 30 volts applied potential the capacitance is of the order of $2(10)^{-7}$ farad per sq. cm.

PROBLEMS

1. Charges of 40 and -40 cgse. units are 4 cms. apart in a vacuum, constituting an electric dipole. Calculate the potential and intensity at a distance of 40 cms. from the midpoint of the dipole, (*a*) in line with the charges, and (*b*) at right angles to the line joining them. In each position first calculate by using equation (44.1) and (44.2). Then use the more exact equation.

$$V = \frac{m \cos \theta}{r^2 - \frac{s^2}{4} \cos^2 \theta}$$

Finally calculate by an exact direct method.

2. The data are as in Problem 1. Calculate the potential when $\theta = 45°$. Calculate the components of the intensity along and normal to the radius vector r, the resultant intensity and the angle it makes with the line joining the charges.

3. The area of the movable plate of a guard-ring condenser is 100 sq. cms. The distance between the plates is 4 mms., and the dielectric has a specific inductive capacity of 3. When the condenser is charged to a difference of potential of 1800 volts what is the flux density D and polarization P?

4. Using the data given in Section 39, calculate the constant m of equation (39.3), and κ at 149 and 334 atmospheres.

Using the same data calculate the constant κ in equation (39.2) for air, and κ for 149 and 334 atmospheres.

5. Tubes of flux enter a medium of specific inductive capacity 3 from air, the angle in air being 45° with the normal. What is the angle in the given medium?

6. Using the data of Problem 3, except that the specific inductive capacity is 1, calculate the energy stored in the electrostatic field between the plates by use of equation (51.1). Then calculate the energy in the charged condenser by use of equation (21.2). Compare the results.

CHAPTER IV

MAGNETOSTATICS

55. Historical. — Magnetism was known to man in remote antiquity. There are two oxides of iron, Fe_2O_3 (hematite), and Fe_3O_4 (magnetite). Magnetite occurs in deposits along with hematite, and is magnetic. It was called a *natural magnet*, and because it possessed polarity it was used as a compass, and was then called *lodestone*. In some manner this iron ore has become magnetized through natural causes. Just how it has been magnetized is still a matter of speculation. There are two possible ways in which this might have been brought about. The earth behaves as a large spherical magnet. Magnetite being magnetic and immersed in the magnetic field of force of the earth, may have become magnetized as a secondary effect, for, whatever may be the cause of the earth's magnetism, it is undoubtedly not due fundamentally to magnetic substances within it. This is the most probable origin of natural magnets. Currents of electricity due to lightning flashes have been suggested as another possible cause. Iron ore was mined and smelted at a very early period, and undoubtedly wherever magnetite was found its magnetic properties were independently observed. Iron first came to Greece from Asia Minor. It was known and used as early as 2900 B.C. Undoubtedly a knowledge of the magnetic properties of magnetite dates back as early as 1200 B.C., for in the iron mines of Phrygia, on the islands of Elba, Crete, and Samothrace Fe_3O_4 was found along with deposits of Fe_2O_3, and was called by the Greeks siderite or ironstone. In the early Greek legends and in connection with religious cults there are mentions of the Samothracian rings, rings of iron magnetized by contact with magnetite, and used in religious rites. These rings are mentioned and discussed by Plato from a philosophical viewpoint. There were early religious cults that made much of the mysterious attraction of magnetite and magnetized iron. Chief among these were the Dactyls and Cabiri. The Dactyls, in Classical Mythology, were supernatural and magical beings living on Mount Ida in Phrygia. To them

115

was attributed the discovery of iron and copper, and the art of working them. In later legends we find them on Mount Ida in Crete, where they were identified with other cults. In these accounts there were first three, the number later being increased to ten and then to one hundred. The Cabiri were beneficent deities in Greek Mythology, of whom little is known. They worshiped in parts of Greece, on the islands of Imbros, Lemnos, and Samothrace. Their rites were secret, very mysterious, and sacred. To them were attributed the inventions of arts, such as ship building, navigation, and the working of iron. That the phenomenon of magnetic attraction was known to the early Greeks, and to other peoples inhabiting the Eastern Mediterranean region, is evidenced by the many fables having their genesis in this attraction. Note the fable of the shepherd Magnes who, on Mount Ida (Island of Crete), was so strongly drawn to earth by the tacks in his sandals and the iron ferrule of his shepherd's staff that he could scarcely pull himself away. He dug into the ground and found a wonderful stone, which, subsequently, was named after him the "magnes stone" or "magnet." In another fable there is mentioned a magnetic mountain which pulled the nails out of ships while at some distance. Pliny relates the construction at Alexandria of a vault with a magnetic roof in the Temple of Arsinoe, built for the purpose of suspending the iron statue of the Queen in mid air. This fable has been variously changed and embellished. Thus, according to the Venerable Bede of England (673–735), Bellerophone's horse, Pegasus, weighing 5,000 lbs. was suspended by magnetic attraction in mid air on the Island of Rhodes. The story of Mohammed's coffin has a similar origin. While, of course, all such fables are pure figments they attest to the fact that this strange property of magnetite was known at a very early period in the Eastern Mediterranean region. So far as can be established, the probable time of the discovery of the attractive property of magnetite is the advent of the Iron Age, and therefore may not extend indefinitely back into prehistoric times.

The Greeks were unacquainted with the fact that magnetite possesses polarity. When this property was first recognized is not known. During the Middle Ages magnetite was suspended and found to orient itself relative to the earth. It then came into use as a compass and was called lodestone. This directive property William Gilbert (1600) called "verticity." Artificial magnets were made of iron by stroking against magnetite and so came into use for compasses. The compass seems not to have had its origin in Greek antiquity. It was known and used at the time of the Crusades. There is mention of its use among the Chinese at an early period.

So far as history records, the first person to make a study of magnetism was Petrus Peregrinus of Picardy, France. In his "Epistola," written in 1269, he relates that he formed a magnet out of magnetite of globular shape and with a small compass needle mapped out the region surrounding it. He found that when lines were drawn upon its surface, connecting the directions as indicated by the needle, they girdled the globular magnet, much as meridians are now known to girdle the earth. There were two points situated on opposite sides of the globe to which all lines converged. Peregrinus called these two points *poles*. He found that the way magnets orient themselves and attract each other depends upon the positions of the poles, as though these points constitute the seat of the magnetic power. Such was the origin of poles and polarization which have played an important role in the development of physics.

The study of magnetism was greatly extended by William Gilbert, Physician-in-Ordinary to Queen Elizabeth of England. In 1600 Gilbert published a treatise, "De Magnete," on magnetism and electricity which marked the beginning of the modern, scientific development of both subjects. He was called by Priestley "The father of modern electricity." Gilbert made the discovery that magnets orient themselves relative to the earth, not because of the intervention of some supernatural being, but because the earth itself behaves as a huge magnet, having poles like the poles of Peregrinus's globular magnet. Thus he found that the compass needle sets itself in a general north-south direction because the north-seeking pole (later called positive) of the compass needle is attracted by the opposite pole of the earth-magnet, and the south-seeking pole (later called negative) is attracted by the opposite pole of the earth-magnet, i.e., the unlike poles of the two magnets attract each other.

"De Magnete" was a compendium of knowledge pertaining to magnetism of the period rather than a mere record of the findings of Gilbert himself. He described the general properties of magnets and discussed the magnetic dip, which was discovered by the German priest, George Hartmann (1544), and announced by Robert Norman in 1576. He, also, discussed magnetic variation or declination, which had been known to navigators since 1436. Gilbert stated that magnetic variation is unchangeable with time. This was later found to be in error, as the secular, annular, and diurnal variations were soon dis-

covered and studied. He pointed out that the earth exerts a couple
on a compass needle but not a single force, a fact noted earlier by
Robert Norman. Here we have the first mention of a field of force, an
orbis virtutis, surrounding a magnet, an idea which was greatly
extended in succeeding years. The demagnetization of iron by bringing it to a red heat was mentioned by Gilbert. It was not until 1776
that the first quantitative measurements of the intensity of the earth's
magnetic field of force were made by Broda (France) by comparing
the vibration periods of compass needles. These measurements were
only comparative measurements; the absolute measurement of the
earth's magnetic intensity was the work of Gauss at a later period
(1834–1842). Thus the foundations were laid for the development of
magnetic theory and the applications of magnetism to practical problems, which will be treated in succeeding pages.

Read   **56. The Place of Magnetostatics in the Subject of Electricity.**
We have seen in the Introduction that, prior to the time of Cardan
(1551), electric effects and magnetic effects were considered to be of
the same physical nature. Cardan for the first time in history distinguished sharply between them. From that time on electric effects
and magnetic effects were categories of natural phenomena and quite
unrelated; consequently our present classifications "electricity" and
"magnetism." However, in the winter of 1819–1820 Oersted made
the discovery that magnetic effects accompany an electric conduction current and in 1876 Rowland showed that the same was true of
convection currents. In 1821 Faraday showed that a current in a
magnetic field of force experienced a mechanical force, and in 1831 he
showed that electric currents (induced) could be produced by varying
the magnetic field in which a closed electric circuit was located. Thus
there was shown to be an intimate relationship between electricity
and magnetism, but which of the two phenomena was the more fundamental was not made clear until the pioneer work of Maxwell
appeared and the later theories of magnetism based upon the modern
electron theory were formulated. It now appears that electricity with
its accompanying field is the fundamental entity, and that magnetism
makes its appearance only when electrostatic fields are varying.
Therefore, a magnetic effect (magnetic field) is secondary and is the
result of a particular behavior of electricity; it is a characteristic of
electricity which it exhibits under certain conditions, or more precisely its field exhibits.

Field Theories. — A. D'Abro defines a "field" as, "the continuous distribution of some 'condition' prevailing throughout a continuum." The mysterious condition surrounding a charged body or a magnet, Gilbert called an "orb of virtue." This was probably the first recognition of a field as such. Modern field theories had their genesis in the experiments in light performed by Thomas Young (England, 1773–1829) and Augustin Jean Fresnel (France, 1788–1827). These experiments suggested a wave motion in an elastic medium. The analogy appeared so striking that Fresnel postulated a space-filling elastic medium, the ether, in which light waves were propagated according to mechanical laws. Fresnel's theory was mechanistic, although based upon a continuous medium, and so fitted into the frame work of the mechanistic philosophy of the eighteenth and nineteenth centuries. Electric and magnetic fields were first thought to be due to strains, produced by charges of electricity and magnets, in the Fresnel ether, which was conceived to fill all space but was not thought of as space itself. Maxwell's field theory was first thought to be of the same general nature as Fresnel's. The electromagnetic fields studied by Maxwell were at first regarded as manifestations of mechanical changes occurring in an elastic ether. However, it was soon realized that an electromagnetic field had no mechanical properties, and so must be distinguished sharply from a material medium pervaded by stresses and strains. The nonmechanical properties of the ether have led most physicists of today to regard the word "ether" as only another name for empty space; and so electric and magnetic fields are due to properties of space itself, and hence space is regarded as an active agent and not a passive void filled with an ether. When Maxwell's electromagnetic field was discovered physicists realized that a new and unsuspected nonmechanical physical reality had been revealed. This was the beginning of the decline in the mechanistic philosophy. H. A. Lorentz in his book, "The Theory of Electrons" (1909), states that though electrons may move, "the ether always remains at rest." He conceives the electron itself to be pervaded by ether, and therefore, that an electromagnetic field may exist inside the electron, the electron being conceived to have a variable density which fades out to 0 at its periphery. This theory was dualistic in nature; there were electrons and fields existing in the ether. The present-day theory is rather a monistic theory, as the fields of electrons and protons are conceived to be integral parts of them.

Electric charges always have electric fields associated with them,

but the field of a negative charge is endowed with the power of annul-
ling the field of a positive charge if the two fields are precisely coterminous and of equal intensity throughout.   Thus an electric charge
and its field is a physical reality and has an independent existence.
However, when electrons and protons are in relative motion, carrying
their fields with them, so to speak, there is developed a magnetic field
which at every point is normal to the electric field which produces it.
Thus we have an electromagnetic field.   Magnetic fields are produced by changing electric fields, and therefore have no other existence.   The converse phenomenon is that a changing magnetic field
produces an electric field, which was Faraday's discovery.

In 1871 W. Weber (Germany) postulated that the magnetic
properties of magnetic substances are due to positive charges rotating
about negative charges in the atoms of the substance.   Today magnetism is accounted for by the assumption that there are negative
charges (electrons) moving about the positive nuclei of the atom.
These moving electrons thus give rise to magnetic fields, and so magnetism is an effect produced by innumerable diminutive solenoidal
currents within the atoms of magnetic substances.   Consequently
some modern writers prefer to treat magnetism as a phase of current
phenomena, which in reality it is, and not give it a separate place.

We fully recognize this fact, but, on the other hand, believe that
the magnetic effects of magnets, treated in the classical manner, are of
sufficient importance from a historical and cultural viewpoint to
merit a separate treatment.   Many instruments depend on permanent magnets and many terms relating to magnetism date back to
the works of Perigrinus, Gilbert, Gauss, and others as a result of their
studies of the properties of permanent magnets.   Because of the close
parallelism between electrostatic fields and magnetic fields of permanent magnets, the one should follow closely upon the other.   This
procedure in no way militates against clarity or the ultimate place-
ment of magnetism in its proper position relative to electric-current
phenonomena.

57. General Considerations. — Magnetism is a universal property
of matter.   All substances respond to magnetic influence to a greater
or less extent when placed in a strong magnetic field of force, as near
to a pole of a powerful electromagnet.   In some cases, however, the
effect is so slight as to require very delicate apparatus to detect it.
From the standpoint of magnetic susceptibility, there are three gen-

eral classes of substances: (*a*) Substances that are weakly attracted by a magnetic pole are called *paramagnetic*. (*b*) Substances that are repelled by a magnetic pole are called *diamagnetic*. (*c*) Substances that are relatively very strongly attracted by a magnetic pole are called *ferromagnetic*. This is by far the most important class from the standpoint of practical applications. In the order of their attractive forces, as also in the order of their practical applications, these substances are iron, nickel, and cobalt. In addition to these elements, there are many alloys which are classified as ferromagnetic substances.

Magnetism is of paramount importance in the extensive applications of electricity to scientific and engineering problems. There are few electric appliances which do not depend upon magnetism in some manner or other for their action. This is apparent when we consider dynamos, motors, electric bells, telephone and telegraph instruments, transformers, etc. In practically all cases iron and its alloys are used to develop strong magnetic fields of force. In high-frequency transformers, such as are used in radio circuits, an air-core transformer is used, but, even here, it is the magnetic field of force which is the medium of energy transfer from the primary circuit to the secondary circuit. In fact, all electric currents, conduction, displacement, and space, are accompanied by a magnetic field of force.

58. Magnetic Poles.   Coulomb's Inverse Square Law. — In the case of both natural and artificial magnets, it was discovered by Peregrinus and confirmed by Gilbert that the magnetic property is confined usually to a small area at either extremity, and that these two areas behave differently toward a third active area. There is no definite point in a magnet which may be identified as a pole. The so-called pole is rather a region, the intensity of action fading out imperceptably with distance from the most active point. Nor is the pole at the surface of the magnet, since the tubes of flux tend to converge to a point beneath the surface. While magnetic poles cannot be definitely localized or isolated, the term magnetic pole is retained in the literature of the subject although it is now known that magnetism is a volume and not a surface effect. Other inappropriate terms, which hark back to the early history of magnetic observations and misty philosophic speculations, are still retained in the literature. The term "density" of magnetism has reference to the early belief that magnetism was an imponderable fluid or effluvium, and the term "flux" goes back to Descartes's attempt to account for magnetism by his vortex theory. He postulated a vortex motion in a magnetic fluid, the fluid of the vortex entering by one pole and leaving by the other. This fluid eddy was supposed to act on iron "by virtue of a special resistance to its motion afforded by the molecules of their substance."

After Gilbert's great work, the next important step in the development of the science of magnetism was the formulation of the law of force between the so-called magnetic poles. This law was experimentally verified and stated by C. A. Coulomb in 1784 by use of his torsion balance. It is of the same form as the law of force between electrostatic charges. Assuming that there are two isolated "point" magnetic poles at a distance of d cms. apart the force between them is given by Coulomb's law, which is

$$F = \frac{mm'}{\mu\, d^2} \text{ dynes.} \tag{58.1}$$

Coulomb's verification of this law by use of the torsion balance was only approximate. He estimated the law to be true to within about 3%. Because of the impossibility of isolating a magnetic pole, or of determining the exact points between which d is to be measured, the precise experimental proof of this law is impossible. However, as will be shown later, Gauss proved the law with a fair degree of accuracy. Our faith in the existence of this law rests ultimately upon the fact that calculations based upon it are found to be correct within the limits of experimental error.

If, in Coulomb's equation, we use the cgsm. system of units, the unit of force, the dyne, is fixed, and the unit of distance, the cm., is also fixed. It remains only to define the other quantities in such a way as to make the equation valid. It is found that the medium between and surrounding the poles has an influence upon the magnitude of the force between them, as with electric charges. μ is a factor of proportionality, called the *permeability* of the medium, which takes account of this effect. The force between two given magnetic poles at a definite distance apart in a vacuum is an invariant. Hence, for a vacuum, μ is arbitrarily taken equal to unity in the cgsm. system of units. Then, if in a vacuum we make $m = m' = 1$, when $F = 1$ dyne and $d = 1$ cm., we have the *unit pole strength* defined. That is, *a magnetic pole has unit strength when, in a vacuum, it repels an equal and like pole with a force of one dyne when the poles are one cm. apart.* It will be shown later that this unit magnetic pole defines the unit electric current in the cgsm. system of units, and hence, also, all other units in the cgsm.

system of units. If m and m' are of the same sign, F is positive; if of opposite signs negative. For all ferromagnetic substances μ is very large and varies greatly, as will be seen in another connection. μ in magnetism is comparable to ϵ in electrostatics.

A magnetic pole has no real existence. It is merely a convenient fiction which served a useful purpose in the past and still has some value. Since all magnetic fields are associated with electric currents, it can be seen that a magnetic pole is merely the point or region from which magnetic flux seems to spring. Although the unit pole strength is defined in the same manner as the unit electric charge and has the same dimensions, it must be remembered that magnetostatic phenomena are quite distinct from electrostatic phenomena; they are alike in form only. It is not until we come to a study of currents that we can establish a relation between these two units.

Coulomb's law for magnetic poles may be treated in the same way we treated Coulomb's law for electric charges. We may write

$$F_0 = \frac{mm'}{\mu_0 d^2},\qquad (58.2)$$

where μ_0 is the permeability in free space when m and m' are expressed in any system of units. On dividing (58.2) by (58.1) we have

$$\frac{F_0}{F} = \frac{\mu}{\mu_0} = \kappa'. \qquad (58.3)$$

The ratio κ' is rarely used and so has no name. R. T. Birge has suggested the name " magnetic specific inductive capacity." Like κ it is the same numerically in all systems of units, and corresponds to specific gravity. In the cgsm. system of units μ_0 is arbitrarily placed equal to unity, and so μ and κ' are numerically equal, but not in any other system of units. With this understanding as to meaning we will use the term permeability, as it is the term in universal use.

The numerical value of μ_0 in (58.2) will depend upon the system of units used. Consider the two fundamental equations:

$$F_0 = \frac{qq'}{\epsilon_0 d^2} \quad \text{and} \quad F_0 = \frac{mm'}{\mu_0 d^2}$$

for free space. If in both equations cgse. units are used,

$$\epsilon_0 = 1 \quad \text{and} \quad \mu_0 = \frac{1}{c^2}.$$

If in both equations cgsm. units are used,

$$\epsilon_0 = \frac{1}{c^2} \quad \text{and} \quad \mu_0 = 1,$$

where c is the velocity of light in free space in cms./sec.

If in both equations the Giorgi mks. (meter-kilogram-second) system of units is used, by putting

$$\mu_0 = 10^{-7}, \quad \epsilon_0 = \frac{10^7}{c^2} = 1.113(10)^{-10},$$

where c is taken as $3(10)^8$ meters/sec. The force is then expressed in newtons. The reader should prove these relations.

59. Magnetic Flux and Intensity. — The region surrounding a permanent magnet, an electromagnet, or an electric current, where a force may be observed to act on a magnetic pole or a magnetic substance, is called a magnetic field of force. There are three fields of force with which we are acquainted which are markedly alike, i.e., the electrostatic field of force, which acts *only* on electric charges; the magnetic field of force, which acts *only* on magnetic substances; and the gravitational field of force, which acts *only* on matter as such. All of these fields of force act through free space. A material medium seems not to be necessary, although its presence modifies to a greater or less extent the actions of the fields, in the cases of electric and magnetic fields, but not in the case of the gravitational field. Fields of force are *never* directly observed in any experiment or otherwise, only the actions of the fields are observed. The existence of a field of force is assumed or postulated because of the observed actions and because observed phenomena can be explained because of this assumption. Although we explain phenomena in terms of a field of force, we cannot explain or describe a field of force or tell of what a field of force consists. However, we know that something exists which we call a field of force and that it is *real*. Free space possesses physical properties and therefore is real, even though we are unable to describe its mechanism or make direct observations of its properties. We may as well say that the fields are excited or are a part of the agents with which they are associated; a medium other than this is unnecessary in our present state of knowledge. To make a distinction between fields of force and space is futile. So far as we now know, or probably ever can know, space cannot be separated from the physical phenomena taking place in space. Some scientists go so far as to say that space has no meaning apart from the physical realities attributed to the region called free space. Descartes once said that if everything inside a hollow vessel were removed its sides would be in contact. Thus he did not separate the metrical and physical properties of space. Although the three fields of force are strikingly similar in many respects, yet in other respects they are quite dissimilar, though we do not know in what the dissimilarity consists. There is little doubt but that there is some element common to these fields of force. In fact, Einstein has attempted to formulate a mathematical field theory which will bring these three fields within the scope of a single treatment, thus unifying them.

Since electrostatic and magnetic fields of force are very similar, we shall expect to find analogous treatments in the two cases, so far as the fields themselves are concerned. In fact, we can develop all of the propositions which were developed for the electrostatic field in the same manner for the magnetic field. Since the days of Faraday it has been customary to represent a field of force, both electric and magnetic, by lines and tubes of force. In a magnetic field of force the intensity H is defined as the force in dynes acting on a unit positive pole. Thus H is a vector quantity, its direction being the direction in which a positive magnetic pole is urged. The unit of intensity is called the *oersted*. The *flux density* in free space is taken equal numerically to the intensity, i.e., in free space at a point where the intensity is H there are taken to be H tubes of flux per sq. cm. normal to the field. However, the treatment in this respect varies somewhat. The unit of flux is called the *maxwell* in the cgsm. system of units, i.e., 4π Maxwells or lines of flux are associated with a unit pole or 4π tubes of flux. Since all material media influence more or less the force between magnetic poles, the flux density in material media is not equal to H, but rather we have

$$B = \mu H. \tag{59.1}$$

The unit of flux density (B) is called the *gauss*. This relationship is analogous to the relationship in electrostatics, $D = \kappa E$, B corresponding to D, μ to κ, and H to E. When considering ferromagnetic media B, the flux density, is called *magnetic induction* or *magnetic flux*. As in electrostatics, the term flux will be used for all media. The only distinction between ferromagnetic media and other media is one of degree, and therefore this relationship is universal. Since for all media, except ferromagnetic media, μ is very nearly equal to 1 in the cgsm. system of units, it is taken equal to 1, and therefore $B = H$. If a pole of strength m is in a magnetic field of intensity H the force acting on it is

$$F = mH \text{ dynes.} \tag{59.2}$$

60. Number of Tubes of Flux Associated with Unit Magnetic Pole. — Let an isolated "point" pole of strength m be surrounded by a sphere of radius r cms. with m at the center. Since the number of tubes of flux per sq. cm. normal to the field in free space is taken equal to H, at any point on the surface of the sphere of radius r

$$H = \frac{m}{r^2}.$$

But since there are $4\pi r^2$ sq. cms. on the surface of a sphere, the total number of tubes of flux passing through the surface of the sphere is

$$N = 4\pi r^2 \left(\frac{m}{r^2}\right) = 4\pi m \text{ maxwells.}$$

One *weber* is 10^8 maxwells. Therefore, because of the manner in which unit pole strength and flux density in free space have been defined, it follows that 4π tubes of flux are associated with each unit magnetic pole irrespective of the medium.

61. Gauss's Law. — The total normal magnetic flux taken over any closed surface in a magnetostatic field of force is equal to $4\pi \Sigma m$, where Σm is the resultant pole strength within the enclosure. Expressed mathematically it is

$$N = \int_s \mu H \cos \theta \, ds = 4\pi \Sigma m.$$

The proof of this law for the magnetostatic field follows the same line as for the electrostatic field, Section 6, and therefore need not be repeated. It may be proved also, as in Section 6, that poles outside the surface contribute nothing to the total normal flux over the surface.

62. Magnetic Potential. — Potential is defined for the magnetostatic field as for the electrostatic field. It is the work done in moving a unit positive pole from a point of zero field strength to the point in question, and difference of potential is the work done in moving a unit positive pole from one point to another in the field. We therefore have, as the mathematical expression for the potential at a point,

$$V = -\int_{\infty}^{r} \frac{m}{\mu r^2} \, dr = \frac{m}{\mu r} \text{ ergs/unit pole.} \qquad (62.1)$$

And also,

$$dV/dr = \frac{d}{dr}\left(\frac{m}{\mu r}\right) = -\frac{m}{\mu r^2} = -H \text{ oersteds.} \qquad (62.2)$$

Thus, potential may be defined as that quantity whose space rate of change in any direction is the intensity of the field in that direction. This is true of all fields of force. Potential is a point function, and therefore the difference of potential between two points is independent of the path followed in moving a unit pole from the one point to the other point. Equipotential surfaces in a magnetic field of force, as in any field of force, are surfaces such that the total intensity is everywhere normal to the surface, i.e., there is no component of intensity tangent to an equipotential surface, and therefore no work is done in moving a magnetic pole along the surface.

The potential at a point in the environs of a number of poles is

$$V = \frac{m_1}{\mu r_1} + \frac{m_2}{\mu r_2} + \frac{m_3}{\mu r_3} + \cdots = \sum \frac{m}{\mu r}. \qquad (62.3)$$

For a distribution of elementary magnetic poles of volume density ρ throughout the volume v and surface density σ over the surface, we have

$$V = \int_{v} \frac{\rho \, dv}{\mu r} + \int_{s} \frac{\sigma \, ds}{\mu r}. \qquad (62.4)$$

Since intensity in the magnetostatic field of force is the space rate of change of potential, we have, as in electrostatics,

$$H_x = -\frac{\partial V}{\partial x}, \quad H_y = -\frac{\partial V}{\partial y}, \quad H_z = -\frac{\partial V}{\partial z}. \qquad (62.5)$$

Similarly, if V is expressed in polar coordinates, we have as the components of H in the directions of increasing r, θ and ϕ

$$H_r = -\frac{\partial V}{\partial r}, \quad H_\theta = -\frac{\partial V}{r \, \partial \theta}, \quad H_\phi = -\frac{\partial V}{r \sin \theta \, \partial \phi}. \qquad (62.6)$$

Omit

63. The Magnetic Shell. — A very thin sheet of ferromagnetic substance of opposite polarity on the two faces is called a magnetic shell. The distribution of magnetism, or magnetic pole strength in this case, is over an extended surface, and hence is said to be *lamellar*. With any magnet the surface density of magnetism is the pole strength per unit area (same as intensity of magnetization I, Section 67). The term surface density had its genesis in the conception that magnetism was a fluid which distributed itself over or through the magnetically active region of the magnet. While the fluid theory of magnetism is now known to be erroneous, the terms and methods built upon this concept still survive, are in use, and give correct results.

Let σ be the surface density of magnetism, t the thickness of the shell, and ϕ the strength of the shell (magnetic moment per sq. cm. of area. The magnetic moment of a magnet is the pole strength times the distance between its poles.) Then, $\phi = \sigma t$, and the total magnetic moment of the shell is

$$M = A \sigma t, \tag{63.1}$$

where A is the area of one face of the shell.

Coulomb's Theorem in the Magnetic Case. — This theorem states that the magnetic intensity H close to the surface of a magnetized area, as close to the surface of a magnetic shell, is

$$H = \frac{4\pi \sigma}{\mu} \text{ oersteds.} \tag{63.2}$$

The proof of this theorem for the magnetostatic field follows the same line as the proof of the cognate theorem for the electrostatic field, and therefore need not be repeated. In the magnetic case, μ is the permeability of the medium surrounding the shell, and H the magnetic field intensity.

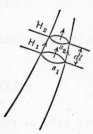

Fig. 45a

Omit

64. Energy in the Magnetostatic Field. — Consider any tube of flux in the magnetic field. The tube terminates at either end upon a magnetized surface of surface densities σ' and σ''. At one end of the tube of flux the pole strength is $\sigma's'$, and at the other end $-\sigma''s''$. Let us take normal sections, s_1 and s_2, Fig. 45a, of a tube of flux at any point in the field in a medium of permeability μ. The flux is normal to the surfaces s_1 and s_2, and there is no flux through the side of the tube. Then, by Gauss's law

$$B_2 s_2 - B_1 s_1 = 0.$$

And therefore,

$$\mu H_2 s_2 = \mu H_1 s_1 = \text{constant}. \tag{64.1}$$

To obtain an expression for the energy in the magnetostatic field, we may take two elementary surfaces, s_1 and s_2, in equipotential planes dl apart, such that $s_1 = s_2 = s$. The field is then uniform and the permeability is constant. The field between s_1 and s_2 will be unaltered if s_1 and s_2 are magnetized, lamellar sheets of surface density σ such that

$$H = \frac{4\pi\,\sigma}{\mu}.$$

We may consider the field to be built up by infinitesimal steps by bringing up elementary poles to the sheets s_1 and s_2, or, what amounts to the same thing, the sheets may be magnetized by infinitesimal increments. In either case, work must be done in creating the field of force and potential energy will be stored in it. In the final state the pole strength over the lamellar surface s is $M = \sigma s$, and the difference of potential between the surfaces is $V = H\,dl$. The energy is

$$dU = v\,dm,$$

where dm is the pole strength of one of the elementary poles and v the corresponding potential difference. The final energy is

$$U = \int_0^M v\,dm. \tag{64.2}$$

v at every instant is proportional to the pole strength, and therefore $v = km$, where k is a constant of proportionality. Hence,

$$U = k\int_0^M m\,dm = \tfrac{1}{2}kM^2 = \tfrac{1}{2}MV = \tfrac{1}{2}\sigma\,sH\,dl = \frac{\mu H^2}{8\pi}\,s\,dl. \tag{64.3}$$

If we now let $s\,dl = 1$ cu. cm., we have as the energy per cu. cm. in the field

$$U = \frac{\mu\,H^2}{8\pi} = \frac{B^2}{8\pi\,\mu} = \frac{BH}{8\pi}\ \text{ergs/cm.}^3, \tag{64.4}$$

when the field is uniform throughout. These expressions for the energy in the magnetostatic field of force are of the same form as the cognate expressions for the electrostatic field, Sections 12 and 51.

In a nonuniform field the energy density varies from point to point being greatest where B is greatest. Let us say that there is a para- or ferromagnetic substance in a magnetic field in air for which μ is one. μ for a para- or ferromagnetic substance is greater than one. Therefore the space occupied by a para- or ferromagnetic substance contains less energy than an equal space occupied by air in the field of force. In a uniform field it makes no difference where the para- or ferromagnetic substance is; the total energy in the field remains constant. In a nonuniform field however the total energy of the system will be least when such a substance occupies a position in the strongest part of the field. As has been stated before, it is a general principle that any system will tend to such a configuration as to make the total potential energy of the system a minimum. Therefore, a para- or ferromagnetic substance when in a nonuniform magnetic field in air will experience a force which tends to move it into the strongest part of the field. On the other hand, a diamagnetic substance experiences a force which tends to move it into the weakest part of a magnetic field of force in air.

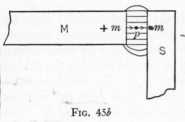

FIG. 45b

Force of Attraction between Magnetic Pole and Soft Iron. — The force of attraction on a magnetized area might be derived as for the electrostatic case in Section 11. However, an alternate method may be used with profit. This method holds equally well for the electrostatic case. Consider the field between the poleface of the magnet M and the soft iron S which is magnetized by induction, Fig. 45b. At a point p in the field of force the intensity is

$$H = \frac{4\pi\sigma}{\mu}.$$

This may be considered to be made up of two parts, $\dfrac{2\pi\sigma}{\mu}$ due to re-

pulsion by the $+m$ pole of the magnet M, and $\dfrac{2\pi\sigma}{\mu}$ due to attraction by the induced pole $-m$ of the soft iron S. But if the unit positive pole at p merges with the $+m$ pole, the force acting on this pole is then only $\dfrac{2\pi \sigma}{\mu}$, and is due to the pole $-m$ alone.   But, since the density of magnetism on the poleface is $+\sigma$, the force on one cm.^{2} of the poleface of M is

$$F = \frac{2\pi \sigma}{\mu} \times \sigma = \frac{2\pi \sigma^2}{\mu} \text{ dynes/cm.}^2$$

[handwritten: $H = \dfrac{4\pi\sigma}{\mu}$. ~$: \dfrac{\mu H}{4\pi}$]

This may be written in the alternate forms

$$F = \frac{\mu H^2}{8\pi} = \frac{B^2}{8\pi \mu} \text{ dynes/cm.}^2 \tag{64.5}$$

[handwritten: $\therefore F = \dfrac{2\pi\mu^2 H^2}{16\pi\mu\mu} = \dfrac{\mu H^2}{8\pi}$]

[handwritten left margin: $H = \dfrac{B}{\mu}$. $\therefore H^2 = \dfrac{B^2}{\mu^2}$ $\therefore F = \dfrac{B^2\mu}{8\pi\mu^2} = \dfrac{B^2}{8\pi\mu}$]

For air $\mu = 1$. The greatest force exists when the soft iron is in actual contact with the poleface. As soon as it is moved away a little the soft iron begins to demagnetize and the field weakens due to leakage. In these expressions σ, the density of magnetism, is the pole strength per sq. cm., and is the same as intensity of magnetization I treated in Section 67.

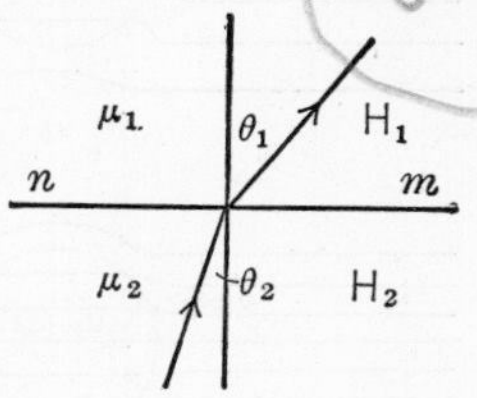

[handwritten right margin: $\sigma = \dfrac{m}{A}$]

[handwritten: Omit]

65. Refraction of Magnetic Tubes of Flux. —

Tubes of magnetic flux are refracted in passing from a medium of one permeability to a medium of a different permeability, Fig. 46. The derivation of the mathematical relationship is similar to the cognate problem in electrostatics, developed in Section 50.

FIG. 46

(*a*) The components of the magnetic intensity parallel to the interface nm in each of the two media are equal. That is,

$$H'_1 = H''_2.$$

And therefore,

$$H_1 \sin \theta_1 = H_2 \sin \theta_2. \tag{65.1}$$

(*b*) The components of the flux densities normal to the interface nm are equal in the two media, and therefore,

$$B'_3 = B''_4, \quad \text{or} \quad \mu_1 H'_3 = \mu_2 H''_4.$$

And therefore,

$$\mu_1 H_1 \cos \theta_1 = \mu_2 H_2 \cos \theta_2. \tag{65.2}$$

Combining equations (65.1) and (65.2), we obtain

$$\frac{\tan \theta_1}{\tan \theta_2} = \frac{\mu_1}{\mu_2}.$$

(65.3)

To illustrate the application of this equation, suppose a ferromagnetic cylinder is placed in a magnetic field in air, as is the practice in the construction of D'Arsonval galvanometers, and ammeters and voltmeters of the D'Arsonval type. A cross section of the cylinder and field is shown in Fig. 47a. In this case the permeability of iron is very much greater than the permeability of air. The Figure shows that, in conformity with equation (65.3), the tubes of flux are bent at the boundary of the iron cylinder in such a manner as to concen-

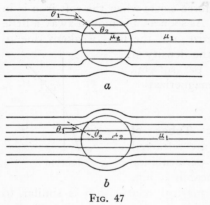

FIG. 47

trate the flux in the cylinder. Thus, the iron cylinder placed between the poles of the permanent magnet concentrates the field between the poles, and also renders it approximately radial so that the galvanometer coil as it swings about the iron cylinder is in a field which is practically constant, and so the deflections are essentially proportional to the currents flowing through the coil.

In Fig. 47b is illustrated a bismuth (most diamagnetic of all substances. $\mu_2 = 0.99997$) cylinder placed in a uniform magnetic field, as between the poles of an electromagnet. In this case $\mu_2 < \mu_1$. The tubes of flux diverge because of the presence of the bismuth cylinder, much as though the air afforded a path of less resistance.

Magnetic shielding is explained by equation (65.3). It is frequently necessary to shield a mechanism from a magnetic field, as, for example, the needle of a galvanometer of a certain type. This is done by enclosing the galvanometer in a thick iron case. However, it has been found that the effectiveness of magnetic shielding is increased by using several concentric shells with air gaps between them, using the same mass of iron. The disturbing magnetic field is concentrated in the iron shielding, as though it were a path of low resistance, and hence most of the flux passes around rather than through the enclosure. The field within the iron enclosure is never entirely removed however, but it is greatly reduced.

66. The Magnetic Dipole. — The magnetic dipole is analogous to the electric dipole. Consider two "point" magnetic poles. Fig. 48, of strength $+m$ and $-m$ distant s apart. A "point" magnetic pole, or any pole for that matter, is a mathematical fiction, as we will see when we study more closely the nature of magnetism, yet the conception of a "point" pole is useful. A point charge of electricity can be realized very nearly; a proton or an electron is essentially a point charge. The "point" magnetic pole has no such independent existence; in fact, *it does not exist at all.* The so-called magnetic poles always occur in pairs, a positive and a negative pole always being associated. Let us then think of

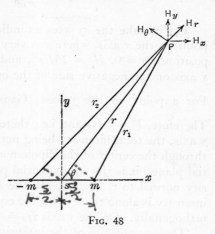

Fig. 48

a magnetic dipole as an extremely short, thin permanent magnet, with the poles exactly at the ends. We may then calculate the potential and the intensity at any point P, Fig. 48, as in the case of the electric dipole, Section 44. Let r be large as compared with the distance s between the poles. The potential at P is

$$V = \frac{m}{r_1} - \frac{m}{r_2} = \frac{m}{r - \frac{s}{2}\cos\theta} - \frac{m}{r + \frac{s}{2}\cos\theta} = \frac{ms\cos\theta}{r^2 - \frac{s^2}{4}\cos\theta}.$$

Neglecting $(s^2/4)\cos^2\theta$, we have

$$V = \frac{ms}{r^2}\cos\theta = \frac{M}{r^2}\cos\theta. \tag{66.1}$$

The product $ms = M$ is called the *magnetic moment* of the magnetic dipole. It is a vector quantity, having as direction the line s and sense taken in the direction from $-m$ to m.

The components of the magnetic intensity in the directions of increasing r and increasing θ are obtained by differentiating (66.1). Thus

$$\left.\begin{array}{l} H_r = -\dfrac{\partial V}{\partial r} = \dfrac{2M \cos \theta}{r^3}, \\[3mm] H_\theta = -\dfrac{\partial V}{r\,\partial \theta} = \dfrac{M \sin \theta}{r^3}. \end{array}\right\} \qquad (66.2)$$

Let us take the xy axes as indicated in the Figure. Then for a point on the x axis, where x is very much greater than $s/2$ (Gauss A position), $\theta = 0$, $H_r = 2M/r^3$, and $V = M/r^2$. At a point on the x axis on the negative side of the origin, $H_r = 2M/r^3$, $V = -M/r^2$. For a point on the y axis (Gauss B position), $H_r = -\dfrac{\partial V}{\partial r} = 0$.

Therefore, $V = $ constant, i.e., there is no component of H along the y axis, the total intensity being normal to it. Thus, a plane passing through the center of the dipole normal to the line s is an equipotential plane; it is the equipotential plane $V = 0$. Consider the intensity normal to r, i.e., H_θ. In the A position $H_\theta = 0$, and the total intensity is along the x axis; the equipotential surfaces cut the x axis orthogonally. On the y axis $H_\theta = M/r^3$.

The components of the intensity in the x direction and in the y direction are

$$\left.\begin{array}{l} H_x = -\dfrac{\partial V}{\partial x} = \dfrac{M}{r^3}\{3 \cos^2 \theta - 1\}, \\[3mm] H_y = -\dfrac{\partial V}{\partial y} = \dfrac{3M}{r^3} \sin \theta \cos \theta. \end{array}\right\} \qquad (66.3)$$

The total intensity at any point P is

$$H = \sqrt{H_x{}^2 + H_y{}^2}. \qquad (66.4)$$

Its direction is given by

$$\phi = \arctan \frac{H_y}{H_x} = \arctan \left\{\frac{3 \sin \theta \cos \theta}{3 \cos^2 \theta - 1}\right\}. \qquad (66.5)$$

Let us resolve the magnetic moment M, as a vector quantity, along and normal to the radius vector r. We obtain $M \cos \theta$ along, and $M \sin \theta$ normal to r. The potential at P for the component $M \cos \theta$

(A position) is therefore, $\dfrac{M \cos \theta}{r^2}$, and for the component $M \sin \theta$ (B position) it is zero. Thus it is seen that a magnetic moment may be resolved as a vector quantity. It has magnitude, sense, and direction, the three characteristics of a vector quantity.

The Unmagnetized or Virgin State. — A ferromagnetic substance when in the virgin state consists of an innumerable number of elementary magnet dipoles oriented in all possible directions. At any point outside the substance the potential of an elementary dipole is given by equation (66.1) and the intensity by equations (66.2). θ may have any possible value, and if we consider a very great number of elementary dipoles oriented at random in all possible directions, $\cos \theta$ and $\sin \theta$ will be as often positive as negative and therefore the potential and the intensity at any point outside the substance will be zero. Thus the virgin state of a ferromagnetic substance is an assemblage of a very great number of elementary magnet dipoles oriented indiscriminately in all possible directions relative to each other.

67. Intensity of Magnetization. — Let us consider a bar of ferromagnetic substance. We may assume that within the substance of the bar there are innumerable elementary magnet dipoles. There may be within the atoms of the substance elements of some kind that function as elementary magnet dipoles. We will not now inquire as to the nature of these elementary magnet dipoles. If an atom is made up of elementary magnet dipoles the magnetic moments of the elementary dipoles may be so oriented relative to each other in the normal atom as to cause the intensity at an outside point to be zero, or there may be an intensity at an outside point with respect to the normal atom (polar atom). Both kinds of atoms may be considered. Now let the substance when in the unmagnetized condition be placed in an external magnetic field of force. The elementary magnet dipoles within the atom will tend to take up the direction of the external field, thus causing the atom to become polarized, if not already partially polarized in the normal state. Within the substance the negative side of one atom faces the positive side of the next atom, and so *within* the substance the elementary magnet poles neutralize each other in pairs. At the ends of the bar, however, there are free poles, negative at one end and positive at the other; the bar as a whole is polarized. At the ends the surface densities are $+\sigma$ and $-\sigma$. The magnetic moment of the bar as a whole is $\sigma\,Al$, where A is its sectional area and l its length.

$Al = v$ is the volume of the bar. Dividing the total magnetic moment of the bar by the volume Al, we obtain σ as the magnetic moment per unit volume. This quantity is called the *intensity of magnetization*, and is usually designated by the letter I. Thus $\sigma = I$. I corresponds to the polarization P in dielectrics. The intensity of magnetization, magnetic moment per unit volume, is therefore a volume effect rather than a surface effect. If a magnetized substance were in the form of a closed ring it would have no free poles, yet, if magnetized, it would have an intensity of magnetization. Very close to the end surface of a magnetized bar we have, analogous to the electrostatics case,

$$H = \frac{4\pi\,I}{\mu}\ \text{oersteds.}$$

68. Induced Magnetism. — When we regard the behavior of a substance when placed in a magnetic field of force, we are struck by the variety of phenomena exhibited as compared with the behavior of dielectrics when placed in an electrostatic field of force. From the viewpoint of behavior of substances when in a magnetic field of force, there are three classes, as we have seen:

1. *Paramagnetic Substances.* — These substances have a permeability which is a little greater than unity, and is constant for fields of force ordinarily obtained. They tend to move into the strongest part of a magnetic field, and so resemble dielectrics.

2. *Ferromagnetic Substances.* — The permeability is much greater than unity, and is not constant. The intensity of magnetization increases to a saturation value, which is relatively large, as the impressed magnetic field increases, thus sharply differentiating this class of substances from paramagnetic substances. The forces acting on them tending to move them into the strongest part of the field are much greater than for paramagnetic substances.

3. *Diamagnetic Substances.* — The permeability is slightly less than unity and constant, and hence the magnetic susceptibility is negative. There is a feeble force acting to move such a substance into the weakest part of the field.

There is another and fundamental difference between the electric and magnetic properties of substances. There is no such thing as a magnetic charge in the same sense as an electric charge. An electron or a proton is a distinct entity, a charge of electricity, which may be isolated in space, whereas a magnetic charge is only a convenient fiction. A magnetic pole cannot be isolated, and has no real existence in the sense that an electron or a proton has. Magnetic poles always exist in pairs, the poles being merely the points of convergence or divergence of tubes of magnetic flux. The basic distinctions between the magnet dipole and the electric dipole will be postponed until we take up the theories of magnetism in Chapter XIV.

Without going into the fundamental nature of magnetism, we may however at this time develop certain relationships. Let us assume that a long bar of ferromagnetic substance, when in the unmagnetized condition, is placed longitudinally in a uniform magnetic field of magnetic intensity H. (*Magnetic force* is probably a better term than *magnetic intensity*, since then there is no confusion with the term *intensity of magnetization*). The elementary magnet dipoles, whether within the atoms, the atoms themselves, the molecules or groups of molecules will become partially or wholly oriented parallel with the impressed field, and so polarized as to be in the same sense. Thus the bar becomes a magnet, and *its tubes of flux* will be added to the tubes of flux of the impressed field. Let us say that the total flux entering the negative end and emerging from the positive end of the bar is ϕ. We will assume the intensity of magnetization to be uniform throughout the bar, i.e., the volume density of free magnetic charge is zero. The number of tubes of flux per sq. cm., the flux density, is

$$B = \frac{\phi}{A} \text{ gausses.} \tag{68.1}$$

It may be seen that the flux density (magnetic induction) B is made up of two components. (1) There are H tubes of flux, which is the exciting field, assumed to be in free space. (2) The magnetized substance will add $4\pi I$ tubes of flux. Thus,

$$B = H + 4\pi I. \tag{68.2}$$

We may write, as in electrostatics, $I = kH$, where k is a factor of proportionality called the *magnetic susceptibility*. Therefore,

$$B = (1 + 4\pi k) H = \mu H. \tag{68.3}$$

Thus,

$$B = \mu H,$$

and

$$\mu = 1 + 4\pi k. \tag{68.4}$$

k expresses the ability of a substance to become magnetized when placed in a magnetic field, or its response to the magnetic field. If either *k* or *μ* can be measured the other can be calculated from equation (68.4). *k* is not constant in case of ferromagnetic substances, since *μ* varies with the magnetizing field *H*. *H* and *I* are vector quantities, and hence *B* is a vector quantity.

In the case of diamagnetic substances *k* is negative, since *μ* is less than one. With this *class* of substances the polarization is reverse to the magnetizing field *H*.

In the foregoing we have assumed uniform magnetization throughout the substance. In such cases the positive and negative poles of the elementary dipoles in the interior of the substance cancel one another, and there is no free magnetization except at the ends of the magnet; the volume density of magnetization within is zero. However, the volume density of magnetism within is not zero in general. We have assumed ideal conditions in the discussion.

Demagnetization. — It has been seen that when a bar is magnetized by being placed in a magnetic field, the ends become poles and these poles will act upon neighboring poles. Each elementary positive pole at the positive end of the magnetized bar will send out tubes of flux, some of which will extend back through the substance of the bar, in a direction reverse to the impressed field *H*, to the corresponding negative elementary pole at the negative end of the bar. Thus, within the substance of the bar this reverse field exerts a demagnetizing effect upon the magnetized bar. This reverse field is called a *demagnetizing field*, since it is in opposition to the impressed field *H*. The demagnetizing field is proportional to the strength of the pole to which it is due, i.e., it is *NI*, where *N* is a factor of proportionality, called the *demagnetization factor*. *N* depends upon the geometrical form of the magnetized body. Thus, if *H'* is the impressed field, the actual magnetizing field *H* within the substance is

$$H = H' - NI. \qquad (68.5)$$

N has been calculated in a few simple cases. It is for the purpose of removing the free poles of a permanent magnet, which produce the demagnetization, that such magnets are provided with keepers. Thus, if two bar magnets of the same length are placed side by side, with unlike poles adjacent, and a soft iron keeper is placed across the poles at each end, the keepers develop poles equal and opposite to the free poles of the magnets, and very close to them, thus neutralizing the demagnetizing fields.

69. Intensity in the Gauss A and B Positions. — In certain experiments it is necessary to know the intensity of the field due to a permanent magnet. The intensity is easily calculated for two positions: (1) A point on the magnetic axis extended, called the Gauss A position. (2) A point on a line drawn normal to the axis of the magnet and passing through its center, called the Gauss B position. These expressions were first derived and used by the German

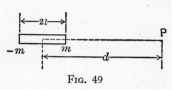

Fig. 49

astronomer and mathematician, Gauss, and published in a paper in 1833 entitled "Absolute Measure of the Earth's Magnetic Field."

By use of Fig. 49 it is easily shown that the resultant intensity in the Gauss A position is

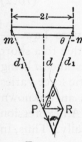

Fig. 50

$$R = \frac{2M\,d}{(d^2 - l^2)^2} = \frac{2M}{d^3} \text{ oersteds,} \qquad (69.1)$$

approximately if d is large in comparison with l. M is the magnetic moment of the magnet, l its half length, and d the distance from the center of the magnet to the point considered.

By use of Fig. 50 the intensity in the Gauss B position may be shown to be

$$R = \frac{M\,l}{(d^2 + l^2)^{3/2}} = \frac{M}{d^3} \text{ oersteds,} \qquad (69.2)$$

approximately if d is large in comparison with l. The derivation of these relations is left as an exercise.

70. The Tangent Law. — If a suspended magnet or compass needle is acted on by two magnetic fields which are normal to each other, a simple relationship for the angular deviation may be found. This applies to the tangent galvanometer as indicated schematically in Fig. 51.

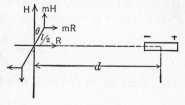

Fig. 51

Let the suspended magnet be acted on by the earth's field H, and, at right angles to H, by a field of intensity R, which is created by a magnet in the Gauss A position, say. The suspended magnet will come to rest in such a position that the opposing couples acting on it are equal. We will then have

$$mlH \sin \theta = mlR \cos \theta.$$

Or

$$R = H \tan \theta, \tag{70.1}$$

where

$$R = \frac{2M}{d^3}.$$

Thus,

$$\text{(1) GAUSS A} \qquad \frac{2M}{d^3} = H \tan \theta.$$

For the Gauss B position

$$\frac{M}{d^3} = H \tan \theta. \tag{70.2}$$

71. Gauss's Experimental Proof of the Inverse Square Law.[1] — This proof is based upon a comparison of the intensities due to a short bar magnet in the A position and in the B position, the distance d being the same in both cases. Gauss assumed that the magnetic force varies as the inverse nth power of the distance, where n is an unknown exponent which is to be determined from experiment. An expression containing n is derived which can be tested experimentally. Thus, in the A position we have

$$R_1 = \frac{m}{(d-l)^n} - \frac{m}{(d+l)^n} = m \left\{ (d-l)^{-n} - (d+l)^{-n} \right\}$$

$$= m \left\{ (d^{-n} + nd^{-(n+1)} l + \cdots) - (d^{-n} - nd^{-(n+1)} l + \cdots) \right\}.$$

If l is small in comparison with d we may neglect the terms containing l^2 and higher powers in this expression. We then have

$$R_1 = \frac{2\,mnl}{d^{n+1}} = \frac{nM}{d^{n+1}}.$$

And, since $R_1 = H \tan \theta$, this becomes

$$\frac{nM}{d^{n+1}} = H \tan \theta_1. \tag{71.1}$$

[1] C. F. Gauss, Poggend. Ann. 38, p. 591, 1833.

For the B position, we have

$$R_2 = \frac{2m}{(d^2 + l^2)^{\frac{n}{2}}} \cdot \frac{l}{(d^2 + l^2)^{\frac{1}{2}}} = \frac{2ml}{(d^2 + l^2)^{\frac{n+1}{2}}}.$$

Neglecting l^2 in the denominator, this reduces to

$$R_2 = \frac{M}{d^{n+1}}.$$

Therefore,

$$\frac{M}{d^{n+1}} = H \tan \theta_2. \tag{71.2}$$

On combining equations (71.1) and (71.2) there results

$$n = \frac{\tan \theta_1}{\tan \theta_2}. \tag{71.3}$$

Equation (71.3) can be tested experimentally since θ_1 and θ_2 can be measured by means of a magnetometer. When tested, Gauss found n to be equal to 2 within the limits of experimental error.

Gauss's method of testing the inverse square law is superior to Coulomb's method by use of the torsion balance, since it does not depend upon locating magnetic poles or measuring the distance between them. Both Coulomb and Gauss tested the law to see if the force between magnetic poles varies directly as the product of the pole strengths, and both found this to be true within the limits of experimental error.

72. Period of Vibration of a Freely Swinging Magnet in a Magnetic Field of Force. — Let us assume that we have a compass needle in the earth's field and that there is no friction at the pivot, or torsional resistance due to a suspension, nor air resistance, i.e., the needle swings with perfect freedom. If the needle is displaced from its equilibrium position in the magnetic meridian and released, it will vibrate about its equilibrium position indefinitely with constant amplitude. This is called undamped vibration, and it is the type of vibration here considered. We will derive an expression for its motion, and from this expression derive a formula for its period.

Elementary Solution. — Let I be the moment of inertia of the compass needle with respect to its axis of rotation, and L the external couple acting on it. From mechanics we have, $L = I\alpha$. The external magnetic couple acting on it is $L = - MH \sin \theta$. (See any text on General Physics). Therefore,

$$I\alpha = - MH \sin \theta. \tag{72.1}$$

If θ is small, we may set $\sin \theta = \theta$ radians without sensible error. Of course, when this substitution is made, the solution gives only an approximately correct solution, but the error is very small if the angular deflection is small. The error increases as the angular deflection increases. θ is substituted for $\sin \theta$ because of mathematical difficulties encountered when the solution is attempted with $\sin \theta$. Making this substitution, we have

$$\alpha = - \frac{MH}{I} \theta, \quad \text{or} \quad - \frac{\theta}{\alpha} = \frac{I}{MH}. \tag{72.2}$$

This is the equation for angular simple harmonic motion. Referring to any college text on General Physics, we find the expression for the period of angular simple harmonic motion to be

$$T = 2\pi \sqrt{- \frac{\theta}{\alpha}}.$$

Therefore, the period of vibration of a freely swinging compass needle in a magnetic field of force is

$$T = 2\pi \sqrt{\frac{I}{MH}}. \tag{72.3}$$

SEE NOTES FOR DERIVATION

Calculus Solution. — Equation (72.2) may be written

$$\frac{d^2\theta}{dt^2} = - n\theta, \tag{72.4}$$

where $n = MH/I$. Multiplying by $2 \frac{d\theta}{dt}$, we have

$$2 \frac{d^2\theta}{dt^2} \frac{d\theta}{dt} = - 2n \theta \frac{d\theta}{dt}.$$

On integrating, there results

$$\left(\frac{d\theta}{dt} \right)^2 = - n\theta^2 + C.$$

For boundary conditions we have, when $t = 0$, $\theta = \theta_0$, $\frac{d\theta}{dt} = 0$.

Then $C = n\theta_0^2$, and

$$\left(\frac{d\theta}{dt}\right)^2 = n(\theta_0^2 - \theta^2).$$

On separating variables, we have

$$\int \frac{d\theta}{\sqrt{\theta_0^2 - \theta^2}} = \sqrt{n}\, t + K. \tag{72.5}$$

To integrate let $\theta = \theta_0 \sin \phi$, and then $d\theta = \theta_0 \cos \phi\, d\phi$. Substituting and reducing, we have

$$\int d\phi = \sqrt{n}\, t + K.$$

Or

$$\phi = \sqrt{n}\, t + K,$$

where

$$\phi = \arc \sin \frac{\theta}{\theta_0}.$$

Therefore,

$$\theta = \theta_0 \sin (\sqrt{n}\, t + K).$$

When $t = 0$, $\theta = \theta_0$, and hence $K = \frac{\pi}{2}$. We then have finally

$$\theta = \theta_0 \sin \left(\sqrt{n}\, t + \frac{\pi}{2}\right) = \theta_0 \cos \sqrt{\frac{MH}{I}}\, t. \tag{72.6}$$

This is the solution of equation (72.4). (72.6) is the equation for simple harmonic motion.

The period is obtained by noting that when the angle changes by 2π the elapsed time T is the period. Therefore,

$$\sqrt{\frac{MH}{I}}\, T = 2\pi, \quad \text{or} \quad T = 2\pi \sqrt{\frac{I}{MH}}. \tag{72.7}$$

Equation (72.4) is a linear differential equation, a type of differential equation often occurring in electric calculations. Its solution by the differential equations method is left to the reader who may be familiar with differential equations.

If the compass needle is suspended by a fiber, the torsional constant of which is k, the equation of motion is

$$I \frac{d^2\theta}{dt^2} + MH\, \theta + k\, \theta = 0. \tag{72.8}$$

The solution of this equation is

$$\theta = \theta_0 \cos \sqrt{\frac{MH + k}{I}}\, t.$$

The period is

$$T = 2\pi \sqrt{\frac{I}{MH + k}}. \tag{72.9}$$

k may be determined by a separate experiment.

73. H by Comparison. — It is frequently necessary to measure the intensity at some point in a magnetic field of force, as, for example, the horizontal intensity of the earth's magnetic field. This is very readily accomplished by use of the expression for the period of a vibrating magnetic needle, if we know the value of H at some definite place. Thus, suppose we wish to obtain the value of H for the earth's field in some location, and that the value of H has been determined at some other place by an absolute method, to be described in the next Section. For the comparison method a magnetoscope is used, which is simply a small bar magnet suspended in a horizontal position by an unspun silk fiber in a glass enclosure to protect it from air currents. T is measured at the place where H is known, and at the place where H is to be determined. We then have, by the use of equation (72.7).

$$\frac{T_1{}^2}{T_2{}^2} = \frac{H_2}{H_1}. \tag{73.1}$$

74. Absolute Determination of M and H. — This method is due to Gauss, and was first used by him in measuring the horizontal intensity of the earth's magnetic field. For the measurement of the horizontal component of the earth's field, we need a short bar magnet and a magnetometer. The magnetometer consists of a short magnet suspended by a fiber, and enclosed in an air-tight container. Above the magnet, and rigidly connected to it, is a small mirror to be used with a telescope and scale, in the usual manner, to measure the angular deflections produced by the short magnet when placed alternately in positions such that the magnetometer magnet is in the A position and in the B position relative to it. The relative positions are indicated in Fig. 52. m is the magnetometer magnet. A and A' show the short bar magnet in the A position relative to m. Thus, a field R is created normal to H, which is directed either east or west depending upon the polarity of the bar magnet. B and B' show the bar magnet in the B position relative to m.

When in this position the field R is normal to H also, and may be directed either east or west depending upon the polarity of the bar magnet.

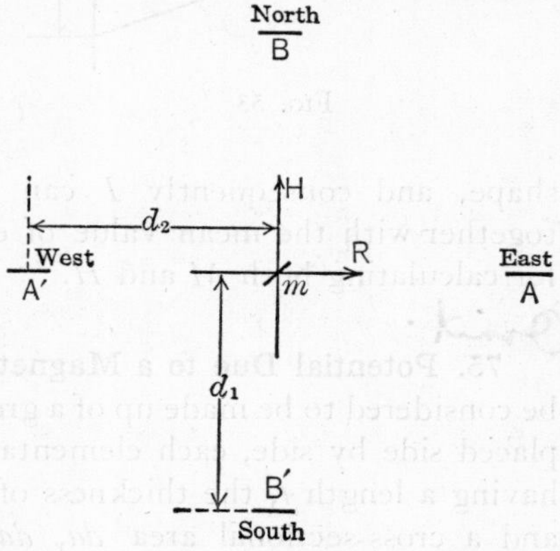

The procedure is as follows: Place the short bar magnet in the B position, say, south of m and at a distance d_1 which will give a workable deflection. Record the scale deflection. Then reverse the bar magnet, again recording the scale deflection. Place the bar magnet an equal distance to the north of m in the B position, and repeat the observations. Average the four scale deflections. Then place the bar magnet a distance d_2 to the east of m in the A position. Read the scale deflection, reverse and read again. Place the bar magnet an equal distance to the west of m, and repeat the observations. Average the four scale deflections.

FIG. 52

For the B position, we have from Section 70,

$$\frac{M}{d_1{}^3} = H \tan \theta_1, \quad \text{or} \quad \frac{M}{H} = d_1{}^3 \tan \theta_1. \qquad (74.1)$$

And for the A position, we have

$$\frac{2M}{d_2{}^3} = H \tan \theta_2, \quad \text{or} \quad \frac{M}{H} = \frac{1}{2} d_2{}^3 \tan \theta_2. \qquad (74.2)$$

From Fig. 53 we see that $s/L = \tan 2\theta$, or $s/2L = \tan \theta$, approximately.

Next suspend the short bar magnet in a horizontal position by a

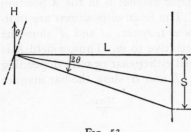

Fig. 53

fiber, in a glass enclosure in the position occupied by the magnetometer magnet m, and determine its period T when swinging through a very small angle. We then have, by Section 72

$$MH = \frac{4\pi^2 I}{T^2}. \qquad (74.3)$$

The bar magnet is of regular shape, and consequently I can be calculated. Equation (74.3) together with the mean value of equations (74.1) and (74.2) suffice for calculating both M and H.

Omit.

75. Potential Due to a Magnetic Shell.

— A magnetic shell may be considered to be made up of a great number of elementary magnets placed side by side, each elementary magnet having a length t, the thickness of the shell, and a cross-sectional area da, da being an element of the surface of the shell turned towards P, Fig. 54, where the potential and intensity are required. The elementary magnets are supposed to be magnetized longitudinally, and all oriented in the same sense so that the positive poles all lie in one face of the shell and the negative poles in the other face.

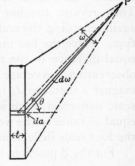

Fig. 54

By Section 63, the strength of a shell is $\phi = \sigma t$, and hence the magnetic moment of one elementary magnet is $\sigma t \, da = \phi \, da$. Therefore, by equation (66.1) the potential at P due to the elementary magnet is

$$dV = \phi \frac{da \cos \theta}{r^2}. \qquad (75.1)$$

But $da \cos \theta / r^2 = dw$ is the solid angle subtended at P by the elementary area da. Therefore, $dV = \phi \, dw$. Then, if ϕ is constant, we have

$$V = \int \phi \, dw = \phi w, \tag{75.2}$$

where w is the solid angle subtended at P by the contour of the shell. The potential is positive if only the positive poles are visible at P, negative if only the negative poles are visible.

If the shell is circular the potential and the intensity are easily calculated for points which lie on

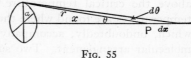

Fig. 55

the axis of the shell, Fig. 55. Let a be the radius of the disc and x the axial distance of the point P from the center of the shell. The solid angle which the shell subtends is

$$w = 2\pi(1 - \cos \theta),$$

where θ is the plane angle subtended by the radius of the disc. The potential at P is, therefore,

$$V = 2\pi(1 - \cos \theta)\phi = 2\pi \phi \left\{ 1 - \frac{x}{(a^2 + x^2)^{1/2}} \right\}. \tag{75.3}$$

On differentiating equation (75.3), we obtain the intensity. Thus

$$H = -\frac{\partial V}{\partial x} = \frac{2\pi \phi \, a^2}{(a^2 + x^2)^{3/2}}. \tag{75.4}$$

By symmetry it will be seen that the resultant intensity at P will be along the x axis.

76. Temperature Effects. — When a permanent magnet is gradually heated it is observed that its magnetic moment changes, and that at a certain temperature it loses its remarkable property and becomes nonmagnetic, or rather paramagnetic, like most substances. The temperature at which a ferromagnetic substance loses its magnetic property is called the *critical temperature*. The critical temperature for iron occurs at about the temperature of dull red heat, but varies with different samples from about 690° C. to 870° C. This variation seems to be influenced in some manner by the carbon content, the critical temperature decreasing as the carbon content increases. The loss of magnetic property, while not taking place abruptly, is extended over only a few degrees. For nickel the critical temperature ranges from 310° C. to 350° C. For cobalt it is about 1150° C.

The critical temperature seems to be associated with a sort of change of state or rearrangement of the molecular structure of the substance. This molecular rearrangement is accompanied by an absorption of heat on rising temperature and an evolution of heat on falling temperature. If an iron wire is heated to a temperature well above the critical temperature and then allowed to cool, several temperatures are found where there is an abnormal evolution of heat, which, undoubtedly, accompany some modification of the internal molecular arrangement. Two such points are particularly marked: One is between 700° C. and 800° C. and corresponds to the critical temperature of magnetism. The other point is at about 660° C. and seems not to be related to magnetism. Other physical properties also change at these transformation points. Thus, the electric resistance undergoes a pronounced change, the thermo-electric power changes, and also the emissive power.

An interesting case of these transformations is afforded by one of the alloys of iron and nickel, the alloy of 25% nickel. When this alloy is raised to a temperature of 580° C. it is no longer magnetic at lower temperatures until −20° C. is reached, when it again becomes magnetic, and remains so until a temperature of 580° C. is reached. Thus, for temperatures between −20° C. and 580° C. this alloy may exist in two different magnetic conditions; one ferromagnetic and the other paramagnetic. Whether a substance is ferromagnetic or paramagnetic seems to depend, in some cases at least, upon its molecular structure.

Magnetic susceptibility is a function of the temperature. In the case of soft wrought iron, for weak fields the susceptibility increases with increase in temperature, while for strong fields the susceptibility decreases with increase in temperature. According to Ewing's findings, there is no temperature hysteresis unless the temperature includes the critical temperature, i.e., on heating and cooling the metal in a magnetic field, the intensity of magnetization is the same at any given temperature whether on rising or falling temperature providing the critical temperature is not included. Curie found other magnetic transformation points for iron than those mentioned above. The most important of these occurs at about 1,280° C.

While ferromagnetic substances lose their magnetic property completely and quite suddenly at the critical temperature, there is a gradual change at lower temperatures. It is found that when a magnet is heated from some low temperature, 0° C. say, its magnetic moment gradually decreases. This change is not constant, but, in general, increases as the temperature rises. Part of this decrease in magnetic moment may be permanent, since the magnet may not regain its full magnetic moment on returning to a lower temperature. However, with proper heat treatment the magnet may be made constant in this respect. If the magnet is repeatedly heated to a given temperature, and each time is remagnetized to the saturation point, it becomes fixed in this respect, i.e., its magnetic moment at a given temperature is constant. Within the limits of atmospheric temperature variations the magnetic moment may be represented by the equation

$$M_t = M_0(1 - at),$$

where M_t is the magnetic moment at any temperature t, M_0 the magnetic moment at 0° C., and a is the temperature coefficient of the magnet, the value of which varies with different magnets, but never exceeds 0.001.

PROBLEMS

1. Comparison of magnetic moments. Two magnets are suspended, when bound together with axes parallel, in an enclosure and the periods are determined, first with like poles in the same direction, and then with the poles reversed. One magnetic moment is known. Derive an expression whereby the other magnetic moment may be calculated.

2. A bar magnet is suspended horizontally by a wire which is controlled by a torsion head. When the torsion head is twisted through an angle of 120° the magnet is twisted through an angle of 30°. What angular twist will turn the magnet through 90°, the field remaining constant?

3. Work out a general relation for the comparison of magnetic moments by the method of Problem 2.

Two magnetic moments are to be compared. The two magnets are suspended in turn from the same torsion head. To twist A through 45° requires a twist of the torsion head of 360°. To twist B through 45° requires a twist of the torsion head of 540°. If the magnetic moment of A is 100, what is that of B?

4. Find approximately the force of attraction or repulsion between two short bar magnets M' and M'' when their centers are r cms. apart, their magnetic axes being along the same line.

5. (a) Two magnets of magnetic moments M' and M'' are placed with their centers r cms. apart. The second magnet is in the A position relative to the first, with its axis normal to that of the first. Derive an expression for the couple acting upon the second magnet.

(b) Find the couple acting upon the second magnet when it is in the B position relative to the first, with its axis normal to that of the first.

6. Derive an expression for the couple L acting on a compass needle, when in the magnetic field of the earth, in terms of the intensity H of the earth's

field, the magnetic moment M of the compass needle, and the angle θ which the axis of the needle makes with the magnetic meridian of the earth. Show that the couple $L = M$ when $\theta = \pi/2$ and $H = 1$.

7. Derive the equations (66.3).

8. Two magnets of magnetic moments M_1 and M_2 are rigidly fastened together at their centers, their magnetic axes making an angle λ with each other. They are mounted on a pivot so as to swing in a horizontal plane in the earth's magnetic field. Show that the magnetic moments M_1 and M_2 combine by the vector law into a resultant magnetic moment such that

$$M^2 = M_1{}^2 + M_2{}^2 + 2M_1M_2 \cos \lambda,$$

and that the period is

$$T = 2\pi \sqrt{\frac{I}{MH}}.$$

9. Show that the solid angle of a disc for a point on its axis Fig. 55, is given by $2\pi(1 - \cos \theta)$, where θ is the plane angle subtended at the point by the radius of the disc.

10. Two short bar magnets are placed relative to each other as shown in Fig. 56. A is fixed in position and B is free to rotate on a pivot about its center. Let the magnetic moment of A be M_1 and B, M_2. Let the distance between the centers of the two magnets be r. Show that the couple L acting on the magnet B due to the field of A is

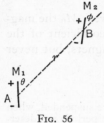

FIG. 56

$$L = \frac{M_1M_2}{r^3} (2 \cos \theta \sin \phi + \sin \theta \cos \phi),$$

and that when $L = 0$, $2 \tan \phi = - \tan \theta$. What is the condition that the couple shall be a maximum?

11. Show that when $L = 0$ in Problem 10, the magnet B is tangent to a tube of flux of the magnet A, and that when $L = $ maximum, the magnet B is normal to a tube of flux of the magnet A.

12. Show that, in Problem 10, the resultant field at B due to A is given by

$$H = \frac{M}{r^3} \sqrt{1 + 3 \cos^2 \theta},$$

and that the angle H makes with H_r is given by $\frac{1}{2} \tan \theta$.

13. A magnetic shell is in the form of a disc of radius 5 cms. Its surface density is 5 poles/cm.^{2}, and its thickness is 5 mms. Calculate the potential and the intensity on the axis of the disc at a distance of 10 cms. from its center.

14. A bar magnet is 4 cms. long and has a pole strength of 100. Calculate the potential at a distance of 40 cms. from the center of the magnet if the radius vector drawn from the center of the magnet makes an angle of 45° with the axis of the magnet. Calculate the total intensity at the point, and the angle it makes with the radius vector and also the axis of the magnet.

15. Very permanent magnets are now made in the Bell Telephone Laboratories out of cobalt steel. The physicists in this Laboratory have made a demonstration apparatus, called a "wobbly bar," consisting of two identical magnets, so arranged that one of the magnets may be suspended above the other in mid air, like Mohammed's coffin, with like poles adjacent. The sus-

pended magnet weighs 16 gms., is 6 cms. long, and, when suspended, the distance between the axes of the magnets is 1.5 cms. Calculate the pole strengths of the magnets.

16. A bar magnet 10 cms. long and having a pole strength of 100 lies with its magnetic axis coinciding with the x axis in a coordinate system, the positive pole of the magnet being at the origin of coordinates, the negative pole being at $x = +10$. Calculate the potential and intensity (magnitude and direction) at (a) the point (50,0). (b) The point (0,50). (c) The point (25,50). Disregard the magnetic field of the earth in each case. (d) If the positive direction of the x axis is in south magnetic direction, calculate the positions of zero intensity if the horizontal intensity of the earth is 0.18. If the intensity of the earth were taken into account, how would the results of (a), (b), and (c) be affected?

17. In Gauss's proof of the inverse square law, Section 71, instead of using the A and B positions, as described, derive an expression which may be tested for n by varying the distance d in either the A or B position.

18. Show that the work done in twisting a suspended magnet or compass needle in a magnetic field is given by $U = MH(\cos \phi_1 - \cos \phi_0)$ ergs, where ϕ_0 is the initial angular deflection and ϕ_1 is the final angular deflection from the equilibrium position.

19. What is the ratio between the magnitudes of the mks. magnetic pole strength and the cgsm. magnetic pole strength?

Then calculate the number of webers that are associated with a unit mks. magnetic pole. See relations on pages 123 and 124.

20. A magnetic pole having a pole strength of one mks. unit is 50 cms. from another magnetic pole having a pole strength of 2 mks. units. Calculate the force between these two poles using Coulomb's equation as written in the mks. system of units and as written in the cgsm. system of units. Show that the force comes out the same whichever form of the equation is used.

21. Suppose we have two isolated point-charges, each of one coulomb, at a distance of one meter apart. What will be the force between them, expressed in either newtons or dynes? Solve first using the mks. system of units (pages 123 and 124), then solve by use of the cgse. system of units and the conversion table given in Sec. 18. Show that the results are the same.

22. Data same as in Problem 21, except that the charges are immersed in a medium of specific inductive capacity $\kappa = 2$. In this case the mks. equation is written $F = \dfrac{qq'}{\kappa \epsilon_0 d^2}$. Solve as in Problem 21 by the mks. equation and then by the cgse. equation coupled with the conversion table in Sec. 18.

23. In the mks. system of units the capacitance of a parallel-plate condenser is given by

$$C = \frac{\kappa \epsilon_0 A}{4 \pi d}.$$

A multiple-plate, parallel-plate condenser (Fig. 19) has an effective area of 2 sq. meters, and the plates are 2 mm. apart. Calculate the capacitance in farads by use of the mks. equation and then by the cgse. equation coupled with the conversion table in Sec. 18. Take $\kappa = 2$.

CHAPTER V

TERRESTRIAL MAGNETISM

77. Historical. — Although natural magnets were known in antiquity, little was known about their properties, save that of attraction. There is no authentic record which shows that the Greeks were acquainted with the polarity of a magnet or of its use as a compass. Bertelli has made a careful examination of the records and has failed to find any mention of use of the directive property of the lodestone by Europeans, in navigation or otherwise, from the 6th century B.C. to the 10th century A.D. There seems, however, to be some evidence to warrant the conclusion that the Chinese were acquainted with the directive property of the lodestone before the beginning of the Christian Era, although this is questioned by some writers. The dates given by various writers for the earliest knowledge of the magnetic compass ranges from 2634 B.C. to 1110 B.C. There is evidence to show that the Chinese were acquainted with the three methods of mounting a compass needle, i.e., by flotation, pivoting, and suspension. It seems that the attractive and repulsive properties, the directive property, and the polarity of the lodestone were discovered independently by the Chinese and Europeans.

The magnetic compass was used for land journeys by the Chinese at an early period, and before it was so used in Europe. Its use by mariners came at a later period, and was undoubtedly delayed by a superstitious awe in which it was held. According to Brunetto Latini, a Florentine encylcopedist, "No master mariner dares to use it, lest he should fall under the supposition of being a magician; nor would even the sailors venture themselves out to sea under his command if he took with him an instrument which carries with it so great an appearance of being constructed under the influence of some infernal spirit." There is little doubt but that the awe in which the compass was held struck terror to the hearts of the sailors on that first historic crossing of the Atlantic ocean by Columbus when it was discovered that the compass no longer pointed to the true north.

Before the time of Gilbert there was a widespread belief that the compass needle pointed north because of a special attraction for iron possessed by the pole star (Polaris). It is not strange that, in an age of mysticism and belief in occult power, the strange and inexplicable behavior of the magnetic compass should be attributed to some mysterious influence beyond the confines of the earth. Gilbert was the first to point out that the magnetic compass orients itself relative to the earth because the earth itself possesses the properties of a magnet. He made a small globe ("terrella" or "little earth") out of magnetite, and with a small compass mapped out the field of force about it, and so showed that the behavior of his "terrella," relative to a small compass, was the same as that of the earth relative to the compass needle. He, however, erroneously assumed the magnetic poles to be at the surface of the earth, and to coincide with the astronomical or geographical poles, although the phenomenon of magnetic declination was known at that time. It is generally considered that Columbus discovered "magnetic variation" or declination during his first crossing of the Atlantic Ocean in 1492, although G. Hellmann concludes that magnetic declination was known in Europe before that date.

The first European to undertake the study of magnetism and to investigate the behavior of magnets by the experimental method was Peregrinus. He made a careful study of magnetism, and in 1269 while serving in the French army in Southern Italy, wrote a letter (Epistola) to a friend in which he set forth his findings and views. This was the first European treatise on magnetism, but unfortunately there were but a few copies made of it, and hence its contents did not become generally known, and therefore many of his findings were later rediscovered independently. In the "Epistola," Peregrinus gave the current beliefs regarding magnetism, and also the results of his own experiments. During his investigations he made use of a spherical lodestone "in the likeness of the heavens," the prototype of Gilbert's "terrella." With this he located the poles of the magnet. He discovered the fact that when a magnet is broken into small pieces each piece is a complete magnet possessing poles. He mounted the compass needle upon a pivot instead of floating it upon water, and used for the first time a graduated circular scale. With this improved compass he had all the means at his disposal for discovering magnetic declination, yet he does not mention it, but states rather that the needle points essentially to the geographic north, which would indicate that at the place where he worked there was no magnetic declination of any consequence. It is interesting to note in passing that Peregrinus proposed to use a magnet in the construction of a perpetual motion machine.

The earliest maps of the Mediterranean coast lines and of Western Europe were made by compass bearings. The dates of some of the earliest maps are 1306, 1324, and 1436. As these charts were made by compass bearings, there are systematic errors in them, owing to magnetic declination, which apparently were not recognized by those who made the charts. Thus, the west end of the Mediterranean is represented too far north relative to the east end. By measuring the angle through which one of these charts must be turned in order that places may fall in their proper geographic relations, Bauer has calculated that in 1436 or earlier the declination at Rome was about 5° E. In later years, after magnetic declination became generally known, it was the practice in many localities to place the compass needle at such an angle relative to the graduated scale that the compass dial would give the true bearings. Such a compass when used at a distant place however would give incorrect bearings.

A real impetus was given to the scientific study of terrestrial magnetism in 1600 with the publication of "De Magnete" by William Gilbert. His interest in the magnetism of the earth was probably aroused by Robert Norman's (London) discovery of magnetic inclination in 1576, and his publication of "The Newe Attractive" in 1581. In "De Magnete" Gilbert assembles the current facts, theories, and vagaries of his day, and also records his own views and experimental findings. Gilbert advanced the theory that magnetite is the fundamental form of matter, that it constitutes all but the outer shell of the earth, and that other forms of matter are derived from it by a process of disintegration. He conceived the earth to be an enormous lodestone having magnetic poles and a magnetic equator, just like his "terrella," but on a much larger scale. Although most of Gilbert's theories pertaining to terrestrial magnetism have been swept away by the investigations of succeeding years, his work is of tremendous importance since it formed the starting point for a sound science of terrestrial magnetism because it introduced the concept for the first time that the earth itself simulates a spherical magnet. However, terrestrial magnetism still remains one of the outstanding, unsolved mysteries in the domain of the Physical Sciences.

78. The Magnetic Elements. — In order to arrive at an understanding of the state of the earth's magnetism, it is necessary to know the intensity, direction, and variation of the magnetic force over the entire surface of the earth. Magnetic observatories have been built at many places, which, unfortunately, are distributed somewhat irregularly over the earth, and magnetic surveys of wide extent have been made and are continuously being made.

In order to determine the magnitude and direction of the earth's magnetism it is necessary to know three things: (1) The magnitude of the horizontal component of the total intensity. This is usually called the *horizontal force* or *horizontal intensity*. (2) The angle that the horizontal intensity makes with the geographical meridian. This angle is called the *declination*, formerly called *magnetic variation*. The trace on the surface of the earth of the vertical plane through the direction of the horizontal intensity is called the *magnetic meridian*. (3) The angle between the total intensity and the horizontal. This angle is called the *dip* or *inclination*. A compass needle mounted on an axis which passes accurately through its center of mass, and so oriented that the axis is normal to the magnetic meridian, will set itself along the line of the

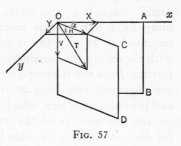

FIG. 57

total magnetic force; the angle which the needle then makes with the horizontal is the dip or inclination. When the horizontal intensity and the dip are known the total intensity is readily calculated. The horizontal intensity, declination, and inclination are the three *elements* which characterize the earth's magnetic state at a given place and time.

The relationship between these three elements will be made clear by reference to Fig. 57. Let the plane *OAB* be the vertical plane through the geographical meridian, and the plane *OCD* the vertical plane through the magnetic meridian. Then the angle α between these two planes is the angle of declination. The total intensity T will be in the direction of the magnetic tubes of flux which lie in the plane *OCD*. The angle i which T makes with the horizontal is the angle of inclination. Thus we have for the horizontal component H

$$H = T \cos i,$$

and for the vertical component V,

$$V = T \sin i.$$

The horizontal component in the plane of the geographical meridian is

$$X = T \cos i \cos \alpha,$$

and the horizontal component normal to this plane is

$$Y = T \cos i \sin \alpha.$$

79. Declination Measurements. — Today measurements of the magnetic elements have reached a high state of accuracy. Declination and horizontal intensity measurements are usually made with the same instrument, a *magnetometer*. The type used by the U.S. Coast and Geodetic Survey is shown in Fig. 58.[1] A hollow cylindrical magnet is suspended horizontally by a stirrup which is hung by a silk or fine metal suspension. A reading telescope is mounted so as to make it possible to bring its axis into alignment with the axis of the suspended magnet. The end of the hollow magnet farthest from the telescope is closed by a piece of plane glass on which are engraved two lines at right angles to each other. The other end is closed by a lens, which makes it possible to focus the telescope on the intersection of the cross lines when the telescope is focused for distant objects. A scale in the telescope permits direct observations of small variations of the magnet. The whole instrument is mounted, when used for field work, upon a theodolite with graduated horizontal scale, which permits the angles between different orientations to be read. Since the axis of figure or geometric axis of the suspended magnet may not coincide with the magnetic axis, the horizontal magnetic direction is read and then the magnet is inverted and another reading is taken. The mean of these two readings gives the direction of the magnetic axis, and hence the direction of the magnetic intensity, or the magnetic meridian.

Since the declination at a given place and time is the angle between the geographic meridian and the magnetic meridian, declination measurements consist in observing these two directions and measuring the angle between them. The magnetic direction is obtained as just stated. The telescope is so mounted as to turn about the central vertical axis, the angular position being indicated by a

[1] Taken from "The Earth's Magnetism," Special Pub. No. 117, p. 28.

horizontal circular scale. The geographic meridian may be determined by observations on the sun or polaris. Sometimes the
geographic meridian is determined by astronomic measurements
and marked on the ground, or the true bearing of some well-defined
distant object is determined, in the case of observatory observations.

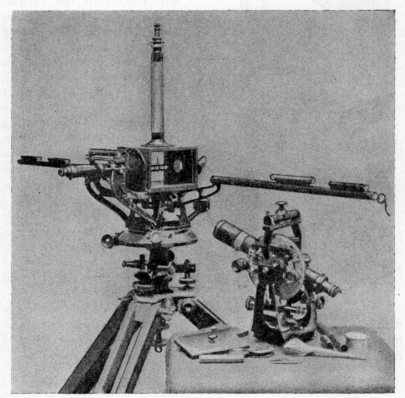

Fig. 58

80. Inclination Measurements. — The angle of inclination is
now usually measured by means of an instrument called a dip circle.
This consists of a magnetic needle mounted on a horizontal axis,
which, when readings are being taken, is placed normal to the magnetic meridian. The needle moves over a graduated scale from which
the angle is read directly. The dip circle which is used by the U. S.
Coast and Geodetic Survey is shown in Fig. 59.

In use the instrument is first leveled, and then the plane of oscillation of the needle is made to coincide with the magnetic meridian. In making this setting use is made of the fact that when the plane of

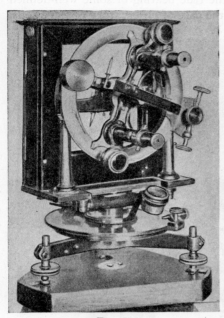

oscillation is normal to the magnetic meridian the needle will remain in the vertical position, since there is then only a vertical force acting on it, the horizontal force being ineffective. The needle is first turned in azimuth until, when set in oscillation, it swings equally on either side of the vertical line when facing south and when facing north. A turn of 90° from this position brings the plane of the circle into the plane of the magnetic meridian.

If observations are made in a plane making an angle α, say, with the magnetic meridian, the relation between the true dip i and the observed dip i' is obtained as follows:

Fig. 59

Let the plane in which the needle oscillates be OAB making the angle α with the magnetic meridian, Fig. 57. In this case α is not necessarily the angle of declination. Then

$$H' = H \cos \alpha, \quad \text{or} \quad H' = T \cos \alpha \cos i. \quad \text{Also } V = T \sin i.$$

But $V/H' = \tan i'$. Therefore,

$$\tan i = \cos \alpha \tan i'.$$

If dip observations are taken in two orthogonal planes making angles α and $90° - \alpha$ with the magnetic meridian, and if i_1 and i_2 are the observed dip angles in the two planes, we have

$$\cot i_1 = \cos \alpha \cot i,$$

and

$$\cot i_2 = \sin \alpha \cot i.$$

Whence

$$\cot^2 i = \cot^2 i_1 + \cot^2 i_2.$$

Thus the dip angle can be measured without determining the plane of the magnetic meridian. This method is of advantage near the magnetic poles where it is difficult to determine the magnetic meridian with accuracy. The method of measuring the horizontal intensity was described in principle in Section 74. As shown there, the measurement requires two operations, called *oscillation* and *deflection*.

81. Isomagnetic Charts. — The results of magnetic surveys are compiled and published in tabular form, or graphically in the form of charts. A chart is more convenient and useful for many purposes than tables of data, since it presents general features to the eye, and gives a more comprehensive mental grasp of the findings. There are three or four main types of maps used to represent the magnetic state of the earth.

Charts upon which lines are drawn through places having the same declination, *isogonic charts*, show the general variations of the compass from the geographic north-south direction over the surface of the earth. Lines of equal declination are called *isogonic lines*, the line of no declination being called an *agonic line*. In the case of declination, the lines are usually drawn 1° of variation apart. The observed angles of declination, as obtained from surveys, seldom fall exactly upon the lines selected to be engraved, and therefore, the location of a line must depend very largely upon interpolated values. On world charts the lines are drawn as smooth curves which show the general regional conditions, but on isogonic charts of land areas which have been surveyed in detail, the lines as a rule are very tortuous owing to local magnetic disturbances; but not all of the local irregularities can be shown even on a detailed chart in many localities. Unusual disturbances in restricted areas are referred to as local in contrast to disturbances which are regional or continental in extent. Very large departures from the regional distribution are sometimes noted in distances of only a few miles. For example, over a small area near Juneau, Alaska, declinations ranging from 175° W to 170° E have been observed where the smooth world isogonics show about 31° 30′ E. At one place in Alaska the dip is 89° 59.4′, and as there is practically no horizontal component the declination cannot be measured. Such marked local disturbances have been observed in other places also. They are generally ascribed to local deposits of magnetic material, such as basalt or magnetite, close to the surface of the ground. In the polar regions the number of observations is limited, and the isogonic lines are of necessity somewhat conjectural, except for the fact that they converge to the magnetic poles.

The places on the earth's surface where the dip needle is vertical are usually called *magnetic poles*. These areas are of two general types. One type is such as was referred to in Alaska where the dip needle is practically vertical. These areas are not the true magnetic poles of the earth, but are considered to be due to local deposits of magnetic material. The other type is characterized by the fact that all isogonic lines converge to them, excepting for a few closed curves as in Siberia which are probably due to local deposits. These poles are two in number, the one in the Northern Hemisphere being in about 71° N latitude and 96° W longitude of Greenwich. The other true magnetic pole, located in the Southern Hemisphere, has never been reached, but the best estimates place it at about 72° S latitude and 155° E longtitude. These magnetic poles are not definite spots, but rather regions of considerable extent, since the dip angle changes very slowly in the vicinity of the pole. Outside the pole area where dip measurements can be made the horizontal component is very weak, thus introducing a relatively large error into the measurements, but from such measurements as have been made, the location of the pole is taken to be the spot to which compass bearings all converge. The magnetic poles of the earth are unlike the poles of a bar magnet; they are not even the places of maximum total intensity. In the Northern Hemisphere there are two places of maximum intensity, the stronger being in Canada at about 52° N latitude and 92° W longitude. There are also two such regions in the Southern Hemisphere. The true magnetic poles are not at the ends of a diameter of the earth; a straight line connecting them misses the center of the earth by about 700 miles, and makes an angle of about 17° with the axis of rotation.

The agonic lines, or lines of zero declination, are of especial interest. One such line girdles the earth in an irregular manner, passing through both magnetic poles and both geographic poles. There is another agonic line of considerable extent which is in the form of an oval (Siberian Oval) in Eastern Siberia. This agonic line, and associated isogonic lines, pass through neither the magnetic nor the geographic pole.

Isogonic charts are used extensively in conjunction with navigation and land surveys when magnetic compasses are used. However, even a casual glance at a chart will convince one of the difficulties involved, and so emphasizes the importance of gyrocompasses, which always set their axes parallel to the geographic meridian in any part of the earth.

Charts on which lines are drawn through places having the same dip angle, *isoclinic charts*, show the general variations of the dip needle from a horizontal position. Lines of equal dip are called *isoclinic lines*, the line of zero dip being called the *magnetic equator*. The magnetic equator crosses the geographic equator twice, once in the Atlantic Ocean and once in the Pacific Ocean. The isoclinic lines are roughly parallel to the magnetic equator, and so correspond to parallels of latitude. North and south of the magnetic equator the isoclinic lines form ever smaller loops encircling the true magnetic poles.

Charts on which lines are drawn through places having the same horizontal intensity, *isodynamic charts*, show the general variations of the horizontal component of the earth's intensity. Lines of equal horizontal intensity are called *isodynamic lines*. The intensity is expressed in dynes per unit pole, and the lines are usually drawn 0.01 dyne apart. The greatest horizontal intensity is in the region of Siam, where a value of 0.4 dyne is observed. Over each magnetic pole, true and apparent, the horizontal intensity vanishes. The isodynamic lines run in a general east-west direction, although many irregularities are observed. The lines are crowded closest in North America to the south of the negative magnetic pole of the earth, and in the region of Australia to the north of the positive magnetic pole.

82. Variations of Magnetic Elements. —

The magnetic elements undergo changes at all points on the earth. These changes may be classified as *secular*, *annual*, and *diurnal*. In addition to these more or less regular and constant variations, there are sudden, irregular, and spasmodic variations which are called *magnetic storms*.

Secular Variations. — Secular variations may be defined as gradual changes in the average daily values of the magnetic elements over a long period of time, several centuries. In 1634 Gellibrand, Professor of mathematics at Gresham College, England, discovered that the angle of declination steadily changed with time. Up to that date it had been supposed that the angle of declination, though changing from place to place upon the earth, was constant with time at any given place. The curve for London seems to point to a periodic character of the variations in the magnetic elements, so that after a period of years (several centuries) the whole process is repeated. However, the curves for other places do not support this conclusion, and, with the accumulation of data, it is seen that the phenomenon is much more irregular and complicated than was at first supposed; the prospect of predicting what changes may be expected from the trend of past events has become ever more remote.

Annual Variations. — There is a variation which is periodic and which takes one year to complete. This variation is superposed upon the secular variation. It occurs simultaneously, but in opposite directions, in the Northern and Southern Hemispheres. In England the maximum easterly declination occurs in August, and the westerly in February, the maximum deviation being about 2.25'.

Diurnal Variations. — The diurnal variation is one that repeats itself with considerable regularity day by day. It is in the main a local phenomenon, apparently depending on the position of the sun above or below the horizon. The major fluctuations occur during daylight, whereas the fluctuations are comparatively small during the night time.

83. Magnetic Storms. — Superposed upon all of the foregoing variations are spasmodic, irregular, and nonperiodic fluctuations. The more marked of these disturbances are called *magnetic storms.* They usually occur at times of maximum sun spot phenomena and auroral displays. Magnetic storms occur at about the same time all over the earth, although the details differ in different places. At the time of some of the most severe magnetic storms telegraphic communications have been interfered with. In the U. S. during a magnetic storm there may be a variation in declination of 0.25° to 1°, and a variation in intensity of as much as 1%. These variations are more pronounced in high latitudes than near the equator. Variations are recorded automatically, the record being called a *magnetogram.*

84. Elementary Mathematical Theory of Terrestrial Magnetism. — An approximate mathematical representation of the magnetic condition of the earth may be arrived at as follows: Consider two spheres, throughout each of which there is a uniform distribution of magnetism of volume density ρ, one positive and the other negative. Let the two spheres occupy the same space, except that one sphere is displaced relative to the other by a small amount oo', Fig. 60. Where the spheres overlap the positive magnetism will neutralize the negative, but at either extremity there will be a crescent of free magnetism, one positive and the other negative. Consider any bar, Fig. 61, with axis parallel to

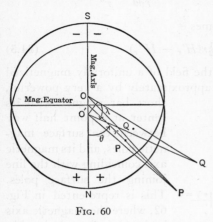

Fig. 60

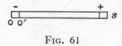

Fig. 61

the line NS, the coalesced spheres imagined to be made up of innumerable bars. At one end of the bar there will be positive magnetism of amount $(oo')s\rho$ and at the other end there will be negative magnetism of the same amount. s is the area of cross section. If oo' is relatively very small these magnetic charges may be considered to be distributed over the ends of the bars. Then $(oo')s\rho = sI$, or $I = (oo')\rho$. The potential due to the positive sphere at any outside point P is $\dfrac{4}{3}\dfrac{\pi a^3 \rho}{o'P}$, and for the negative sphere $-\dfrac{4}{3}\dfrac{\pi a^3 \rho}{oP}$.

The combined potential is

$$V = \tfrac{4}{3}\pi a^3 \rho \left\{ \frac{1}{o'P} - \frac{1}{oP} \right\} = \tfrac{4}{3}\pi a^3 \rho \left\{ \frac{oP - o'P}{r^2} \right\} = \tfrac{4}{3}\pi a^3 \rho \frac{(oo')\cos\theta}{r^2}.$$

But, $M = (\text{volume})I = \tfrac{4}{3}\pi a^3 \rho(oo')$. Hence,

$$V = \frac{M}{r^2}\cos\theta = \frac{M}{r^2}\sin\lambda. \qquad (84.1)$$

For two points P and Q, we have

$$V_P - V_Q = \frac{M}{r^2}(\cos\theta_1 - \cos\theta_2) = \frac{M}{r^2}(\sin\lambda_1 - \sin\lambda_2), \quad (84.2)$$

where λ is the magnetic latitude. Also,

$$H_r = -\frac{\partial V}{\partial r} = \frac{2M}{r^3} \sin \lambda, \quad H_\theta = -\frac{\partial V}{r\partial \theta} = \frac{M}{r^3} \cos \lambda.$$

Thus, in terms of H_r, (84.2) becomes

$$V_P - V_Q = \tfrac{1}{2}r(H'_r - H''_r). \tag{84.3}$$

We see from the above, that the field of a uniformly magnetized sphere may be represented very approximately by a very powerful, short bar magnet with its center at a point half way between the surface magnetic poles, and its magnetic axis coinciding with the line joining the surface poles. This is represented in Fig. 62, where the magnetic axis is shown in its relationship to the axis of rotation.

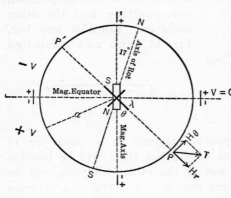

Fig. 62

Equation (84.3) lends itself to experimental test, since the vertical component of the earth's magnetic field can be measured for two stations P and Q, and, if the horizontal intensity H_θ is measured for stations P and Q, $V_P - V_Q$ can be calculated. Other relations may be obtained which can be tested also. Thus, we have

$$\cdot \tan i = \frac{H_r}{H_\theta} = 2 \tan \lambda, \tag{84.4}$$

where i is the dip angle. Further, we have

$$M = (\text{volume})I = \tfrac{4}{3}\pi a^3 I \cdot \tag{84.5}$$

Therefore,

$$H_r = \frac{2(\tfrac{4}{3}\pi a^3)I}{r^3} \sin \lambda, \quad \text{and} \quad H_\theta = \frac{\tfrac{4}{3}\pi a^3 I}{r^3} \cos \lambda.$$

At the surface of the earth at the magnetic poles, $\lambda = 90°$, and $r = a$, the radius of the earth. Hence,

$$T_P = H_r = 2(\tfrac{4}{3}\pi)I, \quad \text{and} \quad H_\theta = 0, \tag{84.6}$$

where T_P is the total intensity at the pole. At the magnetic equator $\lambda = 0$, and hence

$$T_e = H_\theta = \tfrac{4}{3}\pi I, \quad \text{and} \quad H_r = 0, \tag{84.7}$$

where T_e is the total intensity at the magnetic equator. Thus,

$$T_P = 2T_e. \tag{84.8}$$

From (84.5) and (84.7), we have

$$M = T_e a^3. \tag{84.9}$$

The mean value of T_e for the earth is 0.33 oersted. Hence,

$$0.33 = \tfrac{4}{3}\pi I, \text{ and therefore } I = 0.0788.$$

Also, $M = 0.33\ a^3 = 8.8(10)^{25}$. Knowing M, V may be calculated by (84.1).

Schuster has estimated that the maximum intensity of magnetization an iron sphere may acquire is 100. Therefore, a small fraction of the earth is strongly magnetized, or the earth as a whole is magnetized to less than 1/10,000 of the intensity an iron sphere may acquire.[1]

For any point on the surface of the earth, we have

$$H_r = 2T_e \sin \lambda, \quad \text{and} \quad H_\theta = T_e \cos \lambda,$$

and therefore,

$$T^2 = H_r{}^2 + H_\theta{}^2 = T_e{}^2\,(1 + 3\sin^2 \lambda). \tag{84.10}$$

Point Inside the Earth. — For a point inside a uniform distribution of magnetic charge of volume density ρ the intensity ($H = \tfrac{4}{3}\pi\rho r$, Section 9) is directed away from or toward the center depending on whether ρ is positive or negative. In the present case

$$H_+ = \tfrac{4}{3}\pi r'\rho \quad \text{and} \quad H_- = \tfrac{4}{3}\pi r\rho,$$

as shown in Fig. 63. The resultant H is parallel to the magnetic axis for all positions. Hence

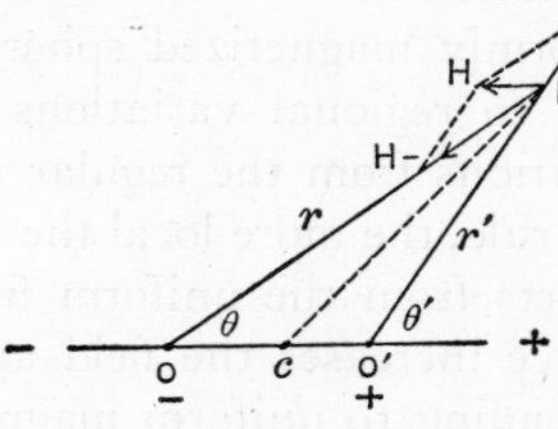

Fig. 63

$$H = \tfrac{4}{3}\pi\rho r' \cos \theta' - \tfrac{4}{3}\pi\rho r \cos \theta = \tfrac{4}{3}\pi\rho(r' \cos \theta' - r \cos \theta) = \tfrac{4}{3}\pi\rho(oo')$$

$$= -\tfrac{4}{3}\pi I. \tag{84.11}$$

[1] Schuster, Phys. Soc. Proc., XXIV, 127, 1912.

The resultant intensity H is, therefore, constant and in the negative direction, i.e., reverse to the polarity of the sphere. Also, if oo' is small relative to r and r', the distinction between θ and θ' is unnecessary, and therefore

$$H_r = -H \cos \theta = \frac{\partial V}{\partial r} \text{ , and } V = -\int_0^r H \cos \theta \, dr = -Hr \cos \theta$$

$$= -Hr \sin \lambda.$$

For any two points P and Q on a sphere of radius r, we have

$$V_P - V_Q = -Hr \cos \theta_P + Hr \cos \theta_Q.$$

But the components toward the center are

$$Z_P = H \cos \theta_P, \text{ and } Z_Q = H \cos \theta_Q,$$

and therefore

$$V_P - V_Q = -r(Z_P - Z_Q). \tag{84.12}$$

The intensity H due to the internal field is negative, and therefore, tends to weaken the field, or to demagnetize. This is the *demagnetizing field*. Assuming the external field to be continuous through the sphere, we have for the resultant, internal field

$$B = -\tfrac{4}{3}\pi I + 4\pi I = \tfrac{8}{3}\pi I, \tag{84.13}$$

which is in the positive sense.

Tests show that the magnetism of the earth corresponds more closely to the relation (84.3) than to (84.12), and therefore the cause of the earth's magnetism lies largely beneath its surface. The actual magnetic field of the earth shows many variations from the field of a uniformly magnetized sphere. These variations range from purely local to regional variations of great extent. In Siberia there are variations from the regular field which amount to as much as 10%. As a rule, the more local the inequality the less the field in that region departs from the uniform field. As the distance above the earth's surface increases the field approaches more closely to the field corresponding to uniform magnetization, so that at a distance of a few diameters of the earth the field is essentially that of uniform magnetization. The more local the deviations from the uniform field the more rapidly do they fade out with distance from the earth.

The preceding theory gives only a rough approximation to the actual magnetic field of the earth. Gauss treated the problem of the earth's magnetism by more rigorous mathematical methods, and obtained expressions which, when tested with observed data, give results more consonant with actual conditions, but his mathematical discussion is beyond the scope of this book.

Whatever the distribution of the magnetism of the earth may be, it has at every point a definite potential, and hence a definite intensity. There is therefore associated with the earth a system of magnetic equipotential surfaces, which are cut normally by tubes of total magnetic flux. If the equipotential surfaces are drawn so as to represent equal potential differences, these equipotential surfaces cut the surface of the earth along lines which may be called *magnetic parallels*, which are at every point perpendicular to the magnetic meridians, and to the total intensity. The magnetic parallels cut the horizontal components orthogonally, and so constitute a system of *equipotential lines*. The magnetic equator corresponds to the intersection of the earth's surface with the equipotential surface $V = 0$. This surface separates points in space for which the potential is positive (Southern Magnetic Hemisphere) from points for which it is negative (Northern Magnetic Hemisphere). The points upon the surface of the earth where the total intensity is vertical are points where the equipotential surfaces are tangent to the surface of the earth, and correspond to surfaces of maximum potential.

85. Theories Concerning the Earth's Magnetism. — The fundamental problem of the cause of the earth's magnetism is one that has for long attracted the attention of scientists. It has been attacked by our ablest men of science, armed with the most powerful weapons known to science, but each and every onslaught has been repulsed by the overwhelming accumulation of observed evidence. One theory after another has been advanced, only to be withdrawn when new evidence rendered it untenable. All fields of science which might have any bearing whatsoever on the problem have been requisitioned, the electron theory, the influence of the sun, the condition and composition of the earth itself, and the possibility of a general space magnetic field, but with little progress. The mystery of the cause of the earth's magnetism is still with us. It will be of interest, however, to review some of the theories that have been advanced and the reasons for their rejection.

The oldest theory is the one advanced by Gilbert, which has found favor in modified forms down almost to the present time.

Gilbert conceived the earth to be composed of magnetite; he thought of it as a huge lodestone uniformly magnetized relative to its axis of rotation. This theory had to be discarded, because, so far as visible rocks are concerned, there is comparatively little magnetite or other magnetic material of any sort, except in local deposits, and there is little likelihood that the interior of the earth is composed largely of ferromagnetic substances. Even if the interior of the earth were composed largely of ferromagnetic substances, the known high temperature would preclude the possibility of its being susceptible to magnetization. Below a depth of about 25 kilometers, assuming the rate of rise in temperature to be 1° C. for every 40 meters, the temperature is higher than the magnetic critical temperature of any ferromagnetic substance, unless conditions there, such as enormous pressure, change laboratory conditions. Magnetite ceases to be magnetic at a lower temperature, which is reached at a depth of about 15 kilometers. If there can be no magnetism below this depth, the theory of permanent magnetism requires a comparatively thin shell near the surface of the earth to be highly magnetized. The secular variations would then be due to changes in the direction of magnetization of this shell; but in order to produce these changes the forces involved would need to be very large owing to the fact that the retentivity would need to be very high in order to preserve the magnetism. Furthermore, there is no satisfactory theory to account for the magnetization in the first place, unless it be due to induction effects from without the earth which are still operative. These difficulties would be lessened if the critical temperatures of ferromagnetic substances were raised by pressure. But, so far as tests that have been made go to show, it seems that an increase in pressure lowers the critical temperature. However, it is possible that very great pressure may change some of the properties of matter, and magnetic susceptibility may be one of them.

Because of the impossibility of accounting for the earth's magnetism in any other way, Nippoldt in 1921, returned to the idea of the earth as a permanent magnet. He advanced the theory that the earth's surface down to a depth of about 20 kilometers is composed of materials susceptible to magnetization, and, in addition, he assumed an interior core composed of iron, nickel, and cobalt, as suggested by geophysicists, which might be susceptible to magnetization in spite of the high temperature in view of the fact that Hale has discovered, through the Zeeman effect, that the sun possesses a magnetic field.

However, even if the earth to a depth of 20 kilometers were composed entirely of magnetite the susceptibility would not be great enough to account for the known field at the surface. If the earth is a magnet, in the ordinary sense, which seems extremely doubtful, we must still account for the fluctuations and changes which are constantly taking place, and show why the retentivity is so high as to effectually resist the demagnetization which takes place with time, which long since would have reduced the magnetism of the earth to zero.

When it became apparent that the earth could not be considered a permanent magnet, the idea was advanced that it might be an electromagnet, the magnetic field being due to currents of electricity flowing around the earth, beneath the surface or in the atmosphere above. Bauer in 1922 came to the conclusion that about 94% of the total magnetic field of the earth comes from an interior system, the balance being external to the earth. If the magnetism of the earth is due to currents, the currents must be largely within the earth, a small portion being in the atmosphere. However, if such currents exist, they cannot be the survival of some past order of events because the rate of attenuation owing to ohmic resistance is by far too rapid. Schuster has calculated that currents within the earth would fall to one eth ($e = 2.718$) of their initial value in two to three days. Currents of electricity capable of producing the earth's magnetic field would need to encircle the earth as a whole in a more or less regular and persistent manner. There are known to be feeble ground currents more or less irregular, but apparently not a part of a regular world system which could account for the magnetic field of the earth. There is no known source of energy within the earth which would maintain a system of currents such as could account for the general magnetic field. Lamont has proposed a possible cause of such internal currents, but principally with reference to the sun. If there were internal currents of matter in meridional planes, these currents, in the presence of a magnetic field no matter how weak, would induce electromotive forces in the moving matter and currents would flow, the currents in turn increasing the magnetic field. The earth would then be comparable to a self-excited dynamo, which builds up from a small residual magnetic field to a fixed value, the energy being derived from the internal circulating matter. While this may be a plausible theory to account for the sun's magnetism, it cannot obtain for the earth because of its extreme rigidity. Even in the case of the sun it is difficult to understand why there should be currents of matter in meridional planes, and, furthermore, the origin of the residual magnetism from which the field is built up remains unexplained. Also, the fluctuations and variations in the magnetic field remain to be accounted for.

Another form of the rotational theory is based upon the fact that a gyroscope on or in a rotating body, such as the earth, tends to set its axis of rotation parallel to the axis of rotation of the body of which it is a part. According to present-day theory the ultimate magnetic elements are electrons in orbital motions about the nuclei of atoms. These revolving electrons should act, therefore, like tiny gyroscopes and set their axes of rotation, and hence also their magnetic axes, parallel to the axis of rotation, leaving the asymmetrical part and the variations to be accounted for in some other manner. Maxwell was the first to point out this possible explanation. Schuster, however, has suggested that this might account for secular variations because of precessional motion, leaving the actual magnetization to be accounted for in some other manner; and Swann has pointed out that this magnetization, if it exists, would be the same for all volume elements, so that the intensity at the surface should be the same whatever the size of the body. Spheres rotated in the laboratory with much greater angular speeds than that of the earth show no comparable magnetic fields. Barnett has recently found that rotation does actually produce magnetization in ferromagnetic substances. The magnetization produced was found to be directly proportional to the angular speed, independent of the size of the rotated body, and the sign was such as could be accounted for on the electron theory. Its magnitude, however, for the slow angular speed of the earth, is far too small to account for the magnetism of the earth, unless some pronounced difference of conditions exist, such as greater freedom of motion in the interior of the earth due to high temperature; but this greater freedom might be more than counterbalanced by enormous pressure. (See Section 208.)

Since all theories that have been advanced to explain terrestrial magnetism have failed to meet all requirements, magneticians have turned to related phenomena in search of an adequate explanation, such as atmospheric electricity, earth currents, auroras, sunspots, and radiation. In particular, magnetic storms have been studied with the hope of connecting them with sunspots and the sun's magnetism. In general, the maximum magnetic disturbances occur at the eleven-year period accompanying sunspot appearances. But, on the other hand, magnetic storms sometimes occur when there are no sunspots in evidence, and again, fail to develop when sunspots are in evidence. There is a close relationship between magnetic storms, sunspots, and auroral displays, and this has suggested the possibility that streams of electrons emanating from the sun and being intercepted by the earth may set up electric currents in the earth's atmosphere, which would produce both auroral displays and magnetic storms. These speculations, like all others, fail to meet all observations. Hale's researches at the Mt. Wilson Observatory have revealed that the sun possesses a magnetic field, in many respects similar to the terrestrial field, with its magnetic axis inclined to the axis of rotation, but by a smaller angle, about 6°. However, the solar magnetic field differs from the terrestrial field in many important respects. It is much stronger, but fades out with distance above the surface of the sun at a more rapid rate, if our evidence is reliable. The sunspots are observed to be magnetic poles, and where sunspots occur in pairs one is usually a positive pole whereas the other is a negative pole. The moon also has a small though definite influence upon the earth's magnetic field.

PROBLEMS

The following data were taken from the U.S. Magnetic Tables for 1925.

	Geographic latitude	Declination	Dip	Horizontal intensity
Urbana, Ill..............	40° 5′	3° 10′	71° 10′	0.1926
Milwaukee, Wis.........	43° 4′	2° 34′	73° 59′	0.1690

1. From the above data calculate the magnetic moment and the intensity of magnetization of the earth. Also, calculate the difference of potential between Urbana and Milwaukee. For each station calculate the magnetic latitude.

2. Calculate the total intensity at Urbana and at Milwaukee. Then calculate the total intensity at the magnetic equator and at the magnetic poles. Compare your results with values given on magnetic charts or obtained from Tables of magnetic data.

CHAPTER VI

DIRECT-CURRENT CIRCUITS

86. — In the first three chapters we have developed the fundamental laws governing charges of electricity when at rest relative to the substance containing them, and we have studied the fields of force surrounding charges of electricity and the influence the medium has on a field of force. This is the division of the subject called electrostatics, and it is the oldest. When charges of electricity are in motion relative to the substance containing them new and very different conditions arise and new phenomena make their appearance. Charges of electricity in motion relative to the conductor containing them constitute a current of electricity. Furthermore, when charges of electricity are in motion relative to material substances magnetic fields of force make their appearance as an accompanying phenomenon. The division of the subject of electricity which treats of the interactions of currents of electricity through the medium of their accompanying magnetic fields, or of the interactions of currents and magnets, is called electrodynamics. From the standpoint of industrial developments this branch of the subject of electricity is by far the most important.

87. The Concept of an Electric Current. — Let us suppose that we have two insulated conducting bodies, A and B, each bearing an electric charge, Fig. 64. Let the charge on A be positive and the

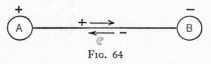

FIG. 64

charge on B negative. If the two bodies be connected by a metal wire a flow of electrons will take place in the direction from B to A, and the flow will continue until the two bodies are at the same potential. Also, in accord with Maxwell's theory, there will be a displacement current in the space surrounding the material system. There was no experimental evidence to guide the early investigators in selecting a direction of flow, and so it was arbitrarily assumed that the flow is from the positively charged body to the negatively charged body, i.e., from A to B. This choice is due to Franklin who postulated that a single "electric fluid" or "electric fire" exists in all bodies. He assumed that a positively charged body contained more and a negatively charged body less of this fluid than an uncharged body. Therefore, when two charged conducting bodies, such as A and B, are connected by a metal wire the flow will be from A to B. Thus A is said to be at a higher potential than B. Had he assumed that the body containing an excess of this electric fluid was negatively charged he would have been in agreement with present-day findings. It is interesting to note in passing that Franklin conceived electricity to be atomic in structure, for he said, "The electrical matter consists of particles extremely subtle since it can penetrate common matter, even the densest, with such freedom and ease as not to receive any appreciable resistance." This reminds us of the atomistic theory promulgated by Democritus. Thus we see that the direction of flow of a current of electricity was fixed arbitrarily at a time when there was no experimental evidence to guide the choice of direction.

Today we have abundant evidence that electricity is atomic in structure, consisting of positive and negative units, the positive unit being called the *proton* and the negative unit the *electron*.[1] The mass of the proton is about 1,840 times that of the electron. Protons are constituents of the nuclei of the atoms of matter, and therefore are fixed in the atoms. In solid conductors the atoms are relatively fixed in position forming lattices, and hence the protons are also fixed in position. Electrons are easily detached from metal atoms, and consequently are relatively free to move through the lattice structure. The body B in Fig. 64 has an excess of electrons and the body A a dearth of electrons. Therefore there is an electric field of force existing between A and B. Electrons in this field of force will be urged in a direction from B to A. However, they are bound to the body B so long as B is insulated, but when a conducting path between B and A is provided, as by a connecting metal wire, electrons will move in a direction from B to A under the influence of the electric field, and this constitutes a current of electricity; in this case a *transient*

---

[1] The discussion at this point does not involve or require the neutron, discovered by Chadwick in 1932, or the positron, discovered by Anderson in 1932.

current, since its duration is only a fraction of a second. In the light of modern evidence it would be better to say that B is at a higher potential than A, if we are to use the terms *high* and *low* to characterize potentials. However, we still retain these terms that have been inherited from the past, and we still say that A is at a higher potential than B, and that the current flows from A to B although we know that it flows in the reverse direction. The reason for this procedure is that when a method in science has been once established and used for several generations it is very difficult to make a change to a more rational method. However, so far as it is possible to do so, consistent with clarity, we will endeavor to present the matter in the correct manner.

If we examine the effects produced by a current of electricity, we shall find that, in general, they are two in number. The conductor is ①*heated*, and it is ②surrounded by a *magnetic field of force*. These two effects always accompany a current of electricity, excepting in the case of superconductivity when heating is negligible. In the case of electrolytic conduction, there is in addition a *chemical action* in the conductor.

A current of electricity in a metallic conductor is a flow of electrons, and therefore, we may express it in terms of the electronic charge e. When a difference of potential exists in a conductor, free electrons experience a force urging them from negative to positive. As they move under the influence of the electric field they are constantly encountering and colliding with the molecules and atoms composing the conductor, and these encounters retard the otherwise free motion. Thus, although the electrons are accelerated between encounters with the molecules, they progress through the conductor with an average constant speed—in case of a steady current—due to these encounters. This average speed v, which characterizes the electric current, is small in comparison with the average random speed of the electrons, which characterizes their heat motions. The drift of the electrons under the electric field, which constitutes the current, is superposed upon the random thermal motions of the electrons. As there can be no accumulation of charge at any point in a conductor, the same charge should cross each section of the circuit which cuts all the stream lines when we take equal finite intervals of time. From the equation $q = it$, we see that i is the charge (expressed in any system of units) which crosses any section of the conductor in unit time. Let the cross section of the conductor be A sq. cms.

Then, if there are n free electrons per cm.^{3}, each bearing a charge e, and the current speed is v cms. per sec,

i = cqc/unit time

$$i = Anev, \qquad (87.1)$$

where i is measured in the same system of units as e. The current i per sq. cm. of section of the conductor, called the current density, is given by

$$i = nev. \qquad (87.2)$$

$i = Ai$

88. General Characteristics of the Electric Current—Constant. —

If the current density i is to be constant over the area of cross section of a conductor we must assume uniform volume distribution of charge throughout the conductor. The density of charge in any system of units in a metallic conductor is so large as compared with the charge of a single electron that we may accept a uniform volume distribution as essentially correct when dealing with currents of ordinary magnitudes in homogeneous conductors. If the conductor is not homogeneous the volume distribution of charge will not be uniform throughout, nor will the current necessarily be constant across a given section of the conductor. Furthermore, the drift of conduction electrons, due to an impressed electric field, will be influenced to some extent by the crystal-lattice structure of the conductor. The fixed lattice structure will contain positive ions, thus rendering the impressed electric field within the conductor nonuniform, and consequently electrons may move in certain crystal directions with greater freedom than in other directions. In such a case the actual flow of electrons at a particular point within the conductor will not necessarily be in the same direction as the impressed field. To this extent the substance is anisotropic. This would be the case when the crystals are large, but the effect is relatively unimportant in ordinary metallic conductors possessing microcrystals. The microscopic resistance to flow, i.e., when considering individual electrons, would depend upon direction, but the average resistance to flow when considering a very large number of electrons, or macroscopic resistance, is the same in all directions. The conductor is then classed as isotropic. However, if the medium is anisotropic the intensity E and i are not in general in the same direction and the relation between them at a point in the medium is not of simple form. If the medium is homogeneous and isotropic, which is true in most practical cases, i is proportional to E and we may write

$$E = \rho i, \quad \text{or} \quad i = \sigma E, \qquad (88.3)$$

conductivity $= \frac{1}{R}$

Resistivity   *Conductivity*

where ρ is the *resistivity* and σ the *conductivity* of the conductor. One is the reciprocal of the other. Equation (88.3) expresses *Ohm's law*, and a medium such that Ohm's law holds is said to be *ohmic*. If the medium is inhomogeneous or anisotropic or both, equation (88.3) does not hold. ρ and σ are then functions of the position in the medium, but for ohmic media ρ and σ are constant and independent of position.

In considering ordinary currents, or macroscopic conditions, a current may be said to be continuous, i.e., the same number of electrons cross a section of a conductor in equal infinitesimal time inter-

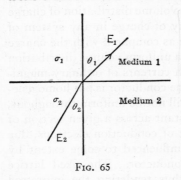

FIG. 65

vals, although even with currents of ordinary magnitudes this probably is not strictly true. However, with extremely small currents we should expect a discontinuity in current flow under certain conditions. Such a condition is actually realized in the case of high gain tube amplifiers. The space current in a radio tube (current between filament and plate) is a stream of electrons in practically free space, and when extremely small currents are highly amplified the atomic nature of electricity is made manifest by discontinuities in the amplified current. This phenomenon is known as the "shot effect." [1]

At the interface separating two homogeneous conductors of different conductivities tubes of flux, and hence also lines of flow, are refracted much as are tubes of flux at the interface separating two dielectrics. Proceeding as in Section 50 we may imagine a very short cylinder enclosing a section of the interface. We may consider that the cylinder is so short as compared with its diameter that the flux and flow through the sides of the cylinder may be neglected. Then the flow through the ends of the cylinder of areas da will be equal, and, by use of equation (88.3) and Fig. 65, we may write

$$\sigma_1 E_1 \cos \theta_1 ds = \sigma_2 E_2 \cos \theta_2 ds,$$

or

$$\sigma_1 E_1 \cos \theta_1 = \sigma_2 E_2 \cos \theta_2. \tag{88.4}$$

[1] See Electron and Nuclear Physics by J. B. Hoag, p. 100.

The tangential components of E are equal, and hence

$$E_1 \sin \theta_1 = E_2 \sin \theta_2. \tag{88.5}$$

Dividing (88.4) by (88.5), we have

$$\sigma_1 \cot \theta_1 = \sigma_2 \cot \sigma_2. \tag{88.6}$$

89. Ohm's Law. — We will consider homogeneous, isotropic conductors only. So long as there is no external field applied to the conductor the average internal field will be zero, since the positive and negative charges in any elementary volume are equal. Therefore, there is only the random thermal motions of the conduction electrons. Now if a field of intensity E is applied to the conductor each electron will experience an acceleration a, which, if the ordinary laws of mechanics obtain, will be of magnitude

$$a = \frac{eE}{m},$$

where m is the rest mass of the electron. This motion is superposed upon the random motion of the electron, and is small in comparison. Since the random motions of the electrons cancel when we consider large numbers, we may consider only the small drift motions due to the external field E. Let t, the *mean free time*, be the average time between successive collisions of an electron with the atoms or molecules of the conductor. t is the time required for an electron to traverse the *mean free path*. t will depend on the structure of the conductor and its temperature.

The electrons will be continually starting due to the field E and stopping due to collisions with atoms and molecules. The collisions have the effect of restoring the random thermal distribution of velocities. Thus, the free electrons are continually starting and stopping, but there will be a definite average drift velocity, when we consider very large numbers of electrons, due to the field E, which is superposed upon the random thermal velocities. We have $v = at$ $= \dfrac{eE}{m} t$ as the velocity at the end of an excursion through the distance of a mean free path. The average velocity is

$$\bar{v} = \frac{0 + \dfrac{eE}{m} t}{2} = \frac{1}{2} \frac{eE}{m} t.$$

If there are n electrons per cm.[3], we have $q = ne$ and $\mathbf{i} = q\bar{v}$, and therefore,

$$\mathbf{i} = \frac{ne^2 t}{2m} E. \tag{89.1}$$

Current Density (handwritten annotation)

Therefore, by equation (88.3), we see that the conductivity is

$$\sigma = \frac{\mathbf{i}}{E} = \frac{ne^2 t}{2m}. \tag{89.2}$$

the resistivity is $\frac{1}{\sigma}$ (handwritten annotation)

Let us now write the differential equation representing the motion of an electron in the x direction, say, the x axis coinciding with the axis of the wire. Thus,

$$m \frac{d^2 x}{dt^2} + k \frac{dx}{dt} = eE_x.$$

m × a · *Force* · *— Retarding Force* · *takes care of starting & stopping due to collisions* (handwritten annotations)

When the steady state is reached the acceleration vanishes, and then

k $\frac{dx}{dt}$ = Ee · *KV = Ee* · *∴ V = $\frac{eE}{K}$* (handwritten annotations)

$$\bar{v} = \frac{e}{k} E_x,$$

and hence $\mathbf{i} = q\bar{v} = \frac{ne^2}{k} E_x.$ Therefore, $\frac{ne^2 t}{2m} = \frac{ne^2}{k}$, and $k = \frac{2m}{t}$.

k is the average effective retarding force per electron per unit velocity.

Also $\sigma = \frac{ne^2}{k}$. If n is known both t and k may be calculated, since σ can be measured.

Returning now to equation (88.3), we have

$$E = \rho \mathbf{i} = \frac{\rho}{A} i,$$

where A is constant for unit length of the conductor. Let us apply this equation to a simple metallic conductor of length l which is homogeneous and of constant cross section throughout its length. E is constant along the flow lines, and in this case, directed along the conductor (wire). El is then by definition the difference of potential between two points along the conductor distant l apart. If the wire is not of uniform cross section throughout the flow lines are not at all points parallel to the axis of the conductor, and hence E and l do not have the same direction at all points. However, we will not follow the argument farther since theories of metallic conduction are

NB · *⊕ current ⊖* · *electrons move up the pot. gradient.* · *e* (handwritten annotations)

beyond the scope of this book. The interested reader will need to consult more extended treatises on this subject.

Multiplying (88.3) by l, we have

$$V = El = \rho \frac{l}{A} i = Ri, \qquad (89.3)$$

Since $E = \rho l$
$\xi \, i = \frac{i}{A}$
$\therefore E = \frac{\rho i}{A}$

where A and ρ are both constant for the length l. This is a statement of Ohm's law in the usual form. Ohm's law may be defined in words as follows: The potential difference between two points in a simple conductor, maintained at constant potential, is directly proportional to the current flowing through it. By simple conductor is meant a homogeneous one in which all of the energy expended appears as heat. In all cases where the energy is not wholly turned into heat in the conductor Ohm's law does not hold. In case the conductor is not of constant cross section throughout, and even ρ may vary, Ohm's law holds if all of the energy is expended as heat in the conductor, but R is not then directly proportional to the length throughout.

$R = \rho \dfrac{l}{A} \cdot$ R is called the ohmic resistance, and may be calculated from this equation if ρ and A are constant throughout. If either ρ or A or both vary R is an average value, i.e., there is some conductor which would have the same resistance for the length l in which ρ and A are constant and represent average values.

Ohm's law as defined holds in any system of units. In the practical system of units V is measured in *volts*, R in *ohms*, and i in *amperes*. These units are defined with reference to the cgsm. system of units in Section 18. ρ is the resistivity measured in ohm-cm., i.e., it is the resistance between the opposite faces of a cm. cube of the substance, and so is a characteristic of the nature of the substance so far as electric resistance is concerned. $\sigma = 1/\rho$ is called the conductivity. $G = 1/R$ is called the conductance, and is measured in *mhos*. Very large resistances are sometimes expressed in megohms, a *megohm* being a million ohms.

90. The Voltaic Cell. — The current of electricity which was considered in Section 87 is a transient current, and the difference in potential giving rise to it is transient. In order to produce a continuous flow for any appreciable time requires that the difference of potential be maintained. The first means which was discovered for maintaining a

$R = \dfrac{\rho l}{A}$
ohm
$ohmcm$

$\rho = ohm \, cms$

difference of potential was the voltaic cell, the difference of potential being maintained by the energy of chemical action.

The voltaic cell leads us immediately to a classification of conductors of electricity. There are two main classes of conductors. Metallic conductors, such as we have been considering, are called *conductors of the first class*. Metallic conduction is such as takes place in metals, and it is not accompanied by a chemical change in the conductor itself. In this type of conduction the conduction electrons within the metal simply migrate under the influence of the electric field. In their migratory motions they collide with the molecules and atoms of the conductor, thus giving rise to thermal agitation of the molecules and atom, and so develop heat. Electrolytes are called *conductors of the second class*. Electrolytic conduction is such as takes place in certain solutions, and it is always accompanied by, and is dependent upon, chemical changes in the conductor. In fact, a transfer of electricity through the electrolyte can take place only when there is a chemical change. Conduction of this type requires a separate treatment, and therefore will be considered at greater length under the heading of "electrolysis." Electrolytic conduction is also accompanied by heating of the conductor and by a magnetic field of force, the two effects of all electric currents.

It was Count Alessandro Volta, Professor of Physics at the University of Pavia, Italy, who explained the cause of the muscular contractions of a frog's legs, in Luigi Galvani's experiments of 1786, as being due to an electric current. Transient electric currents were known prior to this date, and their effects in producing muscular contractions had been observed in connection with static electric generators, which antedate the voltaic cell. Volta showed that an electric current could be produced by placing a piece of copper and a piece of zinc in a solution of H_2SO_4, or some other acid or salt solution. This was about 1800. Here we have the characteristics of all voltaic cells, i.e., if conductors of the first class and conductors of the second class form a closed circuit we have conditions which may give rise to an electric current. The electrodes which form contacts with the electrolyte must be dissimilar, otherwise no current is produced. The number of different voltaic cells that are possible is very great, but only a few have proved to be of any practical value. A current of electricity generated by a voltaic cell is frequently spoken of as a "voltaic current." The term "voltaic current" was originally used to distinguish between a current produced at low potential, as by a voltaic cell, and a current produced at high potential, as by an electrostatic generator, but it does not imply that currents of electricity are inherently different.

The polarity of a voltaic cell was determined by testing the signs of the charges on the exposed electrodes. The electrode which had a charge of the same sign as that on glass when rubbed with silk was said to be positive, and the other was said to be negative, since it had the other kind of charge on it. This fixed the conventional direction of flow of the electric current as from the positive electrode to the negative electrode in the external circuit. This we will call the *conventional current*, as opposed to the actual current which is known to flow in the reverse direction, and which we will call the *electronic current*. So far as results are concerned it makes no difference which current we consider, if we are consistent in our applications, but it is better to think of the actual or electronic current where no confusion in the applications of rules, which have become established through long usage, is involved.

91. Ampère's Law. — In 1819 the Danish physicist, Hans Christian Oersted, performed the fundamental experiments which revealed the presence of a magnetic field of force as a product of the electric current. These experiments consisted in bringing a small compass needle into juxtaposition with a wire bearing a current of electricity and observing its behavior. It was found that if the compass needle were parallel with the wire when no current was flowing it tended to take up a position normal to the wire as soon as a current was established. The existence of a current of electricity had been determined for the previous twenty years by other effects, such as heating and the twitching of muscles, as in Galvani's experiments. Oersted's discovery was of paramount importance in the further development of the science of electricity. As is shown in all books on general physics, the magnetic field about a straight, isolated conductor when bearing a current is circular and concentric with the conductor; the tubes of flux are closed circles about the conductor. If the conductor is not straight and isolated, the flux loops are not, in general, concentric circles, and they are not uniformly spaced. The mutual directions (in conventional usage) of current and tubes of flux may be expressed by a simple rule (due to Fleming), which is as follows: *Grasp the conductor with the right hand, thumb extended. Then the thumb will point in the direction of the current flow if the fingers point in the direction of the* *tubes of flux*, the direction of a tube of flux being that in which a positive magnetic pole is urged.

It was André Marie Ampère who, in 1823, showed that, "Every linear conductor carrying a current is equivalent to a simple magnetic shell, the bounding edge of which coincides with the conductor, and the moment of which per unit area, that is, the strength of the shell, is proportional to the strength of the current." This equivalent shell will be considered later. The potential and the intensity due to a magnetic shell can be uniquely determined at all points, as we have seen in Section 75, and so the magnetic field of force of a current of electricity may be mapped out.

The same results, however, may be obtained by another method. This is accomplished by treating each elementary segment of the current as a current element of length dl, and applying the relation

$$dH = k\frac{i\,dl\sin\theta}{r^2}, \qquad (91.1)$$

Fig. 66. dH is the magnetic intensity at a point P contributed by an elementary segment of length dl, i the current strength, r the distance

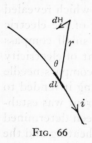

Fig. 66

from the segment to the point P, and θ the angle which r makes with dl. k is a constant of proportionality. It will be noticed that $dl\sin\theta$ is the component of the current normal to r, which alone is effective in developing an intensity at P. dH, in the above expression, is that part of the total intensity at P which is contributed by the element of current of length dl of a continuous current flowing in a closed path. From this expression it is possible, in many cases, to calculate the total effect at P due to the whole current. This will now be done in a simple case, from which is obtained the definition of the cgsm. unit current. The expresion (91.1) is known as Ampère's law.

92. Unit Electromagnetic Current. — The magnetic field strength for a given constant current is constant for any position P. It has been selected, therefore, for the purpose of measuring and defining current strength. The unit field strength, and the unit magnetic pole strength have been defined from Coulomb's law in free space by the relation

$$F = \frac{mm'}{r^2}\ \text{cgsm. units.}$$

We may now define unit current in terms of unit pole strength. Thus, let us say, we have a current flowing in a circle. There is then a definite magnetic intensity at the center of the circle with a given current strength. Equation (91.1) now takes the form

$$dH = ki\frac{dl}{r^2},$$ (92.1)

since $\theta = 90°$ for every current element when we consider the point P to be at the center of the circle. For the total intensity at the center of the circle we have

$$H = \frac{ki}{r^2}\int_0^{2\pi r} dl = k\frac{2\pi i}{r} \text{ oersteds.}$$ (92.2)

Now let us define i as a unit current when both k and r are unity. Then $H = 2\pi$ oersteds. Hence, the cgsm. unit current is defined as *that current which, when flowing in a circle of 1 cm. radius, will develop a magnetic intensity of 2π oersteds at the center of the circle.* The absolute practical unit of current, the *ampere*, is 0.1 of the cgsm. unit current. We might, also, define unit cgsm. current as a current which would be equivalent to a magnetic shell of unit strength.

If instead of a single loop of wire there are n loops, the magnetic intensity at the center is given by

$$H = \frac{2\pi ni}{r} \text{ oersteds,}$$ (92.3)

where i is in cgsm. units. If I is in absolute amperes, we have

$$H = \frac{2\pi nI}{10r} \text{ oersteds,}$$ (92.4)

r being in cms. as before.

The quantity of electricity in the cgsm. system of units, as in all systems of units, is given by

$$q = \int i\, dt, \quad \text{or} \quad i = \frac{dq}{dt}.$$ (92.5)

A unit cgsm. current flowing for one second would cause a unit cgsm. quantity of electricity to cross any section of the conductor, or a current of one ampere would cause one coulomb of electricity to cross a section of the conductor in one second.

The cgsm. difference of potential between two points along a conductor is defined as the work in ergs required to transport one cgsm. unit quantity of electricity from the one point to the other against the impressed electric field. Hence, the unit cgsm. difference of potential is one erg per unit cgsm. charge. The unit difference of potential in the absolute practical system of units is the volt, which is 10^8 times as large as the cgsm. unit. The volt is approximately the emf. of a gravity cell.

It was originally intended to base the practical units on the cgsm. system of units according to the ratios given in Section 18. The system so defined we will call the *absolute practical* system of units. However, the London Conference on Units and Standards (1908) defined a system of practical units which are called the *international units*, and these units have been in use since that date. There is a slight discrepancy between the absolute practical units and the international units. The international units are defined as follows:

1 international ohm is the resistance offered to an unvarying current by a column of pure mercury at 0° C., 14.4521 gms. in mass, of constant cross-sectional area, and 106.30 cms. long.

The ampere is obtained by use of a current balance and then used in conjunction with the standard ohm to calibrate a standard cell.

In 1935 important decisions were made relative to electric units. The International Electrotechnical Commission adopted the Giorgi mks. system of electric units as a system of practical units. The International Committee of Weights and Measures decided that the absolute practical system of units should take the place of the international system, and that the substitution should take place on January 1, 1940.

The most recent experimental relations between the two systems are given below (December, 1939):

1 international ohm = 1.00048 absolute ohms
1 international ampere = 0.99986 absolute ampere
1 international volt = 1.00036 absolute volts
1 international joule = 1.00034 absolute joules.

Precision measurements of the fundamental units are carried out only in standardizing laboratories, such as the Bureau of Standards or the National Physical Laboratory. In these laboratories standard ohms are prepared and calibrated. Currents are measured with a current balance and used in conjunction with standard ohms to calibrate standard cells. The standard ohms and standard cells are then used as laboratory equipment to calibrate ammeters, voltmeters, and wattmeters. Also standards of capacitance and self- and mutual inductance are usually a part of the ordinary laboratory equipment.

93. Resistances in Parallel and in Series. — There are two distinct ways of connecting resistances: (1) Series connection.   (2) Parallel connection.   When resistances are connected in series the whole cur-rent flows through each resistance, Fig. 67. Let r_1, r_2, r_3, etc., be the resistances. i is the same for all of them. Also

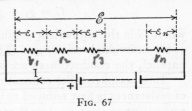

$$\mathcal{E} = \mathcal{E}_1 + \mathcal{E}_2 + \mathcal{E}_3 + \cdots \mathcal{E}_n.^1$$

Fig. 67

By Ohm's law $\mathcal{E}_1 = r_1 i$, $\mathcal{E}_2 = r_2 i$, $\cdots \mathcal{E}_n = r_n i$. Therefore, since $\mathcal{E} = Ri$, we have

$$Ri = r_1 i + r_2 i + r_3 i + \cdots r_n i,$$

and, therefore,

$$R = r_1 + r_2 + r_3 + \cdots r_n. \tag{93.1}$$

That is, the equivalent resistance of n resistances when connected in series is their arithmetical sum.

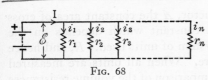

Fig. 68

When the resistances are con-nected in parallel the current divides, as shown in Fig. 68. In this case, the difference of po-tential $\mathcal{E}$ across each resistance is the same, neglecting any small resistance there may be in the connecting wires. The total current, however, is the sum of the currents through the several resistances. That is,

$$I = i_1 + i_2 + i_3 + \cdots i_n.$$

Applying Ohm's law in this case, we have

$$\frac{\mathcal{E}}{R} = \frac{\mathcal{E}}{r_1} + \frac{\mathcal{E}}{r_2} + \frac{\mathcal{E}}{r_3} + \cdots \frac{\mathcal{E}}{r_n},$$

[1] $\mathcal{E}$ and $\mathcal{E}$ will now be used for p.d. as they are in more general use.

and, therefore,

$$\frac{1}{R} = \frac{1}{r_1} + \frac{1}{r_2} + \frac{1}{r_3} + \cdots \frac{1}{r_n}. \qquad (93.2)$$

That is, the reciprocal of the equivalent resistance is the sum of the reciprocals of the individual resistances. Since conductance is the reciprocal of resistance, we may write

$$G = g_1 + g_2 + g_3 + \cdots g_n, \qquad (93.3)$$

where G is the equivalent conductance, g_1, g_2, etc., the conductances of the individual resistances. Thus, when resistances are connected in parallel, the conductances are added arithmetically.

In a series-parallel connection of resistances, each parallel group of resistances is first reduced to its equivalent resistance, and then the equivalent resistances, together with the series resistances, are added.

94. Resistivity and Conductivity. — Measurements show that the resistance of a conductor varies directly as its length and inversely as its area of cross section, and it also depends upon the nature of the conductor. These facts are stated in a simple mathematical equation, as was shown in Section 89. Thus,

$$R = \frac{\rho L}{A}, \qquad (94.1)$$

where L is the length of the conductor, A the constant area of cross section, R its resistance, and ρ a constant which depends on the nature of the conductor and the system of units used. R, and hence also ρ, varies with the temperature. When all units are measured in the same system, ρ serves as a comparison of the volume resistances of the various conductors, and is a very useful constant. The numerical value of ρ will depend upon the system of units used. When L and A are each one, $R = \rho$. If L is measured in cms., A in sq. cms., and R in ohms, ρ is in ohm-cm. This is the most common unit at the present. Other units may be used. Sometimes the length is measured in inches, the area of cross section in sq. inches, and the resistance in ohms. In the mks. system of units the ohm-meter is the unit of resistivity. The reciprocal of resistivity, $\sigma = 1/\rho$, is called the conductivity. Conductivity is measured in various systems of units as well as resistivity. A Table of resistivities is appended for reference. The resistivities are at $0°$ C. From Page and Adams.

Substance	ρ in Ohm-cm.	Substance	ρ in Ohm-cm.
Silver	$1.53(10)^{-6}$	Iron	$10.8(10)^{-6}$
Copper	1.65	Lead	19.3
Gold	2.25	Mercury	94.1
Aluminum	2.88	Brass	6.5
Tungsten	4.44	Manganin	42.0
Tin	10.4	Nichrome	110.0
Platinum	10.3		

95. Ohm's Law for Battery Circuits. — As we have seen, Ohm's law holds in case all of the energy is expended in heat in the conductor. This holds not only for a section of a conductor bearing a current but also for the entire circuit or any part of the circuit. A distinction, however, is made between difference of potential and electromotive force (emf.), although both are measured in the same units. Strictly speaking, a difference of potential exists in an electric field of force, and is measured by the work done in moving a unit positive charge from one point to another against electric forces. An emf. is any action that creates a difference of potential, i.e., an electric field of force in which a difference of potential exists, as, for instance, a battery or dynamo. Thus an emf. exists at a point in a circuit where energy is supplied to the circuit; it creates the electric intensity which may cause a current to flow.

When voltaic cells are joined together they constitute a battery. As in the case of resistances, there are two distinct ways of connecting cells to form a battery: series and parallel. A mixed grouping is called a series-parallel connection. In what follows in this section it is assumed that the circuit is ohmic throughout, i.e., energy is expended in producing heat only. This means that there are no counter emfs. of polarization (explained later) or otherwise against which energy is expended. If there are counter emfs., the $\mathscr{E}$ in the equations is the effective emf. required to drive the current through pure ohmic resistance.

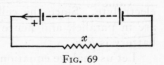

FIG. 69

Series Connection. — Fig. 69 shows a series connection. Let x be the external resistance, b the internal resistance of a single cell, and $\mathscr{E}$ the effective emf. of a single cell. All of the cells are assumed to be identical. Of course, these are ideal conditions which seldom or never actually apply in practice. Applying Ohm's law to the entire circuit, we have

$$n\mathscr{E} = (nb + x)I. \qquad (95.1)$$

Experiments show that the total emf. of a battery of cells, when connected in series, is the algebraic sum of the emfs. of the individual cells composing the battery, and so, when n identical cells are connected in series, the total emf., is $n\mathscr{E}$. Since the cells are connected in series, nb is the total internal resistance. nb is in series with the external resistance x, and so the total resistance of the circuit is $(nb + x)$.

Let us analyze equation (95.1), taking limiting conditions. When $x = 0$, $\mathscr{E} = bI$. That is, one cell will give the same current strength as the entire battery. When $b = 0$,

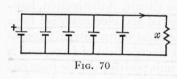

FIG. 70

$n\mathscr{E} = xI$, and the current is n times that for a single cell. Obviously, with low internal resistance and relatively high external resistance, there is an advantage in series connection.

Parallel Connection. — Fig. 70 shows a parallel connection. Applying Ohm's law to the entire circuit, and using the same symbols as before, we have

$$\mathscr{E} = \left(\frac{b}{n} + x\right) I. \qquad (95.2)$$

The effective emf. is that of a single cell, since the emf. of the whole battery is the same as though there were a single pair of plates in a single, large cell, the areas of the plates being equal to the combined areas of the plates of all the cells composing the battery. Experiments show that the size of the plates in a cell has no effect on the emf., the emf. being determined solely by the nature of the electrodes and the electrolyte. Since the cells are in parallel, the internal resistances are in parallel, and hence the equivalent internal resistance of the battery is b/n.

Let us analyze equation (95.2), taking limiting conditions. When $x = 0$, $n\mathscr{E} = bI$. The current strength is n times that of a single cell. When $b = 0$, $\mathscr{E} = xI$. The current strength is the same as for a single cell. Obviously, with low external resistance and relatively high internal resistance there is an advantage in using parallel connection. The question naturally arises, when shall we use series connection, when parallel connection, and when a mixed or series-parallel connection? In order to answer this question let us examine a series-parallel connection.

Series-Parallel Connection. — Let us say that we have m rows of cells connected in parallel, with n cells in each row connected in series. Applying Ohm's law to the entire circuit, we have

$$n\mathscr{E} = \left(\frac{nb}{m} + x\right) I. \tag{95.3}$$

It will be better for our purpose to put equation (95.3) in the following form:

$$I = \frac{nm\mathscr{E}}{xm + nb}. \tag{95.4}$$

There are nm cells in all, and we wish to arrange them in such a manner as to give the maximum current with a given external resistance x and a given internal resistance b per cell. It will be seen from equation (95.4) that I is a maximum when $(xm + nb)$ is a minimum. Since nm is constant, and x and b are assumed to be constant, $xnmb$ is constant. Thus, the denominator is the sum of two terms whose product is constant for any variation of n and m. The sum is, therefore, a minimum when $xm = nb$, or when $x = nb/m$, i.e., when the external resistance is equal to the internal resistance. The same result is obtained by putting $dI/dn = 0$, remembering that $nm = k$, a constant. This proof is left as an exercise.

In the case of maximum current, when $x = nb/m$, the efficiency is, of course 50%, the efficiency being the energy expended in the external circuit divided by the total energy available. It is easily shown that the efficiency is equal to the potential drop in the external circuit divided by the emf. of the battery. The efficiency of a given battery circuit increases as the current decreases, i.e., as the external resistance x increases, the efficiency approaching 100% as x approaches infinity.

In battery circuits the difference of potential across the battery is less when current is flowing than when no current is flowing, i.e., on open circuit. This may be seen by an inspection of any of the equations for the battery circuit. For example, let us consider equation (95.1). We have

$$n\mathscr{E} - nbI = xI.$$

$n\mathcal{E}$ is the emf. on open circuit. nbI is the potential drop within the battery due to the current I flowing through the battery resistance. xI is the potential drop in the external circuit, and is less than the emf. of the battery by the amount nbI.

96. Kirchhoff's Laws.

— About 1860 Gustav Kirchhoff of Germany gave to the world two very useful generalizations, which lead to easy solutions of problems involving networks of conductors in which there are emfs. and resistances. The first law is a statement of the continuity of currents in conductors. The second law is simply an application of Ohm's law to closed loops in networks of conductors.

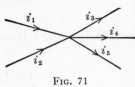

Fig. 71

Law One. — The algebraic sum of all of the currents meeting at a point is zero. This means that in any network of conductors bearing direct currents the sum of all the currents flowing to a junction is equal to the sum of all the currents flowing away from the junction when considering macroscopic conditions. Thus, in Fig. 71,

$$i_1 + i_2 = i_3 + i_4 + i_5,$$

or

$$i_1 + i_2 - i_3 - i_4 - i_5 = 0.$$

That is

$$\Sigma i = 0. \tag{96.1}$$

In equation (96.1) currents flowing toward a junction are taken as positive, and currents flowing away from a junction are taken as negative. If the direction of a current in a branch is not known a direction is assumed for that branch, then, on solving the equations, a positive sign indicates that the correct direction was assumed, whereas a negative sign indicates that the current flows in the reverse direction from that assumed.

Law Two. — Ohm's law must hold for any closed path in a network of conductors, because, whatever increases and decreases in potential there may be, when a loop is traversed the increases must be equal to the decreases. That is, the algebraic sum of the Ri terms around a closed loop is equal to the algebraic sum of the emfs. in the loop.

As an example let us examine the Wheatstone bridge network, Fig. 72. If the bridge is in balance, that is, if the current in the galvanometer branch is zero, c and d are at the same potential, and the current from a to c is the same as the current from c to b. Let the loop $BacbB$ be traversed in the counterclockwise sense. We will then have

$$\mathscr{E} = ri + r_1 i + r_2 i,$$

or

$$\mathscr{E} - ri - r_1 i - r_2 i = 0. \tag{96.2}$$

Let us traverse the circuit $cadc$ in the direction indicated by the small circle. We will then have

$$r_1 i - r_3 i_1 = 0. \tag{96.3}$$

Likewise,

$$r_2 i - x i_1 = 0.$$

Or, in general,

$$\Sigma \text{p.d.} = 0, \tag{96.4}$$

around any closed path. The rule for determining the signs of the terms in equation (96.4) is as follows, using conventional terms: Think of traversing the circuit in a definite direction, clockwise or counterclockwise. *Give the positive sign to terms representing an increase in potential, as when passing from the negative to the positive electrode inside of a battery or when traversing a resistance against the current. Give the negative sign to terms representing a decrease in potential, as when passing from the positive to the negative electrode inside of a battery or when traversing a resistance in the direction of the current.*

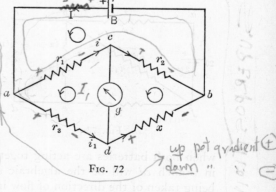

FIG. 72

In order to fix the method of solution, let us solve completely the Wheatsone bridge network of Fig. 72. Let $\mathscr{E} = 1.5$ volts, r (the resistance of the cell) $= 1$ ohm, $r_1 = 2$ ohms, $r_3 = 4$ ohms, $r_2 = 1$ ohm. The resistance x is to be calculated, as are also the currents

I, i, i_1. We may write the following equations for the balanced bridge:

$$\mathcal{E} - rI - r_1i - r_2i = 0$$

$$r_1i - r_3i_1 = 0$$

$$r_2i - xi_1 = 0$$

$$I - i - i_1 = 0.$$

From the second and third of these equations we obtain

$$\frac{r_1}{r_2} = \frac{r_3}{x}, \quad \text{or} \quad x = \frac{r_2r_3}{r_1} = 2 \text{ ohms.}$$

This is the working equation of the bridge as usually stated. On substituting values in the above equations and solving, we obtain $i = \frac{1}{3}$ amp., $i_1 = \frac{1}{6}$ amp., $I = \frac{1}{2}$ amp.

There are several points that may be mentioned in connection with the solutions of these sets of simultaneous equations. The use of determinants will be found to be of advantage. It is a property of all networks of conductors containing emfs. that each emf. acts separately and independently in producing a component current in each branch of the network. Let us consider the network shown in Fig. 73. If the current i_1, in branch cd, say, is calcula-

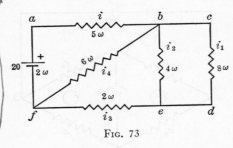

ted with the battery shown acting alone, and then a battery of 10 volts, with internal resistance of 1 ohm, say, is inserted in branch bc, and the current i_1', in branch cd is calculated with this battery acting alone, then when both batteries are acting together in the network the current in branch cd will be the algebraic sum of i_1 and i_1', due account being taken of the direction of flow in each case. The internal resistance of each battery must remain fixed in the branch in which it belongs. Thus each emf. in a network acts independently of all the others in producing the network currents. This property is called the *superposition theorem*. The reader should verify this by carrying out the solutions in the network shown in Fig. 73.

Fig. 73

There is another general property of networks of conductors that may be stated as follows: If an emf. $\mathscr{E}$ in the jth branch of a network produces a current i in the kth branch, then if $\mathscr{E}$ be placed in the kth branch it will produce a current i of the same magnitude in the jth branch. This property is called the *reciprocity theorem*. The reader should prove this by carrying out the calculations in the case of Fig. 73. In setting up equations (96.1) and (96.4) each branch of the network must be included at least once, and the equations must be independent.

97. Energy Relations.

There is a close analogy between an electrostatic field and the field which causes a steady current in the electric circuit. There is, however, one important distinction. A transfer of charge in the electrostatic field is a reversible process. There is no dissipation of energy. The transfer of charge in real conductors is irreversible. There is always dissipation of energy. If conductors and dielectrics were perfect there would be no irreversible losses; all of the energy stored in the electrostatic fields of a charged condenser, say, would be restored on discharge. However, this is not the case with actual materials. It becomes necessary, therefore, to obtain expressions for the transformation of electric energy into other forms, i.e., heat, mechanical energy, and chemical energy. We may proceed as follows:

When one cgsm. unit quantity of electricity is transported from one point in the circuit to another point differing in potential by one cgsm. unit, one erg of work is done. From this definition of work, or expenditure of energy, we obtain expressions for the energy expended in an electric circuit as follows: Using the usual notation, we have

$$dU = \mathscr{E}\,dq = \mathscr{E}i\,dt, \text{ since } dq = i\,dt.$$

Then

$$U = \int_0^t \mathscr{E}i\,dt = \mathscr{E}it \text{ ergs.} \tag{97.1}$$

$\mathscr{E}$ in this equation is the same as V in equation (89.3). On combining this expression with Ohm's law, there results the following expressions for the energy:

$$U = \mathscr{E}it = ri^2t = \frac{\mathscr{E}^2 t}{r} \text{ ergs.} \tag{97.2}$$

The unit of energy in the cgsm. system of units, as in the cgse. system of units, is the erg. This unit is too small for practical purposes, and so a larger unit, called the *joule*, is used. The joule is the energy expended by a current of 1 absolute practical ampere under a difference of potential of 1 volt in 1 second. We may now obtain the relationship between ergs and joules as follows: Let $\mathscr{E}$, i, and r now stand for volts, amperes, and ohms. Then

$$U = \mathscr{E} 10^8 i\, 10^{-1} t = \mathscr{E} i t\, 10^7 \text{ ergs } = \mathscr{E} i t \text{ joules.}$$

Since $\mathscr{E} i t$, in the absolute practical system of units, is expressed in joules, we see that

$$1 \text{ joule } = 10^7 \text{ ergs.} \tag{97.3}$$

Power in the Electric Circuit. — Power, in any system of units, is the time rate of doing work, or expenditure of energy. Hence, in the electric system of units, the power P is

$$P = \frac{\mathscr{E} i t}{t} = \mathscr{E} i \text{ ergs/sec, in cgsm. units.} \tag{97.4}$$

If $\mathscr{E}$, i, and r are measured in absolute practical units, $P = \mathscr{E} i$ joules/ sec $= \mathscr{E} i$ watts. Thus, 1 watt = 1 joules/sec = 10^7 ergs/sec. Combining with Ohm's law we obtain, as in the case of energy, three expressions for power.

$$P = \mathscr{E} i = r i^2 = \frac{\mathscr{E}^2}{r} \text{ watts.} \tag{97.5}$$

Other Relations. —

1 H.P. = 745.7 watts = 0.7457 kilowatt.

1 watt $= \dfrac{550}{745.7} = 0.7375$ ft.-lb./sec., or 1 kw. = 737.5 ft.-lbs./sec.

1 kw. hr., which is an energy unit, is 1000 watts in continuous use for 1 hr., or 3600 secs. Hence, 1 kw. hr. = $2.6552(10)^6$ ft.-lbs. = $3.671(10)^5$ kilogram-meters.

The reader should verify these relations.

Heating Effect of the Current. — We can easily convert heat energy measured in joules into calories as follows: The mechanical equivalent of heat is $J = 4.186(10)^7$ ergs/calorie. Hence,

$$H \text{ (calories)} = \frac{r i^2 t\, 10^7}{4.186(10)^7} = 0.2388\, r i^2 t \text{ calorie.}$$

Or approximately,

$$H = 0.24\, r i^2 t \text{ calorie.} \tag{97.6}$$

The rate at which the temperature of a conductor will rise, due to the heating effect of the electric current, will depend upon its specific heat and its ability to dissipate heat. To aid in the dissipating power of conductors, they are sometimes cooled by air currents, running water, or oil. The case of a transformer is filled with oil for the purpose of dissipating heat energy, and thus preventing undue rise in temperature. Care must always be taken not to use a current sufficiently strong to heat the conductor hot enough to burn the insulation. A safe guide in the use of resistance boxes, and all apparatus using enclosed coils of wire, is to limit the current to such a value that ri^2 shall not exceed 1 watt. If conductors are to be used in the open, they are rated at a higher current carrying capacity than when enclosed in conduits, because open wires can dissipate heat at a higher rate than can enclosed wires.

Energy Consumption of Various Electric Appliances. — We have just seen that there are three expressions for energy and three expressions for power. The question now arises as to the applications of these various forms.

The expressions $\mathcal{E}i$ and $\mathcal{E}it$ are the most general in their

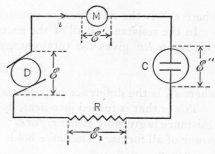

Fig. 74

applications, and will always give the total power or energy between two points differing in potential by $\mathcal{E}$ when a current i is flowing. Thus, suppose a d.c. dynamo D, Fig. 74, is supplying current to a motor M, an electrolytic cell C, and a resistance r, as an electric stove. If we measure $\mathcal{E}$ across the generator and the current i in the line, $\mathcal{E}i$ gives the total power expended in the external circuit. If we measure $\mathcal{E}'$ across the motor M, then $\mathcal{E}'i$ gives the total power expended in the motor. However, the power consumed in the motor is made up of several parts. A part of the power is turned into mechanical work, another part into heat in the windings of the motor, and still another part into the core losses in the iron core of the armature, which consist of eddy-current losses and hysteresis losses. This may be expressed symbolically by the following equation

$$\mathcal{E}'i = ri^2 + m + h,$$

where r is the ohmic resistance of the windings, m the power turned into mechanical work, and h the power turned into heat in the core. It is important to keep the heat losses as low as possible in order to increase the efficiency of the motor. The ri^2 loss is made small by keeping the resistance of the windings small. The h loss is made small by laminating the iron core to reduce the eddy currents, and by using an iron alloy which has low hysteresis loss. Core losses will be considered in a later chapter.

In the electrolytic cell energy is expended in two ways. The cell has ohmic resistance, r' say. Therefore, $r'i^2$ watts are turned into heat due to the current flowing through ohmic resistance. The balance of the power c is consumed in effecting chemical change. Thus, we have

$$\mathscr{E}''i = r'i^2 + c,$$

where $\mathscr{E}''$ is the difference of potential across the cell.

In the resistance R all of the energy is turned into heat, and the expression Ri^2 gives the total energy consumption, that is

$$\mathscr{E}_1 i = Ri^2,$$

where $\mathscr{E}_1$ is the difference of potential across the resistance.

Power that is turned into heat, due to a current flowing through a resistance is given by either ri^2 or $\mathscr{E}^2/r$, whereas $\mathscr{E}i$ measures the total power of all forms. The same holds true for the cognate expressions for energy.

PROBLEMS

1. A wire having a resistance of 5 ohms is drawn out until its length is three times its former length. Assuming that the resistivity remains unaltered, calculate the resistance of the longer wire.

2. A full metallic telegraph line extends between two cities which are 50 miles apart. If No. 10 B & S gauge wire is used, and it requires 0.32 ampere to actuate the telegraph instrument at the receiving end, how many gravity cells connected in series will be required if the emf. of each cell is 1.1 volts and the internal resistance per cell is 1.5 ohms. Neglect the resistance of the telegraph instrument, and take the resistivity of copper as 1.77×10^{-6} ohm–cm. How many lead storage cells would be required, if the emf. of each cell is 2 volts and the internal resistance is 0.05 ohm per cell?

3. Calculate the energy equivalent of a kilowatt hour in (1) joules, (2) Btus., (3) calories, (4) horsepower hours.

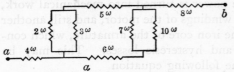

4. Calculate the total resistance between the points a and b in Fig. a. The figures 2, 3, 4, etc., are the resistances in ohms.

15.83 ohms.

15.8 Ω

5. A circuit is arranged as shown in Fig. *b*. When the key K is open the ammeter reads 3 amperes. When the key K is closed the ammeter reads 1.5 amperes. Calculate the resistances r and R, the unknown currents, and the difference of potential across the battery in each case. Am. resistance = 0.

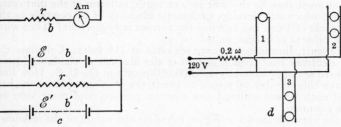

6. A circuit is arranged as shown in Fig. *c*. Solve for the currents in the various branches of the network of conductors when (1) $\mathscr{E} = 1.6$ volts, $b = 3$ ohms, $\mathscr{E}' = 12$ volts, $b' = 2$ ohms, $r = 6$ ohms. (2) All values are the same except that $r = 9$ ohms. (3) All values are the same except that $r = 12$ ohms.

7. In Fig. *d* is shown the plan of a simple house wiring system. The potential at the house switch is 120 volts d.c. Circuit 1 is a stove using 720 watts. Circuit 2 consists of 15–75 watt lamps. Circuit 3 consists of 20–100 watt lamps. The rated watts of each unit are at a potential of 120 volts in each case. Calculate the total current, the current in each line and in each unit, the resistance of each unit, the total equivalent resistance, and the cost of operating at a rate of 6 cents per kilowatt hour.

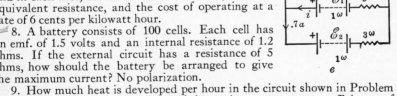

8. A battery consists of 100 cells. Each cell has an emf. of 1.5 volts and an internal resistance of 1.2 ohms. If the external circuit has a resistance of 5 ohms, how should the battery be arranged to give the maximum current? No polarization.

9. How much heat is developed per hour in the circuit shown in Problem 7? What horse power is required if the engine operates at an efficiency of 80%?

10. As in equation (95.4), prove that for any two quantities, xm and nb, whose product is constant for any variations of m and n, that the sum is a minimum when xm equals nb.

11. Water is being heated by an electric heater. The rate at which heat is being supplied is such that 200 liters are raised in temperature 0.5° C. per minute. The p.d. across the heater is 220 volts. Assuming a 20% loss of heat due to conduction and radiation, calculate the current supplied to the heater. If the resistance of the line is 0.1 ohm and the internal resistance of the dynamo is 0.1 ohm, what is the true voltage of the dynamo? If the efficiency of the dynamo is 80% what is the delivered horse power of the steam engine that operates the dynamo? At 5 cents per kilowatt hour what will it cost the consumer (current metered at the load) to heat water at this rate for a period of 24 hours? If coal is $15.00 per short ton, and the steam engine and dynamo combined have an overall efficiency of 10%, what is

the cost to the company? What would it cost the consumer to heat the water directly with a coal burning heater, assuming the heater to have an efficiency of 50%? Heat of combustion of coal is 14,000 Btus. per lb. 252 calories equal 1 Btu.

Orint.

12. Suppose that in the equation $H = \dfrac{2\pi i}{r}$ oersteds, i is measured in cgse. units. What must then be the unit pole strength, in terms of the unit cgsm. pole strength, which will develop a magnetic intensity of 2π oersteds at the center of a circle of 1 cm. radius when the current is 1 cgse. unit? Then what must be the value of μ_0 in cgse. units?

13. A 75 watt, incandescent lamp operates at 115 volts. Calculate the number of electrons that cross a section of the filament of the lamp in one second. There are approximately 130,000,000 people in the U. S. How long would it take this number of people to count the number of electrons just obtained, if each person counted one electron per sec. and there were no cessation in counting?

14. In the network shown in Fig. *e*, calculate the values of the unknown quantities. Calculate the difference of potential across each battery. Calculate the total amount of heat generated.

CHAPTER VII

METALLIC CONDUCTION AND RESISTANCE

In general, a conductor is a substance which readily transmits a current of electricity, and an insulator is a substance which offers a very high resistance to the passage of a current of electricity. There is no sharp distinction, however, between conductors and insulators, as substances differ markedly in their ability to retard the flow of an electric current, and the same substance differs greatly in this respect under different physical conditions. The conductivity of any substance is changed with change in temperature, and also with change of state. Some substances are good insulators at room temperature, and fair conductors at high temperatures. Thus glass, one of the most striking examples of this class, is a high grade insulator at room temperature, but at red heat it is a fair conductor. All metallic conductors undergo a sudden and marked change in resistance on passing from the solid state to the liquid state. Any impurity in a metal changes its resistivity. Alloys do not have the resistivity of any of their constituents.

As we stated in Section 90, there are two main classes of conductors, metallic and electrolytic. These two classes of conductors represent, also, two types of current flow. In metallic conductors the current is, according to our best evidence, a slow drift of free, mobile electrons along the conductor in a direction from negative to positive. In electrolytic conduction, the current consists of positively and negatively charged particles of atomic or molecular size, called *ions*, moving in opposite directions. The researches of Joffé and Pohl have shown that, in certain crystals, conduction is partly of the electronic type and partly of the ionic type. Furthermore, the conductivity of gases represents a type of conduction which is sufficiently distinctive to require a separate treatment. In this chapter metallic conduction alone will be considered. Electrolytic conduction will be treated in the next chapter.

98. Metallic Conduction from the Viewpoint of the Electron Theory.

— A current of electricity of any type is a transfer of electricity, the mode of transfer being different under different conditions. Metallic conduction is a slow drift of free electrons, and is not to be confused with electric waves which travel with very high speeds. According to present-day theory, there are two kinds of electricity, positive and negative, which however are quite distinct from the imponderable fluids of the earlier two-fluid theory. We now have abundant evidence to support the view that electricity is atomic in structure, i.e., it is made up of extremely small, discrete entities, which constitute nature's units of electricity. The positive natural unit is the *proton*, and the negative natural unit is the *electron*. The proton, according to the best evidence we have, is much smaller than the electron but possesses a mass which is about 1,840 times that of the electron. The electron is therefore very light and mobile as compared with the proton. Experimental evidence goes to show that the atoms of all of the elements are composed of protons and electrons grouped together in some pattern or patterns, as yet not fully understood. A neutral atom is one that contains electrons and protons in such numbers and arrangement as to be electrically balanced, whereas an ionized atom is one that has lost one or more electrons from its outermost rim, and is therefore electrically unbalanced, and hence exhibits a positive charge. Although we do not know the exact arrangements of the constituents of the atoms, it is reasonably certain that the relatively heavy protons occupy a central position, called the nucleus, and that the relatively light electrons are grouped about the nucleus. This is the most plausible conclusion to be drawn from Rutherford's researches (1911). The Rutherford atom has been likened to a miniature solar system consisting of a massive, though relatively small, central nucleus, composed of protons with about half as many electrons. However, since the discovery of the neutron, it has been given a place in the nucleus; the nucleus is now thought of as composed of protons and neutrons, the number of protons being equal to the atomic number in the periodic table. The researches of Moseley and Bohr (1913) led to the conclusion that the circumnuclear electrons in each atom are equal in number, in the normal atom, to the "free" positive charges in the nucleus, and that they revolve about the nucleus in stable orbits of elliptic or circular form.[1] The ordinal num-

[1] This was the original Bohr-Sommerfeld conception of the atom. However, we are not at all sure that an electron in an atom is round and corpuscle

ber in the periodic table gives the number of "free" positive charges in the nucleus, and hence also the number of circumnuclear or planetary electrons in the electrically neutral atom. The diameter of an electronic orbit is about 10^{-8} cm., although, of course, it varies somewhat from atom to atom, and for different electrons within the atom. The nucleus has a diameter of the order of 10^{-12} to 10^{-13} cm., and so the atom has a very open structure, comparable, in the case of hydrogen, to one marble revolving about another at a distance of a half mile. Not more than the 10^{-15} part of the space allocated to an atom is occupied by its constituents. Disregarding isotopes for the nonce, the atoms are made up of equal numbers of electrons, protons, and neutrons in increasing complexity beginning with the lightest element, hydrogen. The *regular* atom should then have as many neutrons as protons in the nucleus to account for its mass. Thus hydrogen has a nucleus consisting of one proton accompanied by one planetary electron. Helium has a nucleus consisting of two protons and two neutrons, accompanied by two planetary electrons. Li has a nucleus consisting of three protons and three neutrons, accompanied by three planetary electrons, etc. The He atom is dynamically stable, and therefore He is an inert gas; its two planetary electrons complete the first or innermost shell of electrons. Li has three planetary electrons, and hence one electron is alone in the next outer shell, which requires eight electrons to make the atom dynamically stable. Be has four planetary electrons, and hence two electrons in the second shell, etc. Neon has 10 planetary electrons, with eight in the second shell, thus completing the second shell and giving dynamic stability, and hence an inert element. According to a theory advanced independently by Lewis and Kossel in 1917, an element is in a more dynamically stable state, so far as planetary electrons are concerned, when these electrons conform to the configuration corresponding to the nearest inert element. Thus, all of the metals are just above an inert element in the periodic table, and so they strive to attain

like. The leading physicists of today are not agreed as to the structure of an electron in an atom, nor are they sure that there is an orbital motion of the electron about the nucleus obeying the macroscopic laws of mechanics. It seems reasonably clear, however, that electrons, whatever they may be like, occupy positions outside the nucleus. However, in the absence of knowledge as to the ultimate nature of the electron, the Bohr-Sommerfeld model will serve to give a mental picture of the atom, but Mach has warned us that the models we construct may not be and probably are not anything like ultimate reality, which we may approach but never reach.

dynamic stability by freeing planetary electrons. Since the outermost electrons in metals are held loosely, it is not surprising that they should have free electrons. Those elements that are just below the inert elements in the periodic table strive to attain dynamic stability by picking up electrons whenever possible so as to take on a stable configuration, and therefore these elements have no free electrons. According to this theory, there are two extreme types of elements, outside the inert elements and those that occupy middle positions in the periodic table; those that tend to lose electrons so as to attain dynamic stability, and those that tend to gain planetary electrons so as to attain dynamic stability, i.e., *conductors* and *insulators*. This point will be considered again in connection with electrolytic conduction./

In solid metallic conductors the protons, and hence the positive charges, remain relatively fixed in position, as they compose practically the whole mass of the atom, and hence the identity of the atom. The free electrons fill in the intermolecular spaces, according to the Drude-Lorentz theory. Drude and Lorentz assumed that the free electrons are in a state of thermal agitation analogous to the molecules of a gas, and that they collide with each other and with the molecules of the conductor. In accordance with the equipartition of energy among constituents in thermal agitation, the electrons would possess, on the average, the same kinetic energy as the molecules of a gas at the same temperature, and they would exert a pressure as does a gas. The velocities of the electrons were assumed to be distributed about a mean value represented by the Maxwellian distribution law for gases. Now when the conductor is subjected to a potential gradient the free electrons have superposed upon their random thermal motions a component of motion in the direction of the electric field, i.e., they will drift in the direction from negative to positive. It is this drift velocity component which constitutes the electric current. However, the current component of the velocity of an electron is small as compared with its average thermal velocity. As the potential gradient becomes steeper, and the electrons are driven forward with increased speed, the impacts with the molecules of the conductor become more frequent and violent. This ever increased jostling of electrons and molecules of the conductor, as the current increases, causes an increase in the thermal agitation of the molecules, and hence a rise in temperature. It is reasonable to suppose that electrons are continually leaving atoms and that recombinations are continually taking place, and that therefore the stream of electrons, which is the current, does not remain identical at all times though constant in magnitude. According to Abram F. Joffé, "The most probable model for a solid metal seems to be a lattice of positive ions and negative electrons moving in orbits of such an irregularity that they may be considered on the average as a negative fluid spread continuously over the whole space between the ions."[1] Metals are crystalline and have a structure called a "crystal lattice." The crystal is regarded as a regular arrangement of small units composed of atoms, ions, or molecules, and so related to each other in position and orientation as to possess a minimum energy consistent with stability. The crystal units are supposed to be identical. The crystal lattice is supposed to be a system of electric charges, and it is conceived that there are no other forces than those of electric and magnetic fields.

Another assumption that has been advanced to account for the current of electricity in a conductor requires that the atoms of the conductor keep their full quota of electrons at all times, but that when a potential gradient is established there is an exchange of electrons from atom to atom along the conductor in the direction of electronic flow, i.e., an electron is forced out of one atom and enters its nearest neighbor in the advance direction, etc. The assumption of free electrons is somewhat comparable to the dissociation or spontaneous ionization theory in electrolysis, since it assumes a separation in advance of a potential gradient, whereas the assumption of a progressive exchange of electrons from atom to atom might be compared with the older theory in electrolysis, since it assumes that the dissociation or temporary ionization is dependent on and exists because of an electric field. The Fermi-Dirac distribution law, to be considered later, presents another picture.

One might suppose that the positive residue of the atom would drift also under the influence of the electric field, but in the reverse direction. If any such drift does exist it must be extremely small. One investigator in Germany has reported that he has detected a positive drift in a conductor consisting of an alloy of hydrogen and palladium, which, if authentic, would be composed of the nuclei of hydrogen atoms, or protons. This is the only experimental evidence of a drift of positive ions in a metallic conductor that has come to the attention of the author. If there were a drift of positive ions, we should expect a

[1] The Physics of Crystals by A. F. Joffé.

current of electricity to transport atoms of one metal across the junction between two metals. Careful experiments have been performed to detect such a transfer from one metal to another, but with negative results. Thus, we conclude that the current of electricity in metallic conductors consists of electrons only.

We may cite at this time one line of evidence in support of the electronic theory of metallic conduction. If the temperature of a metal conductor is very high the free, mobile electrons will gain sufficient speed, due to thermal agitation, to carry many of them at the surface of the conductor beyond the confines of the substance out into the space beyond; electrons are veritably boiled out of the conductor, and, if attracted to a positively charged conductor, constitute what O. W. Richardson has called a *thermionic current*. This is the phenomenon which occurs in a radio tube. The free electrons are boiled out of the filament and fly across in empty space to the positive plate of the tube, a new supply of electrons being given to the filament by the current flow. The current between the filament and plate is in empty space, and consequently is called a *space current*. There can be no question in this case that the current is composed solely of electrons moving from the relatively negative filament to the positive plate. We will consider this phenomenon at greater length in a subsequent chapter.

We may think of ohmic resistance as being due to the retarding influence of the atoms and molecules of the conductor as they are buffeted about by the forward stream of electrons which constitutes the electric current. This retardation varies with different substances, owing undoubtedly to some difference in molecular structure or influence, and so accounts for differences in resistivity. The resistance to the flow of electrons increases, in general, with the temperature of the conductor, which may be accounted for by the increased random motions of the molecules owing to thermal agitation. In some substances, such as carbon, electrolytes, and insulators, the resistance decreases with rise in temperature. In these cases the molecular structure or arrangement changes in such a manner with rise in temperature as to give greater freedom of motion to the electrons. This phase of the subject is obscure, and much work remains to be done to clear it up.

The theory of Lewis and Kossel requires that the atoms of insulators or poor conductors attract free electrons in order to attain dynamic stability. Thus, under ordinary potential gradients very little or no current will flow through an insulator as there are no free electrons.

99. Change of Resistance with Temperature. — We have seen that resistance is the ratio between potential and current, that is

$$R = \frac{\mathscr{E}}{I}.$$

In this relationship R is constant only when no chemical or physical changes take place in the conductor. If the temperature of the conductor changes, R changes. R suffers a pronounced change with change of state.

It is customary to define the *temperature coefficient of resistance* of a substance as the change in resistance per degree change in temperature per ohm between 0° C. and 100° C., that is

$$\alpha_0 = \frac{R_{100} - R_0}{100 R_0}.$$

Then the resistance at any other temperature t is given by

$$R_t = R_0(1 + \alpha_0 t). \tag{99.1}$$

This is the slope form of the equation of a straight line, in which $R_0 \alpha_0$ is the slope, R_0 the intercept on the resistance axis, and $-1/\alpha_0$ the intercept on the temperature axis, or the temperature at which the resistance would be zero were the equation to hold for so great a temperature change. The experimental curves for change of resistance with temperature are not straight lines, and therefore this equation can be used with accuracy over only a limited temperature range. Obviously the temperature coefficient of resistance will depend on the initial temperature selected from which to measure the change in resistance. The temperature coefficient of resistance at any temperature may be defined as the change in resistance per degree change in temperature per ohm at that temperature, that is

$$\alpha_t = \frac{R_2 - R_t}{R_t(t_2 - t_1)} = \frac{\Delta R}{R_t \Delta t}, \quad \text{or} \quad R_2 = R_t\{1 + \alpha_t(t_2 - t_1)\}. \tag{99.2}$$

This is also the slope form of the equation of the same straight line as equation (99.1), in which $R_t \alpha_t$ is the slope.

α_0 is the coefficient usually recorded, and it varies greatly with different conductors. Alloys, as a rule, have very small temperature coefficients. Thus manganin (84% copper, 12% manganese, 4% nickel), used extensively for resistors in resistance boxes and standard resistances, has a temperature coefficient of about 0.00001. It has a small thermoelectric effect against copper, and so is suitable for use in circuits where temperature variations occur. Another alloy, German silver, has a temperature coefficient of about 0.0004. In the following table the temperature coefficients, α_0 of equation (99.1), are given for a few metals.

METALS	TEMPERATURE COEFFICIENT	METALS	TEMPERATURE COEFFICIENT
Silver	0.0040	Nickel	0.0062
Copper (hd. dr.)	0.00428	Iron	0.0062
Gold	0.0038	Lead	0.0043
Aluminum	0.0038	Mercury	0.0009
Zinc	0.0037	Bismuth	0.0042
Platinum	0.00367		

α is sometimes negative, as in the case of carbon, electrolytes, and insulators. α is positive for all pure metals in the solid state, and with few exceptions also in the liquid state.

A more accurate expression for the variation of resistance with temperature is the following:

$$R_t = R_0(1 + \alpha t + \beta t^2 + \gamma t^3 + \cdots), \qquad (99.3)$$

where α, β, γ, etc., are constants which depend on the particular metal to which the equation refers. When accuracy is required, a resistance-temperature curve must be used. The temperature-resistance curve for platinum is parabolic over a wide range of temperature.

In applied work, when only approximate results are required, an equation is sometimes used which is comparable to the general gas equation. This equation is derived from equation (99.1) as follows: It is assumed that the resistance-temperature variations are strictly linear. Then the temperature at which R_t is zero, as given by the equation, may be thought of as an absolute zero of temperature for the particular metal in question. Thus

$$0 = R_0(1 + \alpha_0 t_0),$$

or $t_0 = -\dfrac{1}{\alpha_0}$, and therefore $T = t + \dfrac{1}{\alpha_0}$, where T is comparable to an absolute temperature. Introducing T into the equation, we may write

$$R_t = \alpha_0 R_0 \left(\frac{1}{\alpha_0} + t \right) = \alpha_0 R_0 T.$$

But $\alpha_0 R_0 = K$, a constant, and therefore we have

$$R_t = KT. \tag{99.4}$$

As an example of the use of this equation, let us apply it to hard drawn copper. $\alpha_0 = 0.00428$, and therefore $1/\alpha_0 = 233.6$. Hence, this so-called absolute zero of temperature for copper is $-233.6°$ C. Let a wire have a resistance of 40 ohms, say, at $20°$ C. What will be its resistance at $-60°$ C.? On applying equation (99.4), we have

$$40 = K\,253.6$$

$$R = K\,173.6.$$

Therefore $R = 27.4\omega$.

It will be seen from equations (99.1) and (99.2) that the numerical value of the temperature coefficient α depends only on the scale of temperature used and not on the units in which the resistance is measured.

The resistivity of a conducting substance depends on many factors other than temperature. Tables of resistivities are compiled for pure metals and for solutions of definite composition, but it is well not to assume that a given sample has the value given in the tables, since impurities have a marked effect on the resistivity. Alloying has a pronounced influence on resistivity. In relatively few cases the resulting resistivity can be calculated from the percentage composition and the resistivities of the components, but in most cases the resulting resistivity is much greater than any of the constituents, and the temperature coefficient is much smaller. Rolling and drawing into wires changes the hardness of a metal, and so changes its resistivity. An increase in hardness increases the resistivity, whereas annealing a hardened metal lowers the resistivity. Metals are very incompressible, but with great pressure there is a decrease in volume and in resistivity. In general, a decrease in volume means a decrease in resistivity. The resistivity of bismuth, and a few other metals, changes when brought into a magnetic field of force, and selenium has a smaller resistivity when illuminated than when in darkness.

Oxint

100. Resistivities over Wide Ranges of Temperature. — A limited

amount of work has been done on the measurement of resistivities at
very high and very low temperatures. In such measurements great
difficulties are encountered, and the results have little other than
theoretical value at present. Resistivities at high temperatures have
been measured for a few metals by Paul Muller,[1] and for a few other

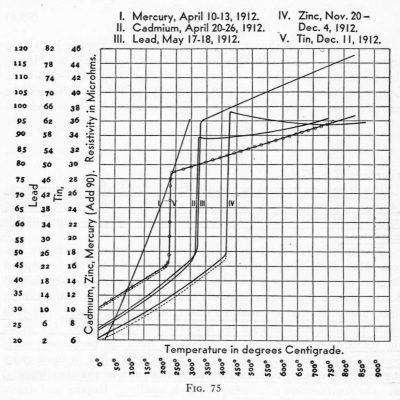

I. Mercury, April 10-13, 1912.	IV. Zinc, Nov. 20 –
II. Cadmium, April 20-26, 1912.	Dec. 4, 1912.
III. Lead, May 17-18, 1912.	V. Tin, Dec. 11, 1912.

FIG. 75

metals by E. F. Northrup and V. A. Suydam.[2] Northrup and Suydam
measured the resistivities of six metals from room temperature up
through the melting point, and to as high a temperature in the molten
state as possible. The curves obtained are shown in Figs. 75 and 76.
It will be seen, Fig. 75, that tin is the only metal investigated that gave

[1] Metallurgie, Halle, 7 pp. 730–755, 1910.
[2] Jour. Franklin Institute, Feb. 1913.

a straight line curve in the solid state and also in the liquid state. All the other metals depart more or less from the linear relationship. Zinc has a negative temperature coefficient in the molten state for most of the temperature range shown. Cadmium has a negative temperature coefficient for a short temperature range just above the melting point. A negative temperature coefficient is very unusual for a pure metal. In the solid state all of the metals shown have positive

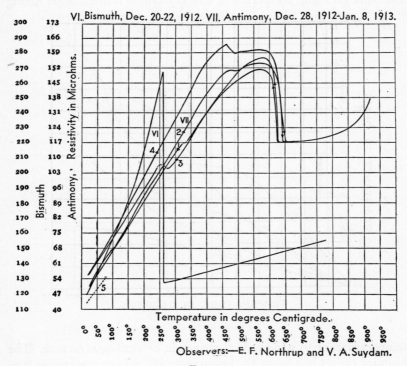

Fig. 76

temperature coefficients. All of the metals shown in Fig. 75 show a very sharp increase in resistivity at the change of state temperature. In each case the resistivity at the end of fusion is approximately double its value at the beginning of fusion.

Fig. 76 shows the curves for antimony and bismuth. Both metals are strongly crystalline and expand on solidification. With both of these metals the resistivity decreased during fusion, but, strangely, the resistivity just after fusion is completed is very nearly half of its value just before fusion begins. Antimony is anomalous since, in the solid state, its resistivity depends on its previous history; the curves do not retrace in the solid state. Arrow tips show rising and falling temperature measurements. There are sharp changes or inflection points in the curves on both rising and falling temperatures, which are evidently due to the breaking down of the crystalline structure on rising temperature, and crystalline formation on falling

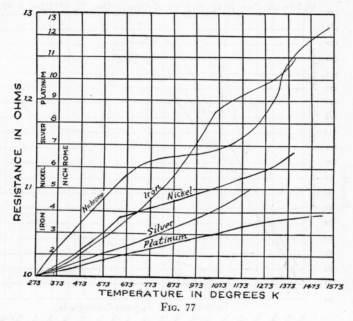

Fig. 77

temperature, or to some radical change in crystalline structure. The rounded curves just below the fusion point indicate an amorphous condition just before melting begins. Curve 5 was obtained from a sample which had cooled rapidly, and therefore, had a somewhat different crystalline structure from the other samples. The crystalline structure is undoubtedly responsible for the variations in the resistivity of antimony.

The curves shown in Fig. 77 were obtained by V. A. Suydam.[1] Platinum has a very regular resistance-temperature curve; in fact it is a

[1] Phys. Rev., Vol. V, No. 6, June 1915.

parabola and is concave to the temperature axis. Nickel has an abrupt change in resistance at about 320° C. This is the temperature at which the magnetic transformation in nickel takes place. Iron shows an abrupt change in resistance at about 620° C. This is the magnetic transformation point for iron. Silver has a regular curve. Nichrome, a high resistivity alloy, has a very irregular curve. It is quite clear from these curves that the resistance-temperature variation is not linear over any very great temperature range, except in a few cases.

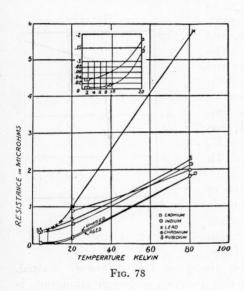

Fig. 78

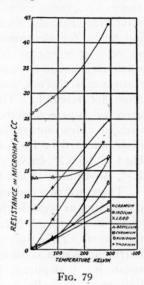

Fig. 79

Resistance measurements at low temperatures are even more difficult to carry out than at high temperatures. Such measurements have been made by H. K. Onnes, Leyden, Holland, Meissner, Charlottenburg, Germany, and J. C. McLennan and C. D. Niven, Toronto, Canada.[2] The curves obtained by McLennan and Niven are shown in Figs. 78, 79, and 80. Cadmium, indium, lead, beryllium, chromium, rubidium, thorium, sodium, potassium, and an alloy of sodium and potassium were tested. These curves show several interesting features. They show that the usual statement that resistivity is proportional to the absolute temperature is, in most cases, far from true. In some cases the resistance abruptly vanishes at a few degrees

[2] Phil. Mag., Vol. 4, No. 21, Aug. 1927.

above the absolute zero of temperature. This extremely low resistance, or extremely high conductivity, at these very low temperatures has been called by Onnes, *superconductivity*. The resistance of lead was so near zero when in this state that when a current of electricity was generated in a lead ring by induction it continued to flow for more than a day with no additional supply of energy. No satisfactory theory to account for this phenomenon has as yet been advanced. It must be that at these low temperatures the crystal lattices of certain metals so arrange themselves as to leave free channels, with no retarding fields, for electronic flow, and so very little energy is lost. The whole mechanism of conduction and resistance is obscure, and so affords room for research. The phenomenon of superconductivity is limited to a few substances. It has been observed in Pb 7.3°, Ta 4.5°, Hg 4.5°, Sn 3.7°, In 3.4°, Ti 2.5°, Th 1.4°, Au-Bi alloy 2.15° K.

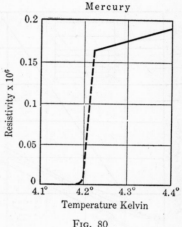

Fig. 80

There are two general classes of conductors as regards the use made of the conductor. Where a conductor is used for the purpose of transmitting power a conductor of low resistivity is required, because the joule loss is energy wasted. Copper is generally used for this purpose, although aluminum is used to some extent for transmission lines. In this case, the heat loss is comparable to the undesirable friction loss in machines. In other uses of conductors high resistivity is required, as in the case of rheostats where current control is the essential thing, and in heating elements of all kinds. This use of electric resistance is comparable to the use of friction in a brake or a friction clutch.

101. Resistance Measurements. — Because of the importance of resistance in the various application of electricity, many methods for the measurement of resistance have come into use. These methods may be classified as follows: *Direct measurements* by use of an ammeter and a voltmeter and the application of Ohm's law; *comparison methods*, where the unknown resistance is compared with some previously measured standard; *absolute methods*, where the resistance is determined in absolute measure without reference to any standard.

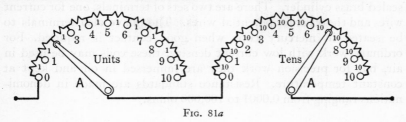

FIG. 81a

Comparison methods are most commonly used, and require for their execution carefully calibrated resistance boxes or single-valued coils. Both *plug* and *dial* resistance boxes are in use, the dial boxes as a rule being the more satisfactory. In Fig. 81a is shown the wiring diagram of a two-dial General Radio Company resistance box. It consists of a number of resistance units, of equal value in each dial, the junction points being connected to a set of metal buttons over which a contact arm *A* slides, thus allowing any number of resistance elements to be included in the circuit. This scheme may be extended to include more dials. Thus a four dial box would have a *units* dial, a *tens* dial, a *hundreds* dial, and a *thousands* dial. Single-valued standard resistances are obtainable from our leading instrument makers. The standard resistances most commonly used in the United States are the Bureau of Standards pattern,[1] and are manufactured by

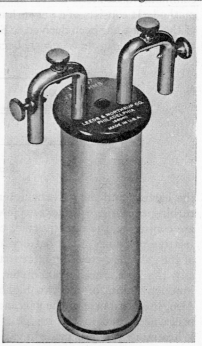

FIG. 81b.

the Leeds & Northrup Co. of Phila. Such a standard is shown in Fig. 81b. These standard resistances are made of manganin wire

[1] B. S. Bul., Vol. 5, p. 413, 1908–09.

wound noninductively on a brass cylinder, carefully insulated from the cylinder by shellac, and immersed in kerosene in a hermetically sealed brass cylinder. There are two sets of terminals, one for current wires and the other for potential wires. They have also terminals to be seated in mercury cups when good contact is required. For ordinary work with low current density, these coils may be used in air, but for precision work they are immersed in oil and kept at constant temperature. Resistance standards are made in denominations ranging from 0.0001 to 100,000 ohms.

102. The Wheatstone Bridge. — The Wheatstone bridge method of measuring resistance is at the same time one of the oldest and most commonly used methods for measuring resistances by the comparison method. It consists of a network of four conductors, Fig. 72. The law of the bridge has been derived in Section 96. The branches cd and aBb are called *conjugate branches*, because they are interchangeable, i.e.,

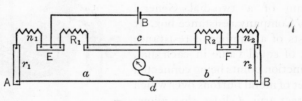

FIG. 82a

the battery and the galvanometer may be interchanged without disturbing the bridge balance. However, although these two branches are conjugate, the sensitivity of the bridge is not independent of the relative positions of the battery and galvanometer. If the resistance of the galvanometer is greater than that of the battery, which is usually the case, the galvanometer should be connected between the junction points of the two highest and the two lowest resistances. Also, the resistance of the galvanometer should be comparable to the resistances used in the bridge if high sensitivity is required. The Wheatstone bridge is made in various types. A common type is

The Slide-Wire or Meter Bridge. — This form of the Wheatstone bridge is shown diagrammatically in Fig. 82a. AB is a high-resistance wire one meter long, hence the name "meter bridge." Let us assume that n_1 and n_2, r_1 and r_2 have zero resistances, i.e., they are heavy brass bars, and that A and B are accurately the 0 and 100 cm. points on the wire. Then, if ρ is the resistance per unit length of wire, assumed constant, we have

$$\frac{R_2}{R_1} = \frac{\rho b}{\rho a} = \frac{b}{a}, \tag{102.1}$$

where R_1, say, is the unknown resistance.

The sensitivity of the bridge is not independent of the values of a and b. It is most sensitive for the point of balance such that $a = b$. This may be proved as follows: Let the true value of the unknown resistance be R_1, and the length of the slide-wire c. Let the true balance point divide the wire into a and b. Then

$$R_1 = R_2 \frac{a}{b} = R_2 \frac{a}{c - a}.$$

Differentiating, and

$$dR_1 = \frac{R_2 c}{(c - a)^2} da, \quad \text{or} \quad \frac{dR_1}{R_1} = \frac{c}{a(c - a)} da. \tag{102.2}$$

$\dfrac{dR_1}{R_1}$ is the variation in R_1 per ohm, and it is expressed in terms of the position on the slide-wire times da, a small change in the balance point on the wire. A better arrangement of this equation for our purpose is

$$\frac{dR_1}{da} = \frac{c}{ab} R_1. \tag{102.3}$$

The condition that $\dfrac{dR_1}{da}$ shall be a minimum is that ab shall be a maximum. $a + b = c$, a constant. The condition that the product of two quantities, whose sum is constant, shall be a maximum is that they shall be equal. Hence, $a = b$ for highest sensitivity.

Example. — $c = 1000$ mms. Let $da = 1$ mm. error in setting.

When $a = b = 500$ mms., $dR_1 = 0.004$ ohm $= 0.4\%$ error.
" $a = 220$ mms., $b = 780$ mms., $dR_1 = 0.0059$ ohm $= 0.59\%$ error.
" $a = 100$ " $b = 900$ " $dR_1 = 0.0111$ " $= 1.11\%$ "
" $a = 20$ " $b = 980$ " $dR_1 = 0.0570$ " $= 5.7\%$ "

We have assumed in the foregoing discussion that n_1, n_2, r_1, r_2, is each equal to zero or very nearly equal to zero, and that the scale is accurately placed relative to the wire. This is not true in an actual bridge, and, if accurate measurements are to be made, corrections must be made. In the ordinary slide-wire bridge n_1 and n_2 are brass bars of low resistance. It is customary in using such a slide-wire bridge to measure R_1, and then interchange R_1 and R_2 and repeat the measurements, and then average the two values obtained. This will eliminate any asymmetry there may be in the resistances of the bridge itself.

If we wish to calculate the connecting resistances at the ends of the bridge, we may proceed as follows: Let the resistance from E to A be equal to a length α of the bridge wire, and the resistance from F to B be equal to a length β of the bridge wire. We then have

$$\frac{R_2}{R_1} = \frac{b_1 + \beta}{a_1 + \alpha}. \tag{102.4}$$

Interchanging R_1 and R_2, we have

$$\frac{R_1}{R_2} = \frac{b_2 + \beta}{a_2 + \alpha}. \tag{102.5}$$

From these two equations α and β are easily calculated, when R_1 and R_2 are known standard resistances which are not equal.

In case we wish to measure a resistance which is quite different from R_1, resistances n_1 and n_2 may be given values, which are expressed in terms of bridge-wire units, and so added to the lengths a and b. This device is equivalent to increasing the length of the slide-wire, and so increasing the range of the bridge.

In using any Wheatstone bridge the battery circuit must be closed first, and then a little later the galvanometer circuit. This procedure is for the purpose of obviating errors which will result if any of the four resistances are inductive. If any of the resistances have inductance in addition to ohmic resistance, and the galvanometer circuit is closed in advance of the battery circuit, there will be a deflection of the galvanometer, even though the bridge is in balance for the ohmic resistances, unless, which seldom obtains, the inductances are so distributed as to make the inductive balance coincide with the purely ohmic

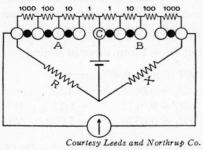

Courtesy Leeds and Northrup Co.

FIG. 82*b*

resistance balance. Inductance in a coil increases its effective resistance during the time the current is varying after closing the key. This point will be considered again under inductance.

The laboratory Wheatstone bridge is usually of the box type, and is then called a "box bridge" or "postoffice box." It is provided with ratio arms as shown in Fig. 82b. In the Figure R is the known arm and is made up of a series of dials, units, tens, thousands, etc. x is the unknown resistance being measured. The ratio between R and x is obtained by adjustment of the plugs in the ratio arms A and B. As shown in the drawing x would be 100 times R. This is a simple scheme, but it illustrates the principle. There are other schemes.

103. Voltmeter Method of Measuring Resistance. — Let the circuit be arranged as shown schematically in Fig. 83. r is a known resistance, x the unknown resistance to be measured, $\mathscr{E}$ the emf. of the source of current supply, assumed constant, and $\mathscr{E}'$ the voltmeter reading, which is equal to the current I times the voltmeter resistance R, or $\mathscr{E}' = RI$. With key k open, we have

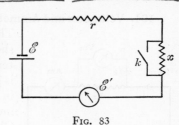

FIG. 83

$$I = \frac{\mathscr{E}}{R + r + x} = \frac{\mathscr{E}'}{R},$$

from which, we obtain

$$\mathscr{E} = \frac{\mathscr{E}'(R + r + x)}{R}. \tag{103.1}$$

Now close the key k, and we have

$$I' = \frac{\mathscr{E}}{R + r} = \frac{\mathscr{E}''}{R},$$

from which, we obtain

$$\mathscr{E} = \frac{\mathscr{E}''(R + r)}{R}. \tag{103.2}$$

Eliminating $\mathscr{E}$ between equations (103.1) and (103.2), we obtain

$$x = \frac{(\mathscr{E}'' - \mathscr{E}')(R + r)}{\mathscr{E}'} \tag{103.3}$$

If the scale readings on the deflection instrument are proportional to the current, we may write $\mathscr{E}' = kd'$, $\mathscr{E}'' = kd''$, and we obtain

$$x = \frac{(d'' - d')(R + r)}{d'}. \tag{103.4}$$

Thus, the deflection instrument need not be calibrated, and hence a galvanometer may be used.

This method is a deflection method, whereas the Wheatstone bridge method is a null or zero deflection method. Null methods are, as a rule, more accurate and easier to use then deflection methods. The voltmeter method is not highly accurate, but for general use in applied work it is convenient as it requires only a voltmeter, since the known resistance r may be zero. It is used to measure fairly large resistances.

104. Voltmeter and Ammeter Method of Measuring Resistance.—

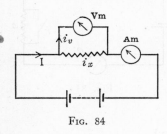

FIG. 84

The arrangement of the apparatus is shown in Fig. 84. The difference of potential across the unknown resistance x is given by the voltmeter and the current in the main circuit is given by the ammeter. We then have approximately by Ohm's law

$$x = \frac{\mathscr{E}}{I}. \tag{104.1}$$

(104.1) does not give an accurate result, since I is not the current through x. To obtain a more accurate expression, we have

$$I = i_x + i_v. \tag{104.2}$$

i_x is the current through x, and therefore the correct value of x is

$$x = \frac{\mathscr{E}}{i_x}. \tag{104.3}$$

Also, $Ri_v = xi_x$, and $i_x = \dfrac{RI}{R + x}$.

Therefore,

$$x = \frac{\mathscr{E} R}{RI - \mathscr{E}}. \tag{104.4}$$

The value of x obtained by equation (104.1) will be too small, since I is greater than i_x. Equation (104.1) may be used with fair accuracy if R is large in comparison with x. This may be seen by putting (104.4) in the following form,

$$x = \frac{\mathscr{E}}{I - \mathscr{E}/R}.$$ (104.5)

If R is large compared with $\mathscr{E}$, the term $\mathscr{E}/R$ may be neglected with small error. If a good grade voltmeter is used, one which has 100 ohms per scale division, the error is usually of the order of 1% to 1.5%. A voltmeter with low resistance will give a large error unless equation (104.4) is used.

105. The Carey-Foster Bridge. — The Carey-Foster bridge is simply a slide-wire bridge with extensions n_1 and n_2, as shown in Fig. 82a. It is used in comparing two resistances, n_1 and n_2, which are very nearly equal. By its use, errors due to the resistances of the leads of the bridge itself, as well as thermal emfs. provided they are constant, are eliminated. This is easily shown in the derivation of the working equation of the bridge. When the bridge is in balance we have

$$\frac{R_1}{R_2} = \frac{n_1 + r_1 + \rho a_1}{n_2 + r_2 + \rho b_1}.$$ (105.1)

Now interchanging n_1 and n_2, we have

$$\frac{R_1}{R_2} = \frac{n_2 + r_1 + \rho a_2}{n_1 + r_2 + \rho b_2}.$$ (105.2)

Therefore,

$$\frac{n_1 + r_1 + \rho a_1}{n_2 + r_2 + \rho b_1} = \frac{n_2 + r_1 + \rho a_2}{n_1 + r_2 + \rho b_2}.$$

By adding 1 to both sides of this equation, we have

$$\frac{n_1 + r_1 + \rho a_1 + n_2 + r_2 + \rho b_1}{n_2 + r_2 + \rho b_1} = \frac{n_2 + r_1 + \rho a_1 + n_1 + r_2 + \rho b_2}{n_1 + r_2 + \rho b_2}.$$

The numerators are equal since $a_1 + b_1 = a_2 + b_2$, and hence

$$n_2 + r_2 + \rho b_1 = n_1 + r_2 + \rho b_2,$$

or

$$n_2 - n_1 = \rho(b_2 - b_1) = \rho(a_1 - a_2). \tag{105.3}$$

ρ, the resistance per unit length of the slide-wire, must first be determined, and then either n_1 or n_2 may be determined if the other

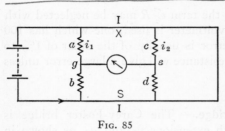

Fig. 85

is known. In the actual bridge an arrangement is provided for quick and easy interchanging of n_1 and n_2. This bridge is suited to both high and low resistance measurements.

106. The Kelvin Double Bridge. — The Wheatstone bridge is not suited to the measurement of very low resistances. The network of conductors shown in Fig. 85 is a device, invented by Lord Kelvin, which is admirably suited to the measurement of very low resistances, since it measures accurately the resistance between two points on a conductor. The equation for the Kelvin double bridge is derived as follows: Since g and e are at the same potential when the bridge is in balance—indicated by zero deflection of the galvanometer—we have

$$\left.\begin{array}{l} ai_1 = XI + ci_2 \\ bi_1 = SI + di_2 \end{array}\right\} \text{ or } \left.\begin{array}{l} XI = ai_1 - ci_2 \\ SI = bi_1 - di_2 \end{array}\right\} \text{ or } \begin{array}{l} XI = a(i_1 - ci_2/a) \\ SI = b(i_1 - di_2/b) \end{array}.$$

If in the construction of the bridge c/a is made equal to d/b, we may write

$$\frac{X}{S} = \frac{a}{b}. \tag{106.1}$$

This is the working equation of the bridge.

107. Principle of the Potentiometer. — The principle of the potentiometer can be explained most clearly by use of a simple diagram, such as that in Fig. 86. ab is a high-resistance wire of, say,

100 cms. in length. *B* is the potentiometer battery. It must have an emf. higher than that of the standard cell, emf. or p.d. to be measured. *R* is a variable control resistance. *R'* is a large resistance required when balancing against the standard cell so as not to draw an appreciable current from it and so cause injury. *R'* may be reduced or cut out when the balance against the standard cell is about perfect, and so secure a sharper balance. *S* is a double-pole, double-throw switch, which makes easy the change from the standard cell $\mathscr{E}_s$ to the unknown emf. or p.d. to be measured. Let the resistance of the wire *ab* per unit length be ρ (constant). Let p_1 be the balance point for the standard cell, indicated by zero deflection of the

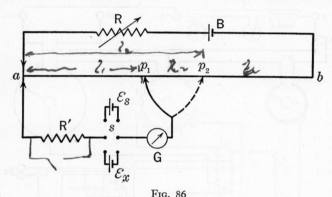

FIG. 86

galvanometer *G*, and p_2 the balance point for the unknown emf. or p.d. Then if l_1 and l_2 are the corresponding distances measured from the end *a* of the wire, we have

$$\frac{\mathscr{E}_x}{\mathscr{E}_s} = \frac{\rho l_2}{\rho l_1} = \frac{l_2}{l_1}. \tag{107.1}$$

$\mathscr{E}_x$ is the only unknown in the equation. It will be noticed that the polarities must be such that the currents are in opposition at the point *a*, and that no current flows in the galvanometer circuit when balance obtains. Then the p.d. along the wire *ab* is equal to the p.d. being measured.

Many types of direct reading precision potentiometers have been designed. The one in most common use in the U. S. is the Leeds and Northrup type *K* potentiometer, a schematic wiring diagram of which is shown in Fig. 87.   The resistances associated with the three dials correspond to the resistance wire *ab* of Fig. 86.   The two dials to the right are used in measurements of unknown p.d.s.   The dial to the left being used for standardizing with a standard cell.   The taps to the central dial are 5 ohms apart, and the dial to the right is a slide-wire on a drum, and also has a resistance of 5 ohms.   Thus the resistance range of the slide-wire is equal to the resistance between the consecutive taps of the center dial, and so permits of measurements of values falling between the tap values.   In use the standard cell dial is first set to the value of the standard cell, the main switch being

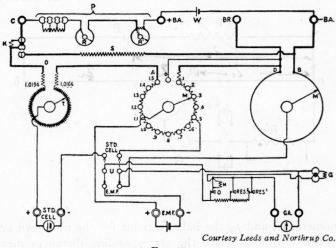

Courtesy Leeds and Northrup Co.

Fig. 87

thrown to the standard cell position.   The variable resistance in the battery circuit, which is within the potentiometer case, is then varied until balance obtains, indicated by zero deflection of the galvanometer.   The current through the potentiometer is then 0.02 amp., and so the p.d. between taps of the center dial is 0.1 volt, and the instrument is direct reading.   The slide wire has 1,000 divisions and may be estimated to 0.1 division.   The resistances in the galvanometer circuit correspond to R' in Fig. 86.   The switch contacts are in the galvanometer circuit, and as these carry no current when balance obtains, thermal emfs. are eliminated.   The plug block, shown in the upper left-hand corner, is designed so that when the plug is in the position marked 1 the readings are as recorded on the dials.   When the plug is in position marked 0.1, the dial readings are 0.1 of the values stated on the dials.

If a voltmeter is to be calibrated having a range not greater than 1.6 volts, it may be connected across R, say, in Fig. 88.   When key k is closed the p.d. between a and b is measured and hence also the correct reading of the voltmeter.   When R is being measured however key k must be open.

108. Measurement of Resistance with Potentiometer. — The potentiometer is an instrument which measures accurately the differ-

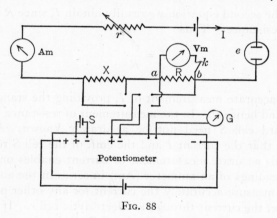

Fig. 88

ence of potential between two points without disturbing the current in the conductor, if difference of potential along a conductor is being measured, or without drawing current from a cell or battery, if difference of potential between the terminals is measured.   It measures difference of potential, without altering the existing difference of potential in the process of measurement.   The principle of the potentiometer was explained in Section 107.   Since the potentiometer measures accurately the difference of potential between two points along a conductor, we see that the difference of potentials across two resistances in series will be proportional to the resistances, since the current is the same in both.   If one of the resistances is known, the other is easily calculated.

The wiring diagram of the hookup is indicated in Fig. 88. The variable resistance r is for the purpose of controlling the current through R and x. R is a known standard resistance, and x is the resistance to be measured. A double-pole, double-throw switch is provided so as to make it easy to connect the potentiometer, first across the known and then across the unknown resistance, and so measure the p.d. across R, which we may call $\mathscr{E}$, and then across x, which we may call $\mathscr{E}_x$. Then by Ohm's law, we have

$$\mathscr{E}_x = xI, \quad \mathscr{E} = RI, \text{ and therefore } x = \frac{R\mathscr{E}_x}{\mathscr{E}}. \tag{108.1}$$

From the second equation we readily obtain I, since R is a known standard resistance. Thus

$$I = \frac{\mathscr{E}}{R}.$$

This is an accurate measurement of I, providing the standard cell is accurate, and hence $\mathscr{E}$. In the measurement of resistance the emf. of the standard cell S need not be accurately known. All that is required is that the current I and the emf. of the cell S remain constant. This accurate measurement of current enables one to check the scale readings of an ammeter (Am) in series in the auxiliary circuit, or to measure accurately the current for any other purpose, as, for example, the current through an electrolytic cell e. If one wishes to check the accuracy of a standard cell S all that is necessary is to make e a standard silver voltameter, and thereby measure I by the application of the law of electrolysis, $m = zIt$, where z is the electrochemical equivalent of silver, 0.00111810. Thus, if I and R are known, $\mathscr{E}$ is known, and then a correction of the emf. of the standard cell may be made. If the range of the ammeter is greater than 1.6 amp. the standard resistance must be less than 1 ohm.

The potentiometer merely balances the potential difference of one circuit or part of a circuit against that of another, and so, when a balance obtains, no current flows in the wires shunted with the resistances R and x, or from a cell or battery if the potentiometer is connected across the cell or battery. This is why conditions are not disturbed in measuring difference of potential with a potentiometer.

Errors in the standard cell cause errors in the absolute measurement of an emf. or a difference of potential, but where the measured difference of potentials enter as ratios, errors in the standard cell are eliminated. The potentiometer is a very useful electric-measuring instrument, as many different applications are made of it.

When a voltmeter having a range greater than 1.6 volts is to be calibrated, a *volt box* must be used in conjunction with the potentiometer. The hookup is shown in Fig. 89. A potentiometer

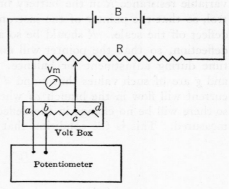

Fig. 89

wire R of large resistance is connected across a battery B forming an auxiliary circuit, thus making it possible to vary the reading of the voltmeter which is being calibrated. The volt box contains a large resistance which is tapped at points a, b, c, d, etc. Let us say that the resistance between a and c is such that the p.d. between a and c is 10 times that between a and b which is measured. Then the p.d. across the voltmeter will be ten times the p.d. measured by the potentiometer, and a p.d. up to 16 volts can be measured. If the ratio is 1 to 100 a p.d. up to 160 volts can be measured. A volt box cannot be used to measure an emf.

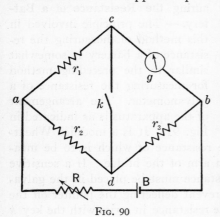

Fig. 90

109. Lord Kelvin's Method of Measuring the Resistance of a Galvanometer. — This method of measuring the resistance of a galvanometer or a millivoltmeter is of use in case only one instrument, the one being measured, is available. A Wheatstone bridge of any type may be used. The instrument being measured is placed in the unknown arm of the bridge, Fig. 90. A key k is placed in the branch cd, which is usually occupied by the galvanometer. The variable resistance R in the battery branch permits of current control, so that the pointer of the instrument being measured will not deflect off the scale. R should be so adjusted as to give a workable deflection, so that the pointer will not deflect off the scale at any time during adjustment for balance. If the resistances r_1, r_2, r_3, and g are of such values that c and d are at the same potential no current will flow in the branch cd when k is closed or opened, and so there will be no change in the deflection of the instrument being measured. This is the condition that

$$g = \frac{r_3 r_1}{r_2}.$$

This method is not suited to the measurement of high resistance instruments, such as voltmeters, as it is too insensitive.

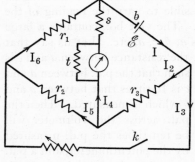

FIG. 91

110. Mance's Method of Measuring the Resistance of a Battery. — The principle involved in this method of measuring the resistance of a battery is somewhat similar to the preceding method for measuring the resistance of a galvanometer. The arrangement of the apparatus is as indicated in Fig. 91. It is a modified Wheatstone bridge. The battery, the resistance of which is to be measured, is placed in the unknown arm of the bridge. If a sensitive galvanometer is to be used, resistance must be placed in the galvanometer branch, as shown, to prevent deflecting the pointer off the scale. It is well also to put some resistance in series with the key k (about equal to $r_2 + r_3$), otherwise I will be too large when the key is closed. There will be a current through the galvanometer at all times, and hence it will show a deflection which can be controlled by the resistances s and t. When a balance obtains, no change in the deflection of the galvanometer will take place when key k is closed.

The equations for this use of the bridge may be derived as follows: Writing Kirchhoff's equations for the two loops of the bridge, we have

$$\mathscr{E} - Ib - r_3I_2 - gI_4 = 0 \qquad (110.1)$$

$$r_2I_5 + r_1I_6 - gI_4 = 0. \qquad (110.2)$$

When key k is closed there will be a change in the currents in all branches excepting the galvanometer branch. Hence, we may write

$$\mathscr{E} - b(I + \Delta I) - r_3(I_2 - \Delta I_2) - gI_4 = 0 \qquad (110.3)$$

$$r_2(I_5 - \Delta I_5) + r_1(I_6 + \Delta I_6) - gI_4 = 0. \qquad (110.4)$$

Subtracting (110.3) from (110.1) and (110.4) from (110.2), we obtain

$$-\Delta Ib + \Delta I_2r_3 = 0 \qquad (110.5)$$

$$-\Delta I_5r_2 + \Delta I_6r_1 = 0.$$

Since the current does not change in the galvanometer branch

$$\Delta I_2 = \Delta I_5 \quad \text{and} \quad \Delta I_6 = \Delta I.$$

Hence, from equations (110.5) and (110.6), we obtain

$$b = \frac{r_1r_3}{r_2}. \qquad (110.7)$$

This is the ordinary Wheatstone bridge equation.

A sufficient variety of resistance measurements has been given to show the general problem. For a very complete discussion of resistance measurement methods, the reader is referred to "Methods of Measuring Electrical Resistances" by E. F. Northrup, McGraw-Hill Book Co., Inc.

111. Electron Theory of Metallic Conduction. — It has been stated that the electric current in metals is a slow drift of electrons in a direction from negative to positive, or in a direction reverse to that conventionally chosen for the direction of the current. Two assumptions have been made as to the manner in which this transport of negative electricity might be brought about. The first supposes that at all times there are many free electrons which occupy the inter-molecular spaces of the conductor, and that they have come into thermal equilibrium, i.e., they have made so many collisions that their mean kinetic energy has become equal to that of a gas molecule at the temperature of the conductor. There is considerable evidence in support of this view, although there is much contradictory evidence, and for this reason its validity is questionable. However, assuming for the present the validity of the electronic-gas theory, we may proceed with the argument. The electrons occupying intermolecular spaces may be assumed to behave as a monatomic gas of extremely small atomic weight obeying the ordinary gas laws. Because of the extremely small mass of an electron, it will have a very large average velocity, due to thermal agitation, as compared with a gas molecule or a molecule of the conductor at the same temperature. It will have a much greater velocity than the drift velocity of the electrons constituting the electric current, i.e., $\bar{u} << U << v$, where $\bar{u}$ is the average drift velocity of the electron current, U the average velocity of a gas molecule due to thermal agitation at the same temperature as the conductor, and v the average velocity of an electron due to thermal agitation. The random motions of the electrons due to thermal agitation go on constantly, whereas the drift velocity, which is superposed upon these motions, is due to the direct action of an electric field and exists only while the field acts.

In order to derive an expression for electric conductivity, on the assumptions made, we may proceed as follows: If $\bar{u}$ is the drift velocity and n the number of free electrons per cm.^{3}, the number of electrons crossing a square cm. of surface, drawn normal to the electric force, per second is $n\bar{u}$, and, if e is the charge of an electron, the current density is given by $i = n\bar{u}e$. If m is the mass of an electron and E the electric field intensity (potential gradient $\mathcal{E}/s$ if the field is uniform), we have $Ee = ma$. The velocity of an electron will increase uniformly under the action of the electric field from zero at the beginning of a free path to u at the end, and, if t is the time between collisions, $a = u/t$. Therefore

$$u = \frac{Eet}{m}, \text{ and the average velocity is } \bar{u} = \frac{Eet}{2m}.$$

If l is the mean free path, we have $t = l/v$. Hence

$$\bar{u} = \frac{Eel}{2mv}, \text{ and therefore, } i = \frac{ne^2l}{2mv} E = \sigma E. \tag{111.1}$$

This is the same as equation (89.1). Thus

$$\sigma = \frac{ne^2l}{2mv}. \tag{111.2}$$

The resistivity ρ is the reciprocal of the conductivity, and therefore

$$\rho = \frac{2mv}{ne^2l}.$$ (111.3)

Thus, so long as the temperature of the conductor remains constant, the resistance remains constant, and therefore, equation (111.1) is a statement of Ohm's law.

If the conductor has a cross-sectional area A, the total current is

$$i = iA = \sigma AE = \frac{AE}{\rho}.$$

If the difference of potential between the two ends of the conductor is $\mathscr{E}$, we have

$$\mathscr{E} = \int_0^s E \, ds = \rho \frac{s}{A} i.$$ (111.4)

The ratio of $\mathscr{E}$ to i is the resistance $R = \rho \dfrac{s}{A}$ of the conductor (Ohm's law). Thus, the resistance is directly proportional to the length s of the conductor and inversely proportional to the area of cross section, as experiment shows.

In order to ascertain the manner in which the resistance varies with the temperature, it will be necessary to introduce the temperature into the expression for ρ. We have, from the kinetic theory of gases,

$$\epsilon = \tfrac{1}{2}mv^2 = \tfrac{3}{2}kT = \alpha T \text{ ergs},$$ (111.5)

where ϵ is the kinetic energy of a gas molecule or electron, T the absolute temperature, k the Boltzmann constant ($1.3803(10)^{-16}$), and α a constant which is the same for all gases.

$$\alpha = 2.0704(10)^{-16}, \text{ and } \epsilon_0 = 5.622(10)^{-14} \text{ erg at } 0° \text{ C.}$$

Combining equations (111.5) and (111.3), we have

$$\rho = \frac{2\sqrt{2m\alpha}\ T^{1/2}}{n\,e^2 l}.$$ (111.6)

We cannot predict on the electron theory as here developed just how ρ varies with the temperature until we know how all of the quantities in the expression vary with the temperature. Therefore, we may conclude that the electron gas theory as here applied is not very satisfying.

112. Ratio of Thermal to Electric Conductivity. Law of Wiedemann and Franz.

— It is a well known fact that good conductors of electricity are likewise good conductors of heat, and that insulators are poor conductors of both heat and electricity. It is natural, therefore, to assume that there is some fundamental, underlying cause for the parallelism. Since the free electrons constitute the electric current, it has been assumed, because of the parallelism just stated, that the free electrons play a major role in thermal conductivity. An attempt has been made to correlate these two phenomena on this assumption.

Let us assume that the conduction of heat is through the medium of the free electrons alone, or that the molecules of the conductor play a negligible role. Suppose one end of a metal rod to be heated. The electrons in the heated end will have their random thermal velocities augmented. The electrons moving away from the heated end will, on the average, possess more kinetic energy than those moving toward it, thus bringing about a transfer of energy in a direction from hot to cold. On the assumption that the free electrons alone take part in thermal conduction, and that the electronic gas in the metal may be treated as an ordinary gas, the thermal conductivity k of the electronic gas should be given by the ordinary expression for the thermal conductivity in an ordinary gas, which is

$$k = \frac{\pi}{8} nv\alpha l,$$

where $\alpha = \frac{1}{2}\frac{mv^2}{T} = \frac{\epsilon}{T}$, and n, v, l, and ϵ have the same meanings as in the previous article.[1] Then the ratio of the thermal to the electric conductivity is

$$\frac{k}{\sigma} = \frac{\pi}{8} nv\alpha l \times \frac{4\alpha T}{ne^2 lv} = \frac{\pi}{2}\left(\frac{\alpha}{e}\right)^2 T = 2.623(10)^8 T. \quad (112.1)$$

This ratio, according to the assumptions that have been made, should be independent of the nature of the conductor at any given tempera-

[1] See O. Meyer's Kinetic Theory of Gases.

ture. This is the *law of Wiedemann* and *Franz*. It shows that this ratio is directly proportional to the absolute temperature.

We can now obtain a value for this ratio at any given temperature and for any metal. For the temperature $T = 273°\ K$, we have from equation (112.1)

$$\frac{k}{\sigma} = 7.16(10)^{10}.$$

The temperature coefficient of this ratio, i.e., the increase in the ratio per degree rise in temperature divided by the value of the ratio at $0°$ C., is $3.66(10)^{-3}$. To show how theory, as here developed, agrees with experiments, the following Table of experimental values obtained by Jager and Disselhorst is given:

Metal	k/σ at $0°$ C.	Temp. Coef.
Copper.............	6.71×10^{10}	3.95×10^{-3}
Silver..............	6.86 "	3.77 "
Gold...............	7.09 "	3.75 "
Zinc...............	6.72 "	3.85 "
Lead...............	7.15 "	4.07 "
Tin................	7.35 "	3.40 "

The agreement of experimental data with theory seems to be quite satisfactory. However, other calculations based upon other assumptions are not in as close agreement. Wiedemann and Franz's law fails conspicuously at low temperatures.

113. Some Difficulties yet to Surmount. — In spite of the apparent success of the foregoing theory there are many points wherein it fails to meet the demands required of an adequate theory of conduction, and therefore, it has failed to command universal respect and support; it has not been generally accepted. The expression for the resistivity ρ has been derived solely on the assumption that electric conduction takes place in an electronic gas, and that the nature of the atoms and molecules of the conductor in no wise influences the process; hence there is no provision in the theory for the known differences in the resistivities of the different metals. Other theories have been developed, starting from different assumptions, but they have been even less successful in a comprehensive solution of the problem. It seems doubtful that the free electrons share in the thermal agitations of the surrounding atoms and molecules of the conductor to the extent required by the classic theory of equipartition of energy, yet the surrounding atoms and molecules do have an influence, as is evidenced by the variations of resistivity. An adequate theory must take account of this fact.

If the free electrons share in the thermal energy of the conductor they must absorb energy with rise in temperature of the conductor. The specific heat should be made up of two parts, one due to the atoms and molecules of the conductor and one due to the free electrons. However, the heat energy absorbed by the atoms and molecules will account for all of the absorption of energy with rise in temperature. In fact, the specific heats of the metals are too small to give any place for absorption of heat energy by free electrons. However, according to the theory just developed, heat conduction, as well as electric conduction, is brought about solely through the agency of the free electrons, and yet the specific heats of the metals are due to the absorption of heat energy by the atoms and molecules. These two processes are too closely associated to be brought about by different agencies.

Superconductivity is a phenomenon which must be included in a comprehensive and adequate theory of electric conduction. This sudden loss of resistance is markedly different from the gradual change in resistance with change in temperature. In explanation of this phenomenon it has been suggested that possibly the number of free electrons might, instead of being approximately equal to the number of atoms, be small in comparison, and therefore, that the mean free path of an electron is much greater than generally assumed due to the small number of electrons, and a possible regular arrangement of the atoms in space lattices. This would provide an explanation of superconductivity. At ordinary temperatures the atoms in the space lattices will be vibrating in much wider excursions about their mean positions, and so will be moving across the free paths of the electrons more frequently, thus causing greater interference. At some sufficiently low temperature, however, this vibratory motion of the atoms may become negligibly small in the case of some metals, thus affording comparatively unobstructed free paths or channels for the electrons. Thus there would be very little retardation of the electrons due to the impact with atoms, and hence, extremely low resistance, assuming, of course, that electric resistance is due to impacts of electrons with atoms. However, it is difficult to conceive of a physical change of this character being so abrupt.

The sudden increase in the resistance of a metal with its change from the solid to the liquid state might be explained as due to the breaking up of the regular arrangement of the atoms in space lattices, thus presenting greater retardation to the onward flow of the electrons which constitute the electric current. However, if this is the explanation, then the decrease in resistance, when antimony and bismuth change from the solid to the liquid state, presents an exception which calls for an explanation. Also, a change from a positive to a negative temperature coefficient of resistance without change of state calls for an explanation. Electric resistance and conductance, in both conductors and insulators, await complete clarification.

PROBLEMS

1. An ammeter when placed in series with a resistance R reads 0.54 ampere. A voltmeter, range 0–150 volts and internal resistance 9500 ohms, when in parallel with the resistance reads 136 volts. Calculate the true value of the resistance R, and its value as calculated by the relation $R = \mathcal{E}/I$.

2. A resistance of 200 ohms is in series with a dynamo. A voltmeter, having a resistance of 500 ohms, gives a difference of potential across the 200 ohm resistance of 110.7 volts. However, when a 500 ohm resistance replaces the 200 ohm resistance the voltmeter reads 114.5 volts. Calculate the internal resistance of the dynamo and its emf.

3. A transmission line 10 miles in length (20 miles total) is made of No. 6 aluminum wire. What is the resistance of this line at 40° C.? At −40° C.? Calculate the so-called absolute zero of temperature for aluminum. What is the ratio of the line loss at 40° C. to the line loss at −40° C., the current being the same in the two cases? How much higher must the emf. of the dynamo be at 40° C. than at −40° C. in order to transmit a current of 40 amperes? (Take the resistivity of aluminum as $2.6(10)^{-6}$ at 0° C. Area of cross section of No. 6 wire is 0.133 cm.² Temperature coefficient of aluminum is 0.0038).

4. Assuming that there are as many free electrons in aluminum as there are atoms of aluminum, calculate the average drift velocity $\bar{u}$ of the electrons in the line conductor of Problem 3. (No. of molecules in one gm. mol. is $6.023(10)^{23}$).

5. A No. 6 aluminum wire has a core of No. 18 steel wire. Calculate the percentage of the current carried by the aluminum and by the steel when this conductor is used as a transmission line.

6. Prove that the product of two quantities, whose sum is constant, is a maximum when the two quantities are equal.

7. Derive an expression for the resistance to radial flow of an electric current from the inner surface to the outer surface of a hollow cylinder of an insulating material whose resistivity is ρ ohm-cm. (submarine cable).

Let the length of the cylinder be l cms., the inside radius a cms., and the outside radius b cms. Assume the resistance of the metal cable to be zero, as well as the surrounding salt water.

$$\text{Ans.} \quad R = \frac{\rho}{2\pi l} \log_e \frac{b}{a}.$$

8. Calculate the resistance of one mile of No. 16 copper wire at a temperature of 25° C. What will be the resistance of one mile of No. 16 aluminum wire at 25° C.? What will be the resistance of one mile of No. 16 iron wire at 25° C.?   *mil fact.*

9. Calculate the resistivity of copper in ohm-inches, in ohm-meters.

10. A copper rod of round section has a resistance of 0.5 ohm. If this rod is drawn out into a wire having a cross section of one one-hundredth that of the rod, what will be its resistance, assuming the resistivity to remain constant?

11. The insulation resistance of a single wire cable from copper core to lead sheathing is 5,500 megohms per 500 feet of length. What is the insulation resistance per mile of length?

523 megre
per mile

12. The resistance of a coil of wire at 0° C. is 2.5 ohms and at 100° C. it is 3.55 ohms. Compute the mean temperature coefficient between 0° C. and 100° C., and also between 30° C. and 100° C.

13. Referring to Section 99, show that the relationship between the temperature coefficients α_0 and α_t is

$$\alpha_0 = \alpha_t(1 + \alpha_0 t).$$

#18 wire = 0.05 ins in diameter

resistivity of steel = 20×10^{-6} ohm cm.

CHAPTER VIII

ELECTROLYTIC CONDUCTION

114. As we have seen, in metallic conduction the current of electricity is a slow drift (averaging about 0.04 cm. per sec.) of free electrons along and through the conductor, and there is not of necessity any chemical change accompanying the passage of current. All conduction of this type is classed as metallic conduction. If a chemical change does take place it is because of some indirect effect, as, for example, heating.

On the other hand, there is a class of conductors in which the transfer of electricity, which constitutes the electric current, has a very different mechanism. This class of conductors, for the most part, consists of solutions of salts and acids. Where the current enters and leaves the solution there are evidences of chemical action having taken place. The carriers of electric charges are of atomic or molecular mass, are of both signs, and travel simultaneously in opposite directions through the conductor, though not necessarily with the same speed. These carriers of charge are called *ions*, and this type of conduction is called electrolytic.

Electrolytic conduction was first studied in the early years of the nineteenth century. To Michael Faraday [1] we owe the nomenclature universally applied to electrolysis (1833). The solution carrying the current is called the *electrolyte*. The conductors by which the current enters and leaves the electrolyte are called *electrodes*; the one by which the current (conventional) enters is called the *anode*, and the one by which the current leaves is called the *cathode*. In the process the molecules of the *solute* break up into charged particles called *ions*. The ions are of two kinds: One is positively charged, the *cation*, and hence migrates to the negative electrode (cathode); the other, the *anion*, is negatively charged and hence migrates to the positive electrode (anode). The process by which the current is carried in this

[1] Experimental Researches in Electricity, London, 1839, Vol I.

class of conductors is called *electrolysis*, and the whole unit is called an *electrolytic cell.*

115. The Dissociation Theory.

— Both Clausius and G. Quincke advanced the theory that the chemical dissociation in an electrolyte is spontaneous, and the result of mere solution. This theory met with little favor, however, until Savante Arrhenius of Stockholm brought forth new and cogent arguments in support of it in 1887.[1] This was the first satisfactory explanation of electrolytic conduction, and so the theory is generally attributed to Arrhenius. According to this theory, the so-called dissociation theory, an acid or salt held in solution breaks up spontaneously into ions *in advance* of an applied p.d. across the electrolytic cell. In order to make the argument specific, let us consider a solution of silver nitrate ($AgNO_3$) in water. According to the theory, most of the molecules of silver nitrate, break up into ions of Ag^+ and NO_3^-. In accordance with a theory advanced by Lewis and Kossel, silver becomes dynamically stable by losing one electron, thus leaving it with a unit positive charge. These free, charged ions exist at all times in the solution *because of the mere fact of solution*. In the light of present-day theory, the atoms composing a molecule are held together largely by electrostatic attraction, i.e., chemical affinity is essentially electrostatic attraction. Clearly, this electrostatic attraction is stronger between some of the atoms of a molecule than between others. Thus, in the example chosen, NO_3 is a very stable grouping, whereas the atom of silver is held to the radicle NO_3 by a relatively weak bond, and so the rupture occurs at the weakest point.

Since the components of a molecule are held together largely by electrostatic attraction, we can see that any influeuce which weakens this attraction will tend to molecular disruption or dissociation. Now the electric force between charged bodies is dependent upon the surrounding medium. This fact is expressed in Coulomb's law,

$$F = \frac{qq'}{\epsilon\, d^2}, \text{ cgse. units.}$$

If ϵ is large the force between the charges is small. Water has a dielectric coefficient of about 80, and therefore, the electric force between charges immersed in water is one 80th of its value in air. Thus,

[1] Zeitschr. Physik. Chemie., Vol. I, p. 631, 1887.

the presence of the water weakens the bond holding the Ag atom to the radicle NO_3, and, aided by impacts of other molecules due to thermal agitation, many molecules of $AgNO_3$ break up. Undoubtedly dissociation and recombination go on continuously, but at any instant there are many free ions, the number probably not remaining constant. This breaking up of molecules into ions is called *ionization*. However, it must be borne in mind that this sort of ionization is different from the ionization which occurs in gases.

Solutions of salts are always good electric conductors — "strong electrolytes". The only solvents that have a generally high solvent action on salts are those that have high specific inductive capacities. Water is the most universal solvent for salts; it has the largest solvent action without decomposition on the greatest number of salts of any known substance. Other solvents having high specific inductive capacities are liquid ammonia, methyl alcohol, formic acid, and formamide. There is a rough parallelism between solvent power and specific inductive capacity, since separation of a salt into ions is dependent upon a weakened electric field, and ionization seems to be a part of the action of solution. In a solvent of high specific inductive capacity, such as water, only a small trace of salt molecules as such is present. Dissociation is practically complete at all ordinary concentrations. Thus the reason that salts dissolve in these solvents is because they favor the separation of the solute into ions, and consequently render the solution conducting. Even the poorest solvents form conducting solutions when they dissolve salts at all.

116. Faraday's Laws. — In electrolytic conduction oppositely charged ions migrate simultaneously in opposite directions through the electrolyte, whereas in metallic conduction the current is, so far as is known, composed of electrons moving in one direction only. We may make the process clear, and at the same time derive Faraday's laws, by considering several electrolytic cells connected in series, as indicated in Fig. 92, the electrodes all being platinum or carbon.

Let the solvent in each case be water, and let the solutes be $AgNO_3$, $CuSO_4$, and H_2SO_4, respectively, as indicated in the Figure. We will here consider only the primary chemical action, i.e., the ruptures of the solute molecules as a result of solution. In the $AgNO_3$ cell we have Ag^+ and NO_3^- ions; in the $CuSO_4$ we have Cu^{++} and SO_4^{--} ions; and in the H_2SO_4 cell we have H^+H^+ and SO_4^{--} ions.

In the case of all salts and acids hydrogen ions and all metal ions are charged positively, and hence migrate to the cathode, whereas the radicles are charged negatively and so migrate to the anode.   In the breaking up of AgNO₃ the radicle NO₃ takes with it one of the valence electrons of the Ag atom, thus giving to the radicle one excess negative charge, and the Ag atom one negative charge less than normal, or an excess of one positive charge.   The valence of Ag is one and the valence of NO₃ is also one.   When CuSO₄ breaks up the radicle SO₄ robs the copper atom of two valence electrons, thus giving the SO₄ ion an excess of two negative charges, and the Cu ion has two negative charges less than normal, or an excess of two positive charges.   The valence of Cu is two and the valence of SO₄ is also two.   When H₂SO₄ breaks up there are two H ions and one SO₄ ion.   The SO₄ radicle robs each of the H atoms of one valence electron, thus giving the SO₄ ion two excess negative charges, and each H ion one less negative charge than

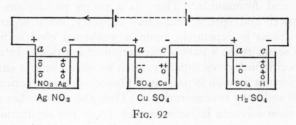

FIG. 92

normal, or an excess of one positive charge each.   Thus, each ion carries a charge numerically equal to its valence.   This is universally true of all ions.   The unit charge here turns out to be numerically equal to that of an electron or proton.   It will be noticed that the carriers of charge in electrolysis, the ions, are of atomic or molecular magnitude.

If a current I is flowing in the circuit of Fig. 92, the strength of the current is the same throughout the circuit, and therefore, the same quantity of electricity must be transported across each cell in the same time.   This will require that for each molecule of CuSO₄ or H₂SO₄ that takes part in the transport of charge through the electrolyte two molecules of AgNO₃ are employed.   Further, to transport a given number of positive charges will require one half as many Cu ions as either Ag or H ions.   Likewise, the SO₄ radicle carries twice the number of negative charges as does the NO₃ radicle, and so would require but half as many ions to transport the same total quantity of charge. Thus, we see that *the mass of an ion required to transport a charge q is proportional to its atomic weight divided by its valence, or proportional to its chemical combining value.*

Let us define a *gram ion* as a quantity in grams of any ion which is numerically equal to the comparative weight of the ion on the basis of $O = 16$. Further, let us define a *gram equivalent* (chemical equivalent numerically) as a gram ion divided by its valence. Thus, we see that *the gram equivalents of all ions transport the same quantity Q of charge through an electrolyte.* Moreover, we see that the mass of any ion delivered to an electrode is proportional to the quantity $q = It$ of charge transported through the cell. Hence, we may write

$$m = zIt. \tag{116.1}$$

This is the mathematical statement of Faraday's first law of electrolysis. z, the *electrochemical equivalent*, is, therefore, the mass in grams of an ion deposited by a current of one ampere in one second, or one coulomb of electricity. For silver, $z = 0.00111810$ gm.

Knowing the electrochemical equivalent of silver, we can calculate the quantity Q of electricity which is transported by one gram equivalent of any ion. Since 0.00111810 gm. of silver transports one coulomb, the number of coulombs which will be transported by one gram equivalent of silver, or of any ion, is given by

$$\frac{107.88}{0.00111810} = 96,494 = Q \text{ coulombs.}$$

Therefore, 96,494 coulombs of electricity will be transported through any electrolyte by one gram equivalent of any ion. This statement may be put in mathematical form as follows:

$$\frac{96,494}{\text{gm. equivalent}} = \frac{It}{m}, \tag{116.2}$$

where m is the mass in gms. deposited by a current of I amperes in t seconds. This is a statement of Faraday's second law of electrolysis. 96,494 is known as the Faraday electrolytic constant, or simply the *Faraday*. Farady's two laws stated in words are as follows:

1. "The amount of decomposition is proportional to the current and to the time for which it passes."

2. "The amounts of different substances liberated by the same current, flowing for the same time, are proportional to the chemical equivalents of the substances."

Knowing the electrochemical equivalent of silver, we may calculate the electrochemical equivalent of any other ion as follows:

$$\frac{0.00111810}{107.88} = \frac{z}{gm.\ equivalent},$$ (116.3)

where z is the unknown electrochemical equivalent. In general, since $107.88/0.00111810 = 96,494 = Q$, we have

$$z = \frac{f}{Q} = \frac{w}{vQ},$$ (116.4)

where f = gm. equivalent, w = atomic weight of the ion (mole), and v = valence. On combining (116.1) and (116.4), we obtain

$$m = \frac{w}{vQ} It.$$ (116.5)

If N is the number of atoms per mole (Avogadro's number) and n is the number of atoms transmitted when a mass of m grams is deposited, we have

$$\frac{w}{m} = \frac{N}{n}.$$

Each ion carries a charge ve. Therefore, $It = nev$, and

$$m = \frac{w}{vQ} nev = \frac{new}{Q}, \quad or \quad \frac{w}{m} = \frac{Q}{ne} = \frac{N}{n}.$$

Thus,

$$Q = Ne.$$ (116.6)

This relation provides the most accurate method of calculating N, since Q and e can be measured with high accuracy. $N = 6.023(10)^{23}$.

117. Mechanism of Metallic and Electrolytic Conduction. — We are now in a position to see how a current of electricity is conveyed throughout a circuit, as, for example, the circuit shown in Fig. 92. Anions carry one or more electrons in excess of the normal number. When an anion arrives at the anode it gives up its excess number of electrons to the anode, thereby becoming normal or neutral. The electrons delivered to the anode by the anions enter the metallic electrode to continue on their way around the circuit as the current in the metallic conductor. The cations are minus one or more electrons, and, upon arriving at the cathode, receive a sufficient number of electrons from the cathode to make them normal or neutral atoms. Since there is no accumulation of charge at any point in the circuit, the same number of electrons must emerge from the metallic circuit at the cathode as enter the metallic circuit at the anode in the same time interval. The neutral atoms or groups of atoms at the anode and at the cathode are either deposited on the electrodes, pass off as gases, or enter into chemical unions after having fulfilled their function as carriers of electric charge. The current in the electrolyte of a battery is exactly the same as in the electrolytic cell, and Faraday's laws are equally applicable.

It may be stated at this point that free electrons do not exist in electrolytic conductors, and that the ions existing in an electrolyte do not enter into the current flow of the metallic conductors through the electrodes, or otherwise.

118. Polarization. — If there were no ions in the electrolyte at the time the difference of potential is applied, it would require a certain minimum difference of potential before any decomposition or dissociation of the solute could take place, and therefore, before any current could flow. On the contrary it is found that any difference of potential, however small, causes some current to flow. The current, however, in some cases will cease, or rather become very small, unless a certain minimum difference of potential is maintained, but in other cases it will not. If the electrolyte is a solution of sulphuric acid in water, this minimum difference of potential is about 1.7 volts. On first thought, one might conclude from this that there are a few free ions present to begin with, and that when these have been removed the current will cease unless the difference of potential is sufficient to effect chemical dissociation.

The real cause of cessation of current, however, is to be found in the layers of dissimilar substances, the products of dissociation, which are deposited on the electrodes. These products of chemical dissociation which are deposited on the electrodes set up a counter emf. of a certain value, depending upon their natures, and, unless the impressed emf. is greater than this minimum counter emf., the current ceases. This phenomenon is called *polarization*. The emf. of polarization may be demonstrated in the following manner: Connect an electrolytic cell e, a battery B, a charge and discharge key K, and a galvanometer G, as shown in Fig. 93. Let the electrolyte be a weak solution of sulphuric acid in water, and the electrodes platinum. On throwing the key K to the contact f a current flows and gases appear at the electrodes. Now throw key K to contact d, thus disconnecting the battery and connecting the galvanometer in circuit with cell e, and the galvanometer indicates that a current is flowing, which continues but for a short time. The electrolytic cell e is now functioning as a voltaic cell, and is driving a current through the galvanometer circuit from the anode a to the cathode c. Thus the polarity is reversed. The hydrogen atoms which have collected on c, and the oxygen atoms which have collected on a, set up a reverse emf., and a reverse current flows for the short interval of time that the gases are disappearing. *The electrolytic cell behaves, during this short interval of time, as a secondary or storage cell, which delivers current after being charged.* It is, in fact, a storage cell of short life. The chemical action, in this evanescent secondary cell, is as follows:

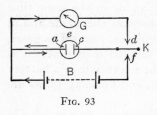

Fig. 93

$$H_2SO_4 \rightleftarrows H^+H^+ + SO_4^{--}, \text{ primary action.}$$

The hydrogen gas collects at the cathode. The SO_4 radicles collect at the anode and there deliver their electrons to the metallic circuit, and then enter into secondary combinations as follows:

$$H_2O + SO_4 \rightleftarrows H_2SO_4 + O, \text{ secondary action.}$$

The free, neutral oxygen collects at the anode.

If, instead of H_2SO_4, $CuSO_4$ is the solute and the electrodes are both copper, we find that no matter how small the p.d. is a current will flow which is proportional to the p.d. In this cell there are no accumulations of gases or other products of dissociation on the electrodes which are dissimilar to the electrodes, and hence there is no counter emf. Since the current is proportional to the impressed p.d., Ohm's law holds. The chemical changes in this case are as follows:

$$CuSO_4 \rightleftarrows Cu^{++} + SO_4^{--}, \text{ primary action.}$$

Copper is deposited on the copper cathode, and hence does not change its character. The SO_4 ions deliver two electrons each to the anode, and then enter into chemical combination with copper from the copper anode, forming $CuSO_4$, thus

$$Cu + SO_4 \rightleftarrows CuSO_4, \text{ secondary action.}$$

The $CuSO_4$ solution remains of the same strength, the anode is consumed and the cathode is built up, but at all times, however, there are two copper electrodes which can develop no counter emf., providing the current density is not too great.

According to Kirchhoff's investigations, any excess emf. above that necessary to balance the counter emf. of polarization develops a current which is strictly proportional to the excess impressed emf., and therefore Ohm's law holds for electrolytic condution. If $\mathscr{E}$ is the impressed emf., $\mathscr{E}'$ the counter emf. of polarization, we have

$$I = \frac{\mathscr{E} - \mathscr{E}'}{R}, \tag{117.1}$$

where R is the true ohmic resistance of the electrolyte.

Polarization takes place in a voltaic cell as well as in an electrolytic cell and for the same reasons. If the products of electrolysis which are deposited on the electrodes of a voltaic cell are unlike the electrodes, counter emfs. are set up which decrease the effective emf. of the cell. This will vary with the strength of the current.

119. Conductivity. — The conductivity of an electrolyte is the reciprocal of the resistivity, as in metallic conductors, and is defined in the same way. In metallic conductors the conductivity is proportional to the drift speed and the number of free electrons per unit volume. In the same manner and for the same reason the conductivity of an electrolyte is proportional to the number of ions per unit volume and the rate at which they travel through the solution. Let c, *the concentration*, be the number of molecules per unit volume of solute, and δ, the *degree of dissociation*, the fraction of the molecules which are ionized. The conductivity σ is then given by $\sigma = Kc\delta$, where K is a constant of proportionality. It is customary in discussing electrolysis to introduce a term, called the *equivalent conductivity* (λ), which is defined as the ratio of the true conductivity σ to the concentration c. Thus,

$$\lambda = \frac{\sigma}{c} = K\delta. \tag{119.1}$$

If δ is constant λ is constant, and therefore independent of the concentration, which means that the conductivity σ is directly proportional to the concentration c. Experiments show that in general, however, λ increases with decreasing concentration, which shows that δ, the degree of dissociation, increases. λ approaches a limiting value asymptotically as c approaches zero. If λ_0 is this limiting value, it must correspond to complete dissociation, in which case $\delta = 1$. Then $\lambda_0 = K$, and

$$\frac{\lambda}{\lambda_0} = \delta. \tag{119.2}$$

σ, and hence λ, is obtained from measurements, and by extrapolation λ_0 is obtained. Then δ is obtained from (119.2).

Let us assume that a salt, such as NaCl, is dissolved in water. Dissociation will then cause a splitting into one positive and one negative ion, each having a charge e. Let there be n' molecules of the salt per unit volume. Then $n'_1 = n'_2 = n'\delta$, when n'_1 and n'_2 are the number of ions of each kind per unit volume. Let u_1 and u_2 be the mobilities (speed per unit potential gradient) of the respective ions. Then, since Ohm's law holds, we have for the current density

$$\mathbf{i} = (n'_1 u_1 + n'_2 u_2)eE \tag{119.3}$$

by (88.3), or

$$\mathbf{i} = en'\delta(u_1 + u_2)E = \sigma E. \tag{119.3}$$

Then

$$\lambda = \frac{\sigma}{c} = \frac{en'\delta(u_1 + u_2)}{c}, \tag{119.4}$$

and λ is proportional to the degree of dissociation and to the sum of the mobilities of the two types of ions. The concentration c of a univalent solute is the number of moles $\left(\dfrac{m}{w}\right)$ per unit volume, or $c = m/wV$, where V is the volume occupied by n ions of mass m. But from Section 116, $\dfrac{m}{w} = \dfrac{n}{N}$. Therefore, $n' = \dfrac{n}{V}$, and $c = \dfrac{n}{NV} = \dfrac{n'}{N}$, and (119.4) becomes

$$\lambda = \frac{\sigma}{c} = \frac{en'\delta(u_1 + u_2)}{n'/N} = Ne\delta(u_1 + u_2) = Q\delta(u_1 + u_2). \tag{119.5}$$

The mobilities u_1 and u_2 can be measured.

There are two classes of electrolytes from the standpoint of degree of dissociation: "Strong electrolytes" and "weak electrolytes."

Strong electrolytes comprise most univalent and many bivalent salts and the so-called strong acids, such as HCl and HNO_3, and the strong bases NaOH, KOH, etc. In the case of strong electrolytes dissociation is practically complete at all ordinary concentrations, and so the variation of λ with concentration is largely due to the variation in the mobilities of the ions. Weak electrolytes are only slightly dissociated in *concentrated* solutions.[1]

120. Ionic Velocities. — According to the dissociation theory, many ions are present in an electrolyte when a p.d. is applied. Immediately on the application of p.d. the negative ions begin to drift toward the anode and the positive ions toward the cathode. For a short time after closing the switch the ions are accelerated, but they soon settle down to a steady, average velocity, the magnitude depending on their size, the potential gradient, and the viscosity of the medium through which they move. Since equal charges are not, in general, associated with equal masses of equal volumes, it is to be expected that the viscous resistance will bring about unequal velocities of the ions. The unequal velocities will cause unequal concentrations of the solution in the vicinity of the anode and in the vicinity of the cathode. The following Table gives a few ionic velocities which have been measured:

Solution in Water at 18° C.	Velocity in cm./sec. for potential grad. of 1 volt/cm.
Li	34.7×10^{-5}
Na	45.1 "
K	67.0 "
NH	66.0 "
Ag	57.0 "
H	325.0 "
Cl	67.8 "
I	68.5 "
NO	64.0 "
OH	178.0 "

It will be observed that the ionic velocities are very small, amounting to only a slow drift. These velocities must not be confused with

[1] For the theory of strong electrolytes see Debye and Huckel, Phys. Zeit., 24, 305 (1923). See also The American Physics Teacher, Vol. 5, p. 198 (1937).

the random, thermal velocities of the ions which are very much larger. The average velocity of a hydrogen atom at 0° C. due to thermal agitation is $18(10)^4$ cms./sec. Ionic velocities increase with rise in temperature.

The change in concentration is easily observed in the case of the electrolysis of a solution of copper sulphate in water, using copper electrodes. The best effect is obtained by placing the electrodes in a horizontal position, the cathode above and the anode below. When the current is flowing it will be observed that the solution near the anode becomes more deeply colored than near the cathode. Sir Oliver Lodge,[1] W. C. D. Whetham,[2] and B. D. Steele[3] have devised experimental arrangements whereby ionic velocities have been measured by direct observations. For a fuller discussion of ionic velocities, see the Dictionary of Applied Physics by Glazebrook, Vol. II, p. 280, and Electricity and Magnetism by S. G. Starling.

121. Ohmic Resistance of Electrolytes. — The true ohmic resistance of an electrolyte could be measured by use of a Wheatstone bridge, by merely placing the electrolytic cell in the unknown arm of

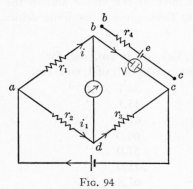

FIG. 94

the bridge and using direct current with a direct current galvanometer in the usual manner, were it not for the counter emf. of polarization which has the effect of an added resistance. The effect of the counter emf. of polarization on the bridge balance is easily shown by aid of the diagram in Fig. 94. Let us assume that a balance obtains. Then

$$r_1 i = r_2 i_1, \quad \text{and} \quad V = r_3 i_1,$$

where V is the sum of the counter emf. and the ohmic potential drop in the arm bc due to polarization and ohmic resistance. On solving for V, we obtain

$$V = \frac{r_1 r_3 i}{r_2}. \tag{121.1}$$

[1] Brit. Assoc., Birmingham, 1886.
[2] Proc. Roy. Soc. 52, p. 283, 1892.
[3] Chem. Soc. Journ., 79, p. 414, 1901.

Let r_4 be the true ohmic resistance of the electrolyte. Then

$$V = r_4 i + \mathcal{E}', \tag{121.2}$$

where $\mathcal{E}'$ is the counter emf. of polarization. On combining (121.1) and (121.2), we obtain

$$r_4 i + \mathcal{E}' = \frac{r_1 r_3}{r_2} i, \text{ and therefore, } r_4 = \frac{r_1 r_3}{r_2} - \frac{\mathcal{E}'}{i}. \tag{121.3}$$

Let us say that $\mathcal{E}'/i = r_5$ is the *equivalent resistance* due to polarization. Then

$$r_4 = \frac{r_1 r_3}{r_2} - r_5. \tag{121.4}$$

On direct current the apparent resistance of the electrolyte, as measured by a Wheatstone bridge in the usual manner, is therefore larger than the true ohmic resistance by the amount r_5. r_5 is a variable and indeterminate quantity, since $\mathcal{E}'$ depends not only on the current density but on the length of time the current has been flowing, and the nature and condition of the electrodes.

In some special cases the counter emf. of polarization is negligible, and r_5 is zero or nearly zero. In such cases the Wheatstone bridge may be used in the usual manner to measure the ohmic resistance of the electrolyte. This is true in all cases where the electrodes are exactly alike and there are no deposits on them which temporarily change their character. Thus, for example, if the electrolyte is a solution of copper sulphate in water and the electrodes are copper, polarization is negligible if the current density is low. If, however, we replace the copper anode with a platinum anode there is a counter emf. of polarization. *In all cases, therefore, where polarization is present the passage of a direct current through the electrolytic cell makes it behave as a voltaic cell with reverse polarity to that of the impressed emf.* Hence, Ohm's law when applied to the electrolytic cell must be of the form

$$I = \frac{\mathcal{E} - \mathcal{E}'}{R},$$

as we have seen.

Because of polarization in the case of most electrolytes, a Wheatstone-bridge hookup using direct current cannot be used for accurate measurement of the resistivity (or conductivity) of an electrolyte.

Consequently alternating currents of comparatively high frequency must be used. Alternating-current bridges will be discussed in a later chapter.

122. The Silver Voltameter. — The silver voltameter is the laboratory instrument for realizing the ampere. Its usual form is indicated in Fig. 95. The electrolyte is held in a platinum crucible c, which is at the same time the cathode. The anode a is of pure silver suspended in the electrolyte. In the early type of silver voltameter the anode was enclosed in filter paper for the purpose of holding back the anode slime, but this was found to introduce impurities and so change the weight of the deposit. In 1899 Richards suspended a

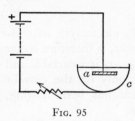

FIG. 95

porous porcelain cup under the anode, thus obviating the introduction of any organic matter into the electrolyte, and at the same time affording a more effective septum. This type of voltameter is known as the Richards porous-cup voltameter. The London Conference of 1908 adopted the following specific specifications for the standard silver voltameter.

"The electrolyte shall consist of a solution of from 15 to 20 parts by weight of silver nitrate in 100 parts of distilled water. The solution must be used only once, and only for so long that not more than 30% of the silver in the solution is deposited."

"The anode shall be of silver, and the cathode of platinum. The current density at the anode shall not exceed $\frac{1}{5}$ ampere per cm.^{2}, and at the cathode $\frac{1}{50}$ ampere per cm.^{2}."

"Not less than 100 cm.^{3} of the electrolyte shall be used in the voltameter."

"Care must be taken that no particles which may be mechanically detached from the anode shall reach the cathode."

"Before weighing, any trace of the solution adhering to the cathode must be removed, and the electrode dried."

"The electrolyte must be free from organic or other reducing substances." The silver nitrate must be highly pure. "The electrolyte when ready for use must be neutral or very slightly acid, as tested by iodeosin." "The cathode shall be a crucible or bowl, preferable of platinum (although gold may be used) of from 125 cm.^{3} to 400 cm.^{3} capacity." "The anode should be of pure silver and is preferably coated with electrolytic silver." "After thorough washing the cathode bowls are dried at about 150° C., preferably in an electric oven, and after cooling are weighed." "The emf. of the standard cell employed is calculated from the weight of silver deposited, and the resistance, and the time, using 0.00111810 gram per second as the electrochemical equivalent of silver." "If a septum between the anode and the cathode is used, it must not contaminate the electrolyte with organic or reducing impurities; it must not produce acid or alkali in the electrolyte, and it must be of sufficiently fine grain to hold back the anode slime without introducing any high resistance in the voltameter." These specifications will aid in the usual laboratory use of the silver voltameter. The silver voltameter is not now used in standardizing laboratories. See circular of the Bureau of Standards, No. 60, page 32 et seq.

If a voltameter is required which will give only approximately correct values, the copper voltameter is very satisfactory. This consists of copper electrodes in a specified solution of copper sulphate in water, the current density being such as to give a firm deposit on the cathode.

123. Standard Cells. — The London Conference of 1908 recommended the use of the Weston Normal Cell as the best method for the realization of the international volt. This Committee determined the emf. of the Weston Normal Cell to be 1.01830 international volts at 20° C. when constructed as specified. An ideal standard cell of any type should conform to the following conditions:

"It must be made up of chemicals which can be purified and reproduced with great exactness."

"No chemical or electrochemical reaction must take place inside the cell, except when a current passes through it."

"When the cell passes through a cycle of temperatures it must give the same emf. at any stated temperature whatever its past thermal history has been, subject to certain limitation of temperature."

"When current passes through the cell its emf. may vary slightly, but it must recover completely within a reasonable time."

No known cell satisfies these requirements completely, but the Clark and Weston cells do very nearly. Many different cells have been used as standards in the past, but the only survivors which fulfill the above requirements with sufficient fidelity to satisfy present-day demands are the Clark and Weston cells.

The Weston Normal Cell. — The Weston cadmium cell was first introduced by Edward Weston in 1892. It is now usually made after the H-shaped pattern designed by Lord Rayleigh, as shown in Fig. 96. In the original form the electrolyte was an unsaturated solution at most working temperatures. In 1908 this cell was made with an electrolyte which was a saturated solution, and it is now universally so made and known as the *Normal Cell*. Mercury is the positive electrode and cadmium amalgam (12.5% of Cd) is the negative electrode. Platinum wires are sealed in the glass to form the + and − poles of the cell. The electrolyte is a saturated solution of cadmium sulphate, with excess crystals to insure saturation at all working temperatures. Mercurous sulphate is the depolarizing agent.

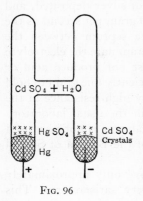

FIG. 96

The value of the emf. of this cell for different temperatures within its working range is given by the following equation:

$$\mathscr{E}_t = 1.01830 - 0.00004075(t - 20) - 0.000000944(t - 20)^2.$$

The emf. of the Weston Normal Cell at 20° C. is 1.0188 volts in terms of the cgsm. unit.

The Clark Cell. — The Clark cell was introduced by Latimer Clark in 1872, and it has undergone many modifications since. It is now usually made after the H-shaped pattern. Pure mercury is poured into one limb of the tube, which constitutes the positive electrode. The negative electrode in the other limb of the tube is an amalgam of zinc (10% of Zn). Above the pure mercury are crystals of mercurous sulphate. The electrolyte, filling the two arms of the tube, is a saturated solution of zinc sulphate, with excess crystals of zinc sulphate.

The emf. of the Clark cell at 15° C. is 1.4326 international volts, and in terms of the cgsm. unit it is 1.4333 volts. At any other temperature t between 10° C. and 25° C. its emf. is given by the equation

$$\mathscr{E}_t = 1.4326 - 0.00119(t - 15) - 0.000007(t - 15)^2.$$

For detailed specifications for the preparation of these cells, see British Association Report for 1905, or Bureau of Standards Bulletins.

The absolute practical units may be obtained from the international units by use of the ratios between the two systems of units given in Section 92.

124. The Primary Voltaic Cell. — The two cells described in the preceding Sections are primary cells of a special design for a special purpose. The primary cell had its origin in a chance observation by Galvani who observed the twitching of freshly skinned frog's legs, when, suspended by a copper wire from an iron balcony, they came into contact with the balcony. Galvani did not see the import of his chance observation, but Volta did, in part at least. Volta showed that the important thing was the junction of two dissimilar metals, forming a part of a closed circuit, with the frog's legs. Here we have the fundamental condition which must be fulfilled in all voltaic cells, *dissimilar metallic conductors in contact with an electrolyte*. In 1799 Volta constructed his voltaic pile, which consisted of discs of zinc, wet cloth, and discs of copper piled alternately one upon the other, as indicated in Fig. 97. What Volta had in reality was a large number of primary cells connected in series. The two dissimilar metals were zinc and copper (conductors of the first class), and the wet cloth was the electrolyte (conductor of the second class). Such a pile gives a comparatively high emf., but the internal resistance is also high. At this time the terms "galvanic electricity" and "voltaic electricity" came into use to distinguish between currents produced at low

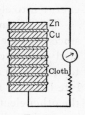

FIG. 97

potential, as from a voltaic pile, and currents or discharges of electricity produced at high potential, as from an electrostatic machine. Later these terms came to have a different meaning in popular usage.

Volta took the next step in the evolution of primary cells when he assembled his "crown of cups," which consisted of a series of cups containing salt water in which stood Zn and Cu plates, the Zn of one cup being connected to the Cu of the next cup. This was simply a number of primary cells connected in series, constituting a battery, and differed from the voltaic pile only in that a free electrolyte in the form of a solution took the place of the wet cloth. From 1800 to about 1879 many combinations of dissimilar metals and electrolytes were investigated, and the phenomenon of polarization was encountered and studied. Of the very large possible number of voltaic cells that may be assembled only two have sufficient merit to possess commercial value, the gravity cell and the so-called dry cell.

125. Fundamental Theory of the Voltaic Cell. — A *primary cell* may be defined as a device for the transformation of chemical energy into electric energy. When the constituents of a *primary* cell are used up they must be replaced with new materials. A *secondary* or *storage* cell is a voltaic cell of such nature that the cell is restored to its working condition by charging, i.e., by sending a current through it in the reverse direction. When acting as a voltaic cell, there is no fundamental difference between it and a primary cell; both types of cells are voltaic cells. In fact, some so-called primary cells, as for example the gravity cell, can be partially restored by sending a current through the cell in the reverse direction. The reverse current simply reverses the chemical action within the cell. A secondary or storage cell may be defined as a reversible device for the transformation of chemical energy into electric energy, although the reversibility is not perfect.

The origin of the emf. of a voltaic cell has been a moot subject since the first voltaic cells were investigated by Volta. Volta discovered that two dissimilar metals, when clean and making good contact, develop a difference of potential even though there is no electrolyte between them. One metal is then said to be electro-positive and the other electro-negative. The chemical elements have been arranged in a series (the electro-chemical series) such that any member of the series is electro-positive to all following elements, and electro-negative to all preceding elements. The farther two elements are separated in this series the greater is the contact difference of potential between them, and this seems to be true also when the two metals are used as electrodes in a voltaic cell. Thus, for a long time the origin of the emf. of a voltaic cell was tied up with Volta's contact potential theory, and, in fact, a quite satisfactory explanation of the behavior of a voltaic cell can be formulated along this line of reasoning, although the magnitudes of the emfs. are too small, and there is no necessity for any chemical action, and hence no accounting for the energy relations involved. Present-day theory, however, views the problem as one which is intimately associated with that of solutions. A number of investigators have worked along the line of the solution theory, including Van't Hoff, Ostwald, Arrhenius, and Nernst, but the theory now accepted seems to be accredited to Nernst.

The *solution theory* involves the solution of atoms, molecules, and ions in a liquid. We have here to do primarily with a solution of ions in water. When ions are dissolved in water, forming a dilute solution, it is found that the dissolved ions behave as a gas quite independently of the solvent, thus exerting a pressure called *osmotic* or *diffusion pressure*, which is proportional to the absolute temperature and to the number of dissolved ions per unit volume. In fact, Avogadro's law for gases apparently holds also for dissolved ions.

According to Nernst, when a metal is immersed in an electrolyte the metal tends to go into solution, i.e., positively charged metal ions leave the metal and go into solution in the electrolyte. The metal ion bears a positive charge because all metals tend to gain dynamic stability by losing one or more electrons, even though by so doing they sacrifice *electric neutrality*. The tendency of the metal to go into solution creates a pressure, which, according to Nernst, can be measured, and which Nernst called the *electrolytic solution pressure*. If ions of the metal are already in solution, one of three things will happen: (1) If the electrolytic solution pressure P is greater than the *diffusion pressure p* of the ions already in solution, which tends to condense ions on the metal, more ions will go into solution. (2) If P equals p, no action takes place. (3) If the diffusion pressure p predominates, there will be a deposit of positively charged metal ions on the metal. In

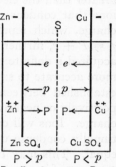

FIG. 98

the first case, where $P > p$, metallic ions will go into solution, thus creating a negative charge on the metal. If the metal electrode is insulated so that the electrons cannot escape, a negative charge builds up which tends to attract positive ions which are in solution. We may call this attractive force per unit area an *electric pressure e*. Thus, when $P = p + e$ the action ceases. In the third case, where $P < p$, metallic ions will be deposited on the metal, thus giving to it a positive charge. If the metal electrode is insulated, a positive charge builds up which will repel the approach of positively charged ions which are in solution, thus creating an *electric pressure e*. Then, when $p = P + e$ the action ceases. As long as the electrolyte contains no like metal ions in solution p is zero.

A concrete example will serve to elucidate the theory. Let a Zn electrode be partly immersed in a dilute solution of zinc sulphate or even pure water, Fig. 98.   Let a Cu electrode be immersed in a strong solution of copper sulphate.   Separating the two compartments of the jar is an unglazed porcelain septum S.   The Zn electrode is an example of the first case cited above.   Solution immediately begins, Zn^{++} ions leave the electrode, two electrons from each atom of Zn remaining behind, thus imparting to the Zn electrode a negative charge.   This will continue until $P = p + e$, when no further solution takes place.   The Zn electrode has acquired a definite potential relative to the solution.

In the case of the Cu electrode in the copper sulphate solution, we have an example of the third case cited above.   The diffusion pressure, which causes Cu^{++} ions to condense on the Cu electrode, is greater than the electrolytic solution pressure of copper.   The Cu^{++} ions that condense on the copper electrode impart to it a positive charge, which repels the positive copper ions in solution.   When $p = P + e$, further deposit of ions ceases and the Cu electrode has acquired a definite potential relative to the solution.   It is probably more accurate to say, in any case, that a condition of equilibrium is established between the electrode and the solution when either a positively or negatively charged electrode has attained its maximum charge.   Ions will continually leave the electrode and ions will continually condense upon it, but in any interval of time t the two are equal.   This may be likened to the evaporation of a liquid in the presence of its saturated vapor.

When equilibrium obtains with respect to each electrode, there is a definite difference of potential between the Zn and Cu electrodes, which is the emf. of the cell.   Now let the exposed terminals of the electrodes be connected through a suitable resistance.   Electrons will immediately begin to migrate in the external circuit from the Zn electrode toward the Cu electrode, thus developing a current of electricity, and concomitantly disturbing the equilibrium of each electrode.   The Zn electrode will lose negative charge, thus permitting more Zn^{++} ions to go into solution.   The Cu electrode will lose positive charge, since electrons will combine with Cu^{++} ions, thus neutralizing them.   This permits further deposition of Cu^{++} ions on the Cu electrode.   Thus, we have a voltaic cell in action. This cell is the original Daniell cell, or the gravity cell of today.   The net result is that neutral Zn atoms continually go into solution at the Zn electrode as zinc ions Zn^{++}, thus continually renewing the negative charge on the Zn electrode as electrons continually leave this electrode and move toward the positive Cu electrode in the external circuit. At the Cu electrode copper ions Cu^{++} are constantly being neutralized and deposited as neutral copper atoms on the electrode, thus permitting the continual deposition of copper ions Cu^{++} from the solution. Chemical energy has been liberated within the cell which appears as electric energy in the external circuit.

The chemical action is as follows: The unglazed porcelain septum permits the ions in solution to pass freely. $CuSO_4$ breaks up into Cu^{++} and SO_4^{--}. The SO_4^{--} ions, which are in solution, combine with Zn^{++} ions, which are also in solution, forming $ZnSO_4$, and Cu^{++} ions being continually deposited on the Cu electrode becoming neutral copper atoms.

The emf. of a voltaic cell depends for the most part on the nature of its electrodes. The nature of the electrolyte affects the emf. to some extent, as does also the concentration of the ions in solution. The emf. is affected slightly by temperature changes. The size of the electrodes and of the cell have no effect on the emf. However, the current that can be delivered by a cell depends very largely on the area of the electrodes exposed to the electrolyte, and on the cross section of the electrolyte that is available for the migration of ions. The potentials of electrodes to electrolytes have been measured in most cases, and can be found in tables of chemical and physical constants.

126. The Concentration Cell. — Concurrent with the solution theory is the possibility of developing an emf. by solution alone, as was first pointed out by Helmholtz in 1878. In this case, the energy is derived from the diffusion between two solutions of different concentrations. The equilibrium condition between an electrode and an electrolyte depends on the diffusion pressure, which is a function of the concentration. Thus, the difference of potential between electrode and electrolyte depends in part on the concentration of the electrolyte. Hence, if a cell can be arranged so that two electrodes of the same metal are in an electrolyte, such that the concentration changes in passing from one electrode to the other, a difference of potential between the electrodes is effected, and we have a kind of voltaic cell in which no chemical action takes place, which is called a *concentration cell*. The emf. is always small, however.

A concentration cell can be made by placing a Zn electrode, No. 1, in a dilute solution of zinc sulphate, and another Zn electrode, No. 2, in a concentrated solution of zinc sulphate, the two solutions being kept separated by a septum S of unglazed porcelain, Fig. 99. The Zn electrode in the concentrated solution will tend to go into solution, thus developing a negative charge on the electrode. The same action will take place at the other electrode, but the diffusion pressure is less in the dilute solution than in the concentrated solution, and, therefore, the electrode in the dilute solution acquires a larger negative charge than the electrode in the concentrated solution. Thus, we

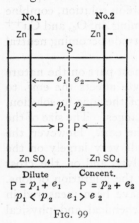

have two electrodes at different negative potentials, the one in the dilute solution being the more negative. Therefore, if the two electrodes are connected externally through a resistance a flow of electrons sets in from electrode No. 1 to electrode No. 2. Because of the current, electrode No. 1 becomes less negative, and so more Zn^{++} ions go into solution. Electrode No. 2 becomes more negative, thus attracting more zinc ions Zn^{++} to it. The net result is that the dilute solution becomes more concentrated, and the concentrated solution becomes less concentrated. This process will continue, with ever decreasing difference of potential between the electrodes, until the concentrations of the two solutions are equalized, and the emf. of the cell sinks to zero. Electrode No. 1 has lost mass and electrode No. 2 has gained mass. The energy appearing in the external circuit has come, for the most part, from the heat of dilution of the zinc in solution, since the net result has been a decrease in concentration of the entire solution. This is not the whole story, however, except in some special cases. In general, the complete energy relations cannot be expressed without recourse to the laws of thermodynamics, which would carry us beyond the purview of this book.

127. Thermo-Chemical Changes and emf.

— If we assume that the chemical action within the cell is the sole source of energy, it is possible to calculate the emf. of a cell by equating the electric energy of the current to the thermal energy of chemical reaction. When one gram equivalent of an ion is formed or broken up in a voltaic cell,

$Q = 96,494$ coulombs of electricity must have passed through the cell, and, if the emf. of the cell is $\mathscr{E}$ absolute practical volts, $Q\mathscr{E}10^7$ ergs of energy are transformed. Assuming that all of the heat of reaction, H calories, is converted into electric energy, we have

$$Q\mathscr{E}10^7 = JH. \text{ Hence, } \mathscr{E} = \frac{4.186\,H}{Q} \text{ volts.}$$

Let us apply this equation to the Daniell cell, in which there are two chemical reactions. At the Zn electrode $ZnSO_4$ is formed with a forward emf. It is found that 1 gm. of Zn develops 1,670 calories of heat in forming $ZnSO_4$. The atomic weight of Zn is 65.37, and its valence is 2. Hence,

$H = 1,670 \times 32.685$ calories per gm. equiv., and $\mathscr{E} = 2.368$ volts.

1 gm. of Cu develops 909.5 calories of heat in forming $CuSO_4$. The atomic weight of Cu is 63.57, and its valence is 2. Hence,

$H = 909.5 \times 31.785$ calories per gm. equiv., and $\mathscr{E} = 1.283$ volts.

The net emf. of the cell is therefore, $2.368 - 1.283 = 1.085$ volts, which is a close value. That so close a value is obtained in this case is owing to the fact that the temperature coefficient of the Daniell cell is negligibly small.

If the temperature of a cell changes with development of current heat is either evolved or absorbed, and this energy change must be taken into account. By the application of thermodynamic methods Helmholtz derived an equation which takes account of the energy involved in temperature changes. *In all calculations involving voltaic cells it must be remembered that Faraday's laws hold in the same form as for electrolytic cells.*

128. Secondary or Storage Cells. — Let us arrange a circuit as in Fig. 93, using lead electrodes instead of platinum. On passing current through such an electrolytic cell, oxygen is liberated at the anode which oxidizes the surface of the lead electrode forming lead oxide, PbO_2. The hydrogen gas liberated at the cathode escapes. After current is passed through the cell for a time it is found that, on disconnecting the battery, the electrolytic cell itself behaves as a voltaic cell, and that the current it supplies passes through the cell in the reverse direction from that of the former current. This voltaic cell has a much longer life, and will furnish a much stronger current, than when platinum electrodes are used in the same manner, and this is because the products of electrolysis are retained in part. When the discharge takes place the PbO_2 is reduced to PbO by the H evolved, which in turn reacts with H_2SO_4 forming $PbSO_4$. If the charging and discharging is repeated many times, it is found that the capacity of the cell to supply current increases. As this process is repeated many times a deep layer of soft lead forms on one electrode, called spongy lead, and a deep layer of lead oxide forms on the other electrode. This process is called *forming* the plates, and is the method which was originally used by Gaston Planté in 1859. On charging, electric energy is stored as chemical energy, and on discharge, the stored chemical energy is transformed into electric energy. On discharge, SO_4^{--} ions migrate to the negative lead electrode, there delivering negative charge, and then entering into chemical union to form lead sulphide, $PbSO_4$. At the positive, lead-dioxide electrode, H^+ ions reduce PbO_2 to PbO, forming H_2O, thereby diluting the sulphuric acid solution. The PbO, in turn, combines with H_2SO_4 forming $PbSO_4$ and H_2O. Thus, $PbSO_4$ forms on both plates, and therefore this reaction is called the *double sulphate* theory, which, however, is not universally accepted, though having the preponderance of support. On charge the chemical actions are all reversed. Since sulphuric acid is decomposed and water is formed on discharge the specific gravity of the electrolyte decreases. Thus the stage of discharge of a lead storage cell can be determined by a specific gravity test. When fully charged the specific gravity of the electrolyte should be about 1.28. On discharge the specific gravity should not be permitted to sink below about 1.15. If the discharge is carried much beyond this point an insoluble form of lead sulphate forms on the electrodes which cannot be decomposed on charging. This reduces the available active material of the electrodes, and hence the capacity of the cell, and, also, raises the internal resistance. When in this condition the cell is said to be *sulphated*. Prolonged idleness will, also, cause sulphation. The emf. of this cell when fully charged is about 2.1 volts, and on discharge the voltage should not be permitted to drop below 1.75 volts. If precaution is exercised in the use of a lead storage cell it will last until mechanical wear and tear dislodges its active material. The internal resistance is made small by making the plates of large area, and separating them by thin, porous separators. At points where the plates are brought close together the current density is high, resulting in rapid eroding at these points. Thus buckling of the plates must be prevented so far as possible. In too rapid charging and discharging the rapid evolution of gases and undue heating of the cell causes loosening of the active material of the plates and buckling which causes local, severe erosion, thus bringing about rapid destruction of the cell.

The capacity of a storage cell is given in ampere-hours, which is the product of amperes times hours the cell will develop on discharge. If a fully charged cell is discharged at constant current, and the discharge occupies 10 hours, it is said to be discharged at the 10 hour rate; if discharged in 8 hours, it is discharged at the 8 hour rate; if discharged in 5 hours, it is discharged at the 5 hour rate, etc. The voltage at which a cell is said to be discharged varies slightly with the rate of discharge, and is furnished by the manufacturer. The capacity is also given in terms of the discharge rate. The lowest, safe voltage limit is usually less with high discharge rate than with low, varying from 1.83 volts for a 10 hour rate to 1.75 volts for a 1 hour rate. The ampere-hour capacity decreases as the discharge rate increases. The figures are roughly as follows, taking the capacity at the 9 hour rate as 100:

Discharge rate	9 hours	6 hours	3 hours	1 hour
Capacity	100	90	73	50

The efficiency of a secondary cell is defined as the ampere-hour efficiency, which is the ratio between the ampere-hours obtained on discharge and the ampere-hours required on charge, or the watt-hour efficiency, which is the ratio between the watt-hours obtained on discharge, and the watt-hours required on charge. The efficiency varies, depending upon the rate of charging and discharging, and also upon previous history. Losses are due to (1) internal resistance, which is small. (2) Polarization, which is also small. (3) A lower emf. on discharge than on charge, due to changes in acid concentration in the pores of the active material. (4) Gassing at the end of the discharge, which is relatively unimportant. The first three of these cause the difference of potential to be higher on charge than on discharge, which is the chief cause of lowered efficiency. The efficiency of a lead cell when properly handled is from 75% to 85%.

The original Planté method of *forming plates* is no longer in use. In order to produce a cheaper plate and in less time Camille Faure prepared red lead (Pb_3O_4) chemically, and, in the form of a paste, pressed it into a lead grid. For the other plate, litharge or lead monoxide (PbO) was prepared, and, in the form of a paste, fixed in a lead grid by pressure. The grid serves merely as a mechanical support. The plates so made are allowed to dry and harden. When sufficiently seasoned, they are assembled in an electrolyte of dilute H_2SO_4, the Pb_3O_4 plate is made the anode and the PbO plate is made the cathode, and a current is passed through it for a considerable time. The Pb_3O_4 is reduced to PbO_2 and PbO is reduced to spongy lead. There are other methods of preparing plates, but in all present-day methods of manufacturing plates most of the work of formation is done chemically.

The *iron-nickel* or *Edison cell* is the only other secondary cell having a commercial value. In this cell, in the charged condition, the positive electrode has oxide of nickel or nickel hydroxide as the active material, and the negative plate has iron as the active material. The electrolyte is potassium hydroxide (KOH) in water. It is not fully established whether the active material on the positive plate is NiO_2 or $Ni(OH)_4$. Assuming that $Ni(OH)_4$ is the active material, we have the following reactions: On discharge the OH^- ions of the KOH go to the negative plate, and the iron is oxidized. The K^+ ions go to the positive plate, and reduce $Ni(OH)_4$ to $Ni(OH)_2$. On charge the action is reversed. The reaction of the cell may be expressed by the following chemical equation

$$Ni(OH)_4 + KOH + Fe \rightleftarrows Ni(OH)_2 + KOH + Fe(OH)_2.$$

It will be seen that the electrolyte remains unchanged and essentially of constant specific gravity. It acts merely as a vehicle for the transfer of the OH^- ions from one plate to the other. Since the specific gravity of the electrolyte does not change materially hydrometer tests are of no avail in determining the extent of discharge. A voltage test must therefore be used. The electrolyte consists of a 21% solution of KOH, to which is added about 50 gms. per liter of lithium hydroxide. The action of LiOH is not understood, but its presence materially increases the capacity of the cell.

All of the metal parts of the Edison cell are sheet steel, nickel plated. The positive electrode consists of tubes held in a nickelled steel frame. The tubes are made of very finely perforated nickelled steel strips, spirally wound, and reinforced with steel rings. The tubes are filled with active material, $Ni(OH)_4$. Since $Ni(OH)_4$ is a poor conductor, thin layers of flaked nickel are inserted at intervals, and then highly compressed. The negative plate is made of finely perforated nickelled steel strips, impregnated with specially prepared iron oxide.

The emf. of the Edison cell when fully charged is about 1.4 volts. The emf. drops gradually on discharge, and the discharge is complete, at the 5 hour rate, when the emf. of the cell drops to 1 volt. The efficiency at the 5 hour rate of discharge is from 75% to 80%. The internal resistance is higher than that of the Planté cell, since the electrolyte is a poorer conductor. The variation of capacity with rate of discharge is small, and therefore the number of ampere hours taken from a cell may be used as a measure of the stage of discharge. The cell is very robust mechanically and electrically. It may be left uncharged, short circuited, and charged at a high rate with impunity.

129. Depolarization. — Polarization in a voltaic cell is brought about by deposition of some of the products of electrolysis on the electrodes, these products being of such a nature as to create a reverse emf. within the cell. These products are usually gases, and they collect more frequently on the positive than on the negative electrode. Gas on an electrode raises the ohmic resistance, and changes the character of the electrode. *Polarization causes a temporary drop in the p.d. of a cell due to its own action.* This limits the usefulness of a cell, and therefore efforts have been made to counteract or lessen it. This is called *depolarization.* There are three chief methods of depolarization that have been tried: (1) Mechanical depolarization. (2) Depolarization by substitution. (3) Depolarization by oxidation.

Two mechanical depolarization methods have been tried: (*a*) As in the Smee cell, which consists of platinum and zinc electrodes immersed in a solution of sulphuric acid. The positive, platinum electrode, instead of being bright and polished, is platinized. A platinized electrode is one which has received a deposit of electrolytic platinum upon it, thereby finely roughening its surface to which hydrogen gas does not readily adhere, and so it more easily escapes. The Smee cell is simple in construction but its emf. is small, being only about 0.5 volt. (*b*) Another method that has been tried is to give a motion to the positive electrode so as to alternately bring portions of it into the air, and then reimmerse it. This method is not feasible for commercial cells.

Depolarization by substitution is illustrated by the Daniell cell. In this case, a harmless ion is substituted for the hydrogen ion. The zinc electrode is immersed in a sulphuric acid solution in one compartment of the cell. The copper electrode in the other compartment is immersed in a concentrated solution of $CuSO_4$, with excess crystals to insure saturation. The two compartments are separated by a porous septum S, which permits free passage of ions, Fig. 100. The action is as follows: When the circuit is closed, SO_4^{--} ions pass to

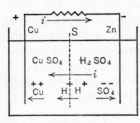

FIG. 100

the Zn electrode, there forming $ZnSO_4$, which passes into solution. The H^+ ions pass through the porous septum and react with $CuSO_4$, forming H_2SO_4 and liberating Cu which is deposited on the Cu electrode. As copper is deposited on copper no polarization will occur, unless the current density is high. The gravity cell is a Daniell cell in which the porous septum is absent, the solutions being kept separated by gravity and the action of the cell. This cell should be kept on closed circuit at low current density.

Depolarization by oxidation depends on placing in the electrolyte some oxidizing agent which will combine chemically with the liberated hydrogen gas, and thus render it innocuous. The oxidizing agent may be in the solid, liquid, or gaseous state. As an example, let us consider the Leclanché cell, or the modified Leclanché cell, called a dry cell. The depolarizer in this case is usually manganese dioxide, MnO_2. The positive, carbon electrode is surrounded by manganese dioxide. The electrolyte is a solution of ammonium chloride, NH_4Cl, and the negative electrode is zinc. The emf. is about 1.5 volts, but on closed circuit the terminal potential difference falls, the amount of drop depending on the current density. The oxidizing action is slow, and, besides, manganese is practically a nonconductor. To render it conducting it must be mixed with a considerable amount of finely granulated carbon or graphite in the form of a paste. The hydrogen gas is slow in coming into contact with the manganese dioxide, and consequently this is not a very effective depolarizer. Owing to the inefficient depolarization, this cell can be used only on open-circuit work. Liquid depolarizers have the advantage that a gas, in general, acts more quickly than with a solid at ordinary temperatures. As an example of a liquid depolarizer, let us consider the dichromate cell. The depolarizer is potassium dichromate, $K_2Cr_2O_7$, or chromic acid dissolved in the electrolyte, which is a solution of H_2SO_4 in water. The positive electrode is carbon and the negative is zinc. Gaseous depolarizers have not been successful. The most recent cell of this type is the Féry cell.

130. Local Action. — When ordinary commercial zinc is used as an electrode with an acid electrolyte it is found to dissolve rapidly even though no current passes through the cell. Pure zinc dissolves very slowly when no current passes through the cell, but pure zinc is too costly to use in this manner. This solvent action serves no useful purpose, and consequently efforts have been made to remedy it. The cause of this solvent action when no current passes, called *local action*, is to be found in the impurities in commercial zinc. Lead is one of the most common impurities. Thus we have within the zinc itself innumerable tiny voltaic cells. Each granule of lead forms with a neighboring granule of zinc a tiny cell, since the acid electrolyte penetrates the zinc to some extent to serve as an electrolyte.

The remedy usually adopted to cure this malady is amalgamation. This is accomplished by bringing mercury into contact with the surface of the zinc electrode in dilute acid, and rubbing so as to cover the surface of the zinc with a thin film of mercury. The film of mercury protects the zinc from electrolytic action, but the zinc is not rendered indefinitely immune, and so amalgamation must be repeated from time to time. The protective action of mercury has not been satisfactorily explained. It might be expected that mercury and zinc would form local cells, and that therefore local electrolytic action would be even greater. The mercury film apparently serves to keep the electrolyte from penetrating the zinc, and also acts as a solvent permitting the zinc to more readily pass into solution in the electrolyte.

131. Stray Electric Currents. — With the extensive use of electricity in cities the currents cannot always be confined to definite channels, and consequently leaks are inevitable. Such leaks are called *stray currents*. Many times these stray currents effect electrolysis with damaging results. Where water mains are laid in the ground along street car lines stray currents are quite apt to return in part by way of the iron water pipes. The current may enter the water pipe at a distant point and leave at a point near the power plant. At a point where the current leaves the metal (anode) and enters the soil corrosion takes place. The pipe is pitted and holes may be eaten through it, or it may be so weakened as to rupture under pressure. Also, at joints stray currents may flow into the soil and back to the pipe in order to get around a point of high resistance. Wherever this occurs the pipe is corroded at points where the current leaves the metal to enter the soil, which serves as an electrolyte.

In some cases where iron pipes are laid in cinders, pieces of coke may come in contact with or lie close to the metal. Since the soil water holds acids and salts in solution, we have here the conditions for electrolysis. Currents will flow from the pipe (anode) through the soil water (electrolyte) to the coke (cathode) and back to the pipe. Any other foreign, dissimilar conductor of the first class will act in a similar manner. This voltaic action effects corrosion of the pipe. The emf. between coke and iron when embedded in soil water is about 0.6 volt. Furthermore, if there are impurities in the pipe itself adjacent points on the surface may develop voltaic action with consequent corrosion. Action of this kind is local action such as occurs in a zinc electrode, but in this case it is called *self corrosion*. It is not easy to distinguish between self corrosion and corrosion that is brought about by stray currents, consequently this has given rise to much litigation. In reinforced concrete buildings the iron reinforcement may serve as a conductor of stray currents with consequent corrosion. Corrosion in this case is less apt to occur where alternating currents are used. Corrosion of this type when sufficiently extended may result in weakening a concrete structure to the extent that collapse may ensue.

132. Electrolytic Rectifiers. — If certain metals are used as electrodes in an electrolytic cell it is found that the current is practically blocked for one direction of flow but passes freely in the reverse direction, as was mentioned in Section 54. Take, for example, the aluminum rectifier. In this rectifier aluminum is one electrode and the other is either lead or iron, in a solution of ammonium phosphate. The current passes readily when the aluminum is the cathode, but when made the anode, the cell is practically nonconducting. Aluminum acts like a valve which permits the current to flow in but one direction. A group of four such cells may be connected as shown in Fig. 101 to form an electrolytic rectifier, where a and l denote aluminum and lead respectively. The rectifier is shown receiving a.c. and delivering d.c., as in charging a storage battery. As arranged, both alternations of the supply are rectified, as will be seen by tracing the currents, remembering that the current passes only when aluminum is the cathode. The variable resistance R is used at starting in order to prevent excessive current. The rectifying action seems to depend on the formation of a thin, nonconducting layer of oxide on the aluminum plate, and this takes a little time to form. After the layer of oxide has formed R is reduced to zero. A rectifier of four cells, as shown, can be used on 120 volt circuits. If higher voltages are to be used a number of cells in series are placed in each position, the number depending on the voltage. Electrolytic rectifiers range in efficiency from 30% to 40%. The cell heats readily and heating lowers the efficiency. For this reason it is necessary to make the cells rather large. With aluminum rectifiers the electrolyte may be a solution of ammonium and alkali salts or acids, such as the tartrates, borates, phosphates, oxalates, citrates, and carbonates. The anodes are usually either lead, iron, or carbon. The electrolytes most commonly used are solutions of sodium acid tartrate, ammonium phosphate, and common borax. A high degree of rectification is obtained only by using high current density at the aluminum electrode.

A number of metals possess an electrolytic valve action, such as is shown by

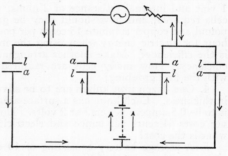

Fig. 101

aluminum. Among these are aluminum, tungsten, tantalum, bismuth, and magnesium. Of these aluminum and tantalum are the most effective, and hence the only ones that have been used to any extent. The tantalum rectifier will deliver a larger current than the aluminum rectifier. The electrolyte in the tantalum rectifier is a solution of potassium carbonate or sulphuric acid. The sulphuric acid electrolyte is preferable because of its low resistivity. Tantalum rectifiers now on the market usually consist of strips of tantalum with a lead or lead oxide electrode in a solution of sulphuric acid of about the same specific gravity as is used in the lead storage cell. The rectifying property obtains almost immediately on the application of an a.c. potential.

For further information on electrolytic rectifiers the reader is referred to "Theory and Performance of Rectifiers," Tech. Paper, B.S., No. 265; "A.C. Rectification" by L. B. W. Jolley; "The Copper Oxide Type of Rectifier" by Grondahl and Geiger, Jour. Am. Inst. of E.E., p. 215, March 1927.

For practical application of electrolysis the reader is referred to "Applied Electrochemistry" by M. de Kay Thompson.

PROBLEMS

1. Calculate, making use of the electrochemical equivalent of silver, the electrochemical equivalents of aluminum, cadmium, gold (valence 3), and lead (valence 2).

2. A gravity cell supplies a current of 0.25 ampere for a period of two hours. How much zinc is consumed, and how much copper is deposited? How much copper sulphate is decomposed? How much zinc sulphate is formed? If the emf. of the cell is 1 volt, and its internal resistance is 2 ohm, what is the efficiency?

3. If 10 incandescent lamps taking 0.5 ampere each at 30 volts, connected in parallel, are to be lighted by gravity cells, each cell having an emf. of 1 volt and internal resistance of 2 ohms, what is the minimum number of cells required, and how should they be grouped? If zinc is 20 cents per pound and copper sulphate 15 cents per pound, what is the cost per kilowatt hour for electric energy when using the minimum number of cells? What is the efficiency? Make another arrangement or grouping having a higher efficiency. How many cells are required? How does the cost compare with the first grouping?

4. One dozen iron knives are to be silver plated with a deposit 0.1 mm. in thickness. Each knife has a surface area of 96 cm.² The current density is to be 0.5 ampere per cm.² at 2 volts. How long a time is required? If silver costs 64 cents per ounce and electricity cost 5 cents per kilowatt hour, what is the cost?

5. A storage battery consisting of 10 cells connected in series is being charged with a current of 10 amperes through an external resistance of 2 ohms. If the counter potential difference of each cell is 2.2 volts, what is the applied voltage? If the internal resistance of each cell is 0.01 ohm, how much of the potential drop is due to ohmic resistance? If 100 ampere-hours are put into each cell, what is the cost of charging at the rate of 5 cents per kilowatt hour?

6. Two electrolytic resistors of 6 and 12 ohms respectively are connected in parallel, and a battery of storage cells of emf. 20.7 volts and internal resistance of 3 ohms sends a current through them. If the counter emf. of polarization is 1.7 volts each, what is the current through each resistor? If the electrolyte is a solution of sulphuric acid in each resistor, how much water is decomposed? What is the difference of potential across the storage battery?

7. The temperature coefficient of the lead storage cell is 0.0004 volt per °C. How much heat does the cell absorb per hour of discharge at 27 °C.?

8. A stray current of 5 amperes leaves an iron pipe for moist earth. How long will it take to remove a pound of iron?

9. Twenty gravity cells, each having an emf. of 1.08 volts and an internal resistance of 2 ohms, are connected in series to a 50 ohm resistance. What is the current in the coil? What is the efficiency?

If these twenty cells are connected in parallel through a 50 ohm resistance, what is the current in the resistance? What is the efficiency?

10. With data as in Problem 9, calculate the amount of zinc consumed per hour in the case of series connection and in the case of parallel connection. Also calculate the amount of copper sulphate that has been decomposed, and the total increase in weight of the copper electrodes.

CHAPTER IX

THERMOELECTRIC EFFECTS

133. Contact Potential. — As was stated in the chapter on electrolysis (Section 125), Volta discovered that when two metals are brought into contact one becomes positive relative to the other. Volta sought to explain the emf. of a voltaic cell on the basis of this observation, and thereby started a protracted discussion as to the exact nature of a contact potential. The contact potentials investigated by Volta may range in magnitude from less than a tenth of a volt to about one volt. It has been contended that if such large differences of potential actually exist as intrinsic potentials, reversible heating effects of comparatively marked magnitudes would accompany the passage of a current of electricity across the junction of two metals. On the contrary, experiments reveal only the very small heating due to the Peltier emf., which is small in comparison with the measured contact potentials. The contact potential for copper and zinc is about 0.7 volt, whereas the Peltier emf. is of the order of 0.0007 volt. Thus, following this line of reasoning, one might argue that the Peltier emf. is the only intrinsic contact potential, and that other concomitant effects contribute to the comparatively large contact potentials.

Contact potentials have been quite generally regarded in the past as being due, in a large measure, to the presence of oxygen from the air which develops a slight chemical action over the surface of contact, and so sets up an emf. in a manner similar to that of a voltaic cell. If this is the cause of contact potential it should decrease or disappear when contact is made in a vacuum. However, vacuum conditions have failed to show the anticipated results, and the failure has been attributed to the difficulty of eradicating occluded oxygen.

At present, due chiefly to investigations by O. W. Richardson and Debye (1901), there is a tendency to view the Volta potential as an intrinsic property of metals, closely related to the emission of electrons from metals. Richardson's statement on this point is "that the balance of evidence is now strongly in favor of the view that the Volta contact emf. is an intrinsic property of pure metals, and not, as is perhaps more widely believed, an accidental development caused by traces of chemical action."[1] He states further, however, that there can be no doubt but "that the actual measured values of the contact emf. is very sensitive to actions of a chemical nature." In the same discussion, Richardson has developed a theoretical equation relating the contact difference of potential to thermionic and photoelectric emission.

At the junction between metals in contact there is another potential, called the *Peltier potential* after the man who discovered it, Jean Athanas Peltier (1834). There is also a difference of potential along a conductor, except in the case of lead, if a temperature gradient exists. This is named, after its discoverer, the *Thomson effect*. At the surface of a metal there is a potential barrier which prevents the conduction electrons from escaping under ordinary conditions. The amount of work required to remove an electron from a metal is called the *work function*, or, as has been suggested, *potential function* might be a better term. All of these potentials depend on the substance, and in most cases on the temperature, although the work function is but slightly affected by the temperature.

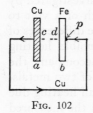

FIG. 102

In order to obtain a relationship between these several potentials, let us consider the arrangement shown in Fig. 102, the whole circuit being in a vacuum. Let a Cu plate a be connected by a Cu wire of negligible resistance to an Fe plate b as shown. Let ϕ_a and ϕ_b be the work functions at the points c and d. The only contact between dissimilar metals is at p. Let the Peltier potential at p be π. Let $\mathcal{E}$ be the contact difference of potential, if any, between the inside faces c and d of the plates. If a unit positive charge is carried around the circuit indicated, the net work must be zero, if we disregard ri^2t losses. ϕ_a and ϕ_b are the work functions per electron, and therefore the work functions per unit charge are

$$\phi_1 = \frac{\phi_a}{e} \quad \text{and} \quad \phi_2 = \frac{\phi_b}{e}.$$

where e is the electronic charge. Since potential difference $\mathcal{E}$ is measured in terms of work, we will have for the complete circuit

$$-\mathcal{E} + \frac{\phi_a}{e} - \frac{\phi_b}{e} - \pi = 0. \tag{133.1}$$

[1] Richardson, Phil. Mag. 23, 261, 1912.

π is always very small, of the order of 0.1 to 1 millivolts, whereas $\mathcal{E}$ is always a few tenths of a volt. Therefore, with negligible error, we have

$$\mathcal{E} = \frac{\phi_a}{e} - \frac{\phi_b}{e} = \phi_1 - \phi_2 \text{ ergs/unit charge.} \qquad (133.2)$$

Thus, the contact difference of potential between two metals is approximately equal to the difference between their work functions. The work function will be considered in the next chapter.[1]

134. The Peltier Effect. — That a difference of potential π exists at a junction point between two dissimilar metals, as at p Fig. 102, was first shown by Peltier. This he did as follows: If a current of electricity from an independent source, as from a battery, is caused to flow across the junction of two dissimilar metals, the junction is heated if the current flows in one direction, cooled if it flows in the reverse direction. Here is a reversible heat effect, quite unlike the Joule heat effect which is irreversible. With a copper-antimony junction Peltier found that there was a rise in temperature of the junction of 10° C. when the current flowed from antimony to copper,

FIG. 103

and a drop in temperature of 5° C. when the current flowed in the reverse direction. Greater changes in temperature were observed with a bismuth-antimony junction. Lenz succeeded in freezing water and lowering the temperature of the ice to $-4.5°$ C.

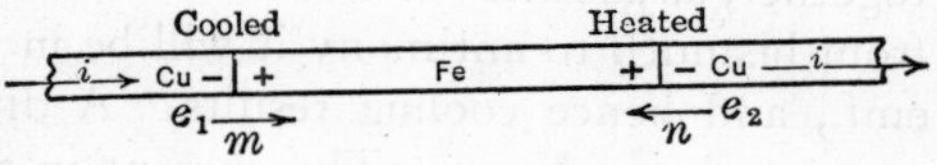

Consider a part of a copper-iron circuit as shown in Fig. 103. A current i (conventional) is caused to flow in the circuit, in the direction indicated by the arrows, by an independent source of emf., as from a battery. At the junction m the current is flowing in the same sense as the Peltier emf. $\mathcal{E}_1$, and hence cooling takes place. This is the same as when a current flows in the normal direction through a battery, in which case the chemical energy, instead of developing heat within the battery, is transferred to the external circuit and there develops heat or does mechanical work. At the junction n the current is flowing in opposition to the Peltier emf. $\mathcal{E}_2$, and hence heating takes

[1] For a discussion of this subject, together with a complete bibliography, see an article by Compton and Langmuir on Electrical Discharges in Gases, Rev. of Modern Physics, Vol. 2, No. 2, April, 1930.

place. This is the same as when a current flows through a battery in opposition to its emf., as in charging a storage battery. The energy of the current is then used in effecting chemical action and in developing heat. In the case of a thermojunction there is no chemical

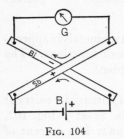

FIG. 104

action, and so heating or cooling is the only energy effect. If the current is reversed the junction *m* is heated and *n* is cooled. Thus the effect is *reversible*. This effect is distinct from the ordinary Joule effect, which is independent of the direction of the current and is always a heating effect, and is therefore *irreversible*. Moreover, the Joule heating occurs in all parts of the circuit, whereas the Peltier effect is restricted to the junction points, and is either an absorption or an evolution of heat, depending on the direction of the current.

Peltier demonstrated this effect by means of a cross, as illustrated in Fig. 104. A cross was made of bismuth and antimony and soldered together, as shown. If current from a cell *B* flows across the junction from bismuth to antimony it will be in the same sense as the Peltier emf., and hence cooling results. A direct-current galvanometer is connected, as shown. The current in the galvanometer is found to flow across the junction from antimony to bismuth, which, as will be seen from the list of metals given in the next Section, indicates that the junction is cooled. Reversing the current reverses the effect. If an alternating current of any frequency is used the junction will be heated and the galvanometer will show a deflection, and in the sense required. This is the principle of the present-day thermocouple galvanometers and ammeters of the cross-wire type which are used extensively in high-frequency current work. Of course, in case a battery is used, as shown in Fig. 104, a small current would flow in the galvanometer circuit even though

FIG. 105

there were no Peltier emf. at the junction since the galvanometer is in parallel with the resistance of the junction. This current is separate from the current produced by the Peltier emf., but superposed upon it.

Another type of thermogalvanometer is shown diagrammatically in Fig. 105. A copper-constantan thermojunction is connected through a direct-current galvanometer or ammeter. The thermojunction is placed close to or in actual contact with a fine wire which is heated by the current that is to be measured or detected.

S. G. Starling has demonstrated the Peltier effect in the following manner: A bar of bismuth is placed endwise between two bars of antimony, the contact surfaces being amalgamated to reduce contact resistance, Fig. 106. A coil of fine, insulated copper wire (about 36 gauge) is wound closely about each junction, and each coil is connected in an arm of a Wheatstone bridge and the bridge is

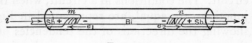

Fig. 106

balanced. The bars are enclosed in a glass tube, as shown, to prevent loss or gain of heat. On causing a current i (conventional) to flow in the direction indicated, the junction m should be heated and the junction n should be cooled. The change in resistance of the coils of wire, due to change of temperature, throws the bridge out of balance, and in such a direction as to indicate that m is heated and n is cooled. Reversing the current reverses the effect.

135. The Seebeck Effect. — In 1822 Thomas Johann Seebeck announced to the Berlin Academy that a ring made of copper and bismuth, soldered together at the two junctions, will furnish an electric current when one of the junctions is at a different temperature from the other. Here we have a case where a current of electricity is produced directly from heat, and for a long time it nurtured a hope, which has never been realized, that currents of electricity of commercial magnitudes might be obtained directly from heat. Currents developed directly from heat were called by Seebeck "thermomagnetic currents." This phenomenon is now called the *thermoelectric* effect, or the *Seebeck effect*. Seebeck was born in Russia, but at an early age moved to Berlin, Germany, to study medicine. Being well to do, he was free to devote himself to a study of science. It was Oersted's experiments in electricity that induced him to investigate electric phenomena, and while engaged in these investigations he discovered the thermoelectric effect, which now bears his name.

Let us consider a closed circuit consisting of two dissimilar metals, say Cu and Fe connected end to end, as shown in Fig. 107. In order to explain the Peltier emf. on the electron theory, it is assumed that the electronic densities in any two metals at the same temperature are, in general, different. When, therefore, two metals are brought into contact an electrostatic field is established between them and hence a potential difference. The strength of the field will depend on the temperature and the metals forming the junction. When the two junctions shown in Fig. 107 are at the same temperature the p.d. at one junction is equal to but opposite in sense to that at the other junction, and hence the net effect is zero and no current flows in the circuit. The conditions in a circuit, when the temperatures of the two junctions are equal, are represented in Fig. 107a, the inside arrows showing the directions of the tendencies of the electrons to move at the two junctions, the outer arrows showing the directions of the conventional emfs.

If the temperature of one junction, m say in Fig. 107b, is higher than that of the other junction n, the Peltier emf. at m becomes greater than at n. The result is that an electronic current flows in the clockwise sense, as indicated by the inside arrows. At the hot junction energy is absorbed and at the cold junction energy is given up. Thus, if the supply of heat to the hot junction were to be cut off a current would continue to flow until the two junctions attained the same temperature.

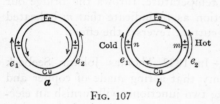

FIG. 107

Heat would be transferred by the current from the hot junction to the cold junction so long as a temperature difference between the junctions existed. This is in accord with the second law of thermodynamics, and is not unlike a heat engine in action. Of course, when a current i flows in a metal of resistance r there is a transformation of electric energy into heat energy which is proportional to the square of the current (Joule heat). The transfer of heat from the hot junction to the cold junction is entirely independent of the Joule effect, which is distributed throughout the length of the conductor. The two effects, however, go on simultaneously.

The Peltier emf. is very small in any thermocouple and is of practical value only where a very small emf. will suffice, as in the measurement of temperature or in the detection and measurement of small currents by means of a galvanometer or milliammeter. One interesting fact, to be discussed later, is that the thermo emf. in a thermocouple circuit, in some cases, increases with temperature difference between the two junctions up to a certain temperature difference, and then decreases to zero and reverses for greater temperature differences. For a copper-iron thermocouple, which has a parabolic temperature-emf. curve, one junction at $0°$ C., the maximum thermo emf. is attained at about $275°$C., the reversal temperature being about $550°$C. These temperatures vary with the metals forming the junction.

In the following list of metals the order is such that, if a thermal junction be made of any two of them, the thermal emf. at the hot junction, in the conventional sense, is from the one preceding to the one following, its value increasing with the distance apart in the list: bismuth, platinum, cobalt, German silver, lead, copper, gold, silver, zinc, iron, antimony.

136. The Thomson Effect. — In 1851 Lord Kelvin, from theoretical considerations, predicted the existence of reversible heat effect in other parts of the thermocouple circuit than at the junctions. He later demonstrated these effects. Consider a copper wire with its ends maintained at the same constant temperature t_1, and the center maintained at a much higher temperature t_2, Fig. 108. Let a current i (conventional) be sent through the wire in the direction indicated. In the section nm heat is absorbed, and hence the current must be flowing up a potential gradient. In the section mo heat is evolved, and therefore the current must be flowing down a potential gradient, the current doing work against an emf. If no current were flowing, a point midway between n and m would be at the same temperature as a point

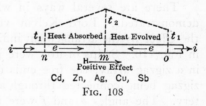

Positive Effect
Cd, Zn, Ag, Cu, Sb
FIG. 108

midway between m and o, due to thermal conduction alone. When a current is flowing, however, as indicated by the arrows, the former point is at a lower temperature than the latter; there has been a transfer of heat, due to the current, and in the direction of current flow. This is analogous to a liquid flowing in a tube heated at one point. The liquid will absorb heat in the section nm and give up heat in the section mo. This is called the *positive Thomson effect*. Thomson called this type of heat effect the *specific heat of electricity*. When the transfer of heat by a current of electricity is in the forward direction it is said that the specific heat of electricity is positive.

Let us next consider an iron wire under the same conditions, Fig. 109. In this case, as in the former case, if no current is flowing in the wire, a point midway between n and m is at the same temperature as a point midway between m and o, due to thermal conduction alone. However, when a current flows in the direction indicated by the arrows, the former point is at a higher temperature than the latter. This can be accounted for if in the section nm there is an emf. directed from m to n and in the section mo there is an emf. directed from m to o. Thus, there has been a transfer of heat, due to the current, and in a direction reverse to the direction

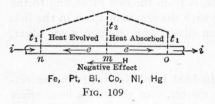

Negative Effect
Fe, Pt, Bi, Co, Ni, Hg
FIG. 109

in which the current is flowing. Thus, if we are to find an analogy with a liquid flowing in a tube, we must imagine the liquid to have a negative specific heat. This is called the *negative Thomson effect*, and, since the current of electricity

was imagined to behave as would a liquid current having a negative specific heat, this effect is called the *negative specific heat of electricity*. The Thomson effect is also sometimes referred to as a convection of heat by a current of electricity, a more appropriate expression it would seem. In any case, if the current is reversed, the Thomson effect is reversed.

There are several ways in which the Thomson effect may be demonstrated. Lord Kelvin verified the effect by the arrangement indicated in Fig. 110. Strips of iron were joined in a zigzag array, the free ends of the zigzag being connected through a battery. The angles b and f were maintained at a low temperature t_1, whereas angle d was maintained at a much higher temperature t_2. Holes for receiving thermometers were drilled in the angles

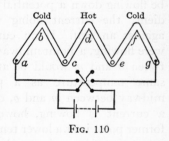

FIG. 110

c and e. When the temperatures of the angles were established, and maintained as indicated, and no current flowed in the circuit, the thermometers at c and e indicated the same temperature, as they should, since the transfer of heat was by thermal conduction alone. However, when a current (conventional) flowed in a direction from a to g through the zigzag the thermometer at c indicated the higher temperature, but when the current was reversed the thermometer at e indicated the higher temperature.

137. Law of Intermediate Metals. — In electric circuits in which electric measuring instruments are used several different kinds of conductors may compose the circuit. It is of importance, therefore, to investigate the effect of several metals in the same circuit, and to formulate a law. The law may be stated as follows: The insertion of additional metals in any circuit does not change the effective emf. in the circuit due to a thermocouple, or other source of emf., provided the added junctions are all at the same temperature. This law is amply verified by experiment. It may also be seen to be a direct consequence of the second law of thermodynamics, for if any number of metals, 1, 2, 3, etc., constitute a circuit, and the temperature is everywhere the same, there can be no current in the circuit since the summation of the thermo emfs. in the circuit must be zero. If a current should flow, for any reason whatsoever, it would cause heating of some junctions and cooling of others. Heat would be transferred, by a self-acting mechanism, from a cold junction to a warm junction, which is in violation of the second law of thermodynamics. In order that such a transfer of energy may take place work must be done on the circuit, i.e., energy must be supplied to it by some outside agency in order to pump heat up a temperature gradient. Therefore, the presence of additional metals in a circuit, at the same temperature as adjacent points, cannot change the effective emf. that may have existed without the additional metals. Thus, if a galvanometer, millivoltmeter, or potentiometer is inserted in a thermocouple circuit the emf. remains unaltered so long as the added parts to the circuit are at the same temperature as contiguous parts.

138. Law of Successive Temperatures. — This law relates to the addition of emfs. when a particular thermocouple is raised in successive temperature steps. It may be stated as follows: For a given thermocouple, the emf. obtained by a temperature difference between the junctions $t_0 - t_n$ is the algebraic sum of the emfs. obtained by the temperature differences $t_0 - t_1$, $t_1 - t_2$, $\cdots$ $t_{n-1} - t_n$. Stated in mathematical form it is

$$\mathcal{E}_0^n = \mathcal{E}_0^1 + \mathcal{E}_1^2 + \mathcal{E}_2^3 + \cdots \mathcal{E}_{n-1}^n.$$

Of course, if there are many junctions at different temperatures, the effective emf. in the circuit is the algebraic sum of the Peltier emfs. and the Thomson emfs.

139. Thermoelectric Curves and Tables. — In a few combinations of metals forming thermoelectric circuits the emf.-temperature curves are sensibly parabolic. In general, however, the curves are represented by an equation of the type

$$\mathscr{E} = at + bt^2 + ct^3 + \cdots.$$

It is usual to record thermoelectric data in tables. Then, by making use of the law for intermediate metals, the equation for any combination of metals or alloys, over the temperature range for which the data hold, is easily obtained from the data given in the tables. The Seebeck effect, the Peltier effect, the Thomson effect, and the thermoelectric power are all profoundly affected by impurities, heat treatment, drawing, rolling, pressure, and tension, and by magnetization for such metals and alloys as are ferromagnetic. Consequently, tables of thermoelectric data must not be relied on too implicitly. For accurate work each individual thermocouple must be calibrated, and values obtained either from an equation or a plotted curve over the range of temperature required.

The following Table of data for elementary substances has been compiled from a more extensive Table to be found in the International Critical Tables, Vol. VI, p. 214. The nomenclature there used has been adopted. The metals are designated by m and r, the thermo emf. by $_m\mathscr{E}_r$, the thermoelectric power by $_mQ_r = d_m\mathscr{E}_r/dt$. The convention which has been adopted in order to obtain a consistent system is as follows: $_m\mathscr{E}_r$ is positive if the current flows from m to r at the junction which is at 0° C., negative if in the reverse direction. Thus, $_r\mathscr{E}_m = -\ _m\mathscr{E}_r$. Also, when other combinations than those appearing in the Table (page 277) are to be made from these data the relationship $_m\mathscr{E}_s = \ _m\mathscr{E}_r + \ _r\mathscr{E}_s$ is to be used. The equations to be used with this Table are

$$_m\mathscr{E}_r = at + \tfrac{1}{2}bt^2 10^{-2} + \tfrac{1}{3}ct^3 10^{-5},$$

$$\frac{d_m\mathscr{E}_r}{dt} = \ _mQ_r = a + bt10^{-2} + ct^2 10^{-5}.$$

$b = 99\%$. $h =$ Heraeus made. $e =$ electrolytic. $g =$ cold drawn and hammered. $m =$ very soft, annealed transformer iron. $r =$ used

TABLE OF THERMOELECTRIC DATA

m	r	t_1	t_2	a	b	c
Ag_b	Pb	0	200	3.3383	0.847	
Al_h	Pb	−200	100	− 0.4717	0.2718	− 2.386
Al	Pb	0	200	− 0.496	0.1734	
Au	Pb	0	200	2.90	0.934	
Bi_e	Pb	−200	100	−81.845	0.599	162.5
Bi	Pb	0	100	−74.42	3.2	
Bi	Pt	0	268	−61.95	4.502	26.82
Cd_g	Pb	−200	100	3.059	2.856	9.00
Cd	Pb	0	100	2.85	3.89	
Cd	Pt	0	320	0.39	0.38	
Co	Cu	0	280	−23.24	−8.26	
Co	Pt	0	1200	−10.70	−5.50	7.50
Cu	Pb	0	100	2.76	1.22	
Cu_m	Pt	0	900	3.13	2.46	
Fe_e	Pb	−230	100	16.65	−2.966	−26.75
F_e	Cu	0	700	13.7	−7.80	6.60
Hg	Pb	0	200	− 8.8103	−3.333	
Ni	Pt	0	313	− 2.891	0.622	
Ni	Pt	0	1200	−17.12	2.46	− 2.193
Pt	Pb	0	100	− 1.788	−3.46	12.6
Sb_r	Pb	0	630	46.24	6.362	−14.33
Sb	Pb	0	100	35.58	14.50	
Sn	Pb	0	200	− 0.168	0.187	
Sn	Pt	0	415	2.87	2.3	
Zn	Pb	0	100	3.047	−0.99	
Zn	Pt	0	450	5.74	3.30	

in cast form, solid rods soldered end to end. t_1 and t_2 temp. °C., range over which given constants hold.

The measurement of a thermo emf. offers some difficulty, since the emf. is always very small. Emfs. of this magnitude may be measured by a high-sensitivity potentiometer, the arrangement being as shown schematically in Fig. 111. The cold junction is usually kept at 0° C. by surrounding it with melting ice, although other fixed temperatures may be used. The other junction, or variable-temperature junction, is heated or cooled as the case may be.

Figure 112 shows several thermoelectric curves. It will be seen that the

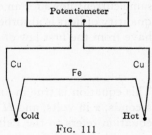

FIG. 111

curves are not parabolic. In fact strictly parabolic thermoelectric curves are exceptional.

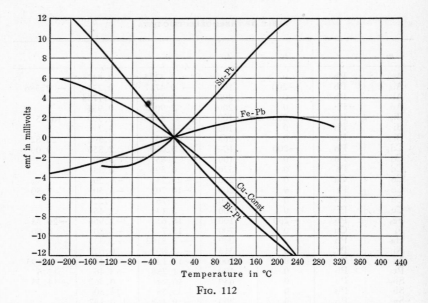

Fig. 112

140. Measurement of the Peltier emf.

140. Measurement of the Peltier emf. — In a thermoelectric circuit there are irreversible heat effects due to a current flowing through a resistance, which are therefore independent of the direction of the current. The heat thus developed is comparable to a friction loss, and is equal to ri^2t joules. If there are fixed or distributed emfs. in the circuit, which exist independently of the current, then there are reversible heat effects. Thus, if there is a drop in potential in the direction of current (conventional) flow heat is evolved, but if the same current flows for an equal time in the reverse direction an equal quantity of heat is absorbed. If the fixed emf. is designated by π, we have from the first law of thermodynamics

$$JH = it\pi = q\pi. \tag{140.1}$$

This equation is true in any system of units. If i is in amperes, t in seconds, π in volts, and H in calories, J is in joules per calorie. This equation refers to the Peltier effect, and π is called the *Peltier coefficient*. It is the difference of potential at a junction, or it is the energy change per unit quantity of electricity crossing the junction.

Since the Peltier heat effect and the Joule heat effect take place simultaneously, it is difficult to separate them. The Peltier heat effect takes place at the junction, but thermal conduction along the wires forming the junction serves to distribute the heat in such a manner as to mask the effect. The Joule heat effect takes place at the junction also, since there is always some contact resistance, and along the conductors adjacent to the junction. Thus, to obtain experimental evidence of and to measure the Peltier heat alone, and hence the Peltier coefficient, presents a problem. The Peltier coefficient cannot be measured directly. Consequently, in the determinations that have been made, the heat which is associated with the passage of a current across a junction is measured, from which the Peltier coefficient is calculated, or else it is calculated from a theoretically derived equation. One method by which π has been determined from heat measurements is to measure the heat change at the junction, and for a short distance on either side, first when a current of definite, known strength flows for a measured time in one direction, and then for the same time in the reverse direction.[1] In one case we will have

$$JH = it\pi + ri^2t,$$

and in the other

$$JH' = - it\pi + ri^2t.$$

On eliminating ri^2t, there results

$$\pi = \frac{J(H - H')}{2it}. \tag{140.2}$$

If H and H' are in calories, t in seconds, J in joules per calorie, i in amperes, π is in volts.[2]

141. Application of Thermodynamics. — Since the Peltier effect is reversible, a thermoelectric circuit may be likened to a heat engine which absorbs a quantity H_2 units of heat at an absolute temperature T_2, a part H_1 of which is given out at a lower temperature T_1, and the difference, $H_2 - H_1$, is used for doing work of some kind. Lord Kelvin (1855) was the first to recognize that a thermoelectric circuit is essentially equivalent to a heat engine, so far as its reversible heat

[1] Le Roux, Ann. Chem. Phys., LV, 10, 1867.

[2] For a determination of the Peltier coefficient by a comparison method, together with a critical discussion of all previous methods and results, see a research by A. E. Casewell, Phys. Rev., 33, p. 379, 1911.

effects are concerned. The thermodynamic condition for a reversible heat engine working between the temperature limits T_1 and T_2 is that

$$\frac{H_2}{T_2} = \frac{H_1}{T_1}. \tag{141.1}$$

When q units of electricity are carried once around the circuit, we have

$$H_2 = \frac{q\pi_2}{J}, \quad \text{and} \quad H_1 = \frac{q\pi_1}{J}$$

by equation (140.1). Therefore, equation (141.1) becomes

$$\frac{q\pi_2}{q\pi_1} = \frac{T_2}{T_1}, \quad \text{or} \quad \frac{\pi_2 - \pi_1}{\pi_1} = \frac{T_2 - T_1}{T_1}. \tag{141.2}$$

$\pi_2 - \pi_1 = \mathscr{E}$ is the thermo emf. in the circuit, providing there are no other than Peltier emfs. present, and hence we may write

$$\mathscr{E} = \frac{\pi_1}{T_1} (T_2 - T_1). \tag{141.3}$$

If T_1 is maintained constant, π_1/T_1 is constant, and therefore $\mathscr{E}$ is proportional to $T_2 - T_1$. However, in general, experiments show this not to be the case, since, in some cases, $\mathscr{E}$ increases to a maximum and then decreases, and finally reverses. From this discrepancy between the data of experiments and the theory thus far developed, Lord Kelvin concluded that the Peltier emfs. are not the only independent emfs. in the circuit, but that there must be emfs. between the junctions. This led to the discovery of the Thomson effect. On the electron theory it is to be expected that thermo emfs. will exist between points differing in temperature, as along a conductor having a temperature gradient, since the electron density should be greater at low than at high temperatures. In some metals, as we have seen, the Thomson emf. is reverse to that in other metals, an anomaly that has not yet received a satisfactory explanation.

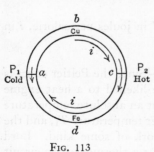

FIG. 113

In order to investigate this matter more fully, let us consider, to be specific, an iron-copper thermocouple circuit, Fig. 113. A current i (conventional) will flow in the direction indicated by the arrows. So far as the Peltier emf. alone is concerned, heat will be absorbed at c and evolved at a, that is, heat is transported from c to a by the current.

In the iron wire the current is flowing from hot to cold, and, since iron exhibits the negative Thomson effect, heat is absorbed, since the current is flowing up a potential slope in the part d of the circuit. In the copper wire the current is flowing from cold to hot, and since copper exhibits the positive Thomson effect, the current is flowing up a potential slope, and heat is absorbed in the part b of the circuit. Thus, heat is absorbed in the sections b and d and at c, and heat is evolved at a. By equation (140.1), the energy change at a and c is of the form $\pi i t$. If we assign the positive sign to heat absorbed and the negative sign to heat evolved at a fixed point, then, so far as the Peltier effect is concerned, the net energy change is

$$\pi_2 i t - \pi_1 i t \equiv (\pi_2 - \pi_1)i t. \tag{141.4}$$

In order to express the Thomson effect in mathematical form we will, following conventional usage, let the symbol σ stand for the coefficient of the Thomson effect, i.e., *the difference of potential due to unit difference in temperature*, which is also called the *specific heat of electricity*. Thus, when a current i flows for t seconds in a particular metal between points differing in temperature by dT, the heat energy change is given by

$$\sigma \, i t \, dT.$$

Since σ is a function of the temperature, and hence variable, the whole energy between points ranging in temperature from T_2 to T_1 is

$$i t \int_{T_1}^{T_2} \sigma \, dT.$$

This integral is taken as positive if the direction of the current is the direction of increasing temperature (or dT positive), and negative if the current flows in the direction of decreasing temperature (or dT negative). σ is positive if the metal exhibits the positive Thomson effect, negative if it exhibits the negative Thomson effect. Let σ_{Cu} and σ_{Fe} stand for the Thomson coefficients in copper and iron respectively. Then, the total energy change in the two wires due to the Thomson effect is

$$it \int_{T_1}^{T_2} \sigma_{\mathrm{Cu}} \, dT - it \int_{T_1}^{T_2} \sigma_{\mathrm{Fe}} \, dT. \qquad (141.5)$$

As the sign of σ is negative for iron, the second term is essentially positive, i.e., heat energy is absorbed in the iron wire as well as in the copper wire. Thus, for the whole circuit, heat energy is absorbed at the hot junction and in the two wires, and heat energy is evolved at the cold junction. Therefore, the total energy change for the entire circuit is

$$\mathscr{E} it = it \int_{T_1}^{T_2} \sigma_{\mathrm{Cu}} \, dT - it \int_{T_1}^{T_2} \sigma_{\mathrm{Fe}} \, dT + it(\pi_2 - \pi_1),$$

or

$$\mathscr{E} = \int_{T_1}^{T_2} \sigma_{\mathrm{Cu}} \, dT - \int_{T_1}^{T_2} \sigma_{\mathrm{Fe}} \, dT + (\pi_2 - \pi_1), \qquad (141.6)$$

which is the energy change when $it = q = 1$ unit charge is transported once around the circuit.

Thermoelectric Power. — Equation (141.6) may be written

$$\mathscr{E} = \int_{T_1}^{T_2} (\sigma_{\mathrm{Cu}} - \sigma_{\mathrm{Fe}}) dT + \int_{T_1}^{T_2} \frac{d\pi}{dT} \, dT. \qquad (141.7)$$

or

$$\mathscr{E} = \int_{T_1}^{T_2} \left(\sigma_{\mathrm{Cu}} - \sigma_{\mathrm{Fe}} + \frac{d\pi}{dT} \right) dT \qquad (141.8)$$

where $d\pi/dT$ is the rate of change of the Peltier coefficient with the temperature. On differentiating equation (141.8), we have

$$\frac{d\mathscr{E}}{dT} = \frac{d\pi}{dT} + \sigma_{\mathrm{Cu}} - \sigma_{\mathrm{Fe}}. \qquad (141.9)$$

$\dfrac{d\mathscr{E}}{dT}$ is the thermoelectric power for the two metals composing the thermocouple.

Disregarding the irreversible Joule heat in the circuit, we may apply the laws of thermodynamics to the entire circuit. From equation (141.9), we have

$$d\mathscr{E} = d\pi + (\sigma_{\mathrm{Cu}} - \sigma_{\mathrm{Fe}}) \, dT, \qquad (141.10)$$

where $d\mathcal{E}$ is the increment in the thermo emf. in the circuit, and $d\pi$ is the increment in the Peltier emf. corresponding to the temperature increment dT. By thermodynamics, the quantity of heat absorbed divided by the absolute temperature at which it is absorbed equals the heat evolved divided by the absolute temperature at which it is evolved. The heat absorbed in the sections of the circuit divided by the absolute temperature is

$$\frac{(\sigma_{Cu} - \sigma_{Fe})dT}{JT}$$

per unit quantity of electricity. To this is to be added a similar expression for the heat absorbed at the hot junction, which is at an absolute temperature $T + dT$, or

$$\frac{\pi + d\pi}{J(T + dT)}.$$

At the cold junction, the heat evolved divided by the absolute temperature is

$$\frac{\pi}{JT}.$$

On equating these expressions, we have

$$\frac{(\sigma_{Cu} - \sigma_{Fe})dT}{T} + \frac{\pi + d\pi}{T + dT} = \frac{\pi}{T}, \tag{141.11}$$

which may be reduced to

$$(\sigma_{Cu} - \sigma_{Fe})dT + d\pi = \frac{\pi}{T}dT. \tag{141.12}$$

Comparing this equation with (141.10), it is seen that

$$d\mathcal{E} = \frac{\pi}{T}dT. \tag{141.13}$$

If the junctions are at the temperatures T_2 and T_1, the thermo emf. in the circuit is

$$\mathcal{E} = \int_{T_1}^{T_2} \frac{\pi}{T}dT. \tag{141.14}$$

It has been pointed out that the direct experimental measurement of the Peltier emf. is impossible. Equation (141.13) affords an indirect method of determining the Peltier emf. Solving for π in this equation, we have

$$\pi = \frac{d\mathscr{E}}{dT} T. \qquad (141.15)$$

For the simple case of a thermocouple having a parabolic curve, we have

$$\mathscr{E} = bt + ct^2.$$

Although not necessary, there are some advantages in changing this equation to absolute temperature.   Thus.

$$\mathscr{E} = b(T - 273) + c(T - 273)^2. \qquad (141.16)$$

And

$$\frac{d\mathscr{E}}{dT} = (b - 546c) + 2cT \equiv e + 2cT. \qquad (141.17)$$

Therefore,

$$\pi = \frac{d\mathscr{E}}{dT} T = eT + 2cT^2. \qquad (141.18)$$

The value of $\sigma_{\text{Cu}} - \sigma_{\text{Fe}}$ may be obtained as follows: From equation (141.12), we have

$$\sigma_{\text{Cu}} - \sigma_{\text{Fe}} = \frac{\pi}{T} - \frac{d\pi}{dT},$$

which may be written

$$\frac{\sigma_{\text{Cu}} - \sigma_{\text{Fe}}}{T} = - \left(\frac{1}{T} \frac{d\pi}{dT} - \frac{\pi}{T^2} \right) = - \frac{d}{dT} \left(\frac{\pi}{T} \right).$$

But $\pi/T = d\mathscr{E}/dT$, by equation (141.15).   Therefore,

$$\sigma_{\text{Cu}} - \sigma_{\text{Fe}} = - T \frac{d^2\mathscr{E}}{dT^2}. \qquad (141.19)$$

Differentiating equation (141.17), we have $\dfrac{d^2\mathscr{E}}{dT^2} = 2c$.   Hence finally

$$\sigma_{\text{Cu}} - \sigma_{\text{Fe}} = - 2cT. \qquad (141.20)$$

Likewise the values of π, and the difference between the values of the Thomson coefficients may be calculated for any thermocouple when the equation for the thermocouple has been obtained.

It may be seen from equation (141.15) that at a temperature such that $\frac{d\mathcal{E}}{dT} = 0$. $\pi = 0$. i.e., the Peltier emf. vanishes at such a point. In the case of parabolic curves this temperature T_n has been called the *neutral temperature*. In the case of any thermoelectric curve, the temperature at which $\frac{d\mathcal{E}}{dT} = 0$ may be called a neutral temperature. In the case of a parabolic curve, we have, by equation (141.17), when $\frac{d\mathcal{E}}{dT} = 0$.

$$0 = e + 2cT_n, \quad \text{or} \quad e = -2cT_n.$$

Introducing this value of e into equation (141.18), we have

$$\pi = -2cTT_n + 2cT^2 = 2cT(T - T_n).$$

Thus, when $T = T_n$, $\pi = 0$. It follows that when the hot junction of a thermocouple is at the neutral temperature there is no Peltier emf. at that junction, i.e., no reversible thermal effects accompany the passage of a current across the junction. Thus, if one junction of a thermocouple were to be held at the neutral temperature, and the temperature of the other junction were permitted to vary, the current would flow in one direction or the other around the circuit depending on whether the temperature of the variable junction were above or below the neutral temperature.

Further, we see that if a junction is below the neutral temperature, π steadily decreases with rise in temperature, becoming zero at the neutral temperature, and then reversing in sign for higher temperatures. However, the Thomson emf. steadily increases in absolute value with rising temperature, and at some particular temperature interval (for a parabolic curve) higher than the neutral temperature the various emfs. in the circuit may sum up to zero.

142. The Transverse Peltier Effect. — Some metals that are strongly crystalline, such as bismuth, are anisotropic relative to thermoelectric properties, i.e., the thermoelectric values depend on the direction which the length of the bar makes with the crystal axis. When a metal bar exhibits this type of anisotropism, a thermoelectric property, other than those already considered, makes its appearance, unless the bar is cut parallel to one of the principal crystal axes. If cut so as to make an angle with one of the principal axes, when a current of electricity is passed longitudinally through the bar there is absorption of heat on one side of the bar and evolution of heat on the other side, the two sides being otherwise at the same temperature. This phenomenon is known as the *transverse Peltier effect*. Conversely, unequal heating on the two sides of the bar will give rise to a longitudinal potential difference.

143. Classic Electron Theory of Peltier Potential. — The theory of free electrons in metals, obeying the ideal gas laws, has met with a large measure of success, although it has failed to meet all requirements. This theory assumes that electrons in metals fill the free spaces in the crystal lattices, that the Maxwellian law of distribution of velocities obtains, and that the electrons share in the thermal energies of the metal atoms, each electron on the average possessing the same energy that a gas molecule would possess at the same temperature. On the basis of these assumptions J. J. Thomson,[1] Drude,[2] and Richardson [3] have derived expression for the Peltier coefficient π. Thomson's derivation, which agrees in its final results with Richardson's derivation, will be given in order to show the method of treatment.

It is assumed that the number of free electrons per unit volume is different in different metals. Hence, considering the electrons to behave as a gas, if the number of electrons per unit volume in one metal is greater than in the other, the electronic or diffusion pressure in one will be greater than in the other. Thus, when two metals are brought into close contact there will be a flow of electrons from one to the other, which will continue until the charge of the electrons so transferred produces a difference of potential sufficient to prevent further transfer.

Let us consider two bars of different metals in contact at junction j, Fig. 114. Let the electron density in bar a be n_1 and in bar b, n_2, both bars being at the same temperature T when brought into contact. Let $n_1 > n_2$. If the gas laws obta n in this case, diffusion pressure (osmotic pressure) will tend to equalize the pressures on the two sides of the junction interface and electrons will be driven from bar a to bar b. The electrons driven to bar b set up an electric field between

[1] Corpuscular Theory of Matter, p. 73.
[2] Ann. der Physik, Vol. 1, p. 590, 1900.
[3] Phil. Mag. 23, p. 269, 1912.

the two bars, bar b becoming more negative, bar a less negative. When the electric-field pressure balances the diffusion pressure equilibrium obtains. There will then be a difference of potential between the two bars which is the Peltier potential π. Using conventional terms, bar b will be at a lower potential than bar a. If electrons are transferred after the limiting potential has been established, as by a

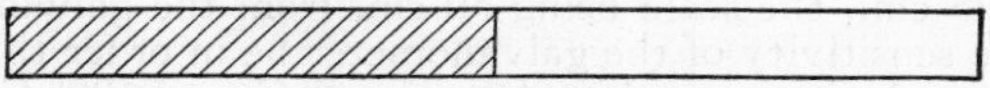

FIG. 114

current of electricity, from bar b to bar a work must be done and there will be heating. If the transfer takes place in the reverse direction there will be cooling. This is the Peltier effect.

In order to derive an expression for the Peltier coefficient, which is the difference of potential at the junction or the work required to transport unit quantity of electricity across the junction, we have

$$\pi = \int_{V_1}^{V_2} p \, dv.$$

By the kinetic theory of gases, $p = \frac{1}{3}nmu^2 = \frac{2}{3}n\alpha T$. Unit quantity of electricity contains $1/e$ electrons, $e = 4.8029(10)^{-10}$ cgse. unit, being the electronic charge. The volume v occupied by unit quantity of charge transferred will be $1/ne$, where n is the number of electrons per unit volume. Therefore,

$$n = \frac{1}{ev}, \quad \text{and} \quad p = \frac{2}{3}\frac{\alpha T}{ev}.$$

Hence,

$$\pi = \int_{V_1}^{V_2} p \, dv = \frac{2}{3}\frac{\alpha T}{e}\int_{V_1}^{V_2}\frac{dv}{v} = \frac{2}{3}\frac{\alpha T}{e}\log_e\frac{V_2}{V_1} = \frac{2}{3}\frac{\alpha T}{e}\log_e\frac{n_1}{n_2},$$

where n_1 and n_2 are the number of electrons per unit volume in the two conductors, and $\alpha T = \frac{1}{2}mu^2$ is the mean kinetic energy of an electron.[1]

[1] See Electricity and Magnetism by S. G. Starting, Chap. VIII, and Textbook of Thermodynamics by Paul S. Epstein, Chapters XVII and XX.

1. An iron-copper thermocouple has the equation

$$\mathscr{E} = 15.81\,t - 0.0288\,t^2 \text{ microvolt.}$$

This thermocouple is connected through a galvanometer such that the resistance of the entire circuit is 120 ohms. When one junction of the thermocouple is held at 0° C. and the other at 100° C., what is the current in the circuit? The galvanometer is of the wall type with the half length of the circular scale 25 cm., the scale being 50 cm. from the galvanometer mirror. What must the sensitivity of the galvanometer be in order that this thermocouple may be used with it, working between 0° C. and 100° C., and just stay on the scale (deflection 25 cms.) at 100° C.? With this setup, what is the deflection of the galvanometer when the hot junction of the thermocouple is 75° C.? When 50° C.? When 25° C.? How could the galvanometer scale be made to read directly in degrees C.?

2. Calculate the neutral temperature and the temperature of inversion of the thermocouple in Problem 1.

3. Calculate the values of π for a Co – Cu thermocouple for the temperatures 273° K., 373° K., T_n, 550° K. Also, calculate $\sigma_{Cu} - \sigma_{Co}$ for the same temperatures.

4. An iron-copper thermocouple has the following equation

$$\mathscr{E} = 15.81\,t - 0.0288\,t^2 \text{ microvolt.}$$

Calculate π and $\sigma_{Cu} - \sigma_{Fe}$ for the following temperatures: 273° K., 373° K., T_n (neutral temperature), 600° K., 700° K. An iron-lead thermocouple has the following equation:

$$\mathscr{E} = 17.15\,t - 0.0241\,t^2 \text{ microvolt.}$$

Calculate π and $\sigma_{Pb} - \sigma_{Fe}$ for the temperatures given just above, and obtain values for the σs.

CHAPTER X

ELECTRONIC EMISSION

144. The Metallic Crystalline State. — Our knowledge of the structure of a metal has advanced materially in recent years. Several contributing lines of evidence have conspired to achieve this end, such as the diffraction of X-rays and electrons by crystals, thermionic and photoelectric emission, electric and thermal conduction, and a more refined study of crystallography. From these contributing fields of research scientists now envisage a crystal as a regular arrangement of atoms forming a so-called space lattice. There may be various types of space lattices. A crystalline substance, e.g., copper, is composed of a large number of small crystals oriented at random with respect to each other. The atoms forming the frame work of a crystal lattice are disturbed more or less by thermal agitation, thus altering the regular arrangement and the distances between the atoms. The distance between the atomic centers is of the order of 10^{-8} cm. which is about equal to the apparent diameter of an atom. However, the atoms themselves are of a very open structure, as we have seen, and consequently the distances between nuclei are very great as compared with nuclear dimensions.

The electrons sharing in the crystal structure occupy positions between the regularly spaced nuclei, and for the most part remain bound to positions determined by the fields of the positive nuclei. They are bound to the system rather than to individual nuclei, which is unlike a gas in which each nucleus has its own complement of electrons. In a metal there are always free electrons, averaging one or two per nucleus, that seem not to be bound to the system but are free to wander about through the space lattice structure of the metal. These are the conduction electrons that are responsible for electric conductivity and to some extent thermal conductivity. Undoubtedly the free electrons change places from time to time with the bound electrons, but on the average the free electrons are conceived to remain of about the same number per mole of metal, although the number may change with temperature.

The influence of the nuclei on the conduction electrons cannot be very great. If these electrons were restrained, they would not move until a certain minimum external field had been applied, and Ohm's law would be violated. This is not the case. On the other hand, if there were no interaction at all between free electrons and atomic nuclei the laws of the conservation of energy and momentum would be violated when an electron absorbs a photon, as in the photoelectric case. It can be shown that if an entirely free electron were to absorb the whole energy of a photon it would be given the speed of light, which by the theory of relativity is impossible since then its mass would be infinite. However, as Tolman and others have shown the electric current in metals is carried by electrons. The streaming electrons through the crystal lattices meet with some opposition and this constitutes ohmic resistance. It is difficult to conceive of the conduction electrons being perfectly free as are the molecules of an ideal gas, and therefore it is questioned that the gas laws obtain as has been assumed in so many theoretical discussions in the past. If charges of electricity behave in a metal as they do outside, there are forces of repulsion between electrons and forces of attraction between electrons and the fixed positive ions composing the crystal lattices. It would indeed be strange if the positive and negative field so completely overlapped at every point as to annul one another and so leave the conduction electrons entirely free as would be the molecules of an ideal gas. The fact that when the gas laws are applied to conduction electrons the theoretical deduction are not wholly in accord with the results of experiments has led to a search for a new and more accurate conception of the behavior of conduction electrons. This will be considered in the next Section.[1]

145. The Fermi-Dirac Distribution. — In 1927 the Fermi-Dirac distribution law based upon the quantum theory appeared, and the following year Sommerfeld introduced a new electron theory of metals based upon the Fermi-Dirac proposition. It is beyond the scope of this book to discuss these theories and their applications in detail.[2] The salient features may be noted, however. The concept of an electron gas within the crystal lattices of a metal is retained in a

---

[1] For complete discussion of this subject, see The Metallic State by Hume-Rothery (Oxford Univ. Press, 1931).

[2] See Photoelectric Phenomena by Hughes and Du Bridge, Chap. VI, and Statistical Theories of Matter, Radiation and Electricity by K. K. Darrow, Rev. of Modern Physics (1929).

much modified sense, but the electron gas no longer obeys the Max-wellian distribution of an ideal gas based upon the kinetic theory. According to the kinetic theory the electrons should all have zero velocity of translation, and therefore zero translational energy, at the absolute zero of temperature. At any temperature $T°$ K. the average energy of an electron should be $\frac{3}{2}kT$. Curves, adapted from "Intro-duction to Modern Physics" by Richtmyer, for an ideal gas obeying the Maxwellian law are shown in Fig. 115. The energy of an electron in electron volts is plotted against the number of electrons per unit of

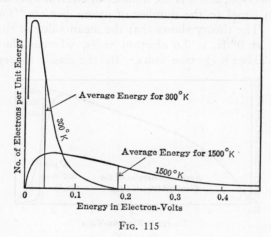

FIG. 115

energy. An electron volt is the energy an electron would acquire in falling through a potential difference of one volt. This energy is

$$\tfrac{1}{2}mv^2 = \frac{Ve}{300} = \frac{4.80329(10)^{-10}}{300} = 1.601(10)^{-12} \text{ erg},$$

where $V = 1$ volt.[3] If $m = 9.1154(10)^{-28}$ gm. is the mass of an electron, then the so-called velocity of one volt is $5.929(10)^7$ cms./sec. The mean energy of an electron is about 0.04 electron volt at 300° K. and 0.19 electron volt at 1,500° K., according to the Maxwellian dis-tribution.

The distribution of energy for the electrons in platinum by appli-cation of the Fermi-Dirac distribution is shown by the curves in

[3] In this Chapter V will be used as the symbol for potential.

Fig. 116. This distribution does not give zero energy and speed for all electrons at absolute zero. The distribution curve starts from zero and rises approximately parabolically to a maximum value W_m, when the temperature is 0° K., given by the equation

$$W_m = \left(\frac{h^2}{2m}\right)\left(\frac{3n}{8\pi}\right)^{\frac{2}{3}},$$

where $h = 6.55(10)^{-27}$ erg-second (Planck's constant), m is the mass of an electron, and n is the number of electrons per unit volume. n was taken equal to the number of atoms per cm.³ for platinum $(6.6(10)^{22})$. The theory shows that the mean value of the energy of an electron at 0° K. is 3.6 electron volts, whereas the maximum value W_m is about 6 electron volts. By the classic theory the mean

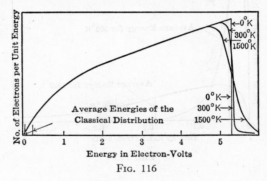

Fig. 116

energy of an electron at 1.500° K. is only 0.19 electron volt. This is a very surprising result.

It will be noticed that as the temperature rises there is no change in the distribution except in the neighborhood of W_m where an increasing number of electrons possess energies greater than W_m. However, this distribution has resulted in much better agreement between theory and experiment in the case of the specific heats of metals, electric conduction, thermal conduction, etc. According to this theory the energy of the electrons in a metal is quantized, so that there are a large number of quantum levels, or "phase states," as they are called. But according to the Pauli exclusion principle there cannot be more than one electron in a given level at the same time. In metals all of the lower quantum levels are filled, and the system is said to be "degenerate." Such a system of electrons is almost incapable of exchanging thermal energy with the surrounding atoms. The theory shows that in the case of metals the contribution of the electrons to the specific heat is less than 1 per cent.

146. Thermionics. — It has been stated that there is a potential barrier at the surface of a metal which ordinarily prevents conduction electrons from escaping from the metal. Under very high potentials electrons will escape at ordinary temperatures. This is the corona effect. It has been known for nearly two centuries that heated bodies are unable to retain an electric charge. However, not much was known about this subject until after 1900. Most of the work in this field in the early part of the present century was done by O. W. Richardson. To him we owe the name *thermionics*, which is applied to this branch of the subject of electricity. He called the current from a heated body a *thermionic current*, and the ions emitted by a heated body *thermions*.

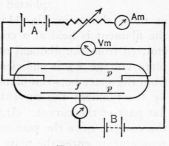

FIG. 117

One of the earliest observations on the emission of electrons was made by Thomas Edison (1885). He sealed an extra terminal in an ordinary carbon electric light bulb, and found that when this extra terminal (now called plate) was connected to the positive terminal of a battery, connected through the filament forming a closed circuit, a current was indicated by a galvanometer in the circuit, but when connected to the negative terminal no current was recorded. This was before the advent of the electron theory, and so the explanation was not forthcoming until Richardson made a thorough investigation of the whole subject of thermionics beginning in 1902.

Richardson's apparatus for the study of thermionic emission from a hot body is shown schematically in Fig. 117. A clean metal filament f is heated in an evacuated cylindrical enclosure by a battery A. The filament is surrounded by a hollow concentric cylinder p. This cylinder is connected through a current-measuring instrument G to the positive terminal of a battery B, the B-battery circuit being connected to the A-battery circuit as shown. The filament acted also as a resistance thermometer to measure its own temperature. A resistance-temperature curve is previously obtained, and then by measur-

ing the p.d. between two points on the wire by means of a high grade
voltmeter or a potentiometer and the current through the filament
by an ammeter, say, the resistance of the wire is obtained by use of
Ohm's law, and hence also the temperature of the filament. Richardson found that at temperatures above red heat electrons were emitted

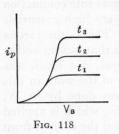

FIG. 118

by the filament and passed across through
empty space to the cold cylinder p (plate), the
strength of the current being measured by the
current-measuring instrument G.

There are three variables in this experiment,
the temperature of the filament t, the plate voltage V_B from filament to plate, and the plate
current i_p. Therefore, two sets of curves may
be plotted which are of interest. If i_p is
plotted against V_B we obtain curves such

as those shown in Fig. 118. Let us say that the temperature of
the filament is held at a constant value t_1. Then electrons will be
emitted from the filament at a constant maximum rate. When the
plate voltage V_B is sufficiently high to remove all of the electrons
from the space between filament and plate as fast as they are emitted
by the filament the current becomes constant (represented by the
flat part of the curve). Any further increase in V_B cannot increase
the current since the maximum number of electrons emitted at that
temperature enter the plate circuit. When the current has reached
this constant value it is said to be *saturated*,
and the corresponding voltage is the *saturation
voltage*. At any voltage less than the saturation value the space between f and p becomes
filled with electrons (space charge) and some
electrons are driven back into the filament or
prevented from escaping by the repulsion of the
space electron-cloud, the number so returning
decreasing as V_B increases, becoming zero at
the saturation-current value. If the tempera-

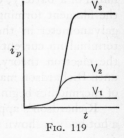

FIG. 119

ture of the filament is raised to a higher constant value t_2, say,
there is another current-saturation value at that temperature, etc.
Thus the shapes of the curves are accounted for.

Let us plot i_p against t, as shown in Fig. 119, giving to the plate
voltage V_B successive constant values, V_1, V_2, V_3, etc. The current i_p
at first increases very slowly as t increases, and then more rapidly,

becoming constant (saturated) at some fixed value V_1 of the plate voltage. If the value of V_B is raised to a higher constant value, V_2 say, there is a higher saturation value for i_p, etc. Up to the saturation value the plate voltage is sufficient to draw all of the emitted electrons over to the plate as fast as they escape from the filament. At temperatures higher than this value, for plate voltage V_1, say, electrons are emitted faster than they can be removed, a space charge builds up which return some of the emitted electrons to the filament, the number returned increasing as the temperature rises above the saturation value.

147. Theory of Thermionic Emission. — It has been found that when a wire is first heated both positive and negative thermions are emitted, but that after the wire has been kept glowing for some time only negative thermions are emitted. Both the charge e and the ratio of charge to mass e/m of negative thermions have been measured and it has been found that these charges are electrons.

If the temperature of a filament is varied, and the plate voltage is maintained greater than that needed for saturation, a curve of the form shown in Fig. 120 is obtained, where i_p represents the *saturation current*. This curve is of much the same form as the saturated vapor pressure curve obtained in the case of ordinary vapors. It is not surprising, therefore, that Richardson and others conceived of electron clouds, both within and without a metal, as gaseous in form and behavior, and that the first theoretical investigations proceeded along this line of argument. Maxwell's law of distribution of the velocities of gas molecules in a gas was well known at that time.

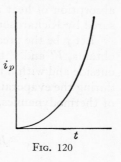

Fig. 120

The electrons within a metal, though moving with comparative freedom, are restrained from escaping through the surface by a potential barrier, and unless an electron possesses sufficient energy to scale this potential barrier it must remain inside the metal. The amount of energy required for escape per electron, ϕ, is usually measured in electron volts. When electrons do escape only those having the highest energies, highest speeds, can make the grade. This means that the escaping electrons have energies represented by the extreme right of the foot of the curve, beyond the energy value W_m

represented in Fig. 116. Measurements of the specific heats of metals do not support the assumption that an appreciable number of the free electrons share in the thermal energies of the molecules. According to Sommerfeld the conduction electrons constitute a highly "degenerate system," incapable for the most part of sharing in the thermal energies of the molecules, and therefore they are not influenced by changes in temperature to the extent required by the classic gas theory. Richardson derived his original equation on the assumption that the electronic gas obeys the laws of an ideal gas. We may derive an expression for the thermionic current by applying the latent heat equation as in thermodynamics.

Let us consider again the evacuated enclosure of Fig. 117. Let us assume that the electrons evaporate from the filament until the space becomes saturated at a given temperature T. Then the number of electrons returning to the filament in any finite time will equal the number emitted in the same time. A state of equilibrium will thus be reached, comparable to that between a liquid and its saturated vapor. In the evaporation of electrons, as in the case of a gas, there is an absorption of heat and a heat of evaporation, which has been measured by Richardson and others, and also a heat of condensation.

Let p be the pressure of the electron atmosphere when equilibrium obtains, V' and v' the volumes of one mole of electrons in the space outside and within the metal respectively, and W the energy absorbed during the evaporation of one mole of electrons. Then from the laws of thermodynamics, we have

$$W = T \frac{dp}{dT}(V' - v') = TV' \frac{dp}{dT}, \qquad (147.1)$$

approximately, since $v' << V'$.

The energy W is made up of two parts: (1) The energy required to surmount the potential barrier at the surface of the metal. This is equal to $N\phi_1$, where ϕ_1 is the work per electron (work function) and N is Avogadro's number, $6.023(10)^{23}$. ϕ_1 is the net work required to extract an electron from the metal and to give it the kinetic energy with which to escape. (2) The work required to overcome the pressure of the electron gas outside the metal. This is equal to pV'. But from the kinetic theory of gases, we have

$$pV' = NkT,$$

where k is Boltzmann's constant, $1.3803(10)^{-16}$. Therefore

$$N(\phi_1 + kT) = TV' \frac{dp}{dT}. \tag{147.2}$$

Eliminating V' by means of $pV' = NkT$, and integrating, we have

$$p = KTe^{\int \frac{\phi_1}{kT^2} dT}, \tag{147.3}$$

where K is a constant. If there are n electrons per cm.^{3} of electron gas, then $p = knT$. Thus

$$n = Ce^{\int \frac{\phi_1}{kT^2} dT}. \tag{147.4}$$

If an electron gas behaves as an ideal gas, the mean square velocity of an electron is given by the equation

$$\tfrac{1}{2}mv^2 = \tfrac{3}{2}kT.$$

If we make the usual assumption that the electrons are traveling in six streams parallel to the six faces of a cube, then it can be shown that the number n_0 striking one cm.^{2} per second is given by

$$n_0 = \frac{nv}{\sqrt{6\pi}}.$$

Then

$$n_0 = \frac{n\sqrt{3k}}{\sqrt{6\pi m}} T^{\frac{1}{2}}. \tag{147.5}$$

Combining equations (147.4) and (147.5), we have

$$n_0 = A_1 T^{\frac{1}{2}} e^{\int \frac{\phi_1}{kT^2} dT} = A_1 T^{\frac{1}{2}} e^{-\frac{\phi_1}{kT}}, \tag{147.6}$$

where A_1 is a constant. This is the form of the equation first obtained by Richardson. The current density of electronic emission will be $i = n_0 e$. Therefore

$$i = A T^{\frac{1}{2}} e^{\int \frac{\phi_1}{kT^2} dT} = A T^{\frac{1}{2}} e^{-\frac{\phi_1}{kT}}, \tag{147.7}$$

where A is a new constant.

If n_0 were the number of electrons absorbed by the metal, it would also be the number emitted when equilibrium obtains between the metal and the saturated electronic gas outside. However, experiments show that a certain amount of reflection of electrons from the surface of a metal takes place, and therefore n_0 is not the number emitted.

Thus the number emitted is a constant times n_0, which may be included in the constant A, and so the form of the equation is not altered.

If we assume that an electron has zero energy within the metal, that it takes an amount of energy ϕ to mount the potential barrier, and that the average energy outside is $\frac{3}{2}kT$, then

$$\phi_1 = \phi + \tfrac{3}{2}kT.$$

Strictly, ϕ is the work function as usually defined. Introducing this value in equation (147.7) and integrating, we have

$$i = AT^2 e^{-\frac{\phi}{kT}}. \tag{147.8}$$

This is the second form of Richardson's equation. The experimental curve for platinum is given in Fig. 120 (Crowther). While equations (147.7) and (147.8) are somewhat different in form it is very difficult to distinguish between them experimentally, since the exponential term is the determining factor. However, recent experiments have shown that equation (147.8) is the more accurate.[1]

Richardson's equation, as modified by application of the Fermi-Dirac statistical distribution, is

$$i = 2\left(\frac{2\pi\, mek^2}{h^3}\right) T^2 e^{-\left(\frac{\omega_a - \omega}{kT}\right)}. \tag{147.9}$$

This equation is of the form

$$i = 2A_0 T^2 e^{-\frac{\phi}{kT}}. \tag{147.10}$$

A_0 is an absolute constant, as it depends only upon m, e, k, and h. If cgse. units are used its value is $1.806(10)^{11}$ cgseu. cm.$^{-2}$ deg.$^{-2}$ sec.$^{-1}$ or 60.2 amp. cm.$^{-2}$ deg.$^{-2}$ $w_a - w = \phi$ is the excess over the maximum energy an electron possesses within the metal at $0°$ K. which it must have in order to surmount the potential barrier at the surface of the metal. It will be seen by referring to Fig. 116 that the most energetic electrons inside platinum at $0°$ K. have energies of about 6 electron volts per electron. This energy is represented by w. w_a is the total energy required for escape providing an electron has zero energy

[1] See The Emission of Electricity from Hot Bodies by O. W. Richardson, 2nd ed. (1916); Ions, Electrons, and Ionizing Radiations, by J. A. Crowther, seventh ed.; Principles of Electricity and Electromagnetism by G. P. Harnwell; Electron and Nuclear Physics by J. B. Hoag.

inside the metal. Thus for platinum $\phi = 5.3$. Therefore $w_a = 11.3$ electron volts approximately. The value of $2A_0$ still presents some difficulties. While for a few metals the value of $2A_0$ may be calculated satisfactorily as indicated above, there are several instances, notably in the case of platinum, where experimental results are widely at variance with theory.[1]

148. The Thermionic Work Function. — Thermionic emission is very largely controlled by ϕ. The presence of a small trace of an impurity which has a small work function will greatly increase the emission. Wires coated with oxides of calcium, barium, strontium, thorium, or a mixture of these oxides have a thermionic emission greatly in excess of the emission of the pure metal. The emission from a coated tungsten wire may be several thousand times as great as from an uncoated wire at the same temperature. Coated wires are used extensively today in radio tubes of all types. Conversely, for the same emission a coated wire may be operated at a much lower temperature thus effecting a saving in electric energy.

Testing Richardson's Equation. — Equation (147.8) may be tested experimentally. A specially designed tube is used in which the filament is so exposed that its temperature may be measured with an optical pyrometer. The current may be measured with a milliammeter. Equation (147.8) is put in another form for use in this experiment. Dividing the equation by T^2 and taking $\log_e$ of both sides, we have

$$\log_e \frac{i}{T^2} = \log_e A - \frac{\phi}{k}\frac{1}{T}. \tag{148.1}$$

This equation is of the form $y = b + mx$. If the exponential form of Richardson's equation is correct the graph of this equation will be a straight line. If we plot the left-hand side of the equation ($y = \log_e(i/T^2)$) as ordinates against $1/T$ as abscissas, the graph is a straight line of slope $m = -\phi/k$. Then $b = \log_e A$ is the intercept on the y axis, from which A may be obtained. If the area of the filament is known, i, the current density, is obtained from current measurements, and hence i/T^2 is obtained. Thus, by measuring the slope of the line, k being a known constant, ϕ is obtained.

[1] For a full account of the present status of this subject see Dushman, Rev. of Mod. Phys. 2, 381 (1930).

If the area of the filament is not known we may still obtain a graph and so test the equation. Let us divide equation (147.8) by aT^2, where a is the unknown area of the filament. We then have

$$\log_e \frac{i}{T^2} = \log_e \frac{A}{a} - \frac{\phi}{k}\frac{1}{T} \tag{148.2}$$

This is also the equation of a straight line. i is the measured current. The graph should be a straight line if Richardson's equation is correct. The intercept on the y axis is now $\log_e(A/a)$. The slope of the line is as before $-\phi/k$, from which ϕ may be obtained.[1] The values for a few metals are given in the following Table:

Surface	A, Amp./cm.² deg.²	ϕ, volts
Barium	60	2.11
Cesium	162	1.81
Copper	65	4.33
Gold	40	4.90
Hafnium	14.5	3.53
Molybdenum	55	4.15
Nickel	1380	5.03
Palladium	60	4.99
Platinum	32	5.32
Silver		4.74
Tantalum	37.2	4.10
Thorium	70	3.38
Tungsten	60–100	4.53
Zirconium	330	4.1
Thorium on tungsten (monatomic layer), approx.		2.7
Cesium on oxygen on tungsten, approx.		1.0

149. Langmuir's Law. — Richardson's equation expresses the relation between the temperature of an emitting filament and the saturation current, i.e., the plate current when the plate potential is so large that all of the emitted electrons are swept over to the positive plate and none return to the filament. If, however, the potential difference between filament and plate is maintained constant, as indicated in Fig. 119, the plate current at first increases according to Richardson's equation, but a limiting value is reached for any fixed plate potential, if not too large. It is this limiting constant current that is expressed in Langmuir's law as a function of the plate voltage, the temperature being sufficiently high so as to give an abundant supply of electrons.

[1] See Electron and Nuclear Physics by J. B. Hoag, and Advanced Laboratory Practice in Electricity and Magnetism by E. M. Terry, 3rd ed.

The limitation of plate current is due to the space charge between filament and plate. At the point where the curves in Fig. 119 begin to depart from the Richardson curve, round off and flatten out, electrons return to the filament in increasing numbers or are prevented from escaping, being repelled by the negative space charge, until eventually electrons leave the filament only so fast as they can be carried away at the plate by the existing plate potential (flat part of curve). Thus the maximum space current between filament and plate, and hence also the plate current, is limited by the plate potential.

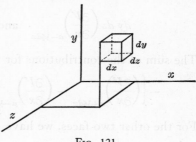

Fig. 121

In order to derive the relation between this limited plate current and the corresponding plate potential we may take a simple case of two parallel plates at a distance d apart, one hot and therefore emitting (cathode), the other cold and collecting charge (anode). Let the hot plate be at zero potential and the cold plate at a positive potential V. The electrons are assumed to stream across in parallel lines from the hot plate to the cold plate. Let this direction be taken as the x direction. Let the negative space-charge density at some point distant x from the cathode be ρ cgse. units per cu. cm.

We may make use of an equation first derived by Poisson in the derivation of Langmuir's equation. Let us first derive Poisson's equation, and then apply it to the case at hand.

Poisson's equation is an extension of Gauss's theorem to a distributed space charge. Consider a cube of sides dx, dy, dz in a coordinate system as shown in Fig. 121, the faces of the infinitesimal cube being taken parallel to the coordinate planes. Then by Gauss's theorem

$$\iint E' \, ds = 4\pi \rho \, dx \, dy \, dz,$$

by (6.1), where ρ is the volume density of charge at the center of the cube. Let the coordinates of the center of the cube be a, b, c. The coordinates of the faces parallel to the yz plane are then $x_1 = a - \frac{1}{2}dx$, $x_2 = a + \frac{1}{2}dx$. Likewise, for the other faces, we have $y_1 = b - \frac{1}{2}dy$,

$y_2 = b + \frac{1}{2}dy$, $z_1 = c - \frac{1}{2}dz$, $z_2 = c + \frac{1}{2}dz$. The x, y, and z components of the intensity E are

$$-\frac{\partial V}{\partial x}, \quad -\frac{\partial V}{\partial y}, \quad -\frac{\partial V}{\partial z}.$$

The Gaussian integral is the sum of the normal components of the intensity over the six faces of the cube. The contributions to the integral for the faces parallel to the yz plane are

$$dy\, dz \left(\frac{\partial V}{\partial x}\right)_{a-\frac{1}{2}dx} \quad \text{and} \quad -dy\, dz \left(\frac{\partial V}{\partial x}\right)_{a+\frac{1}{2}dx}.$$

The sum of the contributions for the two faces is

$$-\left\{\left(\frac{\partial V}{\partial x}\right)_{a+\frac{1}{2}dx} - \left(\frac{\partial V}{\partial x}\right)_{a-\frac{1}{2}dx}\right\} dy\, dz = -\frac{\partial^2 V}{\partial x^2}\, dx\, dy\, dz.$$

For the other two faces, we have

$$-\left(\frac{\partial^2 V}{\partial y^2}\right) dx\, dy\, dz \quad \text{and} \quad -\left(\frac{\partial^2 V}{\partial z^2}\right) dx\, dy\, dz.$$

Hence Gauss's integral yields

$$\left(\frac{\partial^2 V}{\partial x^2} + \frac{\partial^2 V}{\partial y^2} + \frac{\partial^2 V}{\partial z^2}\right) dx\, dy\, dz = -4\pi\rho\, dx\, dy\, dz.$$

Or

$$\frac{\partial^2 V}{\partial x^2} + \frac{\partial^2 V}{\partial y^2} + \frac{\partial^2 V}{\partial z^2} = -4\pi\rho.$$

In the present case the potential is assumed to vary only in the x direction. Therefore

$$\frac{\partial^2 V}{\partial y^2} = \frac{\partial^2 V}{\partial z^2} = 0,$$

and we have

$$\frac{d^2 V}{dx^2} = 4\pi\rho.$$

The space current density will be $i = \rho v$, where v is the velocity with which the electrons are moving. We also have

$$Ve = \frac{1}{2}mv^2.$$

It is assumed that the electrons have zero emission velocity. Hence

$$\frac{d^2V}{dx^2} = 4\pi \, i \sqrt{\frac{m}{2Ve}}. \tag{149.2}$$

An integrating factor is $2(dV/dx)$. On integrating, we have

$$\left(\frac{dV}{dx}\right)^2 = 8\pi \, i \sqrt{\frac{2Vm}{e}} + C.$$

At the cathode $x = 0$, $V = 0$, and therefore $\frac{dV}{dx} = 0$. Consequently $C = 0$, and we have

$$\left(\frac{dV}{dx}\right)^2 = 8\pi \, i \sqrt{\frac{2Vm}{e}}.$$

Integrating again and solving for i, we have

$$i = \frac{\sqrt{2}}{9\pi d^2} \sqrt{\frac{e}{m}} \, V^{3/2} = K V^{3/2}. \tag{149.3}$$ [1]

It may be seen from equations (149.3) that all quantities, excepting $\frac{e}{m}$, may be measured. This gives a means, therefore, of measuring the ratio of charge to mass in the case of thermions, a magnitude of considerable importance in electron physics. This method has been used by Dushman to measure e/m. He obtained $1.76(10)^7$ cgsm./gm. The accepted value is $1.75764(10)^7$ cgsm./gm. A correction must be made in this case for contact potential between cathode and anode and also for the emission velocity of the electrons.

We have considered in this short discussion of thermionics the fundamental principles involved in the modern radio tube. A very extensive industry has been built up which depends directly upon thermionic emission and its control. This phase of the subject will be taken up in a later chapter.

150. Photoelectric Emission. — Another means by which electrons may be caused to be emitted from a metal is through the agency of light of short wavelengths. In the year 1887 Hertz was experimenting with short electromagnetic waves for the purpose of verifying

---

[1] J. A. Crowther, Ions, Electrons, and Ionizing Radiations, 7th ed., p. 122.

Maxwell's electromagnetic theory of light. He was using an induction coil for the purpose of producing a spark discharge between two brass knobs. These discharges were known to be oscillatory, and therefore, according to current theory, should send out electromagnetic waves possessing the properties of light waves. As a detector of electromagnetic waves Hertz used another similar circuit which contained inductance and capacitance. The two circuits are shown schematically in Fig. 122. G_1 is the primary spark gap. When the condenser C_1 is charged to a sufficiently high potential difference V a spark jumps the gap G_1, i.e., electrons are supplied to one knob and removed from the other until the

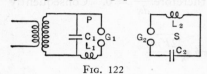

FIG. 122

electric field between the knobs is of sufficient strength to cause a breakdown of the air dielectric between the knobs. The discharge oscillates to and fro between the knobs, the amplitude decreasing with each succeeding surge. This is called a damped oscillation. If electromagnetic waves spread out from spark gap G_1 and envelop the secondary circuit, and the inductance and capacitance of the secondary circuit are such as to produce resonance between the two circuits, a spark will appear at spark gap G_2 at the instant of discharge in circuit P, if not too far away or too wide. Hertz observed, however, that if he interposed a screen between gaps G_1 and G_2 the spark did not occur at gap G_2. By a series of experiments he proved that when he cut off the ultraviolet light emanating from gap G_1 action ceased at gap G_2. Therefore, the ultraviolet light that illuminated the knobs of gap G_2 aided in the discharge in the secondary circuit. Hertz recorded these experiments in a paper entitled, "On an effect of ultraviolet light upon the electric discharge," which was published in 1887.[1] As Hertz was primarily engrossed in experiments on electromagnetic waves, he gave no further attention to the effect of light in producing electric discharges.

However, the following year Hallwachs took up the study of the effect of light in producing a discharge of electricity from metal surfaces, and to him instead of Hertz is usually given the credit for discovering photoelectric emission. Hallwachs found that when an insulated freshly polished surface of zinc was given a negative charge,

[1] See Hertz's Electric Waves.

and then illuminated with ultraviolet light, it lost its negative charge and acquired a positive charge of a certain limited value, but that when given a positive charge it was not discharged, but might be given an even greater positive charge. Clearly ultraviolet light removes negative charge from clean zinc.

The effect of ultraviolet light in causing electronic emission from a metal surface may be illustrated as indicated in Fig. 123. Two zinc plates z_1 and z_2 are enclosed in an evacuated quartz tube, and are connected through a milliammeter A to a battery B. Quartz is used since glass is opaque to ultraviolet light. If one of the zinc plates z_1 is illuminated by ultraviolet light v, as shown, and the positive terminal of the battery B is connected to the plate z_2 the milliammeter indicates the presence of a current but if the battery connections are reversed, no current flows, providing the negative potential is sufficiently large. If z_1 and z_2 are connected to a quadrant electrometer, instead of a battery, and z_1 is illuminated by ultraviolet light the electrometer shows that a difference of potential exists between plates z_1 and z_2, and such that z_1 is positive with respect to z_2. Thus electrons have been transferred from plate z_1 to plate z_2.

151. Stopping Potential. — Let us say that z_1, Fig. 123, is illuminated with monochromatic light of a given intensity. Let the potential difference V between z_1 and z_2 be varied. As V is increased in the positive sense, z_2 positive z_1 negative, there is no appreciable increase in the current i. This shows that practically all of the electrons freed from z_1 reach z_2 at zero potential, and that a small field has no effect in freeing electrons from the metal plate. Now reverse the battery and increase the potential difference in the negative sense, z_1 positive and z_2 negative. As the negative potential increases the current decreases, becoming zero at some negative potential $-V_0$, as shown in Fig. 124. This means that electrons are emitted with speeds varying from practically zero to some maximum represented by the *stopping potential* $-V_0$. The potential required to stop an electron will

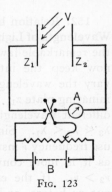

Fig. 123

depend upon its speed. The speed v of the fastest moving electron is given by

$$\tfrac{1}{2}mv_m^2 = V_0 e \qquad (151.1)$$

where V_0 and e are either both in cgse. or cgsm. units. Let us say that the current just considered had a maximum value i_1. Now double the intensity of illumination. A new current-potential curve is obtained with a maximum value i_2 which is $2i_1$. The stopping potential however remains the same. Let the intensity of illumination be tripled. A new curve is obtained of the same general shape, but the maximum current is $3i_1$, the stopping potential remaining the same as before. This illustrates one of the remarkable properties of photoelectric emission. *The photoelectric current is directly proportional to the intensity of illumination, the wavelength of the light remaining constant.* In mathematical form this statement says

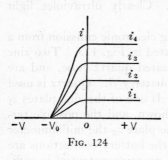

FIG. 124

$$i = KI(\lambda \text{ constant}), \tag{151.2}$$

where K is a constant of proportionality and I is the intensity of illumination. These curves show also that the energy with which the fastest electrons are emitted depends upon the wavelength of the light falling upon the plate. The validity of equation (151.2) gives to the photoelectric cell its chief commercial value.

152. Relation between Maximum Speeds of Photoelectrons and Wavelength of Light. —

With the hookup shown in Fig. 123 another of the remarkable laws of photoelectric emission may be shown. Let us now keep the intensity constant and vary the wavelength of the light illuminating plate z_1. Let us employ three different wavelengths, $\lambda_1, \lambda_2, \lambda_3$, where $\lambda_3 < \lambda_2 < \lambda_1$. Since $c = \lambda\nu$, we may use frequency ν instead of wavelength λ, as it is more convenient. Then $\nu_3 > \nu_2 > \nu_1$. If the experiment is carried out as before, and curves are plotted for the three selected frequencies, curves

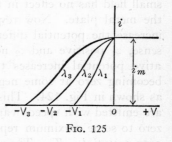

FIG. 125

such as those shown in Fig. 125 will be obtained. The curves show that the higher the frequency ν the greater is the stopping potential $-V_0$, and consequently the greater the energy of the fastest electron. Experiments have shown that *the maximum velocity of emission of photoelectrons (maximum energy) is strictly independent of the intensity of illumination*. This is the second remarkable property of photoelectrons.

153. Theory of Photoelectric Emission. — A very simple linear relationship has been found by Millikan [1] between the frequency of the light and the maximum energy of emission. If a curve is plotted between the maximum energy of emission of an electron $(V_0e = \frac{1}{2}mv_m^2)$ and the frequency (v), a straight line is obtained as shown in Fig. 126. This curve has an intercept v_0 on the frequency axis. v_0 is characteristic of the metal used as emitters, *but the slopes of the curves for all emitters is the same*. The equation of the curve is

$$V_0e = \frac{1}{2}mv_m^2 = hv - hv_0 \text{ ergs,} \quad (153.1)$$

where h is the constant slope of the curves. Each term in this equation is an energy term. hv depends only upon the frequency of the incident light. hv_0 depends upon the kind of emitter used. Equation (153.1) may be written

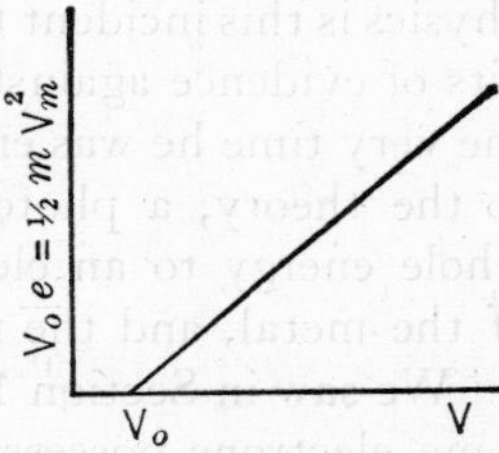

FIG. 126

$$\frac{1}{2}mv_m^2 = hv - w_0. \quad (153.2)$$

This equation was first stated by Einstein in 1905 from theoretical considerations and is known as Einstein's *photoelectric equation*. It is one of the most fundamental and important equations of modern physics.

Equation (153.2) is interpreted as follows: The fastest photoelectrons are emitted with energy $\frac{1}{2}mv_m^2$. *hv is the energy given to the electron by a quantum of radiant energy corresponding to a frequency v.* $w_0 = hv_0$ is the energy required to lift the electron over the potential barrier at the surface of the metal, and is therefore the *work function*. w_0 will differ for different metals. v_0 is the limiting frequency which will enable emission to take place in the case of the particular metal to which it refers. The difference between hv and w_0 is the energy with which the electron leaves the surface of the metal. When $hv = hv_0$, $v_m = 0$ and there is no emission. Hence v_0 is called the *threshold frequency*. Any quantum of light (photon) of frequency

[1] See The Electron, by R. A. Millikan.

less than ν_0 (longer wavelength) of incident light will have an energy value too small to lift an electron over the surface potential barrier for the particular metal. h turns out to be Planck's constant which has a value $6.6283(10)^{-27}$ erg sec. This is a universal constant of wide occurrence. It made its first appearance in Max Panck's theoretical work on radiation. $h\nu$ is the energy value of a quantum of radiation (photon) of frequency ν. In equations (153.1) and (153.2) all terms are measured in ergs, ν is in cycles/sec., m in gms. and ν in cms./sec.

The photoelectric effect can be explained only on a quantum theory of radiation. The electromagnetic wave theory of light is wholly inadequate to explain this phenomenon. Among the ironies of physics is this incident that Hertz uncovered one of the most damaging bits of evidence against the validity of the electromagnetic theory at the very time he was endeavoring to prove its soundness. According to the theory, a photon when incident upon a metal transmits its whole energy to an electron, a part of which lifts the electron out of the metal, and the remainder gives it kinetic energy.

We saw in Section 147 that, according to the Fermi-Dirac theory, some electrons possess while in the metal a very large energy, and therefore, $w_0 = h\nu_0$ is not the whole energy required to lift an electron out of the metal. The equation $w_a - w = \phi$ holds for photoelectric emission as well as for thermionic emission. ϕ of Section 147 corresponds to $w_0 = h\nu_0$ of this Section.

154. The Photoelectric Cell. — A typical photoelectric cell is shown in Fig. 127a. The active substance is deposited upon the concave surface of a cylindrical cathode. The alkali metals are used as active substance when the photoelectric cell is to be used in the visible spectrum, as these metals have smaller work functions than other metals, and hence the threshold frequency is in the red end of the spectrum or even in the infrared. Special photoelectric cells when used only in the ultraviolet range have quartz bulbs and the active substance may then have a larger work function, higher threshold frequency. A photoelectric cell and connections for showing the effect is shown in Fig. 127b.

There are two types of cells used commercially, high-vacuum type and gas-filled type. The high-vacuum cells have a practically instantaneous response but give a small photoelectric current. However, they are not subject to injury by high potentials. Where a large current is required an inert gas (helium or argon) is used in the cell. The advantage of the gas-filled cell is that, through ionization of the gas, a larger current is obtained with the same intensity of illumination than in the other type cell. However, care must be exercised not to apply too great a potential lest the active surface of the cell be impaired. When a high potential is used the positive ions may be driven against the cathode with sufficient force to detach more or less

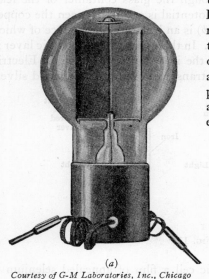

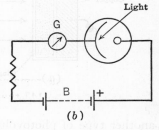

(a)

Courtesy of G-M Laboratories, Inc., Chicago

FIG. 127

of the active material. The response of the gas-filled cell is slower than the high-vacuum type. Photoelectric cells have a wide application both in the commercial field and in the scientific field.[1]

155. The Photovoltaic Effect. — There is a class of boundary surfaces, very much like the rectifying layers mentioned in Section 54, across which there is developed a potential difference when the surface is illuminated. These boundary layers are unidirectional so far as the passage of electrons is concerned. When an electron in the layer absorbs the energy of a photon it moves in one direction rather than the other. Thus when illuminated, electrons move in one direction and so set up a difference of potential between the substances on either side of the layer, which may be used to send a current through an external circuit, a relay let us say, which may close another circuit for the purpose of operating some electric appliance. Two cells of

[1] For a very complete discussion of photoelectric phenomena, see Photoelectric Phenomena, by A. L. Hughes and L. A. Du Bridge.

this type are shown in Fig. 128. The cell (*a*) is very much like the copper oxide rectifier. In this case the copper oxide is the electronic anisotropic layer between a solution of lead nitrate and a block of copper. When illuminated through the glass container of the lead nitrate solution a difference of potential is set up between the copper and lead nitrate solution. Cell (*b*) is an iron disc on one face of which is formed a layer of iron selenide. In this case the photovoltaic layer is the surface of contact between the iron and iron selenide. Electric contact is made by means of a translucent layer of sputtered silver.

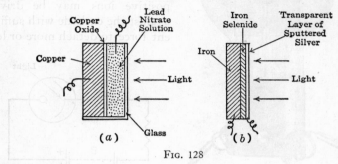

FIG. 128

In another type of photovoltaic cell a film of annealed selenium is formed on a thick disc of iron. Light passing through the thin film of selenium causes electrons to move from the iron to the selenium, thus setting up a difference of potential. Cuprous oxide on a heavy disc of copper acts as a rectifier, permitting current to pass readily from cuprous oxide to copper. This unit also acts as a photovoltaic cell. When illuminated it causes electrons to travel in the reverse direction from that when acting as a rectifier. The cuprous oxide becomes positive to the copper. The "photronic" and "photox" cells belong to this class. Unlike photoelectric cells, these cells require no external battery. The emf. of a photovoltaic cell is small, but it is sufficient to operate miniature relays, which in turn may be used to operate larger relays.[1]

[1] See L. O. Grondahl, Rev. Modern Phys. 5, 141 (1933).

CHAPTER XI

ELECTROMAGNETICS

156. In Sections 91 and 92 there were described the fundamental experiments by which Oersted showed that a current of electricity is always accompanied by a magnetic field of force, and the rule for ascertaining the direction of the field, when the direction of the current is known, was given. Ampère's law was stated and applied in defining the cgsm. unit current. It was shown that the magnetic intensity dH due to a current element dl is given by

$$aH = k\,\frac{idl}{r^2}\sin\theta,$$

and that if we apply this expression, so defining i as to make $k = 1$, to obtain the intensity at the center of a circular loop of wire bearing a current i, we have

$$H = \frac{2\pi ni}{r}, \; i \text{ in cgsm. units,} \quad \text{or} \quad H = \frac{2\pi nI}{10r}, \; I \text{ in amperes.}$$

Starting from this point, a number of relations between currents and and magnetic fields of force will be derived.

157. Magnetic Intensity on the Axis of a Circular Current. — Let it be required to derive an expression for the magnetic intensity at a point P on the axis of a single, circular current loop ae, and distant p
cms. from the center c of the loop,
Fig. 129. The component dH_x of
the intensity along the axis (x axis)
at P due to an element of current dl,
is given by the expression

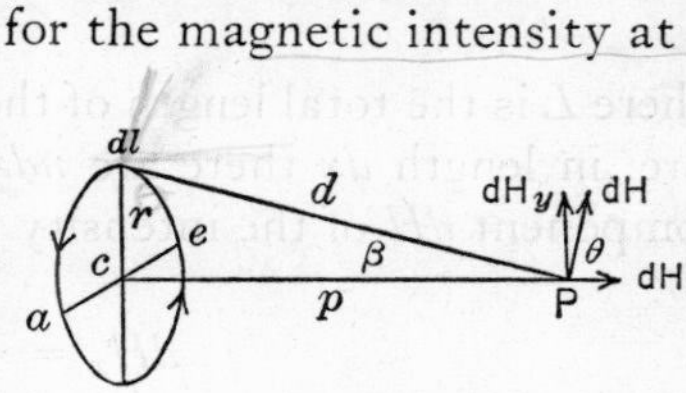

FIG. 129

$$dH_x = \frac{idl}{r^2 + x^2}\cos\theta = \frac{idl}{r^2 + p^2}\sin\beta = \frac{ridl}{(r^2 + p^2)^{3/2}}.$$

And for the whole loop

$$H_x = \frac{ri}{(r^2 + p^2)^{\frac{3}{2}}} \int_0^{2\pi r} dl = \frac{2\pi r^2 i}{(r^2 + p^2)^{\frac{3}{2}}} \text{ oersteds.} \quad (157.1)$$

If the current is expressed in amperes

Intensity on Axis of Coil

$$H_x = \frac{2\pi r^2 I}{10(r^2 + p^2)^{\frac{3}{2}}} \text{ oersteds.} \quad (157.2)$$

The components dH_y of the intensity normal to the axis of the loop at P sum up to zero for the entire loop. Thus the resultant intensity for the whole loop is along its axis. If there are n turns of wire in the loop, so as to constitute a very short solenoid of relatively large radius, the expression becomes

$$H_x = \frac{2\pi n r^2 i}{(r^2 + p^2)^{\frac{3}{2}}} \text{ oersteds.} \quad (157.3)$$

The intensity at the center of the loop is obtained by putting $p = 0$, and is, as in Section 92,

Intensity at Centre Coil

$$H_x = \frac{2\pi n i}{r}, \quad \text{or} \quad H_x = \frac{2\pi n I}{10r}.$$

158. Intensity Due to a Long Solenoid. — Let there be n turns of wire per unit length of the solenoid, N turns in all. Then $n = N/L$,

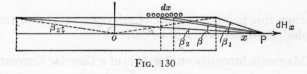

FIG. 130

where L is the total length of the solenoid windings, Fig. 130. Therefore, in length dx there are $ndx = (N/L)dx$ turns. Hence the axial component dH of the intensity at P due to the ndx turns is

$$dH_x = \frac{2\pi \, r^2 \, Ni \, dx}{L(r^2 + x^2)^{\frac{3}{2}}}. \quad (158.1)$$

Now $x = r \cot \beta$, $dx = - r \csc^2 \beta d\beta$, and

$$\sin \beta = \frac{r}{(r^2 + x^2)^{\frac{1}{2}}}.$$

On substituting and reducing, there results

$$H_x = -\frac{2\pi Ni}{L} \int_{\beta_1}^{\beta_2} \sin \beta \, d\beta = \frac{2\pi Ni}{L} (\cos \beta_2 - \cos \beta_1) \text{ oersteds.} \quad (158.2)$$

If the point P be taken at the center O of the solenoid, and the solenoid be very long and of relatively small radius, the angles β_2 and β_1 may be taken as essentially equal to zero and π, and we then have

$$H_x = \frac{4\pi Ni}{L} \text{ oersteds, } i \text{ in cgsm. units,}$$

or

$$H_x = \frac{4\pi NI}{10L} \text{ oersteds, } I \text{ in amperes.} \quad (158.3)$$

L is in cms. in both equations. When the current is in amperes, the product NI is called the total *ampere turns*. If NI is constant with any variation of N and I the intensity H_x remains constant. We may, also, write $H_x = 4\pi ni$ oersteds, or $4\pi nI/10$ oersteds. nI is ampere turns per unit length of the solenoid.

The expression $H_x = 4\pi ni$ or $H_x = 4\pi nI/10$ does not give the correct value for the intensity at the ends of the solenoid, because of the divergence of the tubes of flux and flux leakage. From equation (158.2) we may obtain the approximate intensity at the ends of the solenoid by putting $\beta_1 = \pi/2$. Then if β_2 is taken equal to zero, we have

$$H_x = \frac{2\pi Ni}{L},$$

which is half of its value at the center. The intensity at any point on the axis extended is obtained by assigning the proper values to β_1 and β_2.

If, however, the solenoid is curved around so as to bring the two ends together, thus forming a toroid or anchor ring, the expression $H = 4\pi ni$ gives an approximately correct value for all points within the solenoid. In this case the field outside the solenoid is negligibly small, as it is due solely to flux leakage. The wires are of necessity wound closer together on the inside than on the outside of the toroid, and, consequently, the field will vary within the windings, being greatest on the inside and least on the outside. If r' and r'' are the inside and outside radii of the anchor ring, the number of wires per unit length on the inside is $N/2\pi\, r'$, and on the outside $N/2\pi\, r''$. Hence the intensity varies from $\dfrac{2Ni}{r'}$ to $\dfrac{2Ni}{r''}$.

159. Intensity Due to an Infinitely Long, Straight Current. — Let it be required to calculate the intensity at a point P, Fig. 131, due to an infinitely long, straight current of i cgsm. units. Consider the effect at P due to an element of current of length dl. We have, $dl' = ad\beta$, and $r = a\cos\beta$. Therefore

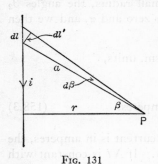

$$dl' = \frac{rd\beta}{\cos\beta},$$

and

$$dH = i\frac{dl'}{a^2} = \frac{i\cos\beta\,d\beta}{r}.$$

FIG. 131

For the whole current $H = \dfrac{2i}{r}\displaystyle\int_0^{\frac{\pi}{2}}\cos\beta\ d\beta = \dfrac{2i}{r}$ oersteds, where

i is in cgsm. units. If the current is in amperes,

$$H = \frac{2I}{10r}\text{ oersteds.} \qquad (159.1)$$

This equation is a statement of the law of Biot and Savart. If the limits of integration are $+\beta_1$ and $-\beta_2$, we have

$$H = \frac{i}{r}\int_{-\beta_2}^{\beta_1}\cos\beta\ d\beta = \frac{i}{r}(\sin\beta_1 + \sin\beta_2). \qquad (159.2)$$

If there are N wires, each bearing a current i, we have

$$H = \frac{Ni}{r}(\sin\beta_1 + \sin\beta_2). \qquad (159.3)$$

160. Work Done in Moving a Magnetic Pole around a Current. — In the preceding Section the expression for the intensity at a point distant r cms. from a cgsm. current i was obtained. Since the force acting on a pole of strength m in a magnetic field of intensity H is $F = mH$, the force acting on a pole of strength m in the field of force due to a current is $F = 2mi/r$. We may use this expression to obtain the work required to move a magnetic pole once around a current in opposition to the magnetic field, or the work done by the current in moving the magnetic pole once around the current with the magnetic field. Since work is force times distance, we have

$$W = \frac{2mi}{r} \, 2\pi \, r = 4\pi \, mi \text{ ergs.} \tag{160.1}$$

If the current is in amperes the work is given by

$$W = 4\pi \, \frac{mI}{10} \text{ ergs.} \tag{160.2}$$

If the pole is a unit pole the work is $W = 4\pi \, i = 4\pi \, I/10$ ergs/pole. Since these expressions are independent of r we see that the same amount of work is done when a magnetic pole is carried around a current no matter what path is followed.

The magnetic potential in the magnetic field due to a current is now readily obtained as follows: Since, in the case of an isolated long, straight current, the lines of magnetic flux are concentric circles about the conductor, the equipotential lines or surfaces are radial. Therefore, the difference of potential between the point a and the point c, Fig. 132, is the work done in moving a unit magnetic pole from the point b to the point c along a line of flux. No work is done in moving the pole from a to b along an equipotential line. If the pole is returned to a by another path, $cdefa$ say, the net work done in the cycle is zero. However, if the return path carries the pole around the current back to the starting point a, the net work done is $4\pi \, i$ ergs irrespective of the path. Therefore, in a magnetic field which is due

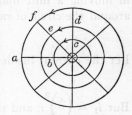

Fig. 132

to a current of electricity, the potential at any point is not a single valued function of the position. It depends upon the number of times the pole has encircled the current.

We may now use the foregoing as another means of determining the intensity inside a long solenoid. Let N be the whole number of turns, and L the length of the solenoid. If n is the number of turns per unit length, $n \, dx$ is the number of turns in a length dx. Let a unit magnetic pole be moved once around the rectangle $abdca$, Fig. 133. Since the work done in moving a unit magnetic pole once around a single current is $4\pi i$ ergs, the work required to move a unit pole once around $n\, dx$ turns is

$$dW = 4\pi\, ni\, dx.$$

Therefore,

$$H = \frac{dW}{dx} = 4\pi\, ni = 4\pi\, \frac{Ni}{L} \text{ oersteds.}$$

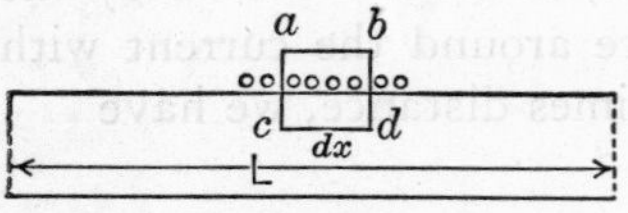

FIG. 133

The only work that is done is in moving from c to d, assuming the flux to be wholly within the solenoid and parallel to its axis, which is the case only if there is no leakage.

161. Magnetic Intensity Inside a Cylindrical Current. — Let a be

the radius of the cylindrical conductor. It is required to find the intensity H_x at a distance x, $x < a$, from the center of the conductor when a current i cgsm. units flows in the conductor, Fig. 134. If the current is a steady, direct current, and the conductor is homogeneous, the current density will be constant over the section of the conductor. The work done in moving a unit magnetic pole once around the circle of radius x is

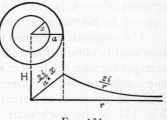

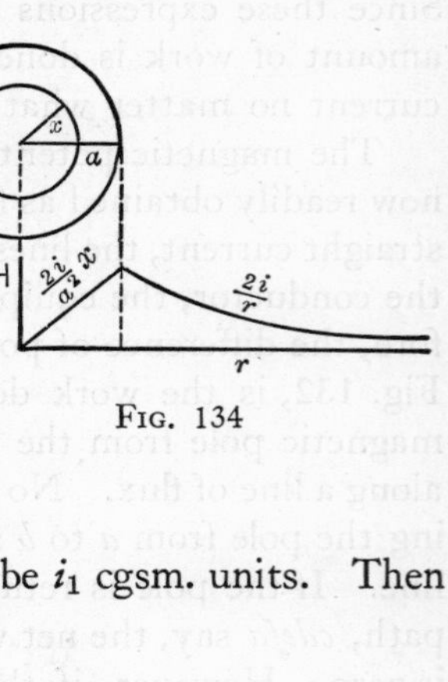

FIG. 134

$$W = H_x 2\pi\, x \text{ ergs.}$$

Let the current inside the circle of radius x be i_1 cgsm. units. Then

$$W = 4\pi\, i_1.$$

But $i_1 = \left(\dfrac{x}{a}\right)^2 i$, and therefore,

$$W = 4\pi \left(\frac{x}{a}\right)^2 i = H_x 2\pi\, x,$$

and hence

$$H_x = \frac{2i}{a^2}\, x \text{ oersteds.}$$

The intensity is, therefore, proportional to the distance from the center of the conductor. The curve in the lower part of Fig. 134 shows the manner in which H varies from the center of the conductor out. It has its maximum value at the surface of the conductor. If the conductor is hollow, the intensity within the hollow space is zero, since there is no current within this space.

In the case of the magnetic field due to a current considered in Section 159 the return current was assumed to be so far away as to have a negligible effect on the magnetic field considered. Let us now consider a conductor cd of radius a, Fig. 135, bearing a current i cgsm. units, the return circuit being a concentric cylinder of radius b. The two circuits may be connected at the ends by conducting plates normal to the conductors. The magnetic intensity inside the conductor cd will be as in the former case. Consider any line of flux, as ef or radius r, between the conductors. For this line of flux, we have

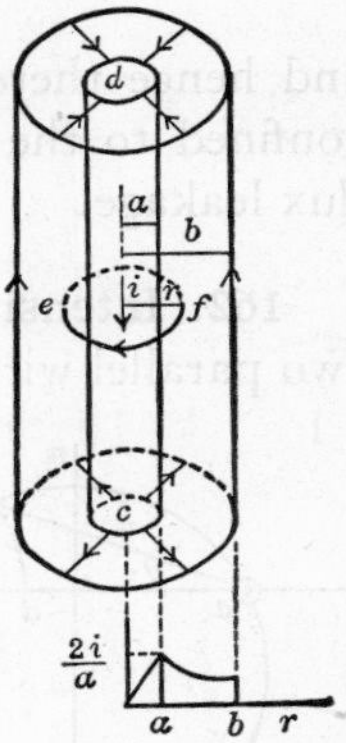

$$2\pi \, r \, H_r = 4\pi \, i, \quad \text{or} \quad H_r = \frac{2i}{r} \text{ oersteds.}$$

For any value of r greater than b, we have

$$2\pi \, rH_r = 4\pi \, i - 4\pi \, i = 0, \quad \text{or} \quad H_r = 0.$$

FIG. 135

Therefore, the magnetic field is entirely within the cylinder of radius b. The intensity curve for this case is shown in the lower drawing of Fig. 135. As the radius b of the outer cylinder is increased we approach the ideal case of an infinitely long isolated current.

Let us next consider, from this viewpoint, the toroid or ring solenoid of mean radius a, Fig. 136, which was considered in Section 158. Clearly, the tubes of flux are circles in planes parallel to the surface of the paper with a common, perpendicular axis passing through o. The toroid is wound with N turns of wire uniformly spaced. The work done in moving a unit pole once around the circle of radius c inside the windings is

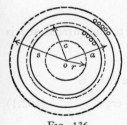

FIG. 136

$$W = H2\pi \, c = 4\pi \, Ni \text{ ergs/unit pole,}$$

or

$$H = \frac{4\pi \, Ni}{2\pi \, c} = \frac{4\pi \, Ni}{L} = 4\pi \, ni \text{ oersteds.}$$

For a circle inside the ring solenoid of radius r, $H2\pi r = 0$, since the magnetic pole does not encircle a current, or $i = 0$. For a path outside the ring solenoid of radius s, we have

$$H2\pi s = 4\pi Ni - 4\pi Ni = 0,$$

and hence there is no field outside the ring solenoid. The field is confined to the space within the windings, assuming, of course, no flux leakage.

162. Intensity and Potential Due to Two Parallel Currents. — Let

two parallel wires s cms. apart, shown in section at a and b, Fig. 137,

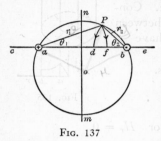

FIG. 137

carry currents i cgsm. units in opposite directions, as in the case of a pair of transmission wires. Let it be required to find the potential at any point P in the magnetic field due to the two currents. The line *cabe* is clearly an equipotential line, and may be taken as the equipotential $V = 0$. From the point f let a unit pole be moved along the arc of the circle with center at a (line of flux) to the point P. Work will be done from f to P of amount

$$w = \frac{2i}{r_1} \times r_1\theta_1 = 2i\,\theta_1 \text{ ergs.}$$

Likewise, the work done because of the field due to the current at b is

$$w = 2i\,\theta_2 \text{ ergs.}$$

Therefore, the potential at P, relative to the line *cabe*, is

$$V = 2i\,\theta_1 + 2i\,\theta_2 = 2i(\theta_1 + \theta_2) \text{ ergs.} \tag{162.1}$$

If V is to remain constant as the point P moves, $\theta_1 + \theta_2 = \pi - \beta$, where $\beta = $ angle aPb must remain constant. This condition requires that P moves along the arc of a circle. Therefore, the equipotential lines are the series of circles passing through the centers of the wires at a and b with centers on the perpendicular bisector *nom* of the line ab.

Lines of magnetic flux cut equipotential lines at right angles. Thus, the lines of magnetic flux are the series of circles having their centers on the lines be and ac, Fig. 138. The tangents to the circular lines of flux are lines drawn from o, the midpoint of ab, and of constant length oa or ob. To construct a line of flux, draw a line from o to any point P on the circle with center at o and radius oa. From P draw a line normal to oP intersecting the line obe at the point e. e is then the center of a particular line of flux of radius eP. This circle will cut all of the equipotential lines orthogonally. Other lines are

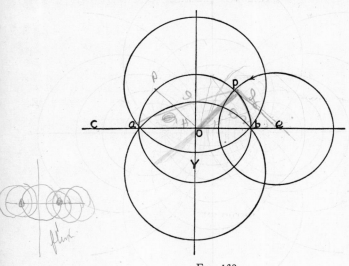

Fig. 138

constructed in the same manner. A more complete set of lines of flux and equipotential lines, constructed in this manner, is shown in Fig. 139.

To obtain the intensity at any point P, Fig. 140, we may proceed as follows: The intensity H, being normal to the equipotential passing through P, will pass through the center o of the circle. The intensities at P of the magnetic fields due to the currents at a and b are e and f, say. We will then have

$$H = e \cos \lambda + f \cos \alpha, \quad \text{and} \quad e \sin \lambda = f \sin \alpha.$$

Now it is easily seen from the construction of the Figure that $\alpha = \theta_2$ and $\lambda = \theta_1$. Therefore,

$$H = e \cos \theta_1 + f \cos \theta_2.$$

But $e = 2i/r_2$, and $f = 2i/r_1$. $\cos \theta_1 = ac/r_1$, and $\cos \theta_2 = bc/r_2$. Hence,

$$H = \frac{2i}{r_2} \times \frac{ac}{r_1} + \frac{2i}{r_1} \times \frac{bc}{r_2} = 2i \left(\frac{ac + bc}{r_1 r_2} \right) = 2i \frac{s}{r_1 r_2}. \qquad (162.2)$$

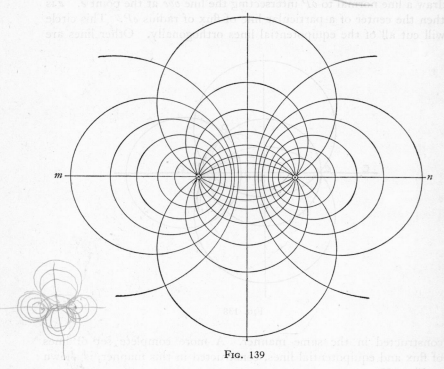

FIG. 139

If the point P is on the line ab, distant x from a, say, then

$$H = 2i \frac{s}{x(s - x)}. \qquad (162.3)$$

Putting $dH/dx = 0$, it is found that H is a minimum at a point on the line ab such that $x = s/2$, i.e., half way between a and b.

The total flux ϕ per cm. of length of line between the inside edges of the wires of radius r is given by

$$\phi = 2i \int_r^{s-r} \frac{s}{x(s - x)} \, dx = 4i \log_e \frac{s - r}{r} \text{ maxwells.} \qquad (162.4)$$

163. Current Circuit Equivalent to a Magnetic Shell. — It was stated in Section 91 that in 1823 Ampère showed that "Every linear conductor carrying a current is equivalent to a magnetic shell, . . ." We will now consider Ampère's equivalent current magnetic shell more at length. Let us first consider the special case of the magnetic field due to a circular current at a point on its axis where the distance from the center of the circle is large as compared with the radius of the circle.

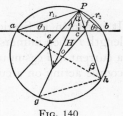

FIG. 140

In Section 157 it was shown that the magnetic intensity at a point P on the axis of a circular current of i cgsm. units is given by

$$H = \frac{2\pi r^2 i}{(x^2 + r^2)^{\frac{3}{2}}} = \frac{2ai}{(x^2 + r^2)^{\frac{3}{2}}},$$

where a is the area of the current circuit, considered to be very small. Then very approximately

$$H = \frac{2ai}{x^3}.$$

Now imagine a very short magnet of poleface area a to be placed within the circular current so that the magnetic axis of the magnet coincides with that of the circular current, the center of the magnet coinciding with that of the circle. At the distance x from the common center of magnet and current circuit the magnetic intensity due to the magnet is given by

$$H = \frac{2M}{x^3}.$$

If the magnetic intensity at P due to the current circuit is to be the same as that due to the magnet, we must have

$$M = ai.$$

That is, a circular current of area a has a magnetic moment of value ai.

A more general and more satisfactory way of arriving at the same result is as follows: Suppose the magnet just considered to be immersed in a uniform magnetic field of intensity H, and that the magnetic axis of the magnet makes an angle θ with the direction of the field. It has been shown that the couple acting on the magnet is given by

$$L = MH \sin \theta.$$

It is shown in Section 169 that the force acting on a conductor of length l when immersed in a magnetic field of intensity H and bearing a current of i cgsm. units is Hil dynes. From this it follows that the couple acting on a current circuit is given by

$$L = Hai \sin \theta,$$

where θ is the angle between the axis of the current circuit and the direction of the magnetic field H. If the couples are to have the same value, we must have

$$M = ai,$$

as before. This will be true whatever the shape of the area a. It need not necessarily be circular.

It was shown in Section 63 that the magnetic moment of a magnetic shell is given by

$$M = a\sigma t = a\phi.$$

Now if the magnet being considered is very short, t small, we may consider it to be a small magnetic shell of area a. But $\sigma t = \phi$, the strength of the shell. Therefore, since $M = ai$, we have $i = \phi$ if the magnetic shell and current circuit are to possess the same magnetic moment, and presumably equivalent magnetic fields. That is, if the magnetic field of the current circuit is equivalent to that of the magnetic shell of the same area a the current i cgsm. units must be numerically equal to the strength ϕ of the magnetic shell.

It was shown in Section 75 that the potential V due to a magnetic shell is given by

$$V = \phi\omega,$$

where ω is the solid angle subtended by the area a at any point P. Hence, for a shell of very small area a, the potential is

$$dV = \phi d\omega.$$

But $\phi = M/a$, and hence

$$dV = \left(\frac{M}{A}\right) d\omega.$$

The current circuit having the same magnetic moment is given by $M = ai$. Therefore,

$$dV = \frac{ai}{a}\, d\omega = i\, d\omega.$$

Now let us consider a current circuit (or magnetic shell) of much larger area A. Let us divide the current circuit of area A into a very large number of meshes, each of area a say, by a network of conductors. If now a current i flows around each mesh, in the counterclockwise sense say, the sides of each mesh, not at the periphery of the area A, will have equal but oppositely directed currents, and hence they will annul each other, leaving only the current around the boundary of the larger area A. A magnetic shell of area A may be considered to be made up of a great number of elemental magnetic shells each of area a. The potential at any point P will then be given by

$$\int_0^V dV = \phi \int_0^\Omega d\omega \quad \text{or} \quad V = \phi\Omega.$$

Likewise, for a current circuit we will have

$$\int_0^V dV = i \int_0^\Omega d\omega \quad \text{or} \quad V = i\Omega,$$

where Ω is the solid angle subtended by the area A of the circular current (or magnetic shell) at the point P. Therefore, if a current circuit having the same periphery as a magnetic shell is to have an equivalent magnetic field the cgsm. current i must be numerically equal to the strength ϕ of the magnetic shell. If there are n turns of wire constituting the current circuit, $V = ni\Omega$, and then $\phi = ni$.

It follows from the foregoing that the potential at any point P due to a magnetic shell depends only upon the strength of the shell and the solid angle subtended by it at the point P. Thus, the potential is independent of the shape of the shell providing the boundary remains fixed. Hence, for example, for a point near an infinite plane the potential is $2\pi\phi$, and also for a hemispherical shell for a point at its center of curvature the potential is $2\pi\phi$, since in either case the solid angle subtended by the shell at the point P is 2π.

Problem. — Starting with $V = i\Omega$, prove that for a circular current, at a point on its axis distant x from its center, the magnetic intensity is given by

$$H = \frac{2\pi r^2 i}{(x^2 + r^2)^{3/2}}. \quad \text{Start with } H = -\frac{\partial V}{\partial x}.$$

The argument just presented is valid only for vacuum conditions. It is shown in more recondite treatises that the magnetic intensity due to a current of electricity is unaffected by a surrounding magnetic medium of permeability μ. However, the magnetic intensity due to a magnetic pole is one μth of its value in a vacuum when surrounded by a magnetic medium of permeability μ. Therefore, if the equivalent magnetic shell is to produce the same intensity and potential at all external points in its magnetic field as a current circuit it must possess a strength equal to μi.[1]

Let us consider one other point. Suppose that we have a current circuit which, for all external points, is equivalent to a magnetic shell whose periphery coincides with that of the current circuit, i.e., $i = \phi$. Let us obtain an expression for the work done when a unit positive magnetic pole is moved from a point on the negative face of the shell around its edge against the field to a point on the positive face of the shell. For a point on the face of a magnetic shell $\Omega = 2\pi$, and therefore, $V = 2\pi\phi$. On the positive face we have $V' = 2\pi\phi$, and on the negative face $V'' = -2\pi\phi$. Therefore, $V' - V'' = 4\pi\phi$. An equal amount of work is done by the field if the pole is moved in the reverse direction. If the pole is moved through a small hole in the shell back to the starting point, the work done in this part of its path is equal to the work done in that part of its path which is outside the substance of the shell, but is opposite in sense. Thus the work done in carrying a pole once around a closed path which is in part outside the substance of the shell and in part within the substance of the shell is zero. However, the work done in moving a unit magnetic pole in like manner with respect to the equivalent current shell is $4\pi i$ ergs, since the pole has been moved once around the current i.

Since the magnetic field of a current circuit at all external points is equivalent to that of a particular magnetic shell the expressions for potential and intensity obtained in Section 66 hold also for a current circuit. Thus, we have for the current circuit

$$V = \frac{Ai}{r^2} \cos \theta, \quad H_r = \frac{2Ai}{r^3} \cos \theta, \quad H_\theta = \frac{Ai}{r^3} \sin \theta,$$

if r is large as compared with the dimensions of A. θ is the angle made with the axis of the current circuit drawn in the positive direction.

[1] Principles of Electricity by Page and Adams, Section 71, p. 253.

1. Two transmission wires 50 cms. apart in a horizontal plane carry currents of 200 amperes in opposite directions. Calculate the magnetic intensity at a point midway between them and 30 cms. above the plane of the wires. What is the direction of the magnetic field at this point? Show by diagram.

What is the magnetic potential at this point, assuming the magnetic potential to be zero on the line joining the centers of the wires.

What is the magnetic potential at an infinite distance above the plane of the wires on the perpendicular bisector of the line connecting the centers of the wires? What is the magnetic intensity at this point?

2. A circular current of 50 amperes has a radius of 5 cms. At a point P on the axis of the circular current distant x cms. from the center of the circle the magnetic potential is 15.7 ergs/pole. Find the value of x. What is the magnetic intensity at this point?

3. A very long wire having a diameter of 2 mm. bears a current of 30 amperes. (*a*) What is the magnetic intensity at the surface of the wire? At a point 30 cms. from the center of the wire? (*b*) How many lines of flux per meter length of wire lie between lines distant 10 cms. and 100 cms. from the axis of the wire?

4. A single wire circuit, bearing a current of 20 amperes, is in the form of a rectangle 30 cms. on one side and 20 cms. on the other side. Calculate the magnetic intensity at the center of the rectangle.

5. Show that the magnetic intensity at the center of a square, the length of each side being a cms., for a single wire bearing a current I amperes is

$$\frac{16\,I}{10\,a\,\sqrt{2}} \text{ oersteds.}$$

6. In Problem 2 calculate the difference of potential between the center of the circular current and a point on its axis at a distance of 20 cms. from the center.

7. What is the total magnetic flux per meter of length of the transmission line of Problem 1 between the wires if they are each 1 cm. in diameter?

8. A long solenoid consists of 500 turns of wire uniformly wound on a wooden cylinder. The length of the windings is 100 cms., and the diameter measured between centers of the wires is 10 cms. When 12 amperes flow in the windings, calculate (*a*) the magnetic intensity on the axis at the center of the solenoid, (*b*) on the axis at one end of the solenoid, (*c*) on the axis 10 cms. beyond the end of the solenoid.

9. Given a circuit having the form of a regular polygon of n sides inscribed in a circle of radius a, show that the magnetic intensity at the center is given by

$$H = \frac{2ni}{a} \tan \frac{\pi}{n},$$

where i is in *cgsm.* units. Show that when n is infinite, $H = \dfrac{2\pi i}{a}.$

10. A wire in the form of a square of sides a bears a current i cgsm. units. Show that the magnetic intensity at a point on the axis of the square at a

distance d from the center is given by

$$H = \frac{2\, i a^2}{\left(\dfrac{a^2}{4} + d^2\right)\sqrt{\dfrac{a^2}{2} + d^2}}.$$

Show that when d is zero this expression reduces to the expression obtained in Problem 5.

11. Using the data of Problem 2, calculate (a) the potential at a distance of $r = 30$ cms. from the center of the circular current. (b) Calculate the intensity H.

12. Referring to Fig. 138, prove that lines of flux, drawn as indicated in Section 162, cut all equipotential lines orthogonally.

13. Referring to Fig. 140, prove that angle α equals angle θ_2 and that angle λ equal angle θ_1.

CHAPTER XII

INDUCED ELECTROMOTIVE FORCES

164. The voltaic cell, discovered by Volta in 1799, was the only known method of developing a sustained emf., and hence a sustained current of electricity of any considerable magnitude, prior to Faraday's discovery of induced emfs. and induced currents in 1831. The voltaic cell, while important, could never produce electric energy on the large scale required for industrial use. Faraday's discovery of induced currents made electricity commercially important, as it led to the development of dynamos, motors, transformers, etc. which have made it possible to change other forms of energy into electric energy which can be transmitted long distances and widely distributed. Induced currents today carry tremendous quantities of energy from water falls, rivers, and coal mines to far distant points to be used in our varied industries and in our homes. Faraday's discovery is among the world's greatest from an economic and industrial standpoint as well as from a scientific standpoint.

165. Faraday's Experiments. — It was pointed out in Section 87 that an electric current consists of a drift of negative electrons in a direction reverse to that of the conventional current. It has, also, been pointed out that when an isolated charge is at rest relative to its surroundings the only field to which it gives rise is an electrostatic field directed radially from the charge and of intensity expressed by Coulomb's law. In 1819 the Danish physicist Oersted discovered that a current of electricity is accompanied by a magnetic field of force, the tubes of magnetic flux being everywhere normal to the direction of the current. *Thus, when a negative electric field is in motion relative to a positive electric field, there is developed a magnetic field.* In 1823 Ampère showed that electric currents act upon each other, and that a current circuit behaves as a magnetic shell. He obtained a mathematical expression (91.1) for the magnetic intensity due to a current element. This has made it possible to obtain expressions for the magnetic field intensity due to electric circuits in some specific cases.

327

Inasmuch as an electric current gives rise to a magnetic field, it occurred to Faraday that the converse effect should obtain under suitable conditions, i.e., a magnetic field should develop an electric current in a closed circuit. In 1831 he found that when a closed circuit, as, for example, a coil of wire in series with a galvanometer, is merely immersed in the magnetic field of a magnet, and at rest relative thereto, no current of electricity is developed, but that if the magnet is moved relative to the circuit, and hence its magnetic field, an electric current is developed which lasts only so long as the relative motion lasts. Faraday's experiments showed that whenever the number of tubes of magnetic flux linked with a closed electric circuit is changed in any manner whatsoever a current of electricity is developed, the magnitude of which is proportional to the time rate of change of magnetic flux. Currents of electricity developed in this manner are called *induced currents*, and the emfs. giving rise to such currents are called *induced electromotive forces*.

There are several ways in which the magnetic flux linked with a circuit may be caused to vary: A permanent magnet close to the circuit may be moved relative to the circuit, or the circuit moved relative to the magnet, thereby causing the magnetic flux threading the circuit to vary. If two circuits, that is, coils of wire, be placed in juxtaposition, and there is a current in one of the coils, an emf. will be induced in the other coil if there is any relative motion between the coils. If the coils are fixed in position and the current is varied in one of them, the *primary*, there is an induced emf. in the other, the *secondary*. The induced emf. always acts in a definite direction relative to the varying magnetic field which produces it. This is stated by Lenz's law, which is: *The induced emf. will cause a current to flow in a closed circuit in such a direction that its magnetic field opposes the change in the magnetic field which produces it.*

166. Relative Sense of Inducing Flux and Current. — The relative senses of *induced current* (conventional) and *inducing flux* may be visualized as in Fig. 141. Fig. 141 (*a*) represents schematically the case where the inducing flux (represented by long arrows) is decreasing. In this case the flux due to the induced current (represented by short arrows) is in the same sense as the inducing flux. Fig. 141 (*b*) represents the case where the inducing flux (represented by long arrows) is increasing. In this case the flux due to the induced current (represented by short arrows) is in opposition to the inducing flux.

KENZES LAW

This follows immediately from the law of the conservation of energy, as expressed by Lenz's law. Let us consider specific cases. Suppose the + pole of a magnet to be advancing toward a closed loop of wire, as from below in Fig. 141 (*b*). The inducing flux due to the magnet will be increasing through the loop. The induced current must flow in such a direction that its flux will oppose the inducing flux, thereby developing opposition and requiring the expenditure of energy to advance the magnet. The lower face of the current loop will correspond to a + magnetic pole, which will repel the + pole of the magnet. The work required to advance the magnet against the opposing field due to the induced current is equal to the energy represented by the induced current. Suppose the + pole of the magnet to be reced-

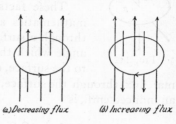

(a) *Decreasing flux*   (b) *Increasing flux*

FIG. 141

ing from a closed loop of wire, as from below in Fig. 141 (*a*). The inducing flux will be decreasing through the loop. The induced current must flow in such a direction as to oppose the motion of recession. Thus, the lower face of the current loop will correspond to a −magnetic pole, and there will be attraction between unlike poles which will oppose the motion of recession; the two magnetic fields will be in the same sense. The energy of the induced current will be equal to the work done in overcoming the attractive force through the distance the magnet has moved. Again, suppose that immediately below the loop of wire in Fig. 141 (*b*) there is a parallel loop of wire in which a current is flowing in such a sense as to produce a field represented by the long arrows. Let the current be increasing, thus increasing the inducing flux through the loop. The induced current will flow in such a direction that its flux will be in opposition to the inducing flux, or the currents in the two loops will be in opposite sense. The energy due to the induced current in the secondary circuit is drawn from the primary circuit, since the primary circuit is increasing its field against opposition. Again, suppose that immediately below the loop of wire in Fig. 141 (*a*) there is a parallel loop of wire in which a decreasing current is flowing. The inducing flux through the loop will be decreasing, and the induced current will flow in such a direction that its flux will be in the same sense as the inducing flux, thereby tending to strengthen it and to prolong the dying away of the current in the primary circuit; the currents in the two loops will be in the same sense. A practical example of this is the transformer. When the current in the primary is increasing the current in the secondary is in the opposite sense, but when decreasing it is in the same sense. _In every case the induced current flows in such a sense as to oppose the change in the magnetic flux which produces it._

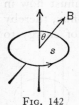

FIG. 142

These facts may be stated in the language of mathematics as follows: Let B be the flux density through a surface s enclosed by the circuit, and θ the angle which the tubes of flux make with the normal to the surface, as indicated in Fig. 142. The total normal flux through the surface, which alone is effective in developing an induced emf., is

$$\phi = \int_s B \cos \theta \, ds. \tag{166.1}$$

Suppose the flux to be decreasing, as in Fig. 141 (_a_). If the upper face of the current loop be taken as positive the flux through it will be positive, and the induced emf. will be in the positive sense, but the flux is decreasing with time. Hence.

$$\varepsilon = -\frac{d\phi}{dt} = -\int \frac{d}{dt}(B \cos \theta) \, ds. \tag{166.2}$$

Thus, Faraday's experiments show that _the emf. ε induced by a change in the normal magnetic flux density through a fixed circuit is equal to the time rate of change of the normal flux._

An electromotive force in any circuit is the work done in carrying a unit charge of electricity once around the circuit, or it is the line integral of the electric intensity E around the circuit. Thus, we have

$$\oint E \, dl = -\int \frac{d\mathcal{B}}{dt} \, ds, \tag{166.3}$$

where $\mathcal{B} = B \cos \theta$ is the normal component of the magnetic flux density through the circuit. The normal flux through the current circuit may be varied by keeping the flux density B constant and varying its direction, or by keeping its direction constant and varying its absolute magnitude, or by varying both simultaneously. Equation (166.3) states that the line integral of the electric intensity around a fixed closed circuit or loop is equal to the time rate of decrease of the normal magnetic flux through the current loop. This will be true whether or not a material circuit coincides with the loop. If a conducting material circuit, as a wire, coincides with the closed loop, forming a closed electric circuit, the electromotive force, represented by the line integral, will cause a drift of electrons (in a sense opposite to that of the conventional current), which is an induced current. Thus, *a varying magnetic flux develops an electric intensity which is normal to the direction of the flux.* The electric intensity, or electric field, is capable of acting on electrons, if present and free to move, and so move them as to develop an electric current. In equation (166.3) both E and $\mathfrak{B}$ must be expressed in the same system of units, cgsm. say.

The converse of equation (166.3) is equation (160.1). To better show the analogy between the two equations we may write equation (160.1) in the form

$$\oint H \, dl = 4\pi \int_s \mathbf{i} \, ds, \tag{166.4}$$

where $\mathbf{i}$ is the current density. Or still better, since $\mathbf{i} = dq/dt$,

$$\oint H \, dl = 4\pi \int_s \frac{dq}{dt} \, ds, \tag{166.5}$$

where q is the charge crossing unit area of the conductor. Thus, the rate of change of electric charge through a closed curve or loop develops a magnetic intensity tangent to the curve. Or, the line integral of the magnetic intensity around a closed curve, within which a current of electricity is flowing, is equal to 4π times the rate of change of electric charge through the curve. In this equation, also, H and q must be expressed in the same system of units.

In equation (166.3) $d\mathfrak{B}/dt$ is the cause and E is the effect. In equation (166.5) dq/dt is the cause and H is the effect.

In the case just considered, where the electric circuit is closed, there is no accumulation of electric charge at any point in the conductor. If, however, the circuit is opened at some point and the free ends of the wire are connected to the two plates of a condenser there will be an accumulation of electrons on one plate of the condenser and a dearth of electrons, or a positive charge, on the other plate, thus bringing about a difference of potential between the two plates which is equivalent to the line integral of the electric intensity along the wire connecting the plates.

167. Electromotive Force by Cutting Lines of Flux. — In the previous Section we have considered the case where an emf. is developed in a fixed circuit by a change of magnetic flux through the circuit. We will now consider the generation of an induced emf. from a slightly different angle.

Equation (166.3) may be illustrated as in Fig. 143. A positive magnetic pole m moving to the right, positive x direction, will develop an electric intensity E in a circular loop of wire, which, at every point, is tangent to the circle. The electric intensity E acting upon the free electrons in the wire will generate a current of electricity, and the line integral of E around the circle is the induced emf. Of course, the electric field E will exist whether the loop of wire is present or not. Thus, a changing magnetic field produces an electric field, the electric field being capable of acting on electric charges and so developing an elec-

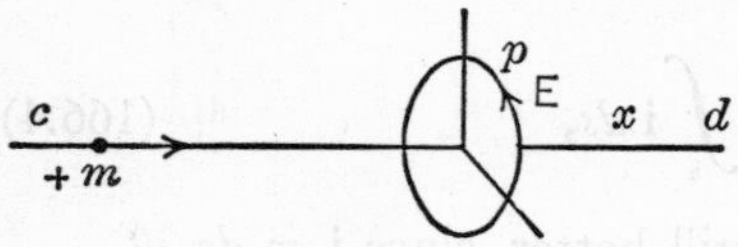

FIG. 143 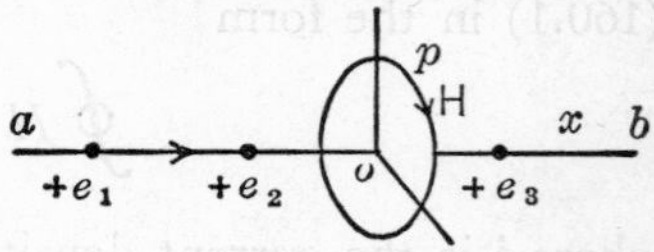   FIG. 144

tric current. This is merely a statement of the law of induced currents which was discovered by Faraday.

Experiments show that there are mutually reciprocal relations between electric fields and magnetic fields. In the previous paragraph we considered the case of an electric field being developed by a changing magnetic field. On the other hand, a changing electric field will develop a magnetic field. This is the familiar magnetic field accompanying a current of electricity, which was discovered by Oersted. Consider a wire coinciding with the x axis, Fig. 144. A stream of electrons in the negative x direction is a current of electricity. Electrically, this is equivalent to an equal stream of positive charges moving in the positive x direction, the conventional current. Consider any charge $+e_1$, a proton say, moving to the right accompanied by its electric field. Now, the only way, so far as we know, that a charge of electricity can produce an effect at a distant point p is through the agency of its electric field. So long as there is no relative motion between the charge $+e_1$ and the point p there is no magnetic field at p. When, however, $+e$ is moving in the positive x direction, as indicated, the electric field at p is changing, and simultaneously, there exists a magnetic field at p, which has a component normal to the x axis, its sense being as indicated by the arrow tip. All points on a circle passing through p with o as center have the same positions relative to $+e_1$. Hence, the magnetic lines of flux are concentric circles around the wire. Other charges, such as $+e_2$, $+e_3$, etc., will, likewise, produce a magnetic intensity at p. Thus, the magnetic field at p must be the sum total of the effects due to all of the charges in the wire having motions in the positive x direction. We must, therefore, view the production of a magnetic field of force around a current as being due in some inexplicable manner to a changing electric flux.

The foregoing discussion is merely a statement of observed facts. It in no wise explains what an electric field is, or what a magnetic field is, or how a magnetic field in relative motion can produce an electric field, or how an electric field in relative motion can produce a magnetic field. These are profound mysteries, and the mere statement of the principles and laws governing them does not make the phenomenon one whit less mysterious. *We discover laws of nature, but we do not thereby reveal ultimate reality.*

168. Induced emf. Mathematical Relations. — As has been stated, whenever the magnetic flux linked with a circuit is varying there is an induced emf. It was shown in Section 97 that the energy of an electric circuit is given by $dU = \mathcal{E}i\,dt$. But $\mathcal{E} = -\,d\phi/dt$. Therefore, for induced currents we have for the energy

$$U = -\int_{\phi_2}^{\phi_1} \frac{d\phi}{dt}\, i\, dt = i(\phi_2 - \phi_1) \text{ ergs.} \qquad (168.1)$$

When the flux is varying in a circuit the total energy is $\mathcal{E}i\,dt$, which is made up of two parts: One part is the energy which is turned into heat and is ri^2dt. The other part is the work done in changing the flux linked with the circuit. Thus,

$$\mathcal{E}i\,dt = ri^2dt + \mathcal{E}i\,dt. \qquad (168.2)$$

$\mathcal{E}$ is the induced emf. which is opposed to $\mathcal{E}$.

If ϕ is the total flux linked with a single turn of wire, then $\mathcal{E}$ is N times as large when ϕ is linked with N turnes of wire, and, therefore, we have

$$\mathcal{E} = -\,N\frac{d\phi}{dt} \text{ cgsm. units.} \qquad (168.3)$$

Or

$$\mathcal{E} = -\left(\frac{N}{10^8}\right)\frac{d\phi}{dt} \text{ absolute practical volts.} \qquad (168.4)$$

This expression is independent of the absolute value of the current in the circuit since it depends only upon the rate of change of flux. If the circuit were open there would still be an induced emf.

Equation (168.3) may be written

$$\mathcal{E} = -\frac{d(\phi N)}{dt} \text{ cgsm. units.} \tag{168.5}$$

The product ϕN is called *flux turns*. In case the total flux does not pass through all of the turns of a coil, the quantities ϕ and N cannot be separated. The product then represents the effective flux turns, a sort of summation.

Fleming's Right-Hand Rule. — When an emf. is induced in a conductor by moving it through a magnetic field of force, the mutual directions of emf., flux, and motion are given by Fleming's right-hand rule, which is as follows:

Place the thumb, index finger, and middle finger of the right hand mutually at right angles. Then if the index finger points in the direction of the flux and the thumb in the direction of motion the middle finger will point in the direction of the induced emf. (conventional). This rule is sometimes called the dynamo rule. It is only the component of motion at right angles to the magnetic flux that is effective in developing an induced emf.

169. Force Acting on a Conductor Bearing a Current when in a Magnetic Field of Force. — Let a conductor of l cms. bearing a cur-

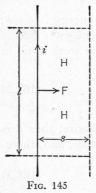

FIG. 145

rent of i cgsm. units be placed in a uniform magnetic field of intensity H in air, the field being normal to the current, Fig. 145. A force of F dynes, say, will act on the conductor which is normal to both the conductor and the field. To obtain the value of F we may assume that the current i is induced in the conductor owing to its motion through the magnetic field. Since a current of electricity represents energy, and energy can be obtained only when work is done against a resistance of some sort, it can be seen that there must be resistance to the motion of the conductor through the magnetic field if thereby a current is induced in the conductor because of such motion. Conversely, if the same current i is caused to flow in a stationary conductor in a magnetic field of force of the same intensity the conductor will experience the same force as was used in moving it through the field to induce the current i. We can, therefore, obtain an expression for the force F by equating the electric energy generated in the conductor to the work done in overcoming the resistance when the conductor is caused to move through the magnetic field. Therefore, we have

$$Fs = Hlsi \text{ ergs.}$$

Or

$$F = Hli \text{ dynes.} \tag{169.1}$$

If either the conductor or the direction of motion is not normal to the magnetic field, then the component of either, as the case may be, normal to the field is alone effective.

Fleming's Left-Hand Rule. — When a conductor bearing a current i is immersed in a magnetic field of force of intensity H there is a force given by equation (169.1) acting on the conductor tending to move it in a direction normal to the magnetic flux. The mutual directions of current, flux, and motion are given by Fleming's left-hand rule, which is as follows:

Place the thumb, index finger, and middle finger of the left hand mutually at right angles. Then if the index finger points in the direction of the flux and the middle finger in the direction of the current (conventional), *the thumb will point in the direction of the force acting on the conductor.* The force F will be perpendicular to the magnetic flux. This rule is sometimes called the motor rule.

170. Force between Currents. — Let the currents be i' and i'' in long, straight conductors which are parallel, and the distance between their centers r cms. Consider the conductor bearing the current i' to be in the field of force of the current i'', which, at a distance r, has an intensity $H'' = 2i''/r$. The force acting on a length of l cms. of the conductor bearing the current i' is

$$F = H''li' = \frac{2i''i'l}{r} \text{ dynes.} \tag{170.1}$$

This equation may be used to define the cgsm. unit current. If the currents are equal,

$$F = \frac{2i^2l}{r} = \frac{2I^2l}{10^2r} \text{ dynes.} \tag{170.2}$$

If the currents are in the same direction, the force is attractive, if in the opposite direction repulsive. The proof of this statement is left to the reader.

171. Coefficients of Self and Mutual Inductance. (*a*) *Mutual Inductance*. — Suppose that we have two coils of wire near together. When a current flows in one of them, the *primary*, the magnetic field envelops the other, the *secondary*. The magnitude of the flux linked with the secondary will depend upon the number of turns of wire in each coil, their cross-sectional areas, and their relative positions. If these factors remain constant the flux turns that are linked with the secondary will be proportional to the current in the primary, and we may write

$$\phi N = Mi, \tag{171.1}$$

where M is a proportionality factor, called the *coefficient of mutual inductance* of the coils. If the current changes, we have, on differentiating,

$$\varepsilon = - \frac{d(\phi N)}{dt} = - M \frac{di}{dt}. \tag{171.2}$$

If ϕ is expressed in maxwells, i in cgsm. units, ε is in cgsm. units, and M is the mututal inductance in the cgsm. system of units. If ϕ is expressed in webers (10^8 maxwells), i in amperes, then ε is in absolute practical volts, and M is the coefficient of mutual inductance in the absolute practical system of units. This unit is called the *henry*, named after Joseph Henry. Equation (171.2) defines the coefficient of mutual inductance in *any* system of units. From this equation we may define the henry as follows:

The mutual inductance between two coils is one henry if, when a current in the primary varies at the rate of one absolute ampere per second, there is developed an induced emf. in the secondary of one absolute practical volt. We will understand by volt, ampere, etc., absolute practical and not international.

For many purposes it is advantageous to define the cgsm. unit of mutual inductance from equation (171.1). Solving for M, we have

$$M = \frac{\phi N}{i} \text{ cgsm. units.} \tag{17.3}$$

Thus, the coefficient of mutual inductance in the cgsm. system is the flux turns linked with the secondary when one cgsm. unit current flows in the primary. Since a volt is 10^8 cgsm. units and the ampere is 10^{-1} cgsm. unit, the henry is 10^9 cgsm. units of inductance.

The negative sign in equation (171.2) may be explained as follows: If the current in the primary is taken as positive, the flux, also, is positive. A current in the secondary that develops flux of the same sense would, also, be positive. As we have seen, a *decreasing* current in the primary (expressed by $-dq/dt$) produces a positive flux in the secondary. On the other hand, an *increasing* current in the primary develops a negative flux in the secondary.

(*b*) *Self Inductance.* — The action of a varying current upon an adjacent coil is not unlike the action of a varying current upon the coil in which the current is flowing. When a current flows in a coil there is linked with the coil itself a certain flux due to its own current, and, therefore, we may write, as before,

$$\phi N = Li, \tag{171.4}$$

where L is a proportionality factor called the *coefficient of self inductance*. On differentiating, we have

$$\varepsilon = -\frac{d(\phi N)}{dt} = -L\frac{di}{dt}. \tag{171.5}$$

This is a defining equation for the coefficient of self inductance in *any* system of units. If i is in amperes, and ε in volts, L is in henrys. Thus, *a coil has a coefficient of self inductance of one henry if, when the current varies at the rate of one ampere per second, there is developed an induced emf. of one volt in the coil itself.*

On a *decreasing* current di/dt is negative and the inducing and induced flux are both positive, i.e., ε is in the same sense as the impressed emf. On an *increasing* current di/dt is positive and the induced flux is negative, i.e., ε is opposed to the impressed emf.

It is sometimes convenient to define the coefficient of self inductance from equation (171.4). Thus,

$$L = \frac{\phi N}{i} \text{ cgsm. units.} \tag{171.6}$$

Hence, the cgsm. unit of self inductance is the flux (in maxwells) turns linked with the coil itself when one cgsm. unit current flows in it.

The coefficient of self inductance of a coil depends upon its cross-sectional area, shape, number of turns, and manner of winding.   It is constant for a given coil if no part of the magnetic circuit contains ferromagnetic substance.   If it does L (and also M) is variable and depends upon the permeability, which depends upon the substance and degree of magnetization.   Since the henry is a large unit a smaller unit is usually used, called the millihenry, which is 10^{-3} henry.

172. Electromagnetic Inertia and Energy. — A variable electric current in a coil behaves as though possessing inertia. There is opposition to any change in the magnitude of the current. When the current is increasing the induced emf. opposes the increase, and when the current is decreasing the induced emf. opposes the decrease, i.e., it prolongs the dying away of the current.   This effect is analogous to inertia in a mechanical system, and so has been called *electromagnetic inertia*.   The inertia effect of the electric current is brought about by its magnetic field, i.e., by inductance.   Any arrangement of a circuit which increases the flux linked with it increases the inductance L and, therefore, the inertia effect.

In a mechanical system any change in velocity of a mass is accompanied by an inertia effect. When a mass m is accelerated the inertia effect opposes the increase in velocity, the effect being proportional to the mass m.   When the mass is decelerated there is an inertia effect opposing the decrease in velocity.   The inertia effect of ponderable matter is given by the familiar expression

$$F = m\frac{dv}{dt}.$$

Likewise, to vary a current of electricity at the rate di/dt requires an impressed emf. of magnitude

$$\mathcal{E} = L\frac{di}{dt}.$$

L in this equation is analogous to m in the mechanical case, and di/dt is analogous to dv/dt. The similarity between the electric and mechanical systems has led some physicists to believe that all inertia effects are of an electromagnetic nature.

The fact that a material mass resists any change in its velocity, coupled with the law of the conservation of energy, leads inevitably to the conclusion that mass in motion possesses a certain amount of energy which is equal to the work done in giving it velocity. Thus,

$$dW = F\,ds = m\,\frac{dv}{dt}\,ds = m\,\frac{dv}{dt}\,v\,dt = mv\,dv.$$

On integrating,

$$W = \int_0^v mv\,dv = \tfrac{1}{2}mv^2. \tag{172.1}$$

Likewise, the fact that an electric current resists any change in its magnitude, leads to the conclusion that electric work is done in increasing a current against an induced emf., and that there is stored in the magnetic field an amount of energy equal to the electric energy which has been expended. The electric energy expended is

$$dW = \mathcal{E}i\,dt = L\frac{di}{dt}\,i\,dt = Li\,di.$$

On integrating,

$$W = \int_0^I Li\,di = \tfrac{1}{2}LI^2 \text{ joules,} \tag{172.2}$$

where I is the maximum or final value of the current in amperes.

If there is no conducting or ferromagnetic substance anywhere in the magnetic circuit the amount of energy $\tfrac{1}{2}LI^2$ is returned to the circuit when the current returns to zero. If ferromagnetic substance is present a part of this energy is dissipated as heat, which is the hysteresis and eddy current losses. If the core is conducting substance but not ferromagnet there will be eddy current losses only.

We may define the coefficient of self inductance in still another way from equation (172.2). Let I equal one ampere, and, solving for L, we have

$$L = 2W \text{ henrys.} \tag{172.3}$$

Thus, L in henrys is twice the magnetic energy in the field in joules when a current of one ampere is flowing. All three ways in which we have defined the coefficient of self inductance L amount to the same thing if the magnetic circuit contains only nonmagnetic substance. This is not the case, however, if the magnetic circuit contains ferromagnetic substance, as will be shown in Section 175.

There is a further relation which may be derived at this point, which is as follows:

$$\mathcal{E} = r\frac{dq}{dt} = L\frac{di}{dt}.$$

And therefore

$$Q = \int_o^i \frac{L}{r}\,di = \frac{L}{r}\,i \text{ cgsm. units.} \qquad (172.4)$$

Thus, when a current i is flowing in a circuit an amount of energy equal to $\frac{1}{2}Li^2$ ergs is stored in the magnetic field. When this current is reduced to zero a quantity of electricity equal to $(L/r)i$ is displaced in the circuit because of the energy stored in the magnetic field. L/r is called the *time constant* of the circuit, the meaning of which will be explained in Chapter XVII.

173. Interacting Circuits. — Let there be two coils coupled as indicated in Fig. 146. It is required to derive an expression for the total energy in the magnetic field when there is a current I_1 flowing in one coil and a current I_2 flowing in the other coil. Let the two currents increase from zero at such a rate that each, at any instant, is the same fraction of its final value as the other, and hence, that they reach their final values at the same instant. Then for circuit (1)

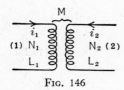

FIG. 146

$$\phi_1 N_1 = L_1 i_1, \quad \text{and} \quad \phi_2' N_1 = M i_2,$$

and for circuit (2)

$$\phi_2 N_2 = L_2 i_2, \quad \text{and} \quad \phi_1' N_2 = M i_1,$$

where i stands for the instantaneous value of a current. Then, on differentiating,

$$\mathcal{E}_1 = L_1\frac{di_1}{dt} + M\frac{di_2}{dt} \qquad (173.1)$$

and

$$\mathcal{E}_2 = L_2\frac{di_2}{dt} + M\frac{di_1}{dt}. \qquad (173.2)$$

The total increment in energy dW is

$$dW = \mathcal{E}_1 i_1 dt + \mathcal{E}_2 i_2 dt. \qquad (173.3)$$

And on substituting from equation (173.1) and (173.2),

$$dW = L_1 i_1 \frac{di_1}{dt} dt + M i_1 \frac{di_2}{dt} dt + L_2 i_2 \frac{di_2}{dt} + M i_2 \frac{di_1}{dt} dt$$

$$= L_1 i_1 di_1 + M i_1 di_2 + L_2 i_2 di_2 + M i_2 di. \qquad (173.4)$$

At any instant i is some fraction β of its final value I. Then

$$i_1 = \beta I_1 \quad \text{and} \quad i_2 = \beta I_2, \qquad di_1 = I_1 d\beta \quad \text{and} \quad di_2 = I_2 d\beta.$$

Substituting in equation (173.4), we have

$$dW = L_1 I_1{}^2 \beta d\beta + M I_1 I_2 \beta d\beta + L_2 I_2{}^2 \beta d\beta + M I_1 I_2 \beta d\beta$$

$$= \{ L_1 I_1{}^2 + 2 M I_1 I_2 + L_2 I_2{}^2 \} \beta d\beta.$$

$$W = \{ L_1 I_1{}^2 + 2 M I_1 I_2 + L_2 I_2{}^2 \} \int_{\beta=0}^{\beta=1} \beta d\beta$$

$$= \tfrac{1}{2} L_1 I_1{}^2 + M I_1 I_2 + \tfrac{1}{2} L_2 I_2{}^2. \qquad (173.5)$$

M is positive or negative depending on whether the flux passes through the two coils in the same or opposite sense.

If the two coils are connected in series so that the same current flows through each coil equation (173.5) becomes

$$W = \tfrac{1}{2} L I^2 = \tfrac{1}{2} L_1 I^2 + M I^2 + \tfrac{1}{2} L_2 I^2, \qquad (173.6)$$

where L is the equivalent inductance. Then

$$L = L_1 + L_2 \pm 2M. \qquad (173.7)$$

This equation may be used to measure mutual inductance from measurements of self inductance. Variable standards of mutual inductance are sometimes made of two cylindrical, coaxial coils so mounted that one coil slides in and out of the other. The relative positions of the two coils determines the mutual inductance, which is marked on a scale with pointer attached. In another form, the two coils are wound on circular, nonmagnetic frames, one of which rotates inside of the other like a variocoupler used in radio work. If the coils are connected in series the combination serves as a variable, standard self inductance. The variation in L is brought about by the variation in M, which depends upon the relative orientations of the two coils. The Ayrton and Perry variable inductor is a standard variable inductance of this type. Brook's inductor consists of six flat coils mounted in pairs in hard rubber discs placed one above the other.

The upper and lower discs are fixed in position and the middle one rotates between them, thus effecting a variation in relative positions, and hence a variation in the mutual inductance. All standards of mutual and self inductance must be free from ferromagnetic substance.

174. Coefficient of Coupling. — Circuits may be coupled together in a variety of ways. When two circuits are coupled as in Fig. 146 the coupling is said to be *inductive*. In general, only a part of the flux having its genesis in one coil is linked with the other coil. There is always more or less leakage. If the leakage is slight the coupling is said to be *close*, and if the leakage is large the coupling is said to be *loose*. A factor which expresses the closeness of coupling is called the *coefficient of coupling*. The coefficient of inductive coupling k is defined as the ratio of the mutual inductance to the square root of the product of the self inductances. Thus,

$$k = \frac{M}{\sqrt{L_1 L_2}}. \tag{174.1}$$

k will vary between 0 and 1. The greatest possible value of the mutual inductance is $\sqrt{L_1 L_2}$. When this condition obtains there is no leakage and $k = 1$.

175. The Effect of Variable Permeability upon the Coefficient of Self Inductance. — We have defined the coefficient of self inductance from the three following equations:

$$(a)\ \ \phi N = Li. \qquad (b)\ \ \varepsilon = L\frac{di}{dt}. \qquad (c)\ \ W = \tfrac{1}{2}Li^2.$$

The value of L is the same when defined by these three equations if the permeability of the magnetic circuit remains constant. If the permeability varies the three equations lead to different values for the coefficient of self inductance. This obtains when there is ferromagnetic substance present in the circuit. Thus, the coefficient of self inductance of a circuit containing ferromagnetic substance is not only variable, but may be defined in different ways, which lead to different values for L. This will be made clear by reference to the magnetization curve in Fig. 147, which shows the relation between flux turns and current i, where i is defined by the equation

$$H = \frac{4\pi Ni}{l}.$$

This curve is of the same form as the B, H magnetization curve (to be explained in Chapter XIV), since i is proportional to H, and ϕN is proportional to B, as $\phi = BA$.

Let us select any point b on the magnetization curve with reference to which L may be defined. From equation (a), we have

$$L = \frac{\phi N}{i} = \frac{oa}{oc} \text{ cgsm. units.} \qquad (175.1)$$

As will be seen, this ratio will vary for different points on the curve.

From equation (b)

$$\varepsilon = L \frac{di}{dt}.$$

Also,

$$\varepsilon = \frac{d(\phi N)}{dt} = \frac{d(\phi N)}{di} \frac{di}{dt}.$$

Now

$$\frac{d(\phi N)}{di} = \frac{cb}{dc},$$

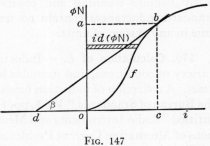

FIG. 147

as db is tangent to the curve at b. Therefore,

$$\frac{cb}{dc} \frac{di}{dt} = L \frac{di}{dt}, \text{ and } L = \frac{cb}{dc} \text{ cgsm. units.} \qquad (175.2)$$

In this case L comes out equal to the tangent of the angle β, or the tangent to the magnetization curve at b.

From equation (c)

$$W = \tfrac{1}{2} L i^2.$$

Now the work done in establishing the current is

$$W = \int_0^t \varepsilon i \, dt = \int_0^t i \frac{d(\phi N)}{dt} \, dt = \int_0^{\phi N} i \, d(\phi N) = \text{area } (ofbao).$$

But also

$$W = \tfrac{1}{2} L (oc)^2 = \text{area } (ofbao),$$

and therefore

$$L = \frac{2 \text{ area } (ofbao)}{(oc)^2} \text{ cgsm. units.} \qquad (175.3)$$

These values of L are all variable and differ from each other. If, however, the curve becomes a straight line, as is the case for nonmagnetic media, all of the values for L are constant and equal to each other. Each expression leads to

$$\frac{cb}{oc} = \frac{\phi N}{i}. \tag{175.4}$$

Thus, with ferromagnetic substance in the circuit, L is not defined uniquely. Its value and meaning depend upon the equation in which it is used, and, with each equation, it varies with the current strength. But in a circuit in which the permeability is constant L has a perfectly definite meaning and constant value. For this reason all standard inductances contain no ferromagnetic substance. This is true in any system of units.

176. Calculation of L. — Induction effects occur under a great variety of conditions, and formulas have been derived to fit different cases. A collection of induction formulas may be found in "Bulletin of the Bureau of Standards," Vol 8, pp. 1–237, 1912. Also, "Circular 74," entitled "Radio Instruments and Measurements." See, also, "Calculations of Alternating Current Problems" by Louis Cohen, Chap. II, and "A Treatise on Alternating Current Theory" by Alex. Russell, Vol. I. Most of the derivations are involved. However, a few simple derivations will serve our purpose here.

(a) *Long Solenoid.* — The flux density B inside a long solenoid as obtained from equation (158.2) is

$$B = \frac{2\pi N i \mu}{l} (\cos \beta_2 - \cos \beta_1).$$

At a point inside the solenoid we have, putting $n = \frac{N}{l}$,

$$B = 2\pi n i \mu \{ \cos \beta_2 - \cos (\pi - \beta_1) \}.$$

And if the point is at a distance x from the left-hand end in Fig. 130, this equation becomes

$$B = 2\pi n i \mu \left\{ \frac{x}{\sqrt{r^2 + x^2}} + \frac{l - x}{\sqrt{r^2 + (l - x)^2}} \right\}.$$

The flux turns due to $n\,dx$ turns is $d\phi = \pi r^2 B n\,dx$ in a length dx. Therefore,

$$\phi = 2\pi^2 r^2 n^2 \mu i \int_0^l \left\{ \frac{x}{\sqrt{r^2 + x^2}} + \frac{l - x}{\sqrt{r^2 + (l - x)^2}} \right\} dx.$$

And hence

$$\phi = 4\pi^2 r^2 n^2 \mu i \left\{ \sqrt{l^2 + r^2} - r \right\}.$$

But

$$\varepsilon = \frac{d\phi}{dt} = L\frac{di}{dt},$$

and, therefore,

$$L = 4\pi^2 \mu r^2 n^2 \left\{ \sqrt{l^2 + r^2} - r \right\} \text{ cgsm. units.} \qquad (176.1)$$

Of course, L has no definite value except when the core is non-magnetic, i.e., when $\mu = $ const. In case of ferromagnetic substance in the core the inductance is variable. Fig. 148 shows the variation of inductance with the magnetizing current under such conditions (Int. Elec. & Transm. Co.). The expression (176.1) is correct within 2%

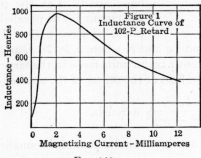

FIG. 148

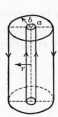

FIG. 149

if l is greater than $10r$. In most cases induction formulas require to be multiplied by a correction factor.

(*b*) *Coaxial Cylinders.* — A circuit consists of two concentric, coaxial, cylindrical shells of radii a and b and common length l, as shown in Fig. 149. Let the cylinders be connected at the ends by flat end plates, thus completing the electric circuit. Since the currents are of the same strength in the two cylinders, but opposite in sense, the field outside the outer cylinder will be zero, since, for any point distant r from the axis of a current, the field strength is $2i/r$. Therefore, the field is confined to the annular space between the cylinders.

The value of H for any point between the cylinders is $2i/r$, and therefore, the total flux for length l of the cylinders is given by

$$\phi = 2il \int_a^b \frac{dr}{r} = 2il \log_e \frac{b}{a} \text{ maxwells.}$$

When i varies

$$\mathcal{E} = \frac{d\phi}{dt} = L\frac{di}{dt} = 2l\log_e\frac{b}{a}\frac{di}{dt}.$$

Therefore,

$$L = 2l\log_e\frac{b}{a}\ \text{cgsm. units.} \tag{176.2}$$

(c) *Mutual Inductance.* — We will take one example of mutual inductance where an approximate expression for the coefficient of

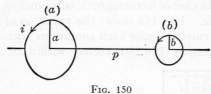

FIG. 150

mutual inductance may be obtained in a simple way. Let there be a pair of circuits as shown in Fig. 150, distant p cms. apart. Let the plane of the circuit (a) be parallel to the plane of circuit (b). Let the circuits be circular and of radii a and b, where $a >> b$, and of one turn of wire each. If a current i cgsm. units flows in the larger circle, then, by equation (157.1), the field at the center of the smaller circle is

$$H = \frac{2\pi a^2 i}{(a^2 + p^2)^{3/2}}\ \text{oersteds.}$$

If we may say that the flux density over the area of the smaller circle is constant and equal to its value at the center, then the flux passing through the circle is given by

$$\phi = \pi b^2 H = \frac{2\pi^2 a^2 b^2 i}{(a^2 + p^2)^{3/2}}.$$

Since

$$\mathcal{E} = \frac{d\phi}{dt} = M\frac{di}{dt},$$

$$M = \frac{2\pi^2 a^2 b^2}{(a^2 + p^2)^{3/2}}\ \text{cgsm. units.} \tag{176.3}$$

If the coils contain n_1 and n_2 turns respectively this expression for M must be multiplied by $n_1 n_2$. A more exact expression may be obtained by the application of Neumann's Theorem, but the development and application of this theorem is beyond the scope of the present treatment.[1] These formulas may be changed to the absolute

---

[1] See Prin. of Elec. and Mag., by Page and Adams, pp. 376–379. Theoretical Physics by W. Wilson, pp. 120–124.

practical system of units by use of the conversion Table given in Section 18.

177. Bridge Method of Comparing Self Inductances. — A self inductance may be measured in a variety of different ways. Only one method will be given here. A self inductance L may be measured by comparison with a known standard of self inductance by use of the ordinary Wheatstone-bridge network. The wiring diagram is shown in Fig. 151, the arrangement being the same as that of the Leeds and Northrup bridge No. 1551. This bridge is used with a battery B and galvanometer for the d.c. balance, and an alternating source of emf., as a microphone hummer, and a telephone as a detector for the a.c. balance. The resistance r is so placed and wired as to make it possible to connect it in series with either the inductance L_1 or L_2 by means of the switch K. The wiring for the transfer of r to one arm of the bridge or the other is placed in the detector branch, because, when a balance obtains, no current flows in this branch and hence there are no induc-

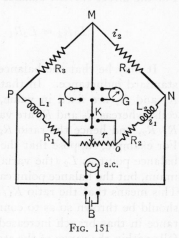

Fig. 151

tance effects due to this part of the circuit. The resistances R_1 and R_2 are the resistances of the inductances L_1 and L_2, which may be measured separately. The resistances R_3, R_4, and r must be free from capacitance and inductance.

To obtain a working equation of the bridge let us assume r to be zero. We will use the differential-equations method of deriving the bridge equation. For a balance the instantaneous p.d. from N to O is equal to that from N to M. Likewise, the p.d. from O to P is equal to that from M to P. This must be true at the same time for direct currents and for varying currents when the coils develop induced emfs.

Therefore, we may write

$$R_2 i_1 + L_2 \frac{di_1}{dt} = R_4 i_2, \tag{177.1}$$

$$R_1 i_1 + L_1 \frac{di_1}{dt} = R_3 i_2. \tag{177.2}$$

Multiplying (177.1) by R_1 and (177.2) by R_2, we have

$$R_1R_2i_1 + L_2R_1\frac{di_1}{dt} = R_4R_1i_2,$$

$$R_1R_2i_1 + L_1R_2\frac{di_1}{dt} = R_3R_2i_2.$$

For the direct current balance $R_4R_1 = R_3R_2$. Therefore,

$$L_1R_2 = L_2R_1 \quad \text{and} \quad \frac{L_1}{L_2} = \frac{R_1}{R_2} = \frac{R_3}{R_4}. \tag{177.3}$$

It may be that the balance lies beyond the range of the variable standard inductance. In that case the variable resistance r is used. R_1 and R_2 are fixed in value, since they are the resistances of the coils, whereas R_3 and R_4 are variable. Therefore, to change the ratio R_1/R_2, and hence the ratio R_3/R_4, the variable resistance r is used. For example, suppose that the detector indicates an approach to the balance point as L_2 (the variable standard) is increased to the maximum, but the balance point cannot be reached or a reversal obtained. This means that the ratio R_1/R_2 is too small. Therefore, the key K should be thrown so as to connect r in the branch OP, and the resistance in that branch increased by an amount such that the balance falls within the range of the standard inductance. If L_2 is decreased to its lower limit and the balance point is approached but not reached, r should be added to R_2. When either R_1 or R_2 is increased a new steady current balance must be obtained.

178. The Carey-Foster Method of Measuring Mutual Inductance.

— The circuit diagram for this method is shown schematically

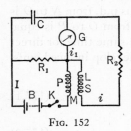

FIG. 152

in Fig. 152. P and S are the primary and secondary of the two coils whose coefficient of mutual inductance is to be measured. G is a ballistic galvanometer, and C is a standard, variable condenser. R_1 and R_2 are variable, noninductive resistances. When the key K is closed two distinct discharges of electricity tend to take place in the galvanometer circuit. By proper connections these discharges may be caused to act in opposite directions. The quantity of electricity Q'

induced in the secondary circuit passes through the galvanometer, and the quantity Q which charges the condenser also passes through the galvanometer, since the galvanometer is common to the two circuits.

The quantity Q that charges the condenser is given by

$$Q = CV = CR_1I,$$

where I is the final steady current in R_1. $R_1I = V$ is the p.d. across the condenser. The charge in the condenser is independent of any current through the galvanometer. By adjusting the resistance R_2 the algebraic sum of the quantities of electricity passing through the galvanometer may be made equal to zero, and there is then no deflection.

By applying Kirchhoff's law, $\Sigma\text{p.d.} = 0$, for the secondary circuit for instantaneous values, we have

$$M\frac{dI}{dt} - L_s\frac{di}{dt} - (S + R_2)i \pm Gi_1 \pm L_g\frac{di_1}{dt} = 0.$$

Integrating between the limits 0 and t, the time for the current in the primary to reach its steady state after closing key K, we have

$$MI - (S + R_2)Q' \pm Gq = 0.$$

$L_s\displaystyle\int_0^{t_1} (di/dt)dt$ and $L_g\displaystyle\int_0^{t_1} (di/dt)dt$ are each equal to zero, since the current is zero at time $t = t_1$ and at time $t = 0$. Since for a balance $p = 0$, we have

$$MI = (S + R_2)Q'$$

and since $Q' = Q$,

$$MI = CR_1I(S + R_2), \quad \text{and finally} \quad M = (S + R_2)CR_1. \quad (178.3)$$

The galvanometer current i_1 need not necessarily be 0 at every instant from 0 to t for a balance. However, the nearer the galvanometer current is to zero during this time interval the steadier the balance. S is the resistance of the secondary coil. When C is measured in farads, R_1 and R_2 in ohms, M is in henrys.

PROBLEMS

1. An earth inductor has a diameter of 30 cms. and 50 turns of wire. At a point where the total intensity of the earth's magnetic field is 0.6 oersted, and the dip angle is 60°, the axis of the earth inductor is placed horizontal and parallel to the magnetic meridian, with the plane of the area of the coil hori-

zontal. If the coil is turned from this position through 180° in 1/50th second, what is the average induced emf. in volts? If the galvanometer to which the earth inductor is connected gives a deflection of 15 scale divisions for this position, what will be the deflection if the axis of the earth inductor is vertical and the time of rotation through 180° is the same as before? What quantity of electricity in coulombs is displaced in the circuit in the first case if the resistance of the circuit is 100 ohms?

2. A coil of wire on the armature of an electric motor contains 10 turns. The length of one side of the coil in the magnetic field is 1 ft., and the distance between the parallel sides is 6 inches. If the density of the magnetic flux is 5000 maxwells per sq. cm., what is the maximum torque in gm-cms. acting upon the coil when the current is 25 amperes? What is the position of the coil relative to the field magnets? Make a diagram showing the relative directions of field, current, and rotation.

CHAPTER XIII

ELECTRIC INSTRUMENTS DEPENDING ON MAGNETIC FIELDS

179. Most electric measuring and current detecting instruments depend for their action upon the interactions of magnetic fields of force; either the magnetic field of a current and that of a permanent magnet, or the magnetic fields of different currents. Galvanometers (current detecting instruments), in general, depend upon a magnetic field of force. In one class of instruments, a permanent magnetic needle is caused to move in the magnetic field of a current (moving-magnet type). In another class, a coil of wire bearing a current to be detected moves in the field of force of a permanent magnet (moving-coil type). In still another type of instrument, a current-bearing coil moves in the magnetic field of another current-bearing coil (dynamometer type). Ammeters are simply calibrated galvanometers of low resistance, and those depending upon a magnetic field of force are usually of the moving-coil type or of the dynamometer type. Indicating wattmeters are of the dynamometer type, one coil of which carries the current and performs the function of an ammeter, and the other is shunted across the line and performs the function of a voltmeter, the current circuit having low resistance and the potential circuit high resistance. Voltmeters are of the same general construction as ammeters, but possess high instead of low resistance, and are generally of the moving-coil type. Integrating wattmeters, or watt-hour meters, are small electric motors geared to a clock-like mechanism with a dial and hands, and calibrated to read in kilowatt hours of energy. There are other types of instruments, however, than those that depend upon magnetic fields, but only the magnetic-field type will be considered in this Chapter.

180. The Tangent Galvanometer. — The tangent galvanometer is one of the oldest galvanometers, but is now little used. It consists of a circular coil of wire having a radius which is large in comparison with the length of the coil, i.e., it is a very short solenoid of large radius. A

351

very small, short magnetic needle is suspended by a fiber or pivoted so that the center of the needle coincides with the center of the coil, the needle swinging in a horizontal plane. The magnetic needle carries a light pointer which moves over a scale graduated in degrees. When in use the coil is placed with its plane accurately vertical and in the plane of the magnetic meridian of the earth. When no current flows in the coil the pointer stands at zero, as the needle is actuated by the earth's field only.

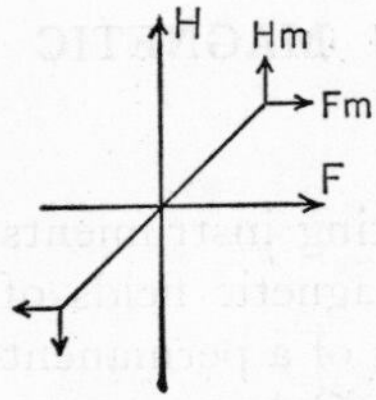

When a current passes through the coil the magnetic field due to the current, of intensity

$$F = \frac{2\pi n i}{r} \text{ oersteds}$$

FIG. 153

at the center, is at right angles to the horizontal component H of the earth's magnetic intensity, Fig. 153. The needle is, therefore, acted upon by two opposing couples, and will come to rest in a position such that the two couples are numerically equal. We, therefore, have

$$HM \sin \theta = FM \cos \theta.$$

Or

$$\tan \theta = \frac{F}{H} = \frac{2\pi n i}{rH}, \tag{180.1}$$

where i is in cgsm. units and r in cms. If the current is in amperes,

$$\tan \theta = \frac{2\pi n I}{10rH}. \tag{180.2}$$

The factor $2\pi n/r$ depends only upon the geometry of the coil and is, therfore, constant. It is called the *galvanometer constant*, and is designated by G. Therefore, expressing the current in amperes, we have

$$I = \frac{10H}{G} \tan \theta. \tag{180.3}$$

For any specific location H is constant, unless, due to near-by fluctuating magnetic fields, it is caused to vary. Putting $10H/G = K$ (reduction factor), we have

$$I = K \tan \theta. \tag{180.4}$$

K may be found experimentally by passing a known current

through the windings. However, if the construction of the instrument is such that n and r can be accurately determined, K can be calculated, since H can be measured by independent means (Section 74). This instrument can and has been used to measure a current *absolutely*. The tangent galvanometer is not a highly sensitive instrument, nor does the tangent law necessarily hold over the whole range of its scale. It is now little used.

Current Sensitivity. — The current sensitivity of the tangent galvanometer is defined as the change in θ produced by a given percentage change in i. That is, the sensitivity is a maximum when $\frac{d\theta}{di/i}$ or $i\frac{d\theta}{di}$ is a maximum. Thus, from (180.1) we have

$$i\frac{d\theta}{di} = \tan \theta \cos^2 \theta = \sin \theta \cos = \tfrac{1}{2} \sin {}^2\theta. \qquad (180.5)$$

This is a maximum when $2\theta = 90°$, or $\theta = 45°$. Thus, the sensitivity increases to a maximum at $\theta = 45°$, and then decreases. Therefore, when accuracy is desired in measuring a current with the tangent galvanometer the deflection should be in the vicinity of 45°.

It has been assumed in the foregoing discussion that the coil of the galvanometer is accurately circular, that the mean radius of the windings is the effective radius, that the center of the needle is exactly at the effective center of the coil, that the field is uniform within the region that the needle swings, that H is known and remains constant, i.e., there are no stray fluctuating magnetic fields, and that there are no control forces acting on the needle, such as pivot resistance or suspension torsion, other than the control field H. The most serious of these defects is the nonuniformity of the field in which the needle swings.

Helmholtz overcame this last difficulty by using two identical coils mounted coaxially with the needle half way between them. The magnetic intensity F at any point on the axis of a coil is given by

$$F = \frac{2\pi nr^2i}{(x^2 + r^2)^{3/2}}, \quad \text{Equation (157.1)}$$

where x is the distance along the axis measured from the center of the coil and r is its radius. The rate at which F varies with x is dF/dx. It is important in this connection to ascertain if there is a point along the axis where this rate is constant. If it is constant at any point, then $d^2F/dx^2 = 0$. Since $2\pi n r^2 i$ is taken as constant, we have

$$\frac{d^2}{dx^2}(x^2 + r^2)^{-\frac{3}{2}} = 0.$$

Or

$$15x^2(x^2 + r^2)^{-\frac{7}{2}} - 3(x^2 + r^2)^{-\frac{3}{2}} = 0, \text{ and } x = \frac{r}{2}.$$

Thus, the point at which dF/dx becomes constant is one half the common radius of the coils from the center of each of the coils. Therefore, Helmholtz placed his coils a distance r apart, i.e., one on each side of the point just found. R is the distance between corresponding turns on the two coils. When so placed the decrease in the field due to one coil compensates the increase in the field due to the other coil, and so a nearly uniform field is obtained between the coils. Putting $x = r/2$ in the above equation for F, multiplying by 2 and reducing, there results

$$F = \frac{32\pi ni}{5r\sqrt{5}}, \tag{180.6}$$

and therefore

$$i = \frac{5rH\sqrt{5}}{32\pi n}\tan\theta. \tag{180.7}$$

The current sensitivity for the Helmholtz tangent galvanometer is obtained in the same manner as for the single-coil tangent galvanometer.

181. The D'Arsonval Galvanometer. — The most commonly used galvanometer of the moving-coil type is the so-called D'Arsonval galvanometer, which was called to the attention of scientists by Deprez and D'Arsonval in 1882. This instrument consists of a rectangular coil of wire suspended between the poles of a strong permanent magnet, Fig. 154. Inside the rectangular coil is a fixed, soft-iron core for the purpose of giving a low reluctance path for the magnetic flux, and consequently, also, so distribute the flux in the air gap as to give a very uniform field over the angular range of the coil. The coil is hung by a fine suspension, which also serves as a control and current lead. Below the coil is a loosely-coiled, metallic spring which serves as the other lead. D'Arsonval galvanometers which are used in a fixed position are provided with leveling screws to adjust the instrument so that the coil swings freely in the proper position. With portable

D'Arsonval galvanometers the coil is held in position by upper and lower lead wires under tension, or the coil may be pivoted and controlled by a hair spring.

The great advantage of the D'Arsonval galvanometer is its freedom from stray magnetic fields and its long uniform scale, and also the ease with which it is damped. Galvanometers of very high sensitivity are made of this type.

Assuming the coil to be rectangular, let the length be l cms. and the breadth b cms. If there are n turns, the total length of active wire

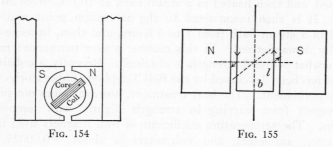

FIG. 154   FIG. 155

in the magnetic field on one side of the rectangle is nl. Since a current i cgsm. units flows up one side of the rectangle and down the other, the force system acting upon the rectangle is a couple, the moment of which is the force on one side times the breadth b of the coil, Fig. 155. Thus,

$$L = nlbHi = nAHi \quad \text{dyne-cms.} \qquad (181.1)$$

This assumes that the field is uniform and radial over the angular range through which the coil swings.   Since the coil is suspended by a wire, the suspension will be twisted when the coil turns, thus acting as a control.   The coil will turn from its equilibrium position until the restoring torsional couple of the wire equals the magnetic couple L. The moment of the restoring couple is $k\theta$, where k is the torsional constant of the suspension.   Thus, for equilibrium

$$k\theta = nAHi. \qquad (181.2)$$

The sensitivity is

$$\frac{d\theta}{di} = \frac{nAH}{k}. \qquad (181.3)$$

The sensitivity, as here defined, is the angle the coil describes with unit change in current.

Thus, the sensitivity increases directly with n, A, and H, and inversely with k. n and A will remain constant with a given instrument. H depends upon the so-called permanent magnet. Magnets lose their strength with age, the aging depending upon the quality of iron used, the design of the magnetic circuit, the temperature variation, and amount of jarring. Any change in the strength of the magnet is a deterioration, and hence detrimental. Therefore, the magnets used in galvanometers, ammeters, and voltmeters are artificially aged. This is accomplished by a heat treatment: The magnet is hardened and then heated in a steam bath at 100° C. from 20 to 30 hours. It is then magnetized to the saturation point and again heated in a steam bath from 4 to 5 hours, and then, in some cases, partially demagnetized. In this manner a very permanent magnet of somewhat reduced strength is obtained. Recently a cobalt-steel magnet has been developed by the Bell Telephone Laboratories which is very permanent. The heat treatment, however, does not prevent the magnet from varying in strength slightly with temperature changes. The temperature coefficient of iron magnets used in galvanometer, ammeters, and voltmeters is about -0.00025. The modulus of elasticity of the suspension decreases with rise in temperature, which, in a measure, compensates for the decrease in strength of the magnet. With phosphor-bronze suspensions the temperature coefficient of elasticity is about -0.0005. The materials most commonly used for suspensions are phosphor-bronze, gold, and steel. The sensitivity is inversely proportional to k, which, for round wires, varies as the 4th power of the radius of the wire. However, the elongation modulus, effective because of the weight of the coil, varies as the square of the radius. The limit to increase in sensitivity, due to decrease in the size of the suspension, is determined by the weight of the coil and frame. However, the sensitivity can be increased, without change in the weight of the coil, by using a flat strip or ribbon instead of a round wire. A ribbon, having a breadth of about ten times its thickness, has approximately one fifth the torsional rigidity of a round wire of the same length and cross-sectional area. Such suspensions are in common use in D'Arsonval galvanometers.

It is important in the use of a galvanometer that it be damped in some manner. Damping of the D'Arsonval galvanometer is easily accomplished by placing on the coil a closed loop of wire or winding the coil on a light metal frame. When the coil swings in the magnetic field a current is induced in the closed circuit, which flows in such a direction that the magnetic fields of current and magnet are in opposition. If there is no closed circuit on the coil damping may be effected by a short-circuiting key across the terminals of the galvanometer. This key and circuit should be free from thermal emfs. The damped D'Arsonval galvanometer is a very good ballistic galvanometer when given a sufficiently long period. Galvanometers are used for two distinct purposes: (1) To measure or detect a current (current galvanometer). (2) To measure a small quantity of electricity, as in the discharge of a condenser or a displacement of electricity in a solenoid. When designed for this purpose they possess a long period, and are called ballistic galvanometers.

182. The Duddell Thermo-Galvanometer. — This galvanometer is a Boy's radio-micrometer which has been adapted to the detection and measurement of small currents, both direct and alternating. The essential features are shown diagrammatically in Fig. 156.

A single loop of silver wire of high conductivity is suspended by a quartz fiber between the poles of a strong permanent magnet. The suspension carries a small mirror by means of which the deflections are read with a telescope and scale or lamp and scale in the usual manner. The lower end of the silver loop is completed through a bismuth-antimony thermocouple. Immediately below the thermocouple, and as near to it as possible without touching, is a *heater* through which the current to be detected or measured is passed. The current generates heat in the heater which is transmitted to the thermojunction by con-

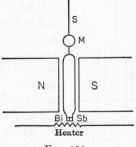

Fig. 156

vection and radiation. This develops a direct current by thermoelectric action in the silver loop, and hence a deflection as in the D'Arsonval galvanometer. The heater is a straight wire or else bent back and forth forming a grid. Several interchangeable heaters come with the instrument. For low resistances the grid is made of fine resistance wire, but for high resistances fine platinized quartz fibers are used. The higher the resistance of the heater the higher the sensitivity of the galvanometer. The sensitivity is varied either by changing the heater or changing its distance from the thermojunction. The inductance of the heater is low, and, therefore, this galvanometer may be used to detect alternating currents of low and high frequencies, as well as direct currents. The resistance of the silver loop is very low and thus it is critically damped electromagnetically. The heating effect varies as the square of the current, but the thermal emf., for small temperature variations, is proportional to the temperature. Therefore, the deflections are approximately proportional to the square of the current. When used as a current measuring instrument or ammeter it is calibrated with direct current and then used equally well for alternating currents. The quartz suspension and silver loop are very delicate, and, consequently, great care must be exercised in handling the galvanometer. The grids are easily burned out and hence must be protected by high series resistance, which may be reduced to the proper value as required. The working parts are enclosed in a case to protect the thermojunction from fluctuations of temperature which cause the zero to drift.

183. Electrodynamometer Instruments.

— Galvanometers, ammeters, voltmeters, and indicating wattmeters, which are of the electrodynamometer type, have one fixed coil and one movable coil which can rotate relative to the fixed coil, as indicated in Fig. 157. The movable coil may be suspended by a fiber or mounted on pivots resting in jewels. When a current flows through the two coils, which are usually connected in series, the movable coil tends to set itself parallel to the fixed coil due to attraction on one side and repulsion on the other side between the parallel currents.

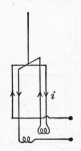

Fig. 157

There are two types of electrodynamometers: (1) The movable coil is always brought back to its initial position by means of a torsion head, as in Siemens's electrodynamometer. (2) The movable coil is allowed to deflect, as in an ordinary galvanometer, the deflection being controlled by the torsional couple of a suspension or of a hair spring.

As has been shown (Section 170), the force between two currents is given by

$$F = \frac{2i'i''l}{r} = \frac{2l}{r}i^2$$

in this case, since the currents are the same, the coils being in series. Since the force between currents varies as the product of the currents (current squared in this case), the couple acting upon the movable system will vary as the square of the current, and, therefore, we have the equation for this type of instrument

$$k\theta = Ci^2,$$

where k and C are constants.

Instruments of this type can be used for both direct and alternating currents, whereas the instruments of the D'Arsonval type can be used only for direct currents.   Since on alternating currents the current reverses in both coils at the same instant, the torque always has the same sense.   For alternating currents, we have

$$k\theta = C(\text{mean } i^2), \text{ and therefore}$$

$$K \sqrt{\theta} = \sqrt{\text{mean } i^2}.$$

But $\sqrt{\text{mean } i^2}$ is the effective value of an alternating current. Hence, the angular deflections, in this type of instruments, are proportional to the square of the effective current, and, therefore, the instruments are calibrated to read effective values directly.

When an electrodynamometer of the second type is shunted with a low, noninductive resistance of proper value it may be calibrated as an ammeter, or if connected in series with a high, noninductive resistance of proper value it becomes a voltmeter when calibrated to read volts.   When used as an indicating wattmeter, one coil is connected in one side of the line, as an ammeter is connected, and the other coil is connected across the line with high series noninductive resistance, as a voltmeter is connected.   It is then calibrated to read in watts.[1]

184. General Characteristics of Galvanometers. — The sensitivity of a galvanometer should be considered in relationship to its particular use. It should be sufficiently sensitive to permit readings to a precision commensurate with other readings in the same piece of work. A galvanometer should not be used which is much more sensitive than the work demands, because such a galvanometer is more difficult to work with and therefore entails a needless waste of time and effort. The damping of a galvanometer should be considered along with its sensitivity. The best working conditions require that the galvanometer be critically damped. Any wide departure from this condition is detrimental. If it is excessively under damped the indi-

---

[1] For descriptions of other types of galvanometers the reader is referred to Electrical Measurements, by Frank A. Laws.

cator oscillates about its rest position for some time before coming to rest. If it is excessively over damped it moves to its rest position so slowly as to make it difficult to tell when it has attained its final position. A critically-damped galvanometer deflects to, but does not pass, its new position, and in the shortest time. It may be necessary to sacrifice sensitivity in order to gain the critically-damped requirement. The designer of the instrument seeks to secure a galvanometer with a short period, except in a ballistic galvanometer, which, because of the nature of its function, requires a long period.

Sensitivity. — In order that galvanometers may be compared and rated it is necessary to define sensitivity quantitatively. There are four definitions that are in common use:

(1) *Current Sensitivity.* — The current sensitivity is defined as the current in amperes required to produce a deflection of 1 mm. on a scale which is at a distance of 1 m. from the galvanometer mirror. The current sensitivity is sometimes expressed in microamperes.

(2) *Megohm Sensitivity.* — This is the number of megohms in the galvanometer and in series with it which will give a deflection of 1 mm. on a scale distant 1 m. from the galvanometer mirror when the impressed p.d. is one volt. The megohm sensitivity is the reciprocal of the current sensitivity expressed in microamperes.

(3) *Voltage Sensitivity.* — This is the impressed p.d. on the galvanometer and any connected external resistance which will give a deflection of 1 mm. on a scale distant 1 m. from the mirror of the galvanometer. The voltage sensitivity is the product of the current sensitivity expressed in amperes and the resistance of the galvanometer circuit expressed in ohms. The voltage sensitivity is usually obtained for the purpose of detecting the presence of extraneous emfs. in the circuit, such as thermal emfs.

(4) *Ballistic Sensitivity.* — This is the quantity of electricity in coulombs which must be suddenly displaced in the galvanometer circuit in order to produce a deflection of 1 mm. on a scale distant 1 m. from the mirror of the galvanometer.

There is a diversity of practice in expressing the period of a galvanometer. The Leeds and Northrup Company use two periods in the rating of galvanometers. For a current galvanometer the period is the time in seconds required for one to and fro swing, i.e., a complete period. For a ballistic galvanometer the period is the time in seconds for the initial deflection away from the zero position to the first full elongation, i.e., a quarter period.

185. The Ballistic Galvanometer. — In measuring the quantity of electricity in a condenser discharge or the quantity of electricity discharged in a circuit with a given change in magnetic flux, a galvanometer is required which gives deflections proportional to the quantity of electricity discharged in the circuit by a transient current. Such a galvanometer is called a ballistic galvanometer, and differs from a current galvanometer in that it has a much longer period, a period so long that the electric discharge is consummated before the coil moves appreciably from its equilibrium position. Ballistic galvanometers are usually of the D'Arsonval type, since this type of galvanometer is uninfluenced by stray magnetic fields. The instrument is read by a telescope and scale, the scale being circular with its center on the axis of the moving system. With such a system the scale reading d is given by $d = r\theta$, where θ is in radians.

In taking readings the coil is brought to rest in its zero position. The electric discharge then takes place in the galvanometer circuit and the first scale deflection is read. Calling the first angular displacement θ_1, we have for the ballistic galvanometer,

$$Q = K_1\theta_1.$$

K_1 is a constant for any particular instrument, and its value depends upon the current sensitivity and the degree of damping.

The long period of the ballistic galvanometer is secured by increasing the moment of inertia I of the moving system, as the moving system is simply a torsion pendulum, the undamped period of which is

$$T = 2\pi\sqrt{\frac{I}{k}}.$$

186. Motion of the Damped Galvanometer Coil. — From the mechanical viewpoint the moving system of a moving-coil galvanometer is a torsion pendulum. Any torsion pendulum is opposed by retarding forces which cause each successive swing to be smaller in amplitude than the preceding. Even the first swing out from the zero position of the coil of a galvanometer is less than it would be were there no retarding forces. For a torsion pendulum we have

$$L = I\frac{d^2\theta}{dt^2}.$$

In the case of the moving system of a ballistic galvanometer L is made up of two parts: (1) The torsion couple of the suspension of value $k\theta$. (2) The retarding couple due to friction, air resistance, and induced currents. This term is usually taken proportional to the angular velocity, and is, therefore, of value $c\, d\theta/dt$. Hence, we have as the equation of motion of the moving system of a galvanometer

$$I\frac{d^2\theta}{dt^2} = -c\frac{d\theta}{dt} - k\theta.$$

Dividing by I, transposing, and adopting new constants, this equation may be written

$$\frac{d^2\theta}{dt^2} + 2K\frac{d\theta}{dt} + \omega^2\theta = 0. \qquad (186.1)$$

To solve this linear differential equation put $\theta = e^{\beta t}$, where e is the Naperian base of logarithms. We then have as the auxiliary equation

$$\beta^2 + 2K\beta + \omega^2 = 0.$$

And therefore

$$\beta_{1-2} = -K \pm \sqrt{K^2 - \omega^2}$$

The complete solution is

$$\theta = Ae^{(-K+\sqrt{K^2-\omega^2})t} + Be^{(-K-\sqrt{K^2-\omega^2})t}, \qquad (186.2)$$

where A and B are constants.

There are three cases to be considered. (1) If $K > \omega$, the exponents are both negative, and the deflection, starting at maximum,

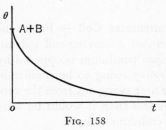

FIG. 158

steadily decreases to zero at time $t = \infty$, as shown in Fig. 158. This is the case of *over damping*. (2) If $K = \omega$, the two exponents are identical and negative. The deflection decreases to zero in the shortest possible time. This is the case of *critical damping*, or the system is said to be *dead beat*. (3) If $K < \omega$, the exponents are complex numbers of the form $x + jy$, where $j = \sqrt{-1}$. Thus equation (186.2) becomes

$$\theta = e^{-Kt}(Ae^{j\omega_1 t} + Be^{-j\omega_1 t}), \qquad (186.3)$$

where $\omega_1 = \sqrt{\omega^2 - K^2}$. This is the condition for *damped oscillations*, and the case we are most concerned with.

In order to free this equation of imaginaries, we introduce the well-known relations

$$e^{j\omega_1 t} = \cos \omega_1 t + j \sin \omega_1 t$$

$$e^{-j\omega_1 t} = \cos \omega_1 t - j \sin \omega_1 t.$$

We then obtain

$$\theta = e^{-Kt}\left\{(A + B) \cos \omega_1 t + j(A - B) \sin \omega_1 t\right\}.$$

In order to free this equation of j we let $(A + B) = C \sin \phi$, and $j(A - B) = C \cos \phi$. Then

$$\theta = Ce^{-Kt}(\sin \phi \cos \omega_1 t + \cos \phi \sin \omega_1 t).$$

Or

$$\theta = Ce^{-Kt} \sin (\omega_1 t + \phi). \tag{186.4}$$

This is the equation of damped, simple harmonic motion, where e^{-Kt} is the damping factor and ϕ is the phase angle. By proper selection of boundary conditions ϕ is made equal to zero, i.e., if $t = 0$ when $\theta = 0$. We then have as the solution of the differential equation,

$$\theta = Ce^{-Kt} \sin \omega_1 t, \tag{186.5}$$

where C is a constant to be evaluated. ω_1 is the so-called angular velocity in the damped, simple harmonic motion, i.e., *it is the angular velocity of the radius vector in the circle of reference.* When the angle changes by 2π, we have the complete damped period

$$T_1 = \frac{2\pi}{\omega_1}. \tag{186.6}$$

If there is no damping $K = 0$, and the undamped period is

$$T = \frac{2\pi}{\omega}. \tag{186.7}$$

Thus, ω is the so-called angular velocity in the simple harmonic motion when there is no damping.

At maximum displacement the angular velocity of the moving system is zero, and therefore,

$$\frac{d\theta}{dt} = Ce^{-Kt_1}\left\{\omega_1 \cos \omega_1 t_1 - K \sin \omega_1 t_1\right\} = 0. \tag{186.8}$$

Therefore, the time taken for the first swing out from the equilibrium position to maximum deflection is

$$t_1 = \frac{1}{\omega_1} \arctan\left(\frac{\omega_1}{K}\right).$$

Let ω_0 be the initial angular velocity of the moving system away from the equilibrium position. We then have, by placing $t = 0$ in equation (186.8),

$$C = \frac{\omega_0}{\omega_1},$$

and the complete solution is

$$\theta = \frac{\omega_0}{\omega_1} e^{-Kt} \sin \omega_1 t. \qquad (186.9)$$

The graph of this equation is represented in Fig. 159, which is the curve for a damped simple harmonic motion. The graph lies between the broken-line curves represented by the equation

$$\theta = \pm\, Ce^{-Kt},$$

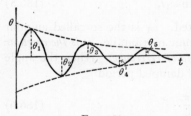

being tangent to them when $\sin \omega_1 t = \pm 1$. In order to evaluate the constants in this equation it is necessary to express them in terms of quantities which can be measured. Referring to equation (186.5) and Fig. 159, we see that at time t_1, $\omega_1 t_1 = \pi/2$, and

FIG. 159

$$\theta_1 = Ce^{-Kt_1}.$$

Also,

$$\theta_2 = Ce^{-K\left(t_1 + \frac{T_1}{2}\right)} = Ce^{-K\left(t_1 + \frac{\pi}{\omega_1}\right)},$$

$$\theta_3 = Ce^{-K\left(t_1 + \frac{2\pi}{\omega_1}\right)}, \text{ etc.}$$

Therefore, we have

$$\frac{\theta_1}{\theta_2} = \frac{\theta_2}{\theta_3} = \text{etc.,} = e^{K\frac{\pi}{\omega_1}} = e^{\delta}, \text{ say.}$$

Hence

$$\delta = \frac{K\pi}{\sqrt{\omega^2 - K^2}}. \tag{186.10}$$

$$\log_e \frac{\theta_1}{\theta_2} = \log_e e^{\delta} = \delta. \tag{186.11}$$

δ is called the *logarithmic decrement*. Thus, in order to obtain δ experimentally, it is necessary merely to observe any two successive deflections. If the damping is small, however, the ratio of successive deflections is nearly unity, and a relatively large error may result. A more accurate value is obtained under these conditions by observing deflections separated by several half periods. We then have

$$\delta = \frac{1}{n-1} \log_e \frac{\theta}{\theta_n}.$$

Eliminating K and ω between equations (186.6), (186.7), and (186.10), we have

$$T = \frac{\pi}{\sqrt{\pi^2 + \delta^2}} T_1. \tag{186.12}$$

We must next obtain an expression for the undamped first angular elongation θ_0. From equation (186.9), we have, when $t = t_1$,

$$\theta_1 = \frac{\omega_0}{\omega_1} e^{-Kt_1}. \tag{186.13}$$

By use of (186.10), we have $\omega_1 = \sqrt{\omega^2 - K^2} = \frac{\omega\pi}{\sqrt{\pi^2 + \delta^2}}$. Also combining the expression for t_1 with (186.10), we have

$$Kt_1 = \frac{K}{\sqrt{\omega^2 - K^2}} \arctan \frac{\sqrt{\omega^2 - K^2}}{K} = \frac{\delta}{\pi} \arctan \frac{\pi}{\delta}.$$

If there is no damping

$$\delta = 0, \quad \text{and} \quad \theta_1 = \theta_0 = \frac{\omega_0}{\omega}.$$

Then,

$$\theta_1 = \theta_0 e^{-\frac{\delta}{\pi} \arctan \frac{\pi}{\delta}},$$

or

$$\theta_0 = \theta_1 e^{\frac{\delta}{\pi} \arctan \frac{\pi}{\delta}}. \tag{186.14}$$

Since δ is usually small, arc tan π/δ is approximately equal to $\pi/2$, and, therefore,

$$\theta_0 = \theta_1 e^{\frac{\delta}{2}}.$$

But

$$e^{\frac{\delta}{2}} = 1 + \frac{\delta}{2} + \frac{\delta^2}{4\underline{|2}} + \frac{\delta^3}{8\underline{|3}} + \cdots = 1 + \frac{\delta}{2} \text{ approximately,}$$

and, therefore, very approximately

$$\theta_0 = \theta_1 \left(1 + \frac{\delta}{2}\right). \tag{186.15}$$

187. The Electric Discharge Q. — Let us consider an undamped, moving-coil ballistic galvanometer. Since the angular deflection of the coil is always small, the deflecting moment at any instant may be taken proportional to the instantaneous current, and, therefore, equal to Gi, where G is a constant depending upon the construction of the instrument. The deflecting moment will be opposed by the inertial moment of the moving system and the torsional moment of the suspension. There will be no opposing moment due to damping. Therefore, we have

$$I\frac{d^2\theta}{dt^2} + k\theta = Gi. \tag{187.1}$$

If we assume that the time of the displacement is so short that the coil has not moved appreciably from its equilibrium position by the time the discharge is completed, we may say that $k\theta = 0$, and, therefore,

$$G\int i\,dt = I\int \frac{d^2\theta}{dt^2}dt.$$

On integrating

$$GQ = I\left(\frac{d\theta}{dt}\right)_{\theta=0} = I\omega_0. \tag{187.2}$$

Thus, the impulse delivered to the coil by the electric discharge is equal to the initial angular momentum of the moving system. The system will turn until the energy given to it by the electric discharge is stored as potential energy in the suspension, i.e.,

$$\tfrac{1}{2}I\omega_0^2 = k\int_0^{\theta_0} \theta\,d\theta = \tfrac{1}{2}k\theta_0^2. \tag{187.3}$$

Combining equations (187.2) and (187.3), we have

$$Q = \frac{\sqrt{Ik}}{G}\,\theta_0. \tag{187.4}$$

The period of an undamped torsion pendulum is $T = 2\pi\sqrt{I/k}$. Combining this expresson for T with the expression for Q, we have

$$Q = \frac{k}{G}\frac{T}{2\pi}\,\theta_0. \tag{187.5}$$

Substituting for T from equation (186.12), and for θ_0 from equation (186.15), we have finally

$$Q = \frac{k}{G}\frac{T_1}{\sqrt{\pi^2 + \delta^2}}\frac{\theta_1}{2}\left(1 + \frac{\delta}{2}\right). \tag{187.6}$$

The galvanometer constant k/G may be found by passing a known, steady current through the galvanometer and observing the angular deflection ϕ radians of the coil. When the coil comes to rest, $Gi = k\phi$, by equation (187.1), and, therefore,

$$\frac{k}{G} = \frac{i}{\phi}.$$

Then finally

$$Q = \frac{i}{\phi}\frac{T_1}{\sqrt{\pi^2 + \delta^2}}\frac{\theta_1}{2}\left(1 + \frac{\delta}{2}\right). \tag{187.7}$$

All of the quantities in this expression for Q can be measured. θ_1 and ϕ are expressed in radians.

The analysis of the ballistic galvanometer shows that the first deflection of the moving system is proportional to the quantity of electricity discharged in the circuit no matter what the degree of damping may be, providing the damping remains unchanged. The major portion of the damping in a moving coil galvanometer is due to currents induced in the coil as it swings in the magnetic field, providing there is a closed circuit. The induced currents are in such a direction that the magnetic field of the current is in opposition to the magnetic field of the magnet (Lenz's law). The magnitude of the induced current is proportional to the angular velocity of the coil, and it also depends upon the resistance of the closed circuit. Thus, when the circuit is kept closed, any change in the resistance of the galvanometer circuit changes the degree of damping, and hence, also, the galvanometer constants, thus necessitating the redetermination of the constants.

188. Condenser and Standard Cell Method of Measuring Q. — The experimental arrangement is as shown in Fig. 160. A standard condenser of known capacitance C is charged to a known potential $\mathscr{E}$ by a standard cell s, and is then discharged through the galvanometer. We then have

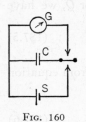

$$Q = Kd, \tag{188.1}$$

where d is the scale deflection. Also, $Q = C\mathscr{E}$. Therefore,

FIG. 160

$$K = \frac{C\mathscr{E}}{d}. \tag{188.2}$$

In obtaining K several different values of C should be used, a curve plotted, Q against d, and the constant K is then the slope of the straight line. If C is in farads, $\mathscr{E}$ in volts, and d in cms., K will be in coulombs per cm.

189. Methods of Measuring Magnetic Flux. — (a) *Standard Solenoid Method.* Let the experimental arrangement be as shown in Fig. 161a. Let the galvanometer G be the same as was used in the pre-

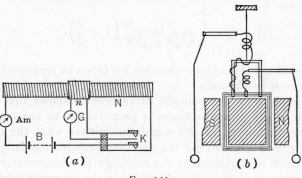

FIG. 161

ceding Section. Let ϕ be the total flux through the secondary of n turns of the standard solenoid when the keys are closed and a current i is flowing in the primary. The keys are so arranged that the primary circuit is opened an instant before the secondary circuit is opened. This time lapse is sufficient for the electric discharge of Q units to be completed in the secondary, due to induction, before it is opened. Since the secondary circuit is open, the moving system will vibrate with the same period it had when the condenser of the preceding Section was discharged. Let R be the total resistance of the secondary circuit and t the time for the electric discharge to take place. Then

$$Q = \int_0^t i\,dt = \int_0^t \frac{\varepsilon}{R}\,dt = \frac{n}{R}\int_0^t \frac{d\phi}{dt}\,dt = \frac{n}{R}\int_0^\phi d\phi = \frac{n\phi}{R} = KD.$$

Substituting the value of K obtained in the preceding Section, we have

$$\frac{n\phi}{R} = \frac{C\varepsilon D}{d}, \quad \text{and} \quad \phi = \frac{C\varepsilon RD}{nd}. \tag{189.1}$$

If ϕ is to be expressed in maxwells, C, ε, and R must be in cgsm. units. Therefore, if C is measured in mf., ε in volts, and R in ohms, we will have

$$\phi = 10^2 \frac{C\varepsilon RD}{nd}, \tag{189.2}$$

D and d being expressed in cms. of scale deflection. If I is the current in amperes in the primary circuit and N the number of turns, the total flux is given, also, by

$$\phi = \frac{4\pi NIA}{10L} \tag{189.3}$$

by equation (204.4), A being the cross-sectional area of the primary solenoid. This last equation will serve to check the preceding equation.

(b) *The Fluxmeter Method.* — The operation of a ballistic galvanometer requires that the electric discharge be essentially completed before the moving system swings appreciably from its zero position. When measuring magnetic flux by means of a coil of wire (exploring coil), which is inserted in the field to be measured and quickly withdrawn, the electric discharge takes too long a time for the use of an ordinary ballistic galvanometer. A galvanometer was designed by M. E. Grassot to meet this requirement. The Grassot fluxmeter is a modified ballistic galvanometer of the D'Arsonval type. The coil of the galvanometer, Fig. 161b, is suspended by a silk fiber which has a restoring couple which is practically zero. The current is conducted to the galvanometer coil by fine springs as shown, the springs being constructed and connected so as to exert as small a restoring couple as possible. The coil is rectangular and the magnetic circuit of the instrument is so designed that the torque produced by a given current is practically independent of the position of the coil. When the galvanometer is connected through an external resistance such that the resistance of the circuit is equal to or a little less than the critical resistance the coil is nearly stationary in any position. However, there is a slow drift back to the zero position which cannot be avoided. When a discharge of electricity takes place in the coil it moves to a new position from whatever position it may be in, and the deflection is proportional to the quantity of electric discharge for relatively long as well as for short periods of discharge. A mechanical device is provided in the instrument to quickly restore it to its zero position.

When used to measure magnetic flux it is provided with external coils. A coil for use with a fluxmeter must have a known number of turns wound on a nonmagnetic frame. A coil is made very thin so that it may be inserted in a narrow gap, as between the armature and pole face of a dynamo. When making measurements a coil is connected to the terminals of the fluxmeter by flexible leads and inserted in a magnetic field to be measured so that its plane is normal to the tubes of flux. The coil is then withdrawn from the field and the deflection of the instrument is read. When multiplied by a constant the change of flux through the coil is obtained. This constant may be obtained as follows:

Let ϕ be the flux through the exploring coil, N its number of turns, L the combined inductance of the exploring coil and galvanometer coil, R the combined resistance of these coils, C the constant of the galvanometer coil. C is the couple acting on the galvanometer coil when the current is one cgsm. unit. Then, by (181.1), $C = Hnlb$. I is the moment of inertia of the galvanometer coil, w its angular velocity at any instant, i the instantaneous current, and θ the angular deflection of the galvanometer due to a change of flux.

As the exploring coil is withdrawn from the field there is an induced emf. in it which at any instant is equal to $Nd\phi/dt$. This is opposed by a counter emf. $L\,di/dt$, and a counter emf. Cw due to the motion of the galvanometer coil through the field of the instrument. Therefore the instantaneous current is

$$i = \frac{N\dfrac{d\phi}{dt} - L\dfrac{di}{dt} - C\omega}{R}. \tag{189.4}$$

The equation of motion of the coil is

$$Ci = I\frac{d\omega}{dt} = \frac{CN}{R}\frac{d\phi}{dt} - \frac{CL}{R}\frac{di}{dt} - \frac{C^2\omega}{R}.$$ (189.5)

This may be integrated between the limits 0 and t, the duration of the change of flux and consequent swing of the galvanometer coil. Thus

$$\frac{CN}{R}\int_0^t \frac{d\phi}{dt}\,dt = I\int_0^t \frac{d\omega}{dt}\,dt + \frac{CL}{R}\int_0^t \frac{di}{dt}\,dt + \frac{C^2}{R}\int_0^t \omega\,dt.$$

The first two terms on the right when integrated will be zero at both limits, and $\int \omega dt = \theta$, the angular deflection of the galvanometer. Therefore, finally

$$\phi_2 - \phi_1 = \frac{C}{N}\theta.$$ (189.6)

The constant C may be determined experimentally by use of a known magnetic field.[1]

190. Q by Use of the Simple Thomson Galvanometer. — This type of galvanometer is an extremely sensitive instrument for detecting direct currents. It was invented by Lord Kelvin (William Thomson) in 1854 for the purpose of receiving signals through submarine cables. Owing to the large capacitance of submarine cables a very sensitive instrument was required. Short submarine cables were in use at that time, but when longer cables were laid it was found that the signals were blurred and unintelligible. This was before science developed a loading system to counteract the capacitance effect.

The astatic Thomson galvanometer is illustrated in Fig. 162. Two sets of short magnets are mounted on a straight glass or quartz rod, together with an observation mirror. The sets of magnets are so mounted on the rigid rod that their poles are in opposition. The whole movable system is hung from a support, not shown, by a quartz suspension. There are two sets of coils, upper and lower. Each set of coils consist of two coils; one back of the magnets, the other in front. Only the rear coils are shown in the drawing. The coils are so wound that when a current passes through them in series the torque has the

[1] Electrical Measurements, by Frank A. Laws, p. 124; Advanced Laboratory Practice in Electricity and Magnetism, by E. M. Terry, p. 31.

same sense for each set of magnets. The coils are set as close as they can be to the magnet and still permit free swinging. A control magnet, as shown, is required as the torques produced by the magnetic field of the earth are not quite equal. The original Thomson galvanometer had only two coils (front and back) and so the control was almost wholly due to the magnet, very little was due to the suspension. This galvanometer we will call the simple Thomson galvanometer.

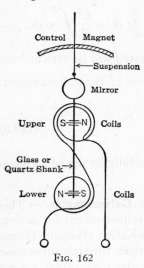

FIG. 162

The Thomson astatic galvanometer is treated in the same manner as the D'Arsonval galvanometer, since the control is due to the torsion couple of the suspension; there is very little magnetic control. In case of the simple Thomson galvanometer, however, the needle is not astatic, and there is only one pair of coils. The control is the earth's field coupled with control magnets. The control due to the suspension is relatively small and will be neglected. An instrument of this pattern is now of little practical use, since, under conditions now quite universal, the local magnetic field varies more or less continuously in both magnitude and direction, thus making the zero and deflections untrustworthy. However, it has some scholastic value. The treatment of this instrument is essentially the same as for the tangent galvanometer, except for the fact that the constant of the galvanometer cannot be calculated from measurements, but must be obtained from experimental data.

Let H be the control field, M the magnetic moment of the needle, and I its moment of inertia. The work done in twisting the needle through the angle θ_0 is

$$U = \int_0^{\theta_0} MH \sin \theta d\theta = MH(1 - \cos \theta_0) = 2MH \sin^2 \frac{\theta_0}{2}.$$

Therefore,

$$2MH \sin^2 \frac{\theta_0}{2} = \frac{1}{2} I\omega^2_0, \tag{190.1}$$

i.e., the work done against the control field is equal to the energy given to the needle by the transient current. At the instant of the electric discharge through the galvanometer $\theta = 0$, and hence $MH \sin \theta = 0$. The momentary impulse given to the needle due to the transient current is equal to the initial angular momentum. Therefore,

$$GM \int i \, dt = I\omega_0,$$

where G is a constant depending upon the construction of the galvanometer. From this equation we obtain

$$Q^2 = \frac{I^2\omega_0^2}{G^2M^2}. \tag{190.2}$$

On combining with (190.1), we have

$$Q^2 = \frac{4MHI}{G^2M^2} \sin^2 \frac{\theta_0}{2}.$$

For an oscillating magnetic needle of small amplitude $T = 2\pi\sqrt{I/MH}$. Therefore,

$$Q = \frac{H}{G} \frac{T}{\pi} \sin \frac{\theta_0}{2}. \tag{190.3}$$

To obtain H/G send a known steady current i through the galvanometer and produce a steady deflection ϕ. Then both fields act simultaneously, and we have

$$MH \sin \phi = GMi \cos \phi,$$

and

$$\frac{H}{G} = \frac{i}{\tan \phi}.$$

191. Galvanometer Shunts. — In the use of a galvanometer it frequently occurs that the instrument is too sensitive or has not sufficient carrying capacity. Under these conditions a resistance is shunted across the terminals of the galvanometer in order to bypass a part of the current. By varying the shunt resistance the desired sensitivity or current carrying capacity is obtained. An ordinary laboratory resistance box may be used which has sufficient variation in resistance. It is always advisable to shunt a galvanometer with a low resistance when making adjustments in order to protect it.

Let r = the resistance of the galvanometer, R = the shunt resistance, I = the line current, i = the current through the galvanometer, and i' = the current through the shunt. Then, applying Kirchhoff's laws, we have

$$I = i + i',$$

$$ri = Ri'.$$

Eliminating i', we have

$$i = \frac{R}{R + r} I. \tag{191.1}$$

The Ayrton-Mather Universal Shunt. — This shunt, which may be purchased complete, is so designed that it may be used with any

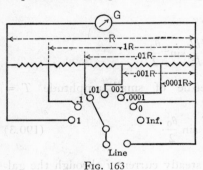

FIG. 163

galvanometer. The change in sensitivity or carrying capacity is effected by merely turning a dial from one stop to another. The wiring diagram is shown diagrammatically in Fig. 163. A high resistance of R ohms is connected across the terminals of the galvanometer, and one terminal is permanently connected to the external circuit. By a suitable arrangement the other line terminal may be connected at will to points along R, as shown. Referring to the Figure, let the movable terminal be set on tap 0.01, say, as shown. The portion of the current going through the galvanometer is then obtained by use of Kirchhoff's laws as follows:

$$I = i + i',$$

$$i' \frac{R}{100} = \left(r + \frac{99R}{100}\right) i.$$

Eliminating i', we have

$$i = \frac{I}{100} \frac{R}{R + r}. \tag{191.2}$$

Therefore, $R/(R + r)$ remains constant for any particular instrument and shunt. Thus, the relative values of i and I are independent of R and r as the switch is moved from one contact to another. However, I will vary in magnitude as the switch is moved from contact to contact, the variation decreasing as the external resistance, exclusive of the shunt, increases. When a galvanometer is used with a shunt it is best to calibrate it with the shunt in the circuit.

192. Ammeters and Voltmeters. — An ammeter, as the name signifies, is an instrument which measures current in amperes, whereas a voltmeter is an electric pressure gauge which measures difference of potential in volts. Ammeters and voltmeters are made for measurements in both direct and alternating current circuits. Ammeters and voltmeters are used in different manners. Since an ammeter measures current it must be connected directly in one side of the line so that the whole current to be measured flows through it, as shown in Fig. 164.

As an ammeter is connected *in the line* it must have a very low resistance so as to cause as little variation as possible in the existing current. A voltmeter, as shown in Fig. 164, is used to measure

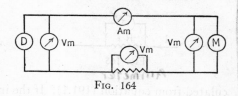

FIG. 164

the difference of potential across a dynamo, across a resistance, and across a motor. A voltmeter must have a high resistance so that it will take a very small current, and, therefore, disturb existing currents in the line as little as possible.

While there are many types of ammeters and voltmeters, most of the d.c. instruments are now of the D'Arsonval type. Such an instrument is a low sensitivity, portable D'Arsonval galvanometer so constructed and calibrated as to measure current or difference of potential, as the case may be. The permanent magnet is of the horseshoe pattern, made of tungsten steel and artificially aged. Soft-iron pole pieces are attached to the magnet and so shaped that the opening between them is cylindrical. Coaxially placed in the opening is a soft-iron cylinder which is fixed in position by a brass yoke attached to the pole pieces. The air gap in which the movable coil rotates is as narrow as possible. In this air gap the coil moves in a field which is essentially radial. (See Fig. 154). The movable coil of copper wire is wound on an aluminum frame, which also serves as an electromagnetic damping device to make the instrument aperiodic. The movable system is mounted on steel pivots which turn in sapphire bearings, which are carried by a yoke attached to the pole pieces. Torsional control is secured by two flat, spiral springs, one above and one below the coil.

These springs are made of nonmagnetic material, and serve, also, to conduct the current to and from the coil. The coil carries a well balanced light aluminum pointer attached to the coil normal to its axis. Parallax in reading the instrument is corrected by the use of a mirror under the pointer near its end. Since the magnetic field in which the coil rotates is essentially radial the scale graduation is nearly uniform. The number of turns of wire on the coil and its size will be determined by the use to be made of the instrument.

The same moving system may be used for either an ammeter or a voltmeter. If the instrument is to be made into an ammeter a resistor of proper magnitude is placed in parallel with the moving coil, as shown in Fig. 165. The value of the shunt resistance R may be cal-

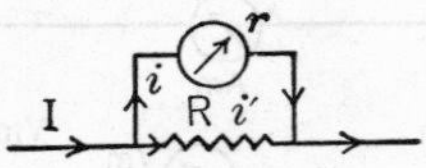

FIG. 165   FIG. 166

Ammeter   Voltmeter

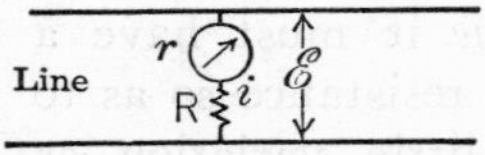

culated from equation (191.1). If the instrument is to be made into a voltmeter a resistor of proper value is connected in series with the moving coil, as shown in Fig. 166. If r is the resistance of the moving coil, R the series resistance, i the current required for full scale deflection, and $\mathscr{E}$ the maximum voltage required, we have

$$ri + Ri = \mathscr{E},$$

and

$$R = \frac{\mathscr{E}}{i} - r. \qquad (192.1)$$

The relationship between any voltage drop $\mathscr{E}$, the voltmeter reading, and the resistance is obtained as follows: Let $\mathscr{E}_1$ be the voltmeter reading, and $\mathscr{E}_2$ the potential drop across the resistor R. Then, $\mathscr{E} = \mathscr{E}_1 + \mathscr{E}_2$. But

$$\mathscr{E}_2 = Ri = \frac{R}{R + r} \mathscr{E}.$$

Then

$$\mathscr{E} = \frac{R + r}{r} \mathscr{E}_1. \qquad (192.2)$$

This equation holds also for an external resistance used with any voltmeter.

A single instrument may have one or more scales depending upon the particular shunt or series resistance which is connected in. It may have one scale as an ammeter and another as a voltmeter, being provided with a double set of binding posts, one binding post being common to both scales. Usually, in Weston instruments, one binding post, the positive in d.c. instruments, is common to all scales, and the other binding posts correspond to the different scales. In Weston instruments of low range the shunt and series resistances are placed inside the instrument case and cannot be changed. High voltage d.c. instruments (Weston) are provided with an external multiplier which is connected in series with the meter. With some ammeters and voltmeters, such as those made by Siemen and Halske and R. W. Paul, the resistors are separate units which may be connected to the instrument as required. The advantage of this arrangement is that a series of shunts and multipliers of proper values enables one to use the same instrument as an ammeter or voltmeter with several ranges for each. The disadvantage is that these separate units may be misplaced or lost.

Alternating current ammeters and voltmeters may be of the electrodynamometer or moving iron type. Such instruments will give a one-way deflection on a.c. as well as on d.c. circuits, since the torque is always of the same sense. These instruments may be used for both a.c. and d.c. circuits. In fact they are calibrated with direct currents and then used on alternating currents. The same general principles outlined for the manner of using d.c. ammeters and voltmeters hold also for a.c. instruments.

In the case of ammeters and voltmeters of the electrodynamometer type the torque acting on the movable coil, which carries the pointer, is nearly proportional to the mean value of i^2, which is the square of the effective current. Since the deflections are proportional to the squares of the effective currents the scale graduations are not uniform, being crowded at the lower end of the scale and widely separated at the upper end. Owing to this defeat a.c. ammeters and voltmeters of the electrodynamometer type covering a wide range are not satisfactory.

193. Power Measurements. — Electric power is measured in watts, which is the product of the current in amperes and the difference of potential in volts, if the current is direct. In this case power may be measured with an ammeter and a voltmeter, connected as shown in Fig. 167, the load in this case being indicated as a d.c.motor M. The voltmeter may be connected on the load side of the ammeter, as from p to p'', or on the line side, as from p' to p''. In either case a small error is introduced, which should be corrected for accurate work. If the voltmeter is connected from p' to p'', it reads the potential drop over the load and ammeter. The potential drop over the ammeter is ri, where r is its resistance and i the current. This potential drop should be subtracted from the voltmeter reading to give the potential drop over the load. If the connection is from p to p'', the ammeter

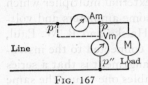

FIG. 167

reading is made up of two parts, i.e., the current through the voltmeter and through the load. The current through the voltmeter is $\mathcal{E}/R$, where $\mathcal{E}$ is the voltmeter reading and R its resistance. This current should be subtracted from the ammeter reading in this connection. However, if the voltmeter is connected from p to p'', and the voltmeter circuit is open when the ammeter is read, no correction is required.

Wattmeters. — A wattmeter, as the name signifies, is a single instrument which measures power in a circuit or part of a circuit in watts. There are three kinds of wattmeters: Indicating wattmeters, recording wattmeters, and integrating wattmeters or watthour meters. An indicating wattmeter measures the rate of expenditure of energy at any instant. A recording wattmeter is an indicating wattmeter which makes a permanent record, on a revolving drum or dial, of the variations of power for a given period of time. A watthour meter is in reality an energy measuring instrument and not a power measuring instrument. It records the energy consumption in killowatt hours, i.e., it integrates the power times the time. Indicating wattmeters for general use are, for the most part, of the electrodynamometer type, which are now to be considered.

An indicating watt meter registers the instantaneous rate of energy consumption, which is $P = \mathcal{E}i \cos \theta$ [1] (alternating currents), where $\mathcal{E}$ is the potential drop, i the current, and θ the phase angle between current and emf. For direct currents and noninductive a.c. loads, $\theta = 0$, and the power is given by $\mathcal{E}i$. Any single instrument which measures watts is essentially an ammeter and a voltmeter combined in one instrument. The electrodynamometer type instrument, shown schematically in Fig. 168, has a fixed coil $a'a$, which is connected in

[1] See Section 240, or any book on general physics.

the line as an ammeter is connected, and hence carries the current to the load. This coil has low resistance, as has any ammeter. The movable coil is connected across the line from p to p'', as a voltmeter is connected. This element must have high resistance, and so a non-inductive resistance R of proper value is connected in series with the coil. The magnetic field associated with the fixed coil is proportional to the total current, whereas the magnetic field associated with the movable coil is proportional to the current in that circuit, which, in turn, is proportional to the potential drop. Since the interacting fields are proportional respectively to the current and potential drop, such instruments may be calibrated to read watts.

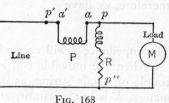

Fig. 168

In alternating current circuits both the p.d. and the current are varying from instant to instant, each passing through a definite cycle of values, and, in general, they are out of step, i.e., there is a phase displacement between them. At a particular moment the instantaneous power is $\mathcal{E}i$, where e and i are instantaneous values. The power measured by an indicating wattmeter is the average value of $\mathcal{E}i$ during a cycle, i.e.,

$$P = \frac{1}{T} \int_0^T \mathcal{E}i \, dt. \tag{193.1}$$

The net area under the power curve (see Figs. 285–287) is proportional to $\int_0^T \mathcal{E}i \, dt$. The time of a complete period T is proportional to the abscissa. Therefore, (193.1) to the proper scale, gives the average ordinate to the power curve. The integral (193.1) depends upon the current and voltage wave forms. If these wave forms are regular, and hence may be expressed in mathematical form, the integral can be evaluated. However, even though the integration cannot be performed mathematically, the electrodynamometer wattmeter performs the integration and gives the correct value. The electrodynamometer wattmeter measures the mean product of the currents in the fixed and movable coils, i.e.,

$$\frac{1}{T} \int_0^T i_1 i_2 \, dt. \tag{193.2}$$

But $i_2 = \mathcal{E}/Z$, where Z is the impedance in the potential circuit. Thus, we have

$$K\phi = \frac{1}{Z}\frac{1}{T}\int^T \mathcal{E}i\,dt = \frac{1}{Z}P. \tag{193.3}$$

If a Siemens type dynamometer is used, where the coils are always brought back into the same relative positions when the reading is taken, the angular twist ϕ required to bring the coil into its initial position is proportional to the power, providing Z is constant, and therefore, we have

$$KZ\phi = P. \tag{193.4}$$

The impedance Z will vary with the frequency.

When the movable coil is allowed to deflect against the control couple of a hair spring, as is the case with Weston indicating watt-meters, K is not constant, and, consequently, the scales of such instruments are not strictly uniform. This nonuniformity of the scale is overcome to some extent by proper proportioning of the fixed and movable coils.

Losses in the Wattmeter. — The wattmeter itself consumes energy, and, where the power being measured is small, this must be allowed for. When the potential terminals are connected from p' to p'' the wattmeter includes the ri^2 loss in the current coil $a'a$, Fig. 168, i.e., the potential drop in the movable coil is larger than when connected from p to p''. When connected from p to p'' the loss in the potential circuit is included in the wattmeter reading.

To avoid the necessity of making corrections for these losses wattmeters are sometimes so designed as to correct them automatically. When so designed the potential terminals are connected from p to p''. When this connection is used the current in the fixed coil $a'a$ is made up of two components, one due to the load and one due to the potential circuit pp''. Thus the current in the coil $a'a$ is too large, and, consequently, its magnetic field is too strong. The component of the magnetic field of the coil $a'a$, which is due to the current through the potential circuit, must be compensated or annulled. This is accomplished by winding on the bobbin which carries the fixed coil a parallel winding, but opposite in sense, connected in series with the potential coil. Thus, the excess field of the current is compensated.

194. Measurement of Power Factor. — In the expression for power,

$$P = \mathcal{E} I \cos \theta$$

$\cos \theta$ is called the *power factor*, and θ is the *phase angle* between current and emf. The power factor and phase angle for a reactive load may be measured with a wattmeter, an ammeter, and a voltmeter connected as shown in Fig. 169. With the ammeter and voltmeter, connected as shown on the load side of the wattmeter, the wattmeter includes the power losses in the ammeter and voltmeter. The wattmeter reading is too high by the ammeter and voltmeter watt consumption. In the above equation $\mathcal{E}$ is the effective voltage across the load, I is the effective current in the load, and P is the watt consumption by the load alone.

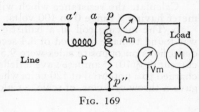

FIG. 169

When the necessary corrections have been made this equation enables one to calculate $\cos \theta$ and θ.

PROBLEMS

1. A standard condenser of 1 mf. capacitance was charged to a potential of 2.8 volts and then discharged through a galvanometer. The first two successive deflections, taken on opposite sides, was found to be 15 cms. and 10 cms. The galvanometer mirror was at the center of a curved scale of 50 cms. radius. Calculate: (1) The quantity of electricity discharged in the galvanometer circuit. (2) The logarithmic decrement. (3) The undamped first scale deflection. (4) The undamped period, the damped period being 5.5 seconds. (5) The undamped angular velocity ω, the constant K, the initial angular velocity of the coil ω_0, and hence obtain the equation of motion.

2. The sensitivity of a ballistic galvanometer was found to be 50 megohms, the period 6 seconds, and the logarithmic decrement 0.8. A certain discharge through the galvanometer gave a deflection of 10 cms. on a circular scale distant 50 cms. from the galvanometer mirror. Calculate the quantity of electricity Q discharged through the galvanometer.

3. A wattmeter, ammeter, and voltmeter were connected as shown in Fig. 169 for the purpose of measuring the power delivered to an induction coil. When the wattmeter was connected alone to the line the reading was 4 watts. When the wattmeter alone was connected to the load the reading was 114 watts. When the wattmeter, ammeter, and voltmeter were all connected to the load as shown the wattmeter read 120 watts, the voltmeter 116 volts, and the ammeter 5.69 amperes. Calculate the true power to the load, the true power factor, and the true phase angle of the load. What percentage error is made by calculating the power to the load using uncorrected simultaneous readings of the three instruments, i.e., when the three instru-

ments were simultaneously connected. The resistance of the voltmeter was 1,910 ohms.

4. Power is being measured on a d.c. line of 120 volts by an ammeter and a voltmeter, as shown in Fig. 167. The load resistance is 5 ohms. Calculate (1) The percentage error when the voltmeter is connected from p to p''. (2) When connected from p' to p''. The resistance of the ammeter is 0.06 ohm and of the voltmeter 2,000 ohms.

5. The deflecting coil of a certain Weston instrument (# 7,637) of the D'Arsonval type was found to have a resistance of 4.7 ohms. The current through the coil required for full scale deflection was found to be 0.014 ampere. Calculate the resistance that will convert this instrument into an ammeter reading from 0 to 15 amperes.

Calculate the resistance which will be required to convert it into a voltmeter having a range 0 to 100 volts.

6. The moving coil of a ballistic galvanometer of the D'Arsonval type was found to have a period of 8.4 seconds for free vibrations. The first two deflections on opposite sides were 9.5 cms. and 4.5 cms. of scale. A steady current of $3(10)^{-4}$ ampere gave a deflection of 12 cms. of scale. A condenser charged to a potential of 120 volts when discharged through the galvanometer gave a throw of 8 cms. of scale. Calculate the capacitance of the condenser.

CHAPTER XIV

THE MAGNETIC CIRCUIT

195. The fundamental principles of the magnetic properties of substances have been set forth in Chapter IV. In this Chapter the magnetic properties of substances will be considered in their relationship to the electric current. In Section 158 an expression was developed for the magnetic intensity H inside a long solenoid which is devoid of magnetic substance. It was shown that

$$H = \frac{4\pi NI}{10L} \text{ oersteds}$$

at the center of a long solenoid. H is the force in dynes acting upon a unit positive magnetic pole, or, because of the manner in which magnetic flux density has been defined, it is numerically equal to the number of tubes of flux (maxwells)[1] per sq. cm. in a vacuum, since μ_0 for a vacuum has been taken equal to unity in the cgsm. system of units. The H tubes of flux per sq. cm. in a vacuum are developed by the current I amperes, and are, therefore, associated with the current. Thus, *a magnetic field of force is one aspect of an electric current*, and, so far as is known, a magnetic field of force has no existence independent of moving electric charges, that is, an electric current, unless it may be said that the oscillating magnetic field forming a component of an electromagnetic wave constitutes an independent existence, but, even there, the magnetic component of the wave has its origin in moving charges of electricity. The fundamental relationship between a current of electricity and its accompanying magnetic field may be elucidated by considering the ring solenoid or toroid.

196. The Simple Magnetic Circuit. — Let a battery B send a direct current through the winding of the ring solenoid shown in Fig. 170. By suitable tests it can be shown that the tubular space within the winding is in that peculiar state which is recognized as a magnetic

---

[1] If one line of flux is assigned to each tube of flux there will be 4π lines of flux as well as tubes of flux associated with a unit magnetic pole.

field of force. It is, also, found that the space outside the solenoid is practically devoid of magnetic effects, and, therefore, the tubes of flux, for the most part, form closed circuits within the winding of the solenoidal current. Such a closed magnetic field, which is linked with an electric circuit, constitutes a *simple magnetic circuit.* Every electric circuit has linked with it a magnetic circuit, but, in the majority of cases, the magnetic circuit is extended and ill-defined, since magnetic flux cannot be confined to a definite channel with the same fidelity that marks the electric current circuit. The ring solenoid affords the best defined magnetic circuit.

The positive direction of a tube of flux has been chosen arbitrarily as the direction in which a positive magnetic pole is urged when placed in the field. The mutual directions of the conventional current

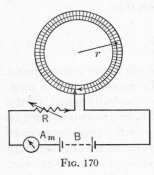

Fig. 170

and tubes of flux is given by the right-hand rule as follows: *Grasp the solenoid with the right hand, fingers pointing in the direction of the conventional current, and the thumb will then point in the direction of the tubes of flux.* This is shown by arrow tips on the current and a tube of flux in Fig. 170. Reversing the current reverses the magnetic field. The equation for the magnetic intensity inside the vacuum-core solenoid shows the flux density to be directly proportional to the strength of the current.

If, however, the solenoid is wound on a ring of ferromagnetic substance, constituting a toroidal electromagnet, the proportionality between current and flux density no longer holds. Further, it is found that the presence of the ferromagnetic substance has very greatly increased the flux density.

Thus, if H is the magnetic intensity (numerically equal to the flux density in a vacuum) with a vacuum core, and B the flux density in the ferromagnetic core, we have

$$B = \mu H \text{ gausses.} \tag{196.1}$$

The magnetic intensity H (force in dynes acting upon unit positive magnetic pole), which is due to the current, is called the *magnetizing field,* (Section 59). The factor μ is called the *permeability* of the medium, and, as here used, is expressed in the cgsm. system of units. Permeability characterizes the physical nature of the medium in which the flux is developed.   As we shall see, μ is not constant for a given ferromagnetic substance, but depends upon the *intensity of magnetization I* of the medium, and therefore, B is not proportional to the current.   We have seen (Section 68) that B, H, and I are related as in the equation

$$B = H + 4\pi I. \tag{196.2}$$

In this equation H is the magnetic intensity due to the current, and $4\pi I$ is the flux density having its origin in the core substance because it has been magnetized by the magnetizing field H.   The flux density B, therefore, is made up of two parts: H tubes of flux per sq. cm. (maxwells) due to the current, and $4\pi I$ tubes of flux per sq. cm. due to the magnetized substance composing the core.   If H is taken as a force, then it requires to be multiplied by the permeability μ_0, taken as unity in a vacuum, to convert it into flux density.   Then, each term in equation (196.2) is a flux density.

The name "oersted" was adopted for the unit magnetic intensity H by the International Electrochemical Commission at their meeting at Oslo in 1930.   The former name for this unit was the "gauss." The Commission adopted the name "gauss" for the unit of flux B. The name "oersted" was formerly used for the unit of reluctance, but now that unit has no name.   Using the new nomenclature equation (196.1) is now written

$$B \text{ (gausses)} = \mu \text{ } (H \text{ oersteds}).$$

Magnetic flux ϕ is measured as formerly in maxwells.

197.   Ohm's Law for the Magnetic Circuit. — The performance of most electrical machines and appliances depends in one way or another upon the magnetic properties of some ferromagnetic substance, i.e., upon magnetic flux in a more or less well-defined circuital path.   It becomes important, therefore, to develop some method for calculating the total magnetic flux in a magnetic circuit.   In order to establish the necessary concepts we may consider the toroidal electromagnet depicted in the previous Section.

Without any reference to equations already established, let us obtain a relationship between the current and the flux, and then translate it into known terms.   Experiments show that the magnetic flux, in case of a nonmagnetic core, remains constant so long as the product of current and turns of wire remains constant, and it in no way depends upon the magnetic history of the core, i.e., the flux has the same value with a given current strength whether approached by a rising or falling current. That is, the current and number of turns of wire may vary in any manner whatsoever, but, so long as their product remains constant, the magnetic flux remains constant. This product creates the magnetizing field. Thus, for example, 200 turns of wire carrying 2 amperes will develop the same flux as 400 turns of wire carrying 1 ampere, or 800 turns of wire carrying 0.5 ampere. This product of current and number of turns of wire is called *ampere turns*. Thus, the ampere turns create and maintain the magnetic flux of the magnetizing field, and, therefore, by analogy with the electric circuit, it has received the name *magnetomotive force* (mmf.).

The mmf. creates and maintains the magnetic flux. The magnetic flux, therefore, corresponds to the current in the electric circuit. We will designate the total flux by ϕ and the mmf. by M. A number of theories have been advanced in the past to explain the physical nature of magnetic flux, such as: (1) Flux is an actual displacement of some subtle, incompressible fluid along the tubes of flux. (2) This incompressible fluid is the so-called ether of space. (3) Magnetic flux consists of infinitely subdivided vortices in the ether, the planes of the eddies being normal to the tubes of flux. Whatever the *real nature* of magnetic flux may be it is very evident that it possesses energy which has its origin in the electric current.

In the cgsm. system of units the unit of magnetic flux is the *maxwell*, as previously defined. In the absolute practical system of units a unit of flux is sometimes used which is 10^8 times larger than the maxwell, which is called the *weber*. Since the magnetic flux ϕ is created by the mmf., we may write

$$M = \mathcal{R}\phi. \tag{197.1}$$

$\mathcal{R}$ is a proportionality factor called the *reluctance* of the magnetic path. Reluctance, therefore, corresponds to resistance in the electric circuit. (197.1) is called *Ohm's law for the magnetic circuit*. This equation merely states an experimental fact, i.e., the relationship between total flux and ampere turns. It takes the *form* of Ohm's law for the electric circuit, but the underlying physical realities are quite dissimilar.

As used by electric engineers the unit of mmf. is one ampere turn, the unit of flux one maxwell, and $\mathcal{R}$ is a proportionality factor which depends upon the medium, its extent and nature, in which the flux is established. The unit of reluctance in the engineering system of units is called by Karapetoff the *rel*. Experiments show that the reluctance of a well-defined circuital path varies directly as the length of the path, and inversely as its area of cross section. Therefore, we may write

$$\mathcal{R} = \nu \frac{L}{A}, \qquad (197.2)$$

which is of the same *form* as for electric resistance. In this equation ν is a constant which depends upon the nature of the medium in which the flux is established, and is called *reluctivity*. Thus reluctivity corresponds to resistivity. We may write (197.1) in the form

$$\phi = \frac{1}{\mathcal{R}} M = \mathcal{P}M, \qquad (197.3)$$

in which $\mathcal{P} = \mu(A/L)$. $\mathcal{P}$ is called the permeance of the magnetic circuit, and $\mu = 1/\nu$ the permeability. Thus, permeance corresponds to conductance and permeability corresponds to conductivity. In the engineering system of units, where the unit of mmf. is taken as one ampere turn, the permeability of free space μ_0 comes out equal to 1.257.

198. The Physicist's System of Units. — The physicist in arriving at equation (197.1) starts out with the work idea, as in the electric circuit. In the electric circuit, emf. is the work done in carrying a unit positive charge once around the electric circuit. Likewise, mmf. is the work done in carrying a unit magnetic pole (fictitious) once around the magnetic circuit. Thus

$$\text{work} = \oint H \, dl = \frac{4\pi}{10} NI = 1.257 \, NI = \text{mmf.} \, (M), \qquad (198.1)$$

where I is in amperes. The unit of magnetomotive force in this system of units is called the *gilbert*, and is equivalent to 0.796 ampere turn. Thus, gilberts = 1.257 ampere turns. The work done in carrying a unit magnetic pole once around a magnetic circuit was called by Maxwell the line integral of the magnetic force, and by Bosanquet the magnetomotive force. The factor 4π which enters equation (198.1) is not due to any quality of the magnetic circuit. It comes from the geometry of space. In calculating the number of maxwells associated with a unit magnetic pole in a vacuum Coulomb's law was used as related to a spherical surface surrounding a unit pole.

The area of the surface of a sphere is $4\pi r^2$. Hence the reason for 4π.

If the toroid is uniformly wound, H in equation (198.1) is constant, and we have

$$H = \frac{M}{L} \text{ oersteds.} \tag{198.2}$$

Thus, the magnetic intensity H is the mmf. per linear cm. of magnetic path. Or, *the oersted is a gilbert per cm.* In case the mmf. is not uniformly distributed over the L cms., H is not constant along the path. The magnetic intensity will be more intense in that part of the circuit where there is the greatest concentration of ampere turns, i.e., where there is the greatest number of ampere turns per cm. of path. In case of nonuniformity of windings, the magnetic intensity should be expressed by

$$H = \frac{dM}{dl}. \tag{198.3}$$

Now $H = B/\mu = \phi/\mu A$, and therefore $\oint H \, dl = \phi \oint dl/\mu A$. Then

$$\phi = \frac{1.257 NI}{\oint \dfrac{dl}{\mu A}} \text{ maxwells.} \tag{198.4}$$

But $\oint dl/\mu A = L/\mu A =$ reluctance providing μ and A are constant throughout the distance L. Since 1930 the unit of reluctance in this system of units has no name. In this system of units the permeability μ_0 for free space is unity.

In case the toroid is uniformly wound (198.4) may be written

$$\phi = \mu \frac{1.257 NIA}{L} \text{ maxwells.} \tag{198.5}$$

If the mmf. is uniformly distributed, and the area of the magnetic circuit is constant, we may write

$$B = \frac{\phi}{A} = \mu \frac{1.257 NI}{L} = \mu \frac{M}{L} \tag{198.6}$$

and, therefore, $B = \mu H$ as before. Before 1930 many writers used H for the flux density in free space, thus using it as a limiting value of B.

When so used B denotes the gausses in a material substance and H denotes the gausses in free space, each for the same ampere-turn value. When used in this sense the magnetic flux in a magnetic circuit containing ferromagnetic substances may be considered to be made up of two superposed fields, one due to the current in the solenoid winding and the other due to electrons in orbital motions or spinning within the atoms of the core substance. However, the International Electrochemical Commission which convened at Oslo in 1930 considered that B and H are essentially unlike physical quantities having unlike dimensions, and that H needs to be multiplied by μ to make it physically equal to B. Therefore, μ is not a pure number, but has dimensions in order that the two sides of the equation may be dimensionally equivalent. However, this question need not concern us in the practical applications of the equations.

In most cases met with in practice the magnetic path is made up of several parts of lengths L_1, L_2, etc. and areas A_1, A_2, etc. in series, and μ varies, in general also from section to section. Then

$$\mathcal{R} = \oint \frac{dl}{\mu A} = \frac{L_1}{\mu_1 A_1} + \frac{L_2}{\mu_2 A_2} + \cdots. \tag{198.7}$$

This equation corresponds in form to that for resistances in series in the electric circuit. Since the *forms* of the equations for the magnetic and electric circuits are the same throughout, it follows that reluctances when in parallel combine in the same way as resistances when in parallel, and thus magnetic flux divides between magnetic conductors or paths as the electric current divides between electric conductors. Therefore, we have

$$\mathcal{P} = \mu_1 \frac{A_1}{L_1} + \mu_2 \frac{A_2}{L_2} + \cdots. \tag{198.8}$$

Equation (198.4) gives the total flux developed. However, the useful flux in any electric appliance is never quite equal to the total flux, since there is always some flux leakage. In case of the toroid, Fig. 170, the leakage is very small. The usual magnetic circuit is somewhat comparable to a metallic conductor traversing a liquid which has small conductivity as compared with the metal. In such a case there would be current leakage. If an air gap exists in a magnetic circuit, as in all dynamos and motors, there is spreading of the flux at the gap, and leakage is enhanced, the amount depending upon the width of the gap. In such cases the amount of leakage is determined and allowed for by use of a *leakage factor*. Leakage factors have been determined for the common electric appliances, and can be used when required.

We must not lose sight of the fact that the concept of a magnetic circuit, from the physical standpoint, is not the same as for the electric circuit. Ohm's law for the magnetic circuit, first conceived by Bosanquet in 1883,[1] is merely an analogy which serves a useful purpose in calculations pertaining to the flux created by a given ampere-turn excitation. Magnetic flux is clearly not a flow of a material substance or an imponderable fluid. All that can be stated definitely in our present state of knowledge is that magnetic flux is that peculiar state of space which we recognize, by indirect means, as a magnetic field of force. We are unacquainted with its real nature. That there is not a flow of an entity in the magnetic field is evidenced by the fact that once the flux is established and remains constant no energy is required to maintain it. There is no continuous energy consumption comparable to the Joule heating effect when a current of electricity flows in a conductor.

The reluctance of a given magnetic circuit is very much less if it consists of a ferromagnetic substance (iron, cobalt, nickel, and to some extent manganese, chromium, and some of the oxides and alloys of these elements) than if it consists of para- or diamagnetic substances. Low reluctance substances are comparable to low resistance substances in the electric circuit. The permeability, and hence the reluctance, varies with the magnetizing field if the circuit is ferromagnetic. Changes in the intensity of magnetization of a ferromagnetic substance involves a kind of magnetic inertia, called *hysteresis*, which is due to the tendency of such a substance to resist any change in a magnetic state already in existence. This causes the intensity of magnetization to be different, with the same magnetizing field, on a rising than on a falling current.

omit.

199. Definitions of Units. — *The Maxwell*. It was shown in Section 60 that 4π lines of flux (maxwells) are associated with a unit magnetic pole. In Section 168, it was shown that the work done, when the magnetic flux linked with a current circuit of i cgsm. units changes, is given by

$$W = i(\phi_2 - \phi_1) \text{ ergs.}$$

[1] Phil. Mag. 15, 205, 1883.

When W is one erg, i one cgsm. unit current, $\phi_2 - \phi_1$ is one maxwell. Therefore, from this equation we may define the maxwell as follows:

The maxwell is the amount of flux change in a circuit when one erg of energy is expended by a current of one cgsm. unit.

This name was adopted for the unit of magnetic flux by the International Electrical Congress which met in Paris in 1900, and it was confirmed by the International Electrochemical Commission which met at Oslo in 1930.

The Gauss. The gauss is defined by the relation $B = \phi/A$ for uniform distribution, or $B = d\phi/dA$ for nonuniform distribution of magnetic flux. Thus,

The gauss is the flux density such that there is a distribution of one maxwell per cm.^{2}, the plane of the area being normal to the direction of the flux.

Reluctance. — By equation (197.1), we have $\mathcal{R} = M/\phi$. Thus, we may define the unit of reluctance as follows: *A magnetic circuit has unit reluctance when unit mmf. is required to establish a flux of one maxwell.*

Prior to 1930 this unit was called the "oersted." Now it has no name.

Permeance. — Permeance is the reciprocal of reluctance.

The Gilbert. — The gilbert may be defined from the equation $M = \mathcal{R}\phi$. Thus, *the gilbert is the mmf. which develops a magnetic flux of one maxwell in a circuit of unit reluctance.*

When μ_0 is taken equal to one for free space the gilbert comes out equal to 0.796 ampere turn. The gilbert has been used for the unit of mmf. by physicists for a long time. However, it was not officially adopted until the meeting of the International Electrochemical Commission at Oslo in 1930.

The Oersted. — "Oersted" is the name adopted by the International Electrochemical Commission in 1930 for the unit of magnetic intensity. It may be defined from the relation $F = mH$. Thus, when m is a unit magnetic pole, as defined by Coulomb's law, and F is one dyne in free space H is one oersted. That is,

The oersted is the magnetic intensity in a magnetic field where a force of one dyne acts upon a unit magnetic pole.

We may, also, define the oersted from equation (198.3), $H = dM/dL$. Hence,

The oersted is the magnetic intensity at a place in the magnetic circuit where the mmf. is one gilbert per cm. of magnetic circuit.

This unit was called the "gauss" prior to 1930. Since B and H have been given different names, it is recognized that they are fundamentally different physical entities, and have unlike dimensions.

200. Magnetization Curves. — In case the core of the ring solenoid shown in Fig. 170 is nonmagnetic the flux ϕ is directly proportional to the mmf. i.e., in the equation $M = \mathcal{R}\phi$, $\mathcal{R}$ is constant for all variations of M. The graph of M against ϕ is a straight line.

On the other hand, if the core of a ring solenoid is iron, say, $\mathcal{R}$ is

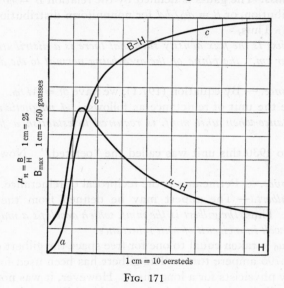

FIG. 171

not constant, but varies as the mmf. varies, i.e., as the intensity of magnetization of the iron changes. If the iron core is completely demagnetized to begin with, and the current is gradually increased from zero, and, step by step, B and H are determined and plotted, a curve is obtained which is of the form shown in Fig. 171. Such a curve for a given ferromagnetic substance, which is the actual curve followed by the substance starting from a state of complete demagnetization, is called its *initial magnetization curve*. If at each step μ is calculated, from the relation $B = \mu H$, and plotted against H the $\mu - H$ curve shown in Fig. 171 is obtained. Thus, μ varies with the intensity of magnetization, and hence, also, $\mathcal{R}$.

The shape of the initial magnetization curve may be explained on the theory that within the atoms of ferromagnetic substances there are diminutive solenoidal currents consisting of electrons in orbital motions, each having a definite magnetic moment, and, therefore, constituting a diminutive, natural unit magnet. In the course of investigations on ferromagnetic substances, P. Weiss [1] came to the conclusion that each atom contains a number of uncompensated electronic orbits each constituting an ultimate magnet having a definite magnetic moment. This ultimate unit he called a *magneton*. Thus, according to this theory, a ferromagnetic substance is made up of discrete unit electromagnets, each being accompanied by its own field of force. In the completely demagnetized or neutral state the magnetic axes of the magnetons are oriented in all possible directions so that their fields overlap in such wise as to annul each other, i.e., if at a point outside the substance the vector sum of the intensities due to all of the magnetons were to be obtained it would sum up to zero.

Now as the exciting current imposes a small magnetizing field upon the ferromagnetic substance only a few of its magnetons become oriented, partly or completely, in the same sense as the magnetizing field, owing to constraints of some kind which prevent complete freedom of motion. As the intensity of the magnetizing field increases the magnetons begin to be oriented in the sense of the magnetizing field in larger numbers, indicated by the increase in the slope in the neighborhood of *a* on the curve. From *a* to *b* on the curve *B* increases very rapidly because of the very large increase in the flux owing to the orientations of magnetons in very large numbers. In the neighborhood of *b*, the beginning of the upper curve, most of the magnetons that can be oriented in line with the magnetizing field have fallen into line. From this point on the slope of the curve gradually decreases until a region *c* is attained of nearly constant slope, where essentially all of the magnetons that can be oriented are in line. The ferromagnetic substance is then said to be *magnetically saturated*. The curve beyond this point is nearly a straight line, the flux added to the circuit coming almost exclusively from the magnetizing current.

201. The Hysteresis Loop. — As has been stated, a ferromagnetic substance possesses the property of tending to maintain any magnetic state which is already in existence. Therefore, if, after the substance has been carried along the initial magnetization curve from *O* to *a*,

[1] Comptes Rendus, 152, 1911.

Fig. 172, the magnetizing field H be gradually reduced the magnetic flux B will at each step have a higher value than when H was being increased.

Let the toroidal electromagnet have an iron core which is in the neutral state, connected as shown in Fig. 170, and let it be magnetized by passing a current through the winding of increasing value until the point a, say, on the magnetization curve has been reached. This

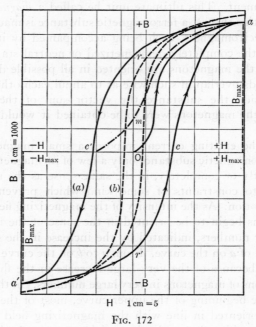

FIG. 172

can be done by decreasing the resistance R. When the state of magnetization represented by the point a on the curve is reached, decrease the current step by step, and, at each step, determine B and H, by a method soon to be given. The curve ar will be obtained, which lies above the initial magnetization curve. When the current has been reduced to zero, and hence H is zero, an amount of magnetization still remains in the iron which is represented by Or on the diagram. This remaining magnetization is called *residual magnetism*, and the property of retaining magnetization is called the *retentivity* of the substance. This remaining magnetism is sometimes, also, called *remanent magnetism*, but the term remanent magnetism is now generally used to mean the magnetism retained by an open-circuit magnet, as, for example, a horseshoe magnet with the keeper removed. The magnetization in the arms of such a magnet is different with the keeper on than when off, since with the keeper on the demagnetization effects are reduced. The magnetization left in an iron ring after the magnetizing field has been removed is called residual magnetism. In this case there are no free poles, and hence no demagnetization effects.

When a point r on the curve has been reached, reverse the current, and, step by step, increase the current in the opposite sense, and, at each step, calculate B and H and plot the curve. At some point c', where the magnetizing field has a value $-H_c$, the flux B is zero. The value of $-H_c$, at which B is reduced to zero, is called the _coercive force_. It is the reverse magnetizing field which is required to overcome the residual magnetism. If the current is still further increased in the negative sense, and the values of B and H are calculated and plotted, the curve $c'a'$ is obtained. If H, corresponding to the point a, is numerically equal to $-H$, corresponding to the point a', B is numerically equal to $-B$. These extreme values on any magnetization curve, or hysteresis loop, are called maximum values, and are designated by H_{max} and B_{max}.

If at the point a' the current is reduced in value, and the calculations carried out as before, the curve $a'r'$ is obtained, which is a duplicate of the curve ar. Thus, Or equals Or', or B_r equals $-B_r$ in absolute value. If now the current is reversed and increased in the positive sense, the curve $r'c$ is obtained, which is a duplicate of the curve rc'. Thus, Oc' equals Oc, and H_c equals $-H_c$ in absolute value. A further increase of the current in the positive sense gives the curve ca, which is a duplicate of the curve $c'a'$. This represents one magnetic cycle. However, a ferromagnetic substance must be put through a number of complete cycles, from 20 to 30, before the curve will close, i.e., it must be put into a _cyclic state_. This closed curve is called the _hysteresis loop_. The cycle may then be repeated any number of times and the curve is retraced, providing H_m is the same each time, and no physical changes have taken place in the substance.

The hysteresis loop reveals the magnetic characteristics of a ferromagnetic substance. The area of the loop is proportional to the energy drawn from the electric circuit, which appears as heat in the core. This energy loss is known as the _hysteresis loss_. In Fig. 172 the solid line hysteresis loop (a) represents more energy loss than the broken-line loop (*b*), if both loops are drawn to the same scale. In the case of transformers and all electric machines, where hysteresis losses merely represent waste energy, a material of low energy loss is selected, such as soft, silicon iron. If, however, the magnetic characteristic required is magnetic permanence, as in the case of magnets used in galvanometers, ammeters, and voltmeters, the material selected is one having high retentivity and coercive force, such as cobalt steel. Many special magnetic alloys have been developed for special uses, and in each case a study of the hysteresis loop has revealed the magnetic quality desired. Thus, *permalloy*, an iron-nickel alloy developed in the Bell Telephone Laboratories, acquires a high degree of magnetization in a weak magnetizing field. This alloy is used in the form of a ribbon to wrap submarine cables, so as to counteract the capacitance of the cable with inductance. Another alloy, *perminvar*, an iron-nickel-cobalt alloy, also developed in the Bell Telephone Laboratories, has the characteristic of being practically nonmagnetic or paramagnetic in weak magnetizing fields, not greater than about three oersteds, whereas in strong fields this characteristic disappears. For fields under about three oersteds the hysteresis loop is nearly a straight line. In stronger fields the hysteresis loop resembles somewhat the characteristic hysteresis loop, save that it has a pronounced constriction at its center.[1]

202. Magnetic History of a Ferromagnetic Substance. — The magnetic state of a ferromagnetic substance clearly depends upon its past magnetic history. Before the substance has been subjected to a magnetizing field, and, hence, is completely demagnetized, it is said to be in the *virgin state*. If, when in the virgin state it is magnetized to saturation and then put through a magnetic cycle, the loop will not close. The cycle must be repeated many times before the loop will close. If, after being put in the cyclic state, it is completely demagnetized it will subsequently form a closed loop if again put in the cyclic state. Once a substance has been magnetized it suffers a permanent change. There is no return to the virgin state. Hence, complete demagnetization after being magnetized, or after having been put in the cyclic state, is magnetically different from the virgin state, and is, therefore, called the *neutral state*.

Again, suppose, as in Fig. 172, the substance has been magnetized

---

[1] For an account of these special alloys, see Arnold and Elmer, Jour. Franklin Inst. 195, 621, 1923; Elmer, Jour. Franklin Inst. 206, 317, 1928.

to saturation by a magnetizing field H_m and the field is then decreased to zero and reversed until the point c' on the curve is reached. The substance is apparently completely demagnetized. But the magnetic condition of the substance at c' is not the same as at O, for if the cycle be stopped at c' and the field $-H_c'$ be reduced to zero, reversed, and increased to $+ H_m$ the broken curve $c'ma$ is followed, and there is a closed loop. But when H equals zero there is magnetization represented by Om. Thus, the substance at c' and c is not in the demagnetized or neutral state. Hysteresis loops of various sizes may be formed, as shown in Fig. 173, by carrying the substance through different amplitudes of H_m. In each case where a loop crosses the H axis there is apparently complete demagnetization, but each point represents a different magnetic state, and in each case, except at o, the substance possesses some degree of magnetization. This argument may be amplified in many ways to show that the magnetic state of a ferromagnetic substance depends upon its magnetic history.

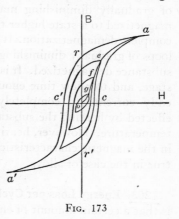

FIG. 173

Let the substance be carried through a series of hysteresis loops of smaller and smaller values of H_m, as shown in Fig. 173. The locus of the cusps of the gradually decreasing hysteresis loops is called the *normal magnetization curve*. This curve is a fictitious curve, since the substance is not actually carried along it magnetically. However, it coincides essentially with the initial magnetization curve, which is the actual curve followed when a completely demagnetized substance is magnetized.

The normal magnetization curve is a very important curve, since it shows the maximum flux that can be obtained with any magnetization field. Also, it is the only means we have of assigning any definite meaning to permeability. The general relation for permeability, $B = \mu H$, holds accurately only for para- and diamagnetic substances. This relation may have almost any value for μ in case of ferromagnetic substances. However, permeability may be given a definite meaning where there is a definite connection between B and H, as along the normal magnetization curve. Thus, for ferromagnetic substances, permeability is defined with reference to the normal magnetization curve, and is $\mu_n = B/H$. This is called the *normal permeability*. Since μ enters into the expression for reluctance, reluctance can have no definite meaning except as defined with reference to the normal magnetization curve.

Figure 173 illustrates the best method for demagnetizing a substance, or bringing it into the neutral state. By this method of demagnetization the substance is placed in a slowly alternating field of gradually diminishing maximum values. The substance is first magnetized to a state higher than in any previous magnetization since complete demagnetization. It is then put through a series of hysteresis loops of gradually diminishing areas which finally vanish leaving the substance demagnetized. It is well to employ several reversals at each stage, and to allow time enough between stages or distinct loops for eddy currents to completely die out. Demagnetization may be effected by heating the substance to a temperature above the critical temperature. However, heating may bring about permanent changes in the magnetic characteristics of the substance, and especially is this true in the case of alloys.

203. Energy Loss per Cycle. — An important feature of hysteresis is that a certain amount of energy must be supplied by the magnetizing current for each cycle, and this energy appears as heat in the substance. The phenomenon of hysteresis is, therefore, an *irreversible* process, as are all cyclic operations where there is a dissipation of energy. If the cycle were reversible the loss of energy during one half cycle would be regained during the subsequent half cycle. If the core is a nonmagnetic substance the operation *is* reversible.

As we have seen, the degree of magnetization in a ferromagnetic substance lags behind the magnetizing field H so that the curve does not follow the same path on a falling current as on a rising current. This lagging of the value of B behind the corresponding value of H is called *hysteresis*, which comes from a Greek word meaning "to lag behind." This lagging effect is accompanied with a dissipation of energy which takes the form of heat in the substance. When the magnetizing current is steady there is only the Joule loss in the solenoid winding. No energy is required to maintain the flux. When, however, the flux is decreased by a decrease in the mmf. not all of the energy in the magnetic field is returned to the circuit. The energy required to magnetize the substance is not completely recoverable when the magnetizing current is reduced to zero. If it were, as is the case for nonmagnetic substances, the cycle would be reversible; the energy required to magnetize the substance would be completely returned to the circuit when the current returned to zero, and the normal magnetization curve would be retraced.

In order to obtain an expression for the electric energy which is turned into heat in a ferromagnetic substance, we must take into account the fact that when a current changes in magnitude in a coil of wire there is an emf. of self in-

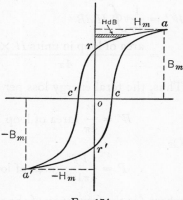

duction, which, *on a decreasing current is in the same sense as the impressed emf., and on an increasing current is in opposition to the impressed emf.* Thus, from a to r, Fig. 174, energy is being returned to the circuit, and the emfs. are in the same sense. From r to c' to a' energy is being stored in the field; the emfs. are in opposition, or work is being done against opposition, which is due to magnetizing the substance in part. From a' to r' energy is being returned to the

Fig. 174

circuit; the emfs. are in the same sense. From r' to c to a energy is being stored in the field; the emfs. are in opposition.

Let us consider the energy returned to the circuit in an infinitesimal change in the flux dB in the part of the cycle ar, corresponding to a change dH in the magnetizing field. Let the total flux at the instant be ϕ maxwells, and the intensity of magnetization H oersteds. The instantaneous induced emf. due to a change in flux $d\phi$ is

$$\mathcal{E} = N\frac{d\phi}{dt} = NA\frac{dB}{dt} \text{ cgsm. units.} \tag{203.1}$$

The change in electric energy is

$$dW = \mathcal{E}i\,dt = NAi\,dB \text{ ergs.}$$

dW is the change in energy in the whole circuit, and hence in the whole volume of the core substance. To reduce this expression to unit volume we have $V = AL$. Therefore,

$$dW' = \frac{dW}{V} = \frac{Ni}{L} \, dB \text{ ergs/cm}^3.$$

Combining this relation with the expression $H = 4\pi Ni/L$, we have

$$dW' = \frac{H \, dB}{4\pi},$$

and on integrating,

$$W' = \frac{1}{4\pi} \oint H \, dB$$

$$= \frac{\text{area of loop in units } H \times B}{4\pi} \text{ ergs per cm.}^3/\text{cycle.} \qquad (203.2)$$

Thus, the total energy loss per cycle is

$$W = \frac{V}{4\pi} \text{ (area of loop in units } H \times B) \text{ ergs/cycle.} \qquad (203.3)$$

Or

$$P = \frac{Vf}{4\pi 10^7} \text{ (area of loop in units } H \times B) \text{ watts,} \qquad (203.4)$$

where f is the frequency of the supply. A graph of the hysteresis loop is made on cross-section paper. The values of B are always much larger than the values of H, and hence B and H cannot be plotted to the same scale. Let x equal the number of H units per cm. of scale and y the number of B units per cm. of scale. Then

$$W' = \frac{xy}{4\pi} \text{ (area of loop in cm.}^2) \text{ ergs per cm.}^3 \text{ cycle.} \qquad (203.5)$$

The area in cm.^{2} may be estimated very approximately by counting the number of cm.^{2} in the area of the loop, or better, the area may be measured accurately with a planimeter.

Equation (203.2) is the form in which Hopkinson developed the expression for the hysteresis loss. Warburg developed the expression

$$W' = \oint H \, dI \qquad (203.6)$$

for the hysteresis loss. It is evident that these two expressions are interchangeable, since

$$B = H + 4\pi I,$$

and, therefore,

$$H \, dB = H \, dH + 4\pi H \, dI.$$

Hence

$$W' = \frac{1}{4\pi} \oint H \, dB = \frac{1}{4\pi} \oint H \, dH + \oint H \, dI. \qquad (203.7)$$

If B and H have the same negative and positive limiting values, $\oint H \, dH = 0$, and, therefore,

$$W' = \frac{1}{4\pi} \oint H \, dB = \oint H \, dI. \qquad (203.8)$$

The shape and size of the hysteresis loop depend upon the character of the ferromagnetic substance. Hard steels have high retentivity and coercivity, and hence the loops have large areas. Soft iron has low retentivity and low coercivity, and the areas of the loops are small. Silicon steel (2.5% to 4% Si) is used for transformers, and is nonaging, i.e., the losses do not increase materially with time and use.

When a ferromagnetic substance is carried through cycles of varying values of B_m the hysteresis loop is larger in area as B_m increases, as is seen from Fig. 173. If the energy loss in

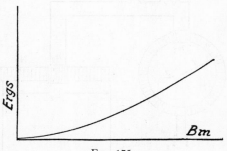

Fig. 175

ergs/cm.^{3}/cycle is calculated for successively larger and larger values of B_m, and W' is plotted against B_m, a curve similar to the one shown in Fig. 175 is obtained. From such a relationship Steinmetz expressed the energy loss by the empirical equation

$$W' = \eta \, B_m^k \text{ ergs/cm.}^3\text{/cycle} \qquad (203.9)$$

k will vary from 1.4 to 1.8 depending upon the character of the ferromagnetic substance, but for most practical cases 1.6 is used. The constant η, called by Steinmetz the *hysteresis constant or coefficient of hysteresis loss*, will vary, also, with different substances. The equation fits experimental data best between $B = 1,500$ gausses and $B = 12,000$ gausses. Above 15,000 gausses the error is large. At best this equation gives only approximate values, and is used principally for rapid checking. A few of the values of the coefficient η are shown in the Table below:

Substance	η	Substance	η
Soft iron.................	0.002	Annealed cast steel.........	0.008
Hardened steel............	0.025	Nickel....................	0.012
Best Silicon steel..........	0.0006	Cobalt...................	0.012
Silicon sheet steel.........	0.001	Hard tungsten steel........	0.058

204. The Rowland Ring Method for Obtaining Magnetization and Hysteresis Curves.

— There are several methods that may be used in measuring the hysteresis losses. However, the Rowland ring method is selected for de-

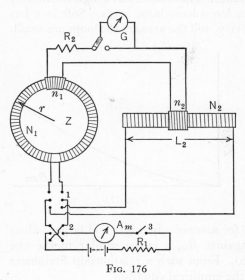

FIG. 176

tailed description since it brings out clearly the physical principles involved. A simple setup for the experiment is shown in Fig. 176. A ring Z, of either circular or rectangular cross section, is made from the substance whose hysteresis curve is to be obtained. Two windings are placed upon this ring, a magnetizing winding of N_1 turns uniformly wound over its entire surface, and a flux coil of n_1 turns localized as shown. The dimensions of the cross section A_1 of the ring are made small as compared with the mean radius r. The mean length L_1 of the magnetic circuit is taken equal to $2\pi r$. A ballistic galvanometer G is connected in series with the flux coil, or secondary coil, to measure the quantity of electricity Q_1 discharged in the secondary coil when a change of flux takes place in the primary circuit.

An expression for the flux density B in the substance may be derived as follows: Let i_1 and $\mathcal{E}_1$ be the instantaneous induced current and emf. in the secondary due to a change of flux in the magnetic circuit brought about by a change in the current of the primary circuit.

Let R be the total resistance of the secondary circuit, which includes the galvanometer and the coils n_1 and n_2. Let the ring be demagnetized, as previously described, by starting with a larger value of B than will be used subsequently. With switch (2) closed and (1) thrown to include the ring Z, switch (3) is closed, Fig. 176. Thus the substance is magnetized to the point a, say, on the curve shown in Fig. 177, by establishing a magnetizing field H_m. Magnetically the substance will pass along the normal magnetization curve from o to a. The

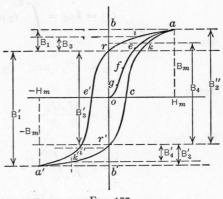

Fig. 177

flux density B will be represented by ob. We have for the ballistic galvanometer

$$Q_1 = kd_1 = \int i \, dt,$$

also

$$\mathcal{E}_1 = Ri_1 = \frac{n_1}{10^8} \frac{d\phi_1}{dt} \text{ volts.}$$

Or

$$i_1 = \frac{n_1}{R10^8} \frac{d\phi_1}{dt} = \frac{n_1 A_1}{R10^8} \frac{dB}{dt} \text{ amperes.}$$

Hence

$$kd_1 = \frac{n_1 A_1}{R10^8} \int_0^B dB = \frac{n_1 A_1 B}{R10^8}. \tag{204.1}$$

k is determined by the flux developed in the standard solenoid having N_2 turns on the primary and n_2 turns on the secondary. Let A_2 be the area of cross section of the standard solenoid, L_2 its length, H_2 the magnetic intensity in the standard solenoid, ϕ_2 the total flux developed, i_2 and $\mathcal{E}_2$ the instantaneous current and emf. in the secondary, I_2 the maximum primary current, M the mutual inductance between primary and secondary, and T the time for the electric discharge to take place. With switch (2) closed and switch (1) thrown to the standard solenoid, switch (3) is closed.   Let d_2 be the throw of the galvanometer by establishing the current I_2 in the primary.   Then

$$Q_2 = kd_2 = \int_0^T i_2\, dt.$$

Also,

$$i_2 = \frac{\mathcal{E}_2}{R}, \quad \text{and} \quad \mathcal{E}_2 = M\frac{dI_2}{dt}.$$

Hence

$$i_2 = \frac{M}{R}\frac{dI_2}{dt}.$$

Therefore,

$$kd_2 = \frac{M}{R}\int_0^{I_2} dI_2 = \frac{MI_2}{R}.$$

The coefficient of mutual inductance M is the flux turns, i.e., maxwell turns, linked with the secondary when unit cgsm. current flows in the primary.   As the secondary is wound upon the primary, we have, assuming no leakage,

$$M = n_2\phi_2 = n_2 H_2 A_2 = \frac{4\pi N_2 n_2 A_2}{L_2} \text{ cgsm. units.}$$

To express M in henrys we divide by 10^9, the ratio between the cgsm. unit of inductance and the absolute practical unit of inductance. Thus, we have

$$kd_2 = \frac{4\pi N_2 n_2 A_2 I_2}{RL_2\, 10^9}. \tag{204.2}$$

k and R will have the same values in (204.1) and (204.2), and therefore, on combining these two equations, we have

$$B = \frac{4\pi N_2 n_2 A_2}{10 L_2 n_1 A_1}\left(\frac{I_2}{d_2}\right) d_1 \text{ gausses.} \tag{204.3}$$

The corresponding value of H is obtained from the equation

$$H = \frac{4\pi N_1 I_1}{10 L_1} \text{ oersteds.} \tag{204.4}$$

An inspection of Fig. 177 will show that on establishing a magnetic field oH_m and then removing it, the galvanometer deflection on removing the flux will be less than on establishing the flux; the deflections will be proportional to rb and ob. The usual method is to reverse the current by means of switch (2). This carries the flux change along the curve $are'a'$, the flux change being $2B$ represented by the ordinate $b'b$. Thus, B is one half of this ordinate. In practice both B and k are obtained by reversing switch (2). This will double the deflection in both of the equations (204.1) and (204.2). Then, in equation (204.3) both d_1 and d_2 will be doubled, thus leaving the equation unaltered. In equation (204.3), I_2/d_2 is the average of a number of readings for different values of I_2. Should the sensitivity of the galvanometer be changed in the course of a set of readings by changing R_2, as is usually necessary in the lower part of the normal magnetization curve, the constant k must be redetermined.

The Normal Magnetization Curve. — Having developed the necessary equations, we may now proceed to their use. The measurements required for the normal magnetization curve are relatively simple. Switch (1) is thrown to include the primary of the ring solenoid. With switch (3) closed, demagnetize the ring as previously described. The current is then increased slightly to give the point g, say, Figs. 173 and 177. Magnetically, the substance passes along the curve from o to g. The current is then reversed, and the deflection of the galvanometer recorded. The values of B and H are calculated for this setting, thus giving the coordinates of the point g. The reversing switch is then thrown back to the starting position, the smallest loop in Fig. 173 has been described, and the loop tip g has been located. The deflection of the galvanometer may be taken on both of these reversals and the average used in computing B. These deflections are opposite in sense, and should be very nearly equal. The substance is now in the magnetic state represented by the point g on the curve. Now increase the current slightly so as to give a point f, say, on the curve. The magnetic change in the substance has been along the curve from g to f. Reverse the current, and then bring the switch back to the starting position. Average the two deflections and calculate B and H thus obtaining the coordinates of the point f. Magnetically, the substance has described the second hysteresis loop in Fig. 173, and the loop tip f has been located to delineate the normal magnetization curve.

With each magnetization field it is well to reverse the current a few times before the readings are taken in order to make sure that the substance is in a cyclic state for that stage of magnetization. At no time should the current be increased and then decreased, because when decreased the substance starts out along a different loop from the one required, and all subsequent readings are invalidated. The galvanometer circuit should be open except when readings are being taken. It is not necessary to make corrections for attenuation of galvanometer deflections since the damping is the same for the calibration and measurements.

The Hysteresis Loop. — In obtaining the hysteresis loop we start with the maximum magnetization field required, represented by the point a, say, on the curve of Fig. 177. With the magnetizing current set at this value, reverse the field several times to make sure that the cyclic state for this magnetizing field has been established and that the substance is following the desired hysteresis loop. Then open switch (3) and observe the deflection. Magnetically, the substance follows the curve from a to the retentivity point r, and the change in flux is B_1. Throw the reversing switch (2), close switch (3) and observe the deflection. The magnetic change in the substance is represented by the curve $re'a'$, and the change in flux is B'_1. Thus, the coordinates of the points a and a' are obtained relative to a horizontal axis passing through the retentivity point r. This will be taken as a temporary axis. Now open switch (3) and observe the deflection. The magnetic change in the substance is represented by the curve $a'r'$, and the change in flux by B'_2, which should be equal to B_1. Throw the reversing switch (2), close switch (3) and observe the deflection. The magnetic change in the substance is represented by the curve $r'ca$, and the change in by flux B''_2, which should be equal to B'_1. Thus, the points a, a', and r' have been located relative to axes passing through the retentivity points r and r'. The magnetic state of the substance is now represented by the point a. With switch (3) still closed, reduce the current by a small amount. The magnetic change in the substance is represented by the curve ai. Now open switch (3) and observe the deflection. The magnetic change is from i to the retentivity point r, and the change in flux is B_3. Throw switch (2), close switch (3) and observe the deflection. The magnetic change is represented by the curve $re'i'$, and the change in flux is B'_3. With switch (3) still closed, *it is now necessary to increase the current to exactly its original value so as to carry the magnetic state of the substance to the point a', and thus keep it on the desired cycle.* Now decrease the current by a small amount so as to bring the substance to k', say. The magnetic change is along the curve $a'k'$. Open switch (3) and observe the deflection. The substance returns to the retentivity point r', the change in flux being B'_4. Throw (2) and close (3). The substance follows the curve $r'ck$, and the change in flux is B_4. Thus, the points i, i', k', and k have been located. Other points may be located on the hysteresis loop by the same procedure. The substance at all times must be kept on the same hysteresis cycle, which means that it must always be carried through the loop tips a and a', and at no time shall the current be increased and then decreased, or vice versa, with switch (3) closed. The curve is plotted with reference to the horizontal axes passing through the retentivity points r and r'. When plotted, the H axis is drawn half way between b and b'.

The formula for the calculation of B must be modified slightly for the hysteresis loop. In this case, instead of reversing the current, the current is either established or reduced to zero. Therefore, to obtain the correct value for B equation (204.3) must be multiplied by 2. Hence we have

$$B = \frac{8\pi N_2 n_2 A_2}{10 L_2 n_1 A_1}\left(\frac{I_2}{d_2}\right) d_1 \text{ gausses.} \qquad (204.5)$$

H is calculated by equation (204.4).

There are a number of other methods for obtaining the normal magnetization curve and the hysteresis loop, such as by the use of Hopkinson's Bar and Yoke, the Double-bar Permeameter, and the Fahy Permeameter. However, the purpose here is to elucidate physical principles rather than to describe experimental methods and laboratory technique.[1]

205. Eddy Current Losses. — Closely associated with the hysteresis losses which occur in electric machines are the eddy current losses. Whenever the magnetic flux in the iron core varies there are induced emfs., not alone in the core windings but also in the iron itself. These currents in the iron, which flow in closed loops, are called *eddy currents*. They cause heating of the iron, and hence loss of energy. In order to reduce the eddy current losses the cores of electric machines are made of thin laminas so oriented relative to the direction of the flux that the induced currents will tend to flow normal to the faces of the laminas, i.e., the faces of the laminas are parallel to the flux lines. This reduces the eddy currents since the electric resistance

---

[1] For experimental methods the reader is referred to Electrical Measurements in Theory and Application, by A. W. Smith, Advanced Laboratory Practice in Electricity and Magnetism, by E. M. Terry, and Advanced Electrical Measurements, by W. R. Smythe and W. C. Michels.

is increased. The laminas are insulated from each other by japan varnish, tissue paper, or simply the iron oxide which forms over the surfaces of the laminas during the process of annealing.

The power loss due to eddy currents may be calculated as follows:

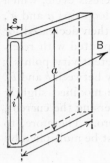 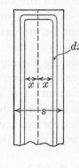

FIG. 178

Let s equal the thickness of a lamina, f the frequency of flux variation, B_m the maximum flux density, a the breadth of the lamina, and l its length, Fig. 178. Let dx equal an element of thickness. The path of an eddy current may be taken as rectangular with sufficient accuracy. Consider a tube of flux of width $2x$ and length l in the direction of the flux. The flux density will vary between $\pm B_m$, and according to the equation

$$b = B_m \sin \omega t.$$

Therefore, the flux linked with a current sheet at any instant is

$$\phi = 2xaB_m \sin \omega t \text{ maxwells.}$$

The induced emf. is

$$\mathcal{E} = \frac{d\phi}{dt} = 2xa\omega B_m \cos \omega t \text{ cgsm. units.}$$

The power represented by this elementary current at this instant is

$$dP = \frac{\mathcal{E}^2}{r} = \frac{4x^2 a^2 \omega^2 B_m{}^2 \cos^2 \omega t}{r}.$$

But

$$r = \frac{\rho(2a + 4x)}{l\,dx} = \frac{\rho 2a}{l\,dx} \text{ approximately.}$$

Therefore,

$$dP = \frac{2\omega^2 B_m{}^2 al \cos^2 \omega t}{\rho} x^2 dx.$$

The average value of $\cos^2 \omega t$ over a half cycle, time $t = T/2 = \pi/\omega$ is

$$\text{av. } \cos^2 \omega t = \frac{1}{\pi/\omega} \int_0^{\frac{\pi}{\omega}} \cos^2 \omega t \, dt = \tfrac{1}{2}.$$

Therefore, the power consumption for the whole lamina is

$$P = \frac{\omega^2 B_m{}^2 al}{\rho} \int_0^{\frac{s}{2}} x^2 dx = \frac{\omega^2 B_m{}^2 als^3}{24\rho} \text{ ergs/sec.}$$

But $\omega = 2\pi f$, $\rho = 10^4$ cgsm. units, $V = als$ cm.^{3}, and 1 watt $= 10^7$ ergs/sec. Therefore,

$$P = \frac{1.6}{10^{11}} (fsB_m)^2 V \text{ watts.} \qquad (205.1)$$

Sometimes cores are made of iron wires, as in the case of induction coils. The eddy current loss in iron wires is found, by a method similar to the above, to be

$$P = \frac{6.17}{10^{12}} (fsB_m)^2 V \text{ watts.} \qquad (205.2)$$

See "Alternating Current Phenomena," by Steinmetz (1908), Chapter XIV.

By Lenz's law the eddy currents create a mmf. in opposition to the mmf. of the magnetizing field. This is a part of the armature reaction in a dynamo. The formulas that have been given for eddy current losses in laminated iron and iron wire hold only when the laminas are thin enough and the wires are small enough to reduce their eddy currents to a value such that their magnetizing fields may be neglected. In large masses of iron the phenomenon is more complicated. The magnetic flux in the interior of the iron is not in phase with the flux at the surface, but lags behind it. The magnetic flux at the surface of the iron is due to the impressed mmf., whereas the flux in the interior is due to the resultant of the impressed emf. and the eddy-current emf., which, of course, will vary with the depth, both in phase and in magnitude. From the surface towards the interior the flux lags more and more and steadily diminishes in intensity. Thus, the surface eddy-current mmf. has a demagnetizing or screening effect for interior points, and, consequently, thick laminas and rods are magnetized more intensely at the surface than at the center.[1]

206. Theories of Magnetism. — The first theories of magnetism, formulated by Poisson and Weber, assumed that the molecules of

---

[1] See Theory and Calculation of Transient Electric Phenomena and Oscillations, by Steinmetz for investigations on the screening effects of eddy currents.

ferromagnetic substances are miniature magnets, and that, when these miniature magnets are to a considerable extent oriented in the same direction the substance as a whole exhibits magnetic properties. Influenced, undoubtedly, by the discovery made by Oersted (1819) that a current of electricity is accompanied by a magnetic field of force, Ampère (1825) advanced the theory of molecular currents to explain why a molecule may behave as a magnet. He assumed that each molecule of a ferromagnetic substance has circulating about it a current of electricity, thus constituting a miniature solenoid. This was before the discovery of the electron, and was therefore, only a shrewd guess at the real explanation of magnetism. The discovery of the electron and its place in the atoms of matter, and the indentification of electrons in motion as a current of electricity inseparably associated with a magnetic field of force, have led to the electron theory of matter, and a more fundamental explanation of magnetism. On the electron theory the varied magnetic properties of matter are now accounted for by the magnetic effects of electrons in orbital motions or spinning within the atoms.

The evidence for the molecular theory of magnetism consists of a few observed facts, namely, the production of new poles when a permanent magnet is broken into smaller and smaller pieces; the saturation that occurs in very strong fields; the loss of magnetism when a magnet is heated to a sufficiently high temperature. These facts find a ready explanation on the molecular theory of magnetism when we consider a magnet to be made up of molecules each one of which is a magnet, which, in the unmagnetized condition, are oriented in all possible directions, but, when the substance is placed in a magnetic field, are oriented in the same sense as the applied field.

If the magnet molecules have perfect freedom of motion they should all rotate immediately into alignment with the external field, even a very weak field, and so the substance should at once reach the condition of saturation. This we know is not the case. To meet this difficulty Weber assumed that each molecule in the unmagnetized condition has taken a position of magnetic equilibrium with its surroundings, and, when displaced from this equilibrium position, is subjected to a restoring couple which is proportional to its angular displacement. This, however, does not explain residual magnetism, because, if the restoring couple is proportional to the angular displacement, and there is perfect freedom of motion, the molecules would take up their original orientations with the removal of the external magnetic field. This they do not do, even in the softest irons. Maxwell tried to explain away this difficulty by assuming that the angular displacement and restoring couple are comparable to strain and stress in elastic solids; for small displacements the return is perfect and there is no hysteresis, but for large displacements the return is incomplete, as when a solid is strained beyond its elastic limit, and we have as a result the phenomenon of residual magnetism and hysteresis. Wiedemann considered that the opposition to rotation is in the nature of mechanical friction between the molecules, which would account for the phenomenon of hysteresis accompanied by a transformation of energy. This, however, requires that there shall be no magnetization for fields of a strength less than that required to overcome the frictional resistance to rotation. However, Lord Rayleigh has shown that this is not the case, except perhaps, for very weak fields.

207. Ewing's Theories of Magnetism. — Prof. J. A. Ewing ("Magnetic Induction in Iron and Other Metals") came to the conclusion, after a long series of experiments, that it is not necessary to postulate anything akin to frictional resistance to account for hysteresis. He advanced a theory which is substantially as follows: The magnet molecules in an unmagnetized, ferromagnetic substance arrange themselves in groups of varied patterns, each group being stable within certain limits of distortion and producing no external field. When a weak magnetic field is applied and gradually increased the first effect is to modify somewhat the configurations, but not to destroy any of them. This corresponds to the lower part of the initial magnetization curve where B is slightly greater than H and μ is but little greater than unity.

As the magnetization field is increased the molecules of each group tend more and more to come under the influence of the external field, and to swing as individual magnets into alignment with the field and away from the group configuration. As a result some of the groups break up. The beginning of the group disintegration is represented by the portion a of the initial magnetization curve, Fig. 171. As the value of H increases the group disintegration is rapidly augmented. This stage is represented by the steep portion of the curve from a to b. When most of the groups have been broken up, in the neighborhood of b on the curve, the substance is entering the stage of saturation. From this stage on there are few groups still to be broken up, but the few remaining groups will be broken up gradually with increase in H, and the substance becomes more and more saturated.

Now, suppose that when the substance is saturated H is gradually decreased. Many of the molecules will persist in their new alignments, as they are quite stable, whereas others will fall back into their old groupings, or form new groups which are magnetically neutral. Thus, when H is reduced to zero, there is some remanent of magnetism remaining. In order to break up these stable alignments of molecules which are responsible for the residual magnetism a reverse field H_c is required. However, as we have seen, this reverse field H_c does not return the substance to either the virgin or the neutral magnetic condition.

In Ewing's theory energy losses are accounted for by supposing that when the groups break up, or reform suddenly, the molecules are set in oscillations about their new positions, and they continue to oscillate until their energies are converted into heat. Thus, the energy loss is greatest during that stage where the groups are rearranging most rapidly, which is represented by the steep part of the curve.

Where a mass of iron is rotated in a strong magnetic field, as in the case of the core of an armature in a dynamo, the groups will not be able to reform after being disrupted. The magnet molecules will be oriented steadily in the direction of the external field as the mass rotates, and will revolve relative to the mass as a whole. Since the formation and breaking up of groups is prevented, there should be no energy loss according to the Ewing theory. Experiments seem to confirm this, in part at least.

Since the advent of the electron theory of matter the theories of magnetism have been recast so as to fit into the new structure which science has built up. Any adequate theory of magnetism must explain the magnetic properties of all substances, not alone ferromagnetic substances. The new theories of magnetism explain the magnetic properties of matter by assuming magnetism to be due to the magnetic fields of electrons in some kind of orbital motions within the atoms or spinning. Thus, in the new theories, the atom, or a subdivision of an atom, is the miniature magnet and not the Weber molecule. The magnetic properties of three classes of substances must be explained by the electron theory. These classes are: (1) Diamagnetic substances. (2) Paramagnetic substances. (3) Ferromagnetic substances.

208. Modified Theories. — According to the modern theory of matter the atoms of all substances are composed of electrons, protons, and neutrons. The relatively heavy protons and neutrons are compactly grouped in the center of the atom constituting the nucleus. The number of protons and neutrons in an atom determine its atomic weight, since the electrons contribute very little to the weight of the atom. The planetary electrons make up the outer shell of the atom, and the total number of electrons in a normal atom is the same as the number of its place in the periodic table of chemical elements. The electrons are supposed to be moving in orbits of some kind about the nucleus. A revolving electron, being equivalent to a circular current of electricity, constitutes a miniature magnetic shell and so exerts a magnetic influence in its immediate environs. The planes of the electronic orbits in an atom may or may not be parallel, and, even if parallel, the sense of rotation of the electrons may not be the same. Thus, an atom as a whole may have a relatively strong field, a weak field, or no field at all, depending upon the relative orientations and strengths of the electronic magnetic shells.

In the early electron theory of magnetism it was generally assumed that the electronic orbits in an atom have definite orientations relative to the structure of the nucleus and rigidly fixed thereto, so that if the planes of orientation of the electronic orbits change there is a corresponding change in the orientation of the atom as a whole.

Diamagnetic Substances. — In 1905 P. Langevin developed a theory of diamagnetism and paramagnetism in terms of electronic orbital motions.[1] In the Langevin theory an atom of a diamagnetic substance is one in which the planes of the electronic orbits are so oriented relative to each other that the atom as a whole is initially magnetically neutral. Thus, the geometric sum of the magnetic moments of the electronic magnetic shells is zero. When, however, a magnetizing field is applied the perfect balance of the magnetic moments within the atom is upset and the electronic orbits shift slightly relative to each other, but in such wise as to bring about a negative magnetic moment of the atom as a whole. Thus, a diamagnetic substance, such as bismuth, is feebly repelled by a powerful magnet and sets itself transverse to the lines of flux when placed between the poles of a strong magnet. The following are some of the diamagnetic substances: Bismuth, antimony, phosphorus, mercury, zinc, lead, tin, copper, silver, gold, sulfur, selenium, alcohol, air, hydrogen.

[1] Annales de Chem. et de Phys. (8), V, 70, 1905.

All substances should show this diamagnetic effect but it is masked in some cases by the much stronger para- and ferromagnetic effects.

Paramagnetic Substances. — In the Langevin theory a paramagnetic substance is one wherein the electronic magnetic moments within the atom do not initially quite sum up to zero, and so there is a very small magnetic moment for the atom as a whole. Under the influence of a magnetizing field the atoms orient themselves in the same sense as the magnetizing field, and so the substance is feebly magnetic, the induced magnetism being proportional to the magnetizing field, and vanishes when the field is reduced to zero. There is, therefore, no residual magnetism. In these substances the magnetic fields of the atoms are very feeble, so feeble indeed that the atoms do not act upon one another in any pronounced manner to form magnetically stable groups or aggregations, but in a strong external field do become oriented in the same sense as the field. The following are some of the paramagnetic substances: Manganese, cerium, platinum, oxygen, titanium, palladium, osmium, and many salts and ores of these metals.

Ferromagnetic Substances. — The extension of Langevin's theory to ferromagnetic substances was made by Weiss.[1] In these substances the atom magnets are relatively strong and act upon each other in a pronounced manner, and, therefore, form groups or aggregations which in the unmagnetized condition are magnetically neutral, as in Ewing's original theory. However, when subjected to a magnetizing field these groups break up and permit the individual magnet atoms to become oriented in the sense of the external field. Residual magnetism, hysteresis, and coercive force are explained as in the Ewing theory. Three elements, iron, cobalt, and nickel belong to this class. These are consecutive elements in the periodic table of elements, atomic numbers 26, 27, 28, and they all belong to the cubic system of crystallization.

Temperature Effects. — P. Curie investigared the change in susceptibility with temperature.[2] He found that the susceptibility per unit mass (specific susceptibility) of diamagnetic substances is independent of the field, and generally of the temperature. The specific susceptibility of paramagnetic substances is independent of the field, and varies, as a first approximation, inversely as the absolute temper-

[1] Journal de Phys. VI, 661, 1907.
[2] Annales de Chem. et de Phys. (VII), V, 298, 1895.

ature. This inverse variation of the susceptibility with the absolute temperature is known as Curie's law.

Ferromagnetic substances pass into paramagnetic substances at a sufficiently high temperature. In the case of ferromagnetic substances the variation of specific susceptibility with temperature may be shown approximately by a curve, Fig. 179, where susceptibility is plotted along the vertical axis and temperature along the horizontal axis. The curve shows that the susceptibility is very large for low temperatures and decreases rapidly until a temperature T_c is reached where there is a rather sharp change (point c), and from that point on for higher temperatures the Curie temperature law for paramagnetic substances holds. The temperature at which this change takes place is called the *critical temperature*. This is the transformation point at which ferromagnetic substances change to paramagnetic substances. This is not an abrupt change but takes place over a short temperature interval. Investigators differ as to the cause of this change, but there seems to be support for the belief that thermal agitation in some way changes the character of the sub-

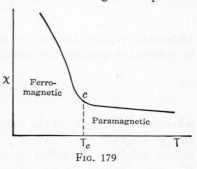

FIG. 179

stance so as to cause it to offer a high resistance to magnetization which characterizes paramagnetic substances. In the space lattice of the cubic system the magnet atoms seem to be capable of such orientations as will render the substance susceptible to magnetization. At the critical temperature, which is also the recalescence temperature, the crystalline structure evidently suffers a profound change, and this is accompanied by other changes, such as change in energy content, change in electric resistance, and change in emissivity.

Ewing has recently modified his original theory. In his original theory it was assumed that the molecule is the miniature magnet. It is now recognized, however, that the atom is responsible for magnetism. Ewing now assumes that a single atom may contain one or more elemental magnets, due to electronic orbital motions, each possessing a definite magnetic moment. In this new Ewing theory it is not the atom itself which turns under the influence of the external field but something within the atom.[1]

[1] Proc. Roy. Soc., Feb. 1922.

The condition for the magnetic property of a substance may be expressed in terms of μ and k by means of the relation.

$$\mu = 1 + 4\pi k.$$

For a vacuum $\mu = 1$, and, therefore, $k = 0$. For para- and ferromagnetic substances $\mu > 1$, and $k > 0$, both being positive. For diamagnetic substances $\mu < 1$, and k is negative, but as k is always very small μ is never negative, but is less than 1. k for bismuth, the strongest diamagnetic substance, is $-1/400,000$.

In Section 67 intensity of magnetization was defined as magnetic moment per unit volume, i.e.,

$$I = \frac{M}{V}.$$

Instead of referring intensity of magnetization to unit volume, it may be referred to unit mass, whence

$$J = \frac{M}{V\rho} = \frac{I}{\rho},$$

where ρ is the density of the substance. J is called the *specific intensity of magnetization*. When J is multiplied by the molecular or atomic weight of the substance the product is called the *molecular or the atomic intensity of magnetization*. The susceptibility may, also, be referred to unit mass instead of unit volume. Thus,

$$\chi = \frac{J}{H} = \frac{I}{H\rho} = \frac{k}{\rho}.$$

χ is called the *specific susceptibility* or *susceptibility per unit mass*. When χ is multiplied by the molecular or atomic weight the product is called the *molecular* or *atomic susceptibility*.

More recent investigations indicate that the orbital motions of electrons within the atoms fail to explain all observed phenomena. In general, an atom will possess both an angular momentum and a magnetic moment due to electrons, each of charge e and mass m, which are in orbital motions about the positive nucleus. There are certain types of atoms, however, for example helium, in which the effects of the circulation of electrons exactly annul one another, thus leaving the atom as a whole devoid of net angular momentum and magnetic moment. However, in general, an atom will behave as a *magnetic spinning top.* Because of revolving electrons possessing mass it behaves as a gyroscope, and because of negative charges revolving about a positive nucleus it behaves as a miniature magnetic shell. In addition to this *gyromagnetic* behavior of the atom as a whole, there is a *gyromagnetic* behavior of the *internal electrons* which are closely bound to the atoms, as perhaps also the free electrons. From many lines of evidence in the domain of atomic physics it seems that an electron is possessed of a *spin* about an axis passing through its center. It is to this *spin* that the largest part of the magnetic effects in ferromagnetic substances is now attributed. That magnetism in these substances is very largely due to *electron spin* is shown by the fact that the ratio of magnetic moment to angular momentum in ferromagnetic substances is approximately that of a spinning electron. Every modern theory of magnetism that has been advanced postulates an *elementary electromagnet* of atomic or subatomic magnitude. The solution of the problem is still far from complete. For further account of this intricate subject the interested reader must consult treatises or current articles on atomic magnetism.[1]

Since magnetic effects are ostensibly due to the spin and circulation of all of the electrons in a ferromagnetic substance, both bound and free, it is to be expected that there will be torsional reactions to the orientations of the elemental gyromagnets. This type of magneto-mechanical effect has been obtained experimentally. When a specimen of ferromagnetic substance is rotated the elemental gyromagnets should swing into line so that their axes of spin or revolution are parallel to the axis of rotation of the rotating mass, thus magnetizing the substance. Barnett performed this experiment and developed a magnetic moment in the specimen by rotation alone. This is known as the *Barnett effect.* Conversely, if a magnetic field is established around a ferromagnetic substance it should experience a mechanical torque. This effect was obtained experimentally by Einstein and de Haas, and is known as the *Einstein-de Haas effect.* There is another effect that points to the electronic origin of magnetism. Ferromagnetism is observed only in crystalline forms; it is associated with the crystalline structure. Groups of crystals apparently conspire to form magnetic units, or *crystal domains.* Now magnetization in certain field-strength

[1] See, Stoner, E. C., *Magnetism and Matter*, Methuen and Company, Ltd., London, Eng., 1934; Bitter, *Introduction to Ferromagnetism*, McGraw-Hill Book Co., Inc., New York, 1937; Van Vleck, *The Theory of Electric and Magnetic Susceptibility*, Oxford, Eng., 1932.

regions, as on the steep part of the magnetization curve, is not a continuous process, but takes place in a series of minute discrete steps. This can be shown by wrapping a coil of wire around a specimen of ferromagnetic substance which is connected through a tube amplifier to a loud speaker. If the magnetizing field surrounding the specimen is slowly increased clicks will be heard in the loud speaker. This is due to small flux increments in the specimen which are due to the orientations of the crystal domains. This is known as the *Barkhausen effect*.

209. Magnetostriction. — Generally, when a ferromagnetic substance is magnetized there is a slight mechanical deformation. The investigations of this phenomenon have been confined almost exclusively to the change in length of a rod of the material when subjected to a magnetizing field. The first observations were made on iron by Joule in 1847, and hence this phenomenon is sometimes called the *Joule effect*. The curves of Fig. 180 show the nature and magnitude of the effect in a few substances.

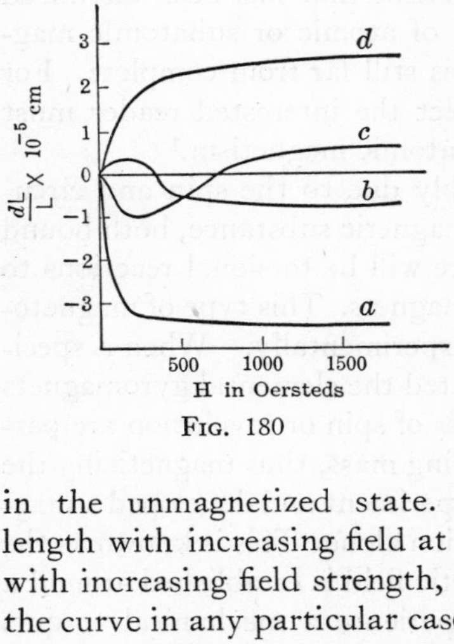

FIG. 180

Nickel decreases in length with increasing field, but soon approaches a steady state where no further change takes place. Iron increases in length at first, then decreases, eventually becoming shorter than in the unmagnetized state. The iron-nickel alloy increases in length with increasing field at first. In all cases the effect diminishes with increasing field strength, eventually becoming nil. The form of the curve in any particular case is influenced markedly by heat treatment, crystalline structure, and other physical conditions.

Since magnetization produces a change in length it is to be expected that, conversely, a longitudinal tension or compression of a rod will bring about a change in its state of magnetization when in a magnetizing field. This has been observed, and is known as the *Villari effect*. Thus, the intensity of magnetization of nickel is increased by longitudinal compression, and decreased by extension. Iron, which shows a Joule reversal, also shows a Villari reversal, its itensity of magnetization being increased by extension in fields up to the reversal field strength, and decreased for stronger fields, providing the deformation is not too great. Accompanying the longitudinal change in dimension is a transverse change in dimension, which, in general, brings about a change in volume (*Barrett effect*). Other effects have been observed. Thus, the simultaneous application of a longitudinal field and a circular field produce a twist (*Wiedemann effect*).

The causes underlying these effects are obscure, and no adequate theoretical interpretation of the experimental results has as yet been advanced. However, it seems reasonable to suppose that the effects are in some manner tied up with the crystalline structure of the substance. Undoubtedly the reorientation of electronic orbits consequent to magnetization will distort to some extent the crystal structure, or, conversely, a mechanically produced distortion of the crystal will influence the electronic orbits, and so influence the magnetization.

210. Magnetic Properties of Ferromagnetic Substances. — Iron

is the most strongly magnetic of all of the elements, but the different grades of iron differ markedly in magnetic properties. The magnetic properties of iron undergo profound changes when alloyed with other elements. We will, therefore, consider very briefly some of the magnetic properties of iron and its alloys.

Cast Iron. — The maximum permeability of cast iron is about 500. From the magnetic standpoint cast iron is a very poor substance, but it has been used in dynamos and motors because of its cheapness.

Cast Steel. — This is much superior magnetically to cast iron. Its maximum permeability is about 1,500. Cast steel is used for the yokes and frames of electric machines. The magnetic properties of all grades of steel vary greatly depending upon impurities and heat treatment. *Bessemer steel* is used for laminated poles because of its cheapness, but finds little other use. Its maximum permeability is about 1,900. Its hysteresis loss is about 0.10 joule per kilogram per cycle. *Open-hearth steel* is used very largely for the cores of transformers and rotating machines. This is known as *dynamo steel*, and is produced in various grades and under different trade names. It has a silicon content of 1% or less. As it comes from the mills it has a maximum permeability of from 3,000 to 6,000. By suitable heat treatment its maximum permeability may be increased to from 4,000 to 8,000. In general, the higher the silicon content the lower the saturation flux density. The hysteresis loss varies from 0.03 to 0.04 joule per kilogram per cycle.

Silicon Steel. — Under this heading are steels having a silicon content in excess of 1%. *Medium silicon steel* has a silicon content of from 2% to 3%, and *high silicon steel* has a silicon content of from 3.5% to 4.5%. Medium silicon steel is used in motors and generators to a considerable extent, and in transformers. Its maximum permeability is a little higher than that of open-hearth steel. Its hysteresis loss is from 0.025 to 0.03 joule per kilogram per cycle. In high silicon steel impurities are kept very low in order to decrease hysteresis losses. The hysteresis loss is from 0.015 to 0.025 joule per kilogram per cycle. Aluminum when alloyed with steel has about the same effect upon the saturation flux density as has silicon, but for some reason it does not improve the magnetic properties in other respects.

Silicon steel was introduced by Hadfield in 1903, but no material improvement was made in it until 1914 when T. D. Yensen made very pronounced improvements in silicon steel alloys by preparing them in a vacuum furnace, annealing them in a vacuum, and reducing the impurities to a minimum, especially carbon. A maximum permeability of 40,000 was obtained, and the hysteresis loss was about one fourth that of the best previous grades of silicon steel. Low hysteresis loss is accompanied by low coercivity and high maximum permeability. The hysteresis loss is affected by carbon impurity more than by any other impurity. For low carbon content the hysteresis loss is approximately proportional to the percentage carbon content, and approaches zero for zero carbon content. In general, hysteresis losses increase with increase in carbon content. Sulfur affects the hysteresis loss, and even in small amounts is harmful. Manganese and phosphorus have very little effect. A large grain crystalline structure improves the magnetic properties; this is the chief function of silicon.

Nickel and Iron-Nickel Alloys. — Nickel of itself is of very little commercial value from the magnetic standpoint. It finds its chief value as an alloy with iron. The maximum permeability of nickel is about 400.

The iron-nickel alloys, however, form an important series. Yensen found that by varying the nickel content almost any desired magnetic property might be realized. At a nickel content of about 30% the alloy undergoes a sharp decrease in magnetizability and is nearly nonmagnetic. This is explained as being due to a change in crystalline structure at this particular nickel content.[1]   The hysteresis loss and coercivity are a minimum at a nickel content of about 50%.

Recently there has been developed an iron-nickel alloy possessing very remarkable magnetic properties which has been christened *permalloy*. This was accomplished by G. W. Elmer in the Research Laboratories of the Western Electric and American Telephone and Telegraph Companies.[2]   This is a very pure iron-nickel alloy having a nickel content of 78.5%.   The remarkable feature of this alloy is its high permeability in low magnetizing fields.   It has an initial permeability of about 9,000 in a weak field, and a maximum permeability of 100,000 or over in a field of flux density of about 5 kilogausses. Fig. 180*a* shows a comparison of permalloy (curve *d*) with armco iron (curve *a*) for low magnetizing fields.   In a magnetizing field of about 0.04 oersted it has a permeability of about 90,000, or about 200 times the permeability of the best grade of iron at this low mag-

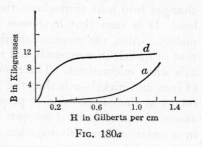

FIG. 180*a*

netizing field. Ewing concluded from his studies that no substance with higher permeability than iron would ever be found, yet the unexpected has been realized.   This high permeability is dependent upon proper heat treatment. It is probably for this reason that it remained so long undiscovered.   Permalloy is very sensitive to mechanical strain, i.e., the permeability varies in a pronounced manner with mechanical strain.   The electric conductivity, also, varies markedly with strain, as does the degree of magnetization.   The electric conductivity decreases as the magnetizing field increases.   So great is the change in electric conductivity that the earth's magnetic field can be measured to within 1%.   On the other hand, magnetostriction is zero within the permalloy range of nickel content.   Other physical properties, however, show no peculiarities at this composition.   Permalloy has found a place in telegraph work.   In the form of a ribbon it is wrapped spirally around, and adjacent to, the metallic conductors of long submarine cables.   This has the

[1] See X-Ray Analysis of Three Series of Alloys, Phys. Rev., Vol. XVIII, p. 245, 1921.
[2] Jour. Franklin Inst., Vol. 195, p. 621, May, 1923.   The Bell System Tech. Jour. Vol. II, July 1923.

effect of neutralizing the capacitance of the cable and so increasing the working speed about fivefold.

An explanation of the anomalous magnetic properties of permalloy is given by L. W. McKeehan, which runs somewhat as follows:[1] Magnetization of iron, cobalt, and nickel must be accompanied by interatomic forces. This is evidenced by a minute change in overall dimensions amounting to but a few parts in 100,000. A change in dimensions due to magnetization is called *magnetostriction* as we have seen. Now if the change in interatomic forces takes place suddenly and simultaneously at widely different points energy should be changed into heat throughout the substance. This is the hysteresis loss. It is seen that hysteresis losses are abnormally low in permalloy. Also, the magnetostrictive effect in iron is in opposition to that of nickel; iron expands and nickel contracts along the magnetic axis when magnetized. Therefore, there must be some composition of iron and nickel such that the Joule effect is zero. This actually occurs at the composition of permalloy. With this composition the atoms of iron and nickel conspire in little groups to make their shifts in orientation smoothly together rather than by sudden jumps separately, and thus the sudden changes are avoided which result in oscillations with consequent energy losses.[2] There are several grades of permalloy now standardized, each being characterized by its percentage of nickel content. Thus, 45 permalloy contains 45% of nickel; 78 permalloy contains 78% of nickel. Each grade has its individual characteristics and uses.

Cobalt and Iron-Cobalt Alloys. — Like nickel, cobalt of itself is of little importance as a magnetic material, but it is of very great importance as an alloy of iron. Cobalt, however, has one unique property: Its magnetic transformation point is higher than that of any other ferromagnetic substance, being about 1,150° C. Its maximum permeability is about 150.

The most important iron-cobalt alloy has a composition of 34.5% of cobalt. This composition increases the saturation value about 12%. For very pure vacuum-fused alloys the maximum permeability is about 13,200. The hysteresis loss is about 0.17 joule per kilogram per cycle. Recently the Bell Telephone Laboratories have developed

[1] Bell Laboratory Record, Vol. III, Dec. 1926.
[2] For a more extended discussion of this interesting subject the reader is referred to articles by McKeehan in the Jour. Franklin Inst., Vol. 202, pp. 737–773, 1926; Vol. 204, pp. 501–524, 1927.

a cobalt steel which has a very high coercivity, from three to four times that of tungsten steel which has been standard for permanent magnets. This alloy is now being used in some of the Western Electric telephone receivers. However, cobalt is expensive, and, therefore, the cobalt alloys will of necessity have a restricted use.

Iron-Manganese Alloys. — These alloys have no commercial value but they are of scientific interest because, as the percentage of manganese increases the saturation flux density decreases until at about 15% manganese the alloy is nonmagnetic.

Heusler Alloys. — These are ferromagnetic alloys whose constituents are paramagnetic. They are composed of a number of different elements. The most strongly magnetic of these alloys is composed of copper, manganese, and aluminum. The permeability is about that of poor cast iron, and the hysteresis loss is about that of poor cast steel. The magnetic transformation extends over a range of about 50° C., and occurs in the neighborhood of 300° C. Manganese and aluminum seem to be responsible for the magnetic properties; copper acts as a solvent, and to a small extent influences the magnetic properties. An alloy of 72.2% copper, 10.3% aluminum, and 17.5% manganese has its transformation point at 0° C. The theoretical explanations of these alloys is incomplete and unsatisfactory.

It is possible to produce alloys of iron that are practically nonmagnetic. Thus, 30% of nickel with a small amount of manganese or carbon results in an alloy that is very nearly nonmagnetic. Other alloys of this kind have been formed. The effect of alloying in these cases is to lower the transformation point below room temperature.

In addition to the alloys mentioned there is a series of special alloys used for permanent magnets. The steels used for permanent magnets are: Carbon-manganese steel, tungsten steel (5% to 6% tungsten), and cobalt steel. The last two are expensive.[1]

PROBLEMS

1. There are 40,000 ampere turns on a ring solenoid, as shown in Fig. 170, and the total flux developed is 2,000 maxwells. When the mmf. is measured in gilberts, what is the reluctance? What is the ratio between the reluctance when the ampere turn is the unit of mmf. and the reluctance when the gilbert is the unit of mmf.? Assume no leakage.

2. If in Problem 1 the area of cross section of the tubular space inside the solenoid is 1.2 cm.², what is the mean length of the path, the permeability being 1? What is the mean diameter of the ring? Would the mean diameter of the ring be different if the ampere turn were taken as the unit of mmf.?

[1] For further information see Properties and Testing of Magnetic Materials, by Thomas Spooner.

3. If in Problem 1 the core is cast iron having a permeability of 500, how many ampere turns are required to develop the same flux, the gilbert being taken as the unit of mmf.? If the ampere turn is taken as the unit of mmf., what would the permeability be, and hence, what is the ratio between the permeabilities in the two systems of units?

4. Let it be assumed that the ring solenoid shown in Fig. 170 has an air gap of 1 cm. in the otherwise solid iron core. Let $\mu = 500$ as before, and $Ni = 40,000$. Calculate the flux ϕ. Calculate ϕ when there is no air gap.

5. In the preceding Problem, assume that the core is a hollow iron tube, the area of cross section of the iron being 0.6 cm.² and the cross section of the air core within the iron 0.6 cm.² With the data otherwise as in Problem 4, calculate total flux ϕ.

6. The core of a transformer has a cross section of 22 cm.², and the mean length of the closed magnetic circuit is 70 cm. Let the core of the transformer be made of iron whose hysteresis loop under operating conditions is shown in Fig. 172 (heavy line). The area of the loop as measured with a planimeter is 123.2 cm.² What is the hysteresis power loss in watts when the frequency is 60 cycles/sec.? From these data calculate the Steinmetz hysteresis constant, and then calculate the power loss when the maximum induction is 8,000 gausses, using 1.6 as the value of k in (203.9). What would be the hysteresis loss at 25 cycles/sec.?

7. Suppose the transformer core in Problem 6 were made of a grade of iron whose hysteresis loop is the broken line loop Fig. 172, which has an area of 21.93 cm.² Calculate the core loss at the maximum induction indicated on the curve, and obtain the Steinmetz hysteresis constant, k being 1.6.

8. If the core of the transformer of Problem 7 is laminated iron 1 mm. thick, what is the eddy current loss at 60 cycles/sec., the maximum induction being 11,200 gausses?

9. In the magnetic circuit shown in the accompanying figure the flux required passes through the air gap between the two steel bars. A part of the flux is shunted by way of the cast iron member. What total mmf. is

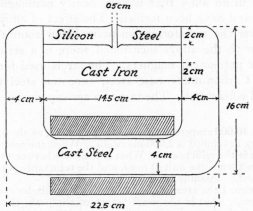

needed to establish a flux density of 1 kilogauss in the air gap? All dimensions perpendicular to the paper are 4 cms. The permeability for silicon steel is 1,000, for cast iron 400, and for cast steel 800. What is the total flux through each member of the magnetic circuit? Assume no leakage.

CHAPTER XV

MOVING CHARGES AND THE ELECTROMAGNETIC FIELD

211. Whenever an electric charge is accelerated it must radiate energy according to the requirements of the electromagnetic theory. Consequently, the planetary electrons within the atoms of matter should be radiating energy continuously so long as they are being accelerated. According to the classical picture of the atom, there is a central nucleus around which electrons are revolving in orbits of some kind. From the purely mechanical viewpoint the electron is accelerated so long as it is moving in a curved path. If this were the true state of affairs the planetary electrons would eventually lose their store of energy and become inactive as an integral part of the nucleus, and further there would be no definite and sharp frequency of radiation as is shown by spectral lines. Thus the electromagnetic theory does not supply a mechanism of radiation, nor does it account for the quantum character of radiation. There are two aspects of electricity which we must constantly bear in mind: There are discrete units or concentrations which we call natural charges—electrons and protons— and intimately related to these in some manner there are fields of force extending beyond their confines in decreasing intensity, theoretically to an infinite distance. If a charge is at rest relative to its environs only an electrostatic field is manifest. If, on the other hand, a charge is moving relative to its environs, there is developed also a magnetic field. If the motion is an accelerated motion electromagnetic waves are generated which carry energy. In the present chapter there will be brought together a few classical developments relating to charges and the fields that inevitably accompany them. While the fundamental assumptions hark back to the period of the ether theory of electricity, the conclusions are in line with modern views.

212. The Magnetic Field of a Moving Charge. — According to Maxwell, a displacement current in free space produces magnetic effects the same as those of a conduction current. Both Maxwell and

Faraday suggested the possibility of showing experimentally that a moving charge does develop a magnetic field. However, Rowland was the first person who actually performed the experiment. The method of the experiment was to rotate an ebonite disc which had alternate charged gilt sectors and observe the behavior of a magnet placed near it. The magnet showed a deflection of the same kind as would be produced by a current of electricity. A reversal of rotation or a change of the sign of the charge reversed the deflection. The magnitude of the magnetic field produced by a moving charge may be derived mathematically as follows:

We have from Section 41, equation (41.3), the expression for a displacement current in free space, (current density),

$$i = \frac{1}{4\pi} \frac{dE}{dt},$$

expressed in cgse. units. This equation states that, "if at any point in free space the intensity E is changing at the rate dE/dt the phenomena accompanying this change are identical with what would occur in the surrounding space if a current i per cm.^{2} were actually flowing through the same space in the direction in which E is changing." If the field is uniform over an area A, we may write

$$i = iA = \frac{A}{4\pi} \frac{dE}{dt} = \frac{1}{4\pi} \frac{d\phi}{dt}, \qquad (212.1)$$

when the area A is perpendicular to E. Since in these equations E is numerically equal to the flux per unit area, $A\,dE = d\phi$ is the change in flux through the area A. Now, if the rate of change of ϕ with respect to t, $d\phi/dt$, can be calculated we obtain the equivalent current through A. This may be accomplished as follows:

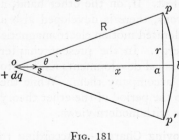

Let a charge $+ dq$ be moving with a speed s cms./sec. at the origin o in the positive x direction along the x axis, Fig. 181. It is required to obtain an expression for the magnitude of the magnetic field H at a point p distant R from o due to the moving charge dq. If the speed

Fig. 181

s is small compared with the speed of light, we may assume a symmetrical distribution of the tubes of flux about dq, i.e., equal areas on the surface of a sphere of radius R will contain the same number of tubes of flux. Let the area A be the spherical cap pbp' of the cone of plane angle θ. We may calculate the total flux through this cap, and then the rate of change of the flux due to the motion of dq. The area of the cap is

$$A = 2\pi R^2 \int_0 \sin \theta \, d\theta = 2\pi R^2 (1 - \cos \theta).$$

At the distance R the intensity is $E = dq/R^2$. The total flux through the area A is $\phi = EA$, since for free space the flux density is numerically equal to the intensity. Therefore,

$$\phi = \frac{dq}{R^2} (2\pi R^2) (1 - \cos \theta)$$

$$= 2\pi \, dq \, (1 - \cos \theta).$$

Now

$$\cos \theta = \frac{x}{\sqrt{r^2 + x^2}},$$

and, therefore,

$$\phi = 2\pi \, dq \left(1 - \frac{x}{\sqrt{r^2 + x^2}}\right).$$

Differentiating with respect to t, we have

$$\frac{d\phi}{dt} = -\frac{dx}{dt} 2\pi \, dq \left\{ (r^2 + x^2)^{-\frac{1}{2}} - x^2 (r^2 + x^2)^{-\frac{3}{2}} \right\}.$$

But $-dx/dt = s$, since x is taken as the distance between o and a, and therefore decreases as t increases. Therefore,

$$\frac{d\phi}{dt} = \frac{2\pi s \, dq}{R} \left(1 - \frac{x^2}{R^2}\right),$$

since $(r^2 + x^2)^{\frac{1}{2}} = R$. Further $x/R = \cos \theta$, and therefore,

$$\frac{d\phi}{dt} = \frac{2\pi s \, dq}{R} (1 - \cos^2 \theta) = \frac{2\pi s \, dq}{R} \sin^2 \theta.$$

And finally by (212.1)

$$i = \frac{s \, dq}{2R} \sin^2 \theta \quad \text{or} \quad i' = \frac{s \, dq'}{2R} \sin^2 \theta, \qquad (212.2)$$

since $vi' = i$ and $vq' = q$, the relationships between the two systems of units. Primed symbols indicate cgsm. units, whereas unprimed symbols indicate cgse. units. v as used here is the ratio between quantities when expressed in the two systems of units. i' is the equivalent displacement current through the spherical cap pbp', and also the current through the circular area pap'. Now, if the current i' is equivalent to a conduction current it is surrounded by a magnetic field. This magnetic field of intensity H at p is tangent to the circular circumference enclosing the area pap' of radius r, and, because of symmetry, it has the same magnitude at all points on the circumference. H is normal to the paper and acting outward at p. The work done in carrying a unit magnetic pole once around the area pap' against H is $W = 2\pi r H$ ergs. This work is also

$$W = 4\pi i' = 4\pi \frac{s\,dq'}{2R} \sin^2 \theta \text{ ergs.}$$

On equating these expressions for the work, we have

$$2\pi r H = 2\pi \frac{s\,dq'}{R} \sin^2 \theta,$$

or

$$H = \frac{s\,dq'}{R} \frac{\sin^2 \theta}{r} = \frac{s\,dq'}{R} \frac{\sin \theta}{r} \frac{r}{R}.$$

And therefore,

$$H = \frac{s\,dq'}{R^2} \sin \theta \text{ oersteds,} \qquad (212.3)$$

or

$$H = \frac{s\,dq}{vR^2} \sin \theta \text{ oersteds.} \qquad (212.4)$$

Equation (212.3) is of the same form as Ampère's law, Section 91, which is

$$dH = \frac{i'\,dl}{r^2} \sin \theta.$$

Thus the product $s\,dq'$ is equivalent to the current element $i'\,dl$, Fig. 182. This is seen to be true since

$$i'\,dl = \frac{dq'}{dt}\,dl, \quad \text{and} \quad s\,dq' = dq' \frac{dl}{dt} = \frac{dq'}{dt}\,dl.$$

The magnetic intensity H at p is directly proportional to $s\,dq'$ and to $\sin\theta$, and inversely proportional to the square of the distance R. We see from (212.3) that H is zero for all points on the x axis ($\theta = 0$), and a maximum when $\theta = \pi/2$, as in Ampère's law.

Converse Theorem.—Since a moving charge creates a magnetic field, which is capable of exerting a force upon a magnetic pole, it follows from Newton's law of action and reaction that a magnetic field should exert a force upon a moving charge. If a magnetic pole of strength $+ m$ were to be placed at p, Fig. 181, it would experience a force, acting outward normal to the plane of the paper, of magnitude

$$F = mH \text{ dynes.}$$

The force acting on the moving charge dq', due to the field of the magnetic pole m, is equal and opposite, or

$$F' = -mH = -m\left(\frac{s\,dq'}{R^2}\right)\sin\theta, \text{ by (212.3).} \qquad (212.5)$$

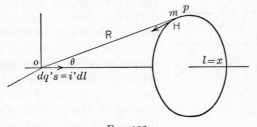

Fig. 182

It will be noticed that the charge dq' must be in motion relative to m in order that there may be a reaction between the magnetic field of m and the charge, this being due to the fact that one magnetic field reacts to another magnetic field but not to an electric field. When the magnetic pole m is placed at p the moving charge at o is in the magnetic field of m. The moving charge at o is equivalent to a current element $i'dl$ making an angle θ with the direction of the field due to m, Fig. 182. The intensity of the field at o due to m is

$$\frac{m}{R^2} = H'.$$

Therefore (212.5) becomes, omitting the minus sign,

$$F' = H' \, s \, dq' \sin \theta = H'i' \, dl \sin \theta \text{ dynes.} \quad (212.6)$$

When $\theta = 0$, $F' = 0$, and when $\theta = \dfrac{\pi}{2}$, $F' = H's \, dq' = H'i'dl$. $\quad$ (212.7)

Equation (212.7) is the familiar equation for the force acting on a current element when in a magnetic field, Section 169. From this consideration we should expect a freely moving charge in a magnetic field to experience a force acting upon it which would deflect it from its rectilinear path, if it has a component of velocity normal to the magnetic field. This, as we shall see, is the case when an electron or positive ion moves through a magnetic field.

213. Total Energy in the Magnetic Field of a Moving Charge. —

As we have seen, a magnetic field is a seat of energy, and, since a moving charge develops a magnetic field, there is a certain amount of

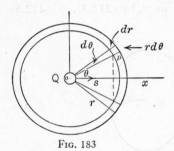

FIG. 183

energy in the magnetic field which is associated with the moving charge. An expression for this energy may be derived as follows: Let a charge Q cgse. units of electricity be uniformly distributed over the surface of a very small sphere of radius ρ with center at o, the origin of coordinates, Fig. 183. We will assume the center of the sphere to be moving in the positive x direction, at the instant considered, with a speed s.

By equation (212.4) the magnetic intensity H at a point p is

$$H = \frac{Qs}{vr^2} \sin \theta \text{ oersteds.} \quad (213.1)$$

The energy per cm.³ of a magnetic field in free space is $W = H^2/8\pi$ ergs. Therefore, the energy contained in an elementary volume dV at a distance r from o is,

$$dW = \frac{H^2}{8\pi} \, dV \text{ ergs.} \quad (213.2)$$

If the speed s is small compared with the speed c of light we may assume the field about o to be symmetrical. Hence the element of volume dV may be taken as a circular zone with center on the line of motion ox. This elementary volume is

$$dV = 2\pi r^2 \sin \theta \, dr \, d\theta.$$

Therefore, equation (213.2) becomes

$$dW = \frac{Q^2 s^2 \sin^3 \theta}{4v^2 r^2} \, dr \, d\theta. \tag{213.3}$$

Hence the total energy in the magnetic field is

$$W = \frac{Q^2 s^2}{4v^2} \int_\rho^\infty \int_0^\pi \frac{\sin^3 \theta}{r^2} \, dr \, d\theta = \frac{Q^2 s^2}{3\rho v^2} \text{ ergs.} \tag{213.4}$$

Equation (213.4) may be put in the form

$$W = \frac{1}{2} \left(\frac{2Q^2}{3\rho v^2} \right) s^2 = \frac{1}{2} \left(\frac{2Q'^2}{3\rho} \right) s^2 \text{ ergs.} \tag{213.5}$$

Comparing this equation with the familar expression for kinetic energy, $\frac{1}{2}ms^2$, we see that the moving charge behaves as though it had a mass equal to $2Q^2/3\rho v$ or $2Q'^2/3\rho$ gms. This apparent mass is due to the magnetic field developed by the motion of the charge, and is, therefore, quite independent of any mass in the ordinary sense of the word that may be associated with the charged sphere. Thus any body possessing charges of electricity should have an apparent increase in mass with increase in speed. Hence the electromagnetic theory accounts for an increase in the mass of a moving body. This is one of the main tenets of the Theory of Relativity.

The seat of this equivalent mass which has just been calculated is not in the charged sphere but in the space surrounding it, according to the argument here presented. The magnetic field which has been brought into being by the moving charge possesses energy, and this energy is equal to the added work which must be done upon the sphere in giving it velocity owing to the fact that it possesses a charge of electricity, or, in other words, it is the work required to give the charge a velocity. Thus, the magnetic field created by the motion of the charge has the effect of mass or inertia in the ordinary or mechanical sense, and therefore we call this kind of mass *electromagnetic mass*, and this kind of inertia *electromagnetic inertia*. It is still a moot question as to whether there is any other kind of inertia. If it is eventually proved that electrons and protons possess no mechanical mass as such, then all inertia is electromagnetic since atoms are mere aggregations of electrons and protons. This is, of course, on the assumption that the neutron is an electron and a proton in close union, which however, is still an open question.

In the case of an electric charge we may visualize tubes of electric flux streaming out symmetrically in all directions, and when the charge is given a speed s the tubes of electric flux drag, so to speak, upon a surrounding medium of some sort, which was formerly thought of as the ether of space, and to overcome this drag requires the expenditure of energy. The ether in this connection may be and in all probability is the sum total of the electric fields of all other electric charges. In some manner, the mechanism of which is unknown, the electric field associated with the charge when passing through space, or rather a distributed electric field, develops a magnetic field which is at every point normal to the electric field, and it is the creation of this magnetic field which requires the expenditure of energy upon the charge to give it speed.

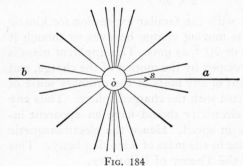

Fig. 184

It was assumed in the derivation of equation (213.4) that the tubes of electric flux were symmetrically distributed about the charge Q. This assumption is justified only when $s < < c$, the velocity of light. As s increases, it is assumed that the tubes of flux tend to move from the polar regions oa and ob and concentrate more and more in the regions (equatorial regions) at right angles to ba, Fig. 184. (The spacing of the tubes of flux, represented by lines, is to indicate the relative strengths of the field.) But the polar regions are the regions where H is small and the equatorial regions are the regions where H is relatively large as indicated by equation (213.1). Thus the effect of speed is to strengthen the electric field in the equatorial regions and to weaken it in the polar regions. This has the effect of increasing the electromagnetic mass, since it is only the component of the electric intensity normal to the direction of motion that is effective in developing a magnetic field. The expression for the electromagnetic mass was obtained on the assumption that the tubes of electric flux are symmetrically distributed, which would obtain only when the speed is small. However, as the speed of the charge increases the electric flux shifts more and more into the equatorial regions, and hence, the electromagnetic mass increases. J. J. Thomson has expressed the electromagnetic mass in the form

$$m_2 = a \, \frac{2Q'^2}{3\rho},$$

where the coefficient a is a variable, being essentially 1 for low speeds, increasing as the speed increases, and becoming very large as the speed of the charge approaches the speed of light. From electromagnetic considerations, Oliver Heaviside [1] has derived an expression for a which is

$$a = \frac{1}{\sqrt{1 - s^2/c^2}}.$$

Thus when $s = c$, $a = \infty$, and the electromagnetic mass is infinite.

That electromagnetic mass is a function of the speed of the moving charge has been proved experimentally by Kaufmann, Bucherer, Neumann, and others. Radium emits β particles. The β particles (electrons) move with speeds comparable with the speed of light, and therefore, these particles are suitable for testing whether or not there is an increase in the apparent mass with increase in speed. Kaufmann used these particles to apply the test. He measured the ratio e'/m for particles of various speeds and found that this ratio decreased as the speed increased. e' is the charge carried by the β particle and m is its mass in grams. Since it is very unlikely that e' varies, the conclusion is that m varies, i.e., increases as the speed increases. Sir J. J. Thomson [2] and M. Abraham [3] have calculated this increase in mass from electromagnetic considerations and found it in close agreement with Kaufmann's experimental results. The following Table, taken from "The Corpuscular Theory of Matter" by J. J. Thomson, gives comparative values:

Speed of particle in cms./sec.	Ratio of mass to that of slow speed particles	a
2.36×10^{10}	1.65	1.50
2.48 "	1.83	1.66
2.59 "	2.04	2.00
2.72 "	2.43	2.42
2.85 "	3.09	3.10

[1] Oliver Heaviside, Electromagnetic Theory, Vol. 1.
[2] Sir J. J. Thomson, Recent Researches in Electricity and Magnetism.
[3] M. Abraham, Phys. Zeitschr., 4, p. 57, 1902.

The second and third columns in the Table are almost identical. The second column expresses the ratio of the whole mass at the given speeds to the mass of a very slow moving particle, whereas the third column gives the coefficient a for the same speeds as calculated. From these results Thomson draws the conclusion that the whole mass of the β particle or electron is electromagnetic, which is quite largely in the region surrounding the electron and not in the very small volume we *think of* as being occupied by the electron itself. What we *think* the electron to be is in all probability quite unlike what the electron actually is. Thus, from this viewpoint, each electron may be said to occupy the whole Universe, and therefore all electrons occupy the whole Universe simultaneously (Thomson).

If the whole mass of the electron is conceived to be concentrated in a small sphere the radius of this sphere may be calculated from the relation

$$m = \frac{2}{3}\frac{Q'^2}{\rho}.$$

Taking as data $Q'/m = 1.75764(10)^7$, $Q' = 1.6022(10)^{-20}$, then $\rho = 1.878(10)^{-13}$ cm. The radius of the atom is usually taken as about 10^{-8} cm. Hence the radius of the atom is about 10^5 times as large as the radius of the electron, according to this method of calculation. The value of Q'/m for the proton is about 10^4, which is essentially the same as the ratio Q'/m for the hydrogen ion in the electrolysis of dilute solutions. The rest mass of the electron is $9.1154(10)^{-28}$ gm. The rest mass of the proton is $1.6726(10)^{-24}$ gm. The radius of the proton is $1.03(10)^{-16}$ cm. Hence the proton has a mass 1,835 times that of the electron, and a radius 1,835 times smaller. These results follow from the theory here developed according to the assumptions that have been made.

One of the results of the Theory of Relativity is the dependence of mass upon speed. It is a consequence of the Einstein theory that mass is dependent upon velocity according to the equation

$$m = \frac{m_0}{\sqrt{1 - s^2/c^2}}.$$

This equation is of the same form as that derived by Heaviside from the electromagnetic theory cited above.

CHAPTER XVI

ATOMIC CONSTITUENTS

MOVING CHARGES IN MAGNETIC AND ELECTRIC FIELDS

214. The era of electronics followed closely upon the epochal discoveries of Maxwell and Hertz, and opened up the way for other discoveries, inventions, and developments which made possible the full utilization of electromagnetic waves in a world-wide intercommunication system with which we are now so familiar. In this chapter we shall consider briefly some of the uses made of magnetic and electric fields in connection with their interactions with moving charges of electricity for the purpose of still further extending our knowledge of the atomic structure of electricity and matter.

Throughout the preceding pages we have had many occasions to refer to the fundamental, natural units of electricity, the *electron* and the *proton*. These terms have become so much a part of our current, everyday physics that we accept them without question, and, for the most part, without inquiry as to the original discoveries and their import. We will now outline some of the outstanding interesting events which have led up to our present state of knowledge of the structure of matter and of electricity, and we shall describe a few of the classical researches that have had to do with the identification and delineation of electrons and protons. It will serve to orient our thought, however, if we run through in rapid review the salient events in atomistic theory from antiquity down to the present time.

215. Origin and Development of Atomistic Theory. — At a very early period in man's intellectual life there appears the conception of a world made up of a limited number of fundamental units, which through multivaried combinations produce the multiplicity in form and color which go to make up our habitat. All through the classical Greek and Roman times this thought prevailed with the philosophers of that age, and it has persisted and grown ever more acute down to the present moment. Among the earliest of philosophers to converse about natural philosophy is Thales of Miletus (born about 640 B.C.).

435

While he left no writings, others coming at a later period have recorded his sayings, mainly Diogenes Laertius. Thales is given credit for these words: "There must be some great unifying principle which links together all phenomena and is capable of making them rationally intelligible; that behind all the apparent variety and change of things there is some primordial element, out of which all things are made and the search for which must be the aim of all natural science." This was a serious attempt to reduce the obvious complexity of the physical world to simpler terms by the introduction of a unifying principle or substance, which Thales thought to be *water*. This was the first step in the creation of a science, i.e., a recognition of and a faith in a definite order of nature. Other members of the Ionian school suggested other substances. For example, Anaximenes considered *air* to be the unifying substance. The conception of a world made up of *atoms* in incessant motions was advanced by the Greek philosophers Democritus (420 B.C.) and Epicurus (370 B.C.) and the Roman Lucretius (50 B.C.). The views of Democritus are especially interesting, since with some changes they might pass muster today. In the words of Democritus

> "The atoms are infinite in number and infinitely varied in form; they strike together and their lateral motions and whirlings which thus arise are the beginnings of worlds ... The only existing things are atoms and empty space; all else is mere opinion . . . The varieties of all things depend upon the varieties of their atoms, in number, size and aggregation . . . The soul consists of fine, smooth, round atoms like those of fire. These are the most mobile of all. They interpenetrate the whole body and in their motions the phenomena of life arises."

In the philosophy of Democritus there were many and varied atoms. However, Empedocles (460 B.C.), as well as Aristotle, conceived the cosmos to be explicable in terms of only four elements, viz., *earth, air, fire,* and *water*. To these four elements Empedocles added two *divine powers*; the principles of *attraction* and *repulsion* which he assumed to pervade the entire universe. The four elements of Empedocles are not elements in our use of the term; they are rather different states of matter, i.e., solid, liquid, and gas, fire being not a substance at all. We find other similar classifications among the ancient writers. These four elements played a leading role in philosophy for many centuries, and only vanished completely when it was shown in the latter part of the eighteenth century that earth, air, and water are composed of yet other constituents, and that fire is a chemical process.

These views, however, were the fruition of misty philosophizing and proved to have no permanent value and little in common with present-day atomic theory, yet it is difficult to say to just what extent they have down through the ages stimulated thought, and in modern times inspired experimentation. Our atomic theory rests upon experimentally ascertained facts. The ancients with few exceptions did not submit their reasonings to tests through experiments. To them the testimony of observation and experimentation carried little weight in the higher court of reason. To resort to experiment was to stoop; the senses were not to be trusted; reason was the only reliable guide. The Greek atomic theory rests upon an entirely different foundation than does our atomic theory. Their chief aim was to build up a system of thought which was free from logical contradictions, with little concern as to its accordance with the facts of observation. On the other hand, we claim for the modern viewpoint a close accordance with the facts of observation; observations and experiments are to be the reliable guides. Yet one wonders in connection with the ultra-modern phases of physics, for instance the new wave mechanics of the atom which reduces atoms and their constituents to wave groups, to what extent mathematical abstractions are taking us backward into metaphysical speculations, eliminating physical pictures and reality from physics and reducing it to a pure process of reasoning; but, of course, always with the test of experimentation to guide our reasoning.

Down through the ages no progress was made in atomic theory until the eighteenth century; in fact, through the Middle Ages the Greek atomic theory was in disfavor and practically forgotten. Modern atomic theory may be said to begin with the work of Daniel Bernouilli (1700–1782), although Pierre Gassendi (1592–1655), French philosopher and mathematician, is frequently mentioned as a pioneer in modern atomic theory. Gassendi's work reveals little more than a resurrection of the ideas of Democritus and Epicurus. Bernouilli, member of a famous Dutch-Swiss family, in his treatise, "Hydrodynamics," published in 1738, sets forth the fundamental ideas of the modern kinetic theory. This was not a mere adumbration of the modern kinetic theory, which is based upon the incessant random motions of discrete particles (molecules and atoms), but a real anticipation of the work of Boyle, Charles, and Gay-Lussac. Not until the work of Dalton, however, is the atomic structure of matter fully established on a firm experimental basis.

In the closing years of the eighteenth century alchemy, upon which chemistry had rested for centuries, had gone into decline, and a fierce warfare was in progress among chemists over the *phlogiston doctrine*. The doctrine of the older chemistry was that of Becher and Stahl, that the only kind of combustible substance is a kind of matter called phlogiston which enters into the composition of other substances in varying degrees, thus determining their degree of inflammability. At this time the four primordial elements of Empedocles, earth, air, fire, and water, were still the foundation stones of chemical philosophy. Only a few acids and alkalis were known, and gases other than air not at all. Hydrogen, discovered by Cavendish (1776) by the electrolytic process, was called inflammable air and was thought to be phlogiston. A flame was thought to be a union of phlogiston and heat (caloric). Earth, air, and water were soon shown to be composed of constituents, and with this discovery the phlogiston doctrine was attacked and finally overthrown. Oxygen was discovered by Priestley (England) and Scheele (Sweden) in 1774, but neither saw its relation to the phlogiston doctrine. Lavoisier (France) found that oxygen is consumed in combustion, and this discovery was the death knell to the phlogiston doctrine, although Priestley clung to it to the end of his life. Lavoisier, together with Berthollet, Morveau, and Fourcroy developed a new chemistry which was published in 1788. This work began the naming and classification of the chemical elements and compounds.

The name that stands out above all others during this period in connection with the atomic theory is that of John Dalton in England. He began his observation by a study of the weather, and was led into the atomic theory of matter by observations on evaporation. His reasoning was about as follows: Water goes into the air as vapor, hence it must exist as discrete particles or atoms, and the air itself must be composed of atoms which mingle with the atoms of water. About 1803 Dalton came to a full conception of the chemical atom, and this laid the foundation of modern chemistry, and also the kinetic theory of matter. Dalton made many tests on the combining properties of the elements, and as a result announced his law of multiple proportions. In 1810 he published the results of his researches in a treatise entitled "A New System of Chemical Philosophy."

Gay-Lussac showed that hydrogen and oxygen combine in definite proportions, i.e., two volumes of hydrogen to one volume of oxygen. From this and related facts Avogadro stated his now famous law (1811): "Under the same physical condition as to temperature and pressure every gas contains the same number of particles (molecules) in the same volume." This law, which has played a prominent part in modern physics, was lost sight of for a generation. A combination of atoms in close union forming a unit or particle Avogadro called a *molecule* (1828), thus differentiating between atoms and molecules. The atomic theory was on trial at this time, and in its stead the law of multiple proportions found favor. The atomic theory was stoutly upheld by Thomas Thomson, a professor at Edinburgh, and John Berzelius, the noted Swedish chemist, supported it valiantly. Berzelius made many tests on proportional parts (combining weights), and these combining weights came to be known by common consent as "atomic weights." Sir Humphrey Davy, Professor of Chemical Philosophy, Royal Institute, London, separated many compounds electrolytically. He referred to the then known elements as "undecompounded" bodies, thus showing that he thought that these elements might eventually be resolved into still smaller units. The migration of ions in electrolysis was unexplained at that time. Davy, however, asserted that some ions are positive, others are negative, and gave to these ions the names *electropositive* and *electronegative*, and thus formulated the hypothesis of the union of electropositive and electronegative ions to form chemical compounds. Berzelius made this the basis of his famous system of theoretical chemistry ("Dualistic Theory of Binary Combinations"). Faraday (1833) showed the definite relationship between the quantity of electricity passed through a solution and the amount of decomposition in the electrolyte (Faraday's laws of electrolysis). It was supposed at that time that the organic compounds could be synthesized only by a so-called "vital force," but Wohler (Germany) synthesized urea, and so brought organic compounds under the ordinary laws of "chemical affinity," and so cast doubt upon the existence of a "vital force."

The leading chemists of that time refused to admit that the so-called elements were in reality elements. One of the first hypotheses advanced in support of this contention was promulgated by Dr. William Prout in England (1815). Dr. Prout was an enthusiastic supporter of the atomic theory and a chemist. He pointed out that many atomic weights were almost exactly whole numbers, and went so far as to predict that all the elements are made up out of hydrogen, which he conceived to be the protyle of ancient atomistic philosophy. Prout's hypothesis was published originally in a magazine devoted more to the observations of amateurs than to research by scientists. The hypothesis was considered at the time as a wild though interesting theory. Prout's idea gained ground to some extent until atomic weight measurements became so exact as to show that the atomic weights of all the elements cannot be considered as multiples of hydrogen. His theory, however, stimulated exact atomic weight determinations, and so served a useful purpose. Dumas (1840) supported and revised Prout's hypothesis, but was finally forced to admit that probably a smaller unit than hydrogen was the primordial element.

In 1863 J. A. R. Newlands (London) pointed out the recurring properties of the elements in intervals of eight when the elements are arranged in the order of atomic weights. This was called the "law of octaves." Later Hinrichs (U. S.), Meyer (Germany), in 1870, and Mendeleeff (Russia) in 1869 took up the study of this law of octaves. Mendeleeff made a very careful study of all of the known facts and gave expression to his findings under the title of the "Periodic Law." Professor J. H. Goldstein said of this law, "It forces upon us the conviction that the elements are not separate bodies created without reference to one another, but that they have been originally fashioned, or have been built up, from one another according to some general plan." The discrepancies in Prout's hypothesis are largely due, as we now know, to isotopes which have been revealed to us by the works of J. J. Thomson, Aston, Dempster, and Bainbridge, and also to loss of mass due to what is called the packing effect. Of course, hydrogen is not the primordial element. It is composed of one electron and one proton, yet almost the entire mass is in the proton, and consequently the atomic weights of the higher elements should come out essentially multiples of hydrogen, were it not for the discrepancies mentioned.

Prior to 1833 there were two theories of electricity, the Du Fay two-fluid theory and the Franklin one fluid theory. In either theory ordinary matter and electricity were separate and distinct entities, though they were thought of as being closely associated. There was no thought that electricity in any way entered into the structures of the atoms of ordinary matter. If there were a primordial element smaller than that of hydrogen it was thought to be of the nature of matter and not electricity. Electricity was thought of as a fluid or fluids which resided on bodies or interpenetrated their structure. In the two fluid theory there was no mention of the fluids being granular or atomic in structure. Franklin (1750), however, unquestionably believed in a particle or atom of electricity, for he says, "The electrical matter consists of particles extremely subtle, since it can penetrate common matter, even the densest, with such freedom and ease as not to receive any appreciable resistance." Here we have the conception of electricity as a material substance, atomic in structure, and not an imponderable. Franklin's atomic electricity, which could freely interpenetrate ordinary matter, was similar to Democritus's fine, smooth atoms which could permeate matter, and it may be his ideas were gained from those of an earlier period. Franklin's statement, however, was pure speculation as there was no experimental evidence in support of it at the time.

The first experimental evidence that appeared in support of Franklin's prophecy as to the atomic structure of electricity came in 1833 when Faraday found that with the liberation of a gram atom in the process of electrolysis there was always associated a definite quantity of electricity for a univalent element, twice that amount for a bivalent element, three times that amount for a trivalent element, etc., i.e., the quantity of electricity carried by an element is proportional to its valence. But in all gram atoms there are the same number of units, and hence each univalent ion carries a definite quantity e of electricity, each bivalent ion carries a quantity $2e$, etc. Here was tangible evidence of a granular structure of electricity, but the prevailing opinion at the time did not so interpret it. The thought was that each univalent ion had a definite capacity for carrying the electric fluid, each bivalent ion had twice that capacity, etc. Hence the ions took from the store of electric fluid on or in the electrode, negative or positive as the case might be, their full capacity. Davy's assertion some thirty years earlier that the ions in an electrolytic solution are either positive or negative did not carry with it the idea that there was associated with each ion a definite quantity of electricity, positive or negative, but simply that the ions were charged.

Striking as was the evidence given by the laws of electrolysis of a granular structure of electricity, it did not carry weight at the time. This evidence was presented at the very time when thought was being directed away from the electric fluids themselves to the fields of force about them, i.e., to imaginary strains in a hypothetical ether. Due to Faraday's experiments with induced currents, Maxwell's field equations, and Hertz's experiments with electromagnetic waves the fields of force were overemphasized to the extent that they were thought of as the whole show, i.e., an electric charge was merely and solely a state of strain in a supposititious ether. Thus, from this viewpoint, an electric current in a wire was pictured as a continuous "slip" or "breaking down of a strain" in the medium within the wire. The wire acted merely as a guide to a "breaking down" of ether strain, rather than as a carrier of an electric fluid. Thus, between about 1840 and near the close of the century electrolytic conduction and metallic conduction were thought of as two different and distinct processes. Electrolytic conduction was the transport through an electrolyte of electric fluids in definite portions; metallic conduction was a "breaking down" of a strained ether within the conductor, thus giving direction to a flow of energy which in reality took place in the medium surrounding the conductor. A reconciliation of these conflicting ideas had to await the advent of the electron theory. In some books on electricity and magnetism of today these ideas of slipping or breaking down of strains in an ether are still portrayed in drawings of lines of force, and the accompanying description of the lines slipping along a conductor and collapsing, as when a condenser is discharged. This is simply a survival of a former period. It does no harm if understood, but the immature student is quite apt to take it too literally.

Of course, this dualistic view of electric conduction called forth discussion at the time and the inconsistency was recognized, but the hiatus was too great to be bridged by the means at hand; there were many and varied explanations but none were adequate. Faraday's experiments on electrolysis did not show that there was a transport of the electric fluid along or through the metallic part of the circuit, or that the electric fluid in the metallic conductor consisted of definite units or granules. All that was shown was that ions in the electrolyte took unto themselves definite quantities, according to their valence, of a hypothetical electric fluid due to some specific property they possessed; there was no evidence that the quanta of electricity remained intact and continued to move along or through the metallic part of the circuit. Our reasons for believing that a current of electricity in a metallic conductor is a flow of corpuscles of electricity (electrons) is that an accumulation of evidence points irresistibly to that conclusion; but the evidence has been brought into court since Faraday, and Maxwell, and Hertz retired from the case.

There is one other phase of the two-fluid theory of electricity, and also the one-fluid theory, which deserves mention in passing. In the two-fluid theory two equal and opposite charges on or in a body completely annulled one another and removed the electric fields of force. In the one-fluid theory the normal amount of electricity on or in a body caused the electric field to vanish. This peculiar phenomenon was inexplicable then, and remains so in light of our present-day knowledge. Why should equal quantities of opposite kinds of electricity, be the structure fluid, corpuscular, or wave groups, in the same position or in juxtaposition cause the associated electric fields of force to vanish? Of course, we say that for any point in space the vector sum equates to zero, but that is a mathematical abstraction which in no way carries a physical picture or supplies a mechanism. Perhaps this is as clear a picture of overlapping fields of force as we shall ever be able to obtain; they are merely regions in space where forces are observed to act, and the vectors representing these forces may or may not sum up to zero.

Thus far in the historical development there has been no suggestion that electricity enters into the structure of the atoms of ordinary matter. Electricity was thought of as a fluid, and by Franklin as granular, which was capable of penetrating matter, but there is no indication that it was considered a constituent of the atoms of matter. However, in 1871 Wilhelm Weber introduced this idea to explain magnetism. As early as 1825 Ampère had explained magnetism as being due to minute currents of electricity flowing continuously within the atoms or molecules of magnetic substances, thereby making the atom or molecule a miniature electromagnet. Ampère's theory associated electricity closely with the atoms of magnetic substances, but this was not extended to other substances. The hypothetical currents in Ampère's molecular magnets (there was no sharp distinction between atoms and molecules in these theories) are replaced in Weber's molecular theory of magnetism by rotating positive charges about heavy negative charges. Here we have the rudiments of the modern explanation of magnetism, except that the signs of the charges are reversed. Evidence coming at a much later date seems to confirm Weber's postulate. For example, a revolving electric charge possessing inertial mass is equivalent, from the electrical standpoint, to a tiny magnetic shell, and from the mechanical standpoint to a gyroscope. If this interpretation be true it should be possible by quickly reversing the polarity of a freely suspended soft-iron rod to turn it by a detectable amount. This was first recognized by Einstein, and in 1915 Einstein and the Holland physicist, de Haas, successfully performed the experiment. The reverse effect of the discovery made by Einstein is to magnetize a soft-iron bar by rotating it rapidly about its axis. This was accomplished by Barnett.

In 1874 G. Johnson Stoney read a paper entitled, "On the Physical Units of Nature," before the British Association at Belfast. In this paper, which was published in 1881,[1] Stoney states the atomic theory of electricity very clearly. He even calculated approximately the value of the atom of electricity, and obtained $0.3 (10)^{-10}$ cgse. unit. This was accomplished, by a method which will be indicated in the next Section, by knowing the quantity of electricity required to separate from a solution one gram molecule of hydrogen together with the number of atoms in a gram molecule of hydrogen as estimated from the kinetic theory of gases. In 1891 Stoney gave the name "electron" to this unit quantity of electricity which is associated with a hydrogen ion or any univalent ion in electrolysis. The inertia or mass associated with the unit quantity of electricity was not included in the term "electron" as used by Stoney. Stoney's use of the term "electron" came at a time when electricity and ordinary matter were thought of as separate and distinct entities; electricity was thought to "ride" on matter. The terms "negative electron" and "positive electron" (proton) were used at that time to distinguish between the two units of electricity as such. The term "positive electron" is now used for the "positron," which was discovered by Carl Anderson at the California Institute of Technology in 1932. At a meeting of the British Association held at Cardiff in 1920 E. Rutherford suggested that the positive charge (nucleus of the hydrogen atom) be named "proton." Thus, today the term electron means the natural unit of negative electricity, and the term proton means the natural unit of positive electricity, both terms including also the associated inertia or mass. There has, furthermore, been a tendency among physicists of today to conceive of no other form of matter than electricity, i.e., all matter is electricity. If, however, it is eventually proved that a neutron exists in its own right, and is not an electron and a proton in close union, matter as such may come to be recognized.

In 1881 Helmholtz delivered the Faraday lecture in the Royal Institute in London. In this lecture he pointed out the conclusions as to the atomic structure of electricity which may be drawn from the

[1] Stoney, Phil. Mag. XI, Ser. 5, p. 384, 1881.

laws of electrolysis, which were stated by Faraday in 1833. However, even in this same lecture, Helmholtz makes statements which indicate that he considers metallic conduction as something quite different from electrolytic conduction.

The conclusion that electric charges entered into the structure of atoms of matter, and that, therefore, metallic conduction, like electrolytic conduction, is a transport of atoms of electricity gained important support from two concepts introduced into the theory of electricity in about 1880. These are, the conception of convection currents and the conception of electromagnetic mass. Rowland in 1876 showed, as already stated, that moving charges of electricity produce magnetic effects of the same kind as those discovered by Oersted in connection with currents of electricity in wires (conduction currents). This so-called convection current has the same properties as regards a magnetic field as has a current in a wire.

From the conclusion that a convection current, so far as its magnetic field is concerned, is the same as a conduction current, J. J. Thomson made a very important deduction. As we have seen, according to Maxwell's electromagnetic theory, a certain amount of energy is associated with every electric and magnetic field of force. On the other hand, a moving electric charge produces a magnetic field, as was shown by Rowland's experiment. The magnetic field together with its energy comes into being when charges of electricity are set in motion. But this requires the expenditure of energy by the law of the conservation of energy. Thus, an electric charge possesses the property of inertia or it has inertial mass, as was shown in the preceding Chapter. Thus the idea of mass was associated with electric charges. From this it follows that every convection current, and hence also every conduction current, represents a mechanical process (electric charges in motion), and an electromagnetic process (the creation of a magnetic field of force by charges of electricity in relative motion). It is precisely this electro-mechanical parallelism which unites electrolytic conduction (transport of electric charges) and metallic conduction which was then thought of solely as a "breaking down" of ether strains. Thus, it turned out that electrolytic conduction and metallic conduction are not two distinct processes but rather similar processes, the transfer of electric charges. This conception gave rise to a new series of relations which were brought out by the Holland physicist, H. A. Lorentz in his "Theory of Electrons". This theory had its beginning in 1880, but was not published until 1895. Lorentz's electron theory is based upon the idea that currents of electricity are moving charges of electricity. It postulates that electric charges (electrons) are constituents of the atoms of all matter, and that the change in positions of these electrons constitutes the electric current. Each electron is an elementary quantum of electricity which always retains its identity. The Lorentz electron theory retains the essentials of the Maxwell electromagnetic theory, which was fundamentally a theory of the electromagnetic field, but by the introduction of the electron it was possible to explain phenomena which the original Maxwell theory had failed to explain. The Maxwell theory did not include electrolysis nor did it explain the discharge of electricity through rarefied gases.

One outstanding problem which Maxwell's theory in its original form had failed to solve was the phenomenon of optical dispersion, i.e., the variation of the index of refraction with wavelength. The explanation of dispersion offered the greatest difficulties both to the elastic solid theory of light and to the electromagnetic theory. If light be regarded as an electromagnetic wave motion, we must look for the origin of light waves in vibrating electric charges. Since matter under various modes of excitation sends out light waves the implication is that it contains electric charges which are capable of executing vibrations of the range of frequencies to be found in light. An explanation of dispersion was found when it was assumed that electrically charged particles possessing inertia are contained within the atoms of matter, and that these particles are capable of executing mechanical vibrations. If electrons are contained in the atoms of matter and are executing vibratory motions, and they are acted upon by light waves, which by the electromagnetic theory are varying electric intensities, they will be acted upon by forces which vary periodically. Thus there will be the superposition of two vibratory motions which will lead to the phenomenon of resonance or forced vibrations. A theory of dispersion was worked out along this line, but the complete treatment of the subject is beyond the scope of this book. For an excellent treatment of the subject the reader is referred to Houston's "Treatise on Light."

In 1750 Franklin envisaged the atomic structure of electricity. This idea became more securely entrenched as time went on until in 1895 Lorentz made it the basis of his electron theory of matter. But apart from the direct evidence furnished by electrolysis, and the inferences drawn from magnetism and the electromagnetic theory, there was a dearth of convincing evidence. By 1895 the time was ripe for the accumulation of convincing proof through experimentation, and therefore since that date we have witnessed a series of brilliant experiments which have completely isolated the electron and identified it as a constituent of all matter; not alone that, but many physicists of today have gone even farther and now conceive electricity to be matter itself. Thus, Arthur Haas in "The New Physics" says, "In the modern system of physics electricity no longer stands alongside of matter; it has taken the place of matter. The new physics can descry in electricity that unadulterated primordial something for which scientists sought through thousands of years, and from which all things amenable to sense-perception are formed." To the evidence for the atomic structure of electricity, and its relation to matter we will now direct our attention, selecting only a few outstanding experiments.

216. Evidence from Electrolysis. — As has been pointed out, the laws of electrolysis, formulated by Faraday in 1833, imply that there is associated with each univalent ion in the process of electrolytic conduction an elementary charge e, with each bivalent ion a charge $2e$, etc. If this were not so we would not always find the electrolytic deposit proportional to the equivalent weight. While we cannot calculate the absolute value of the charge e from electrolytic data alone, we can calculate the ratio of the charge e to the mass m of the ion.

A gram atom or gram molecule (mole) of any substance contains N atoms or molecules. N is called the Avogadro constant, sometimes called the Loschmidt number (in Germany) after the Viennese physicist, Joseph Loschmidt who first determined (1865), from the kinetic theory of gases, the absolute magnitude of a molecule. However, the Loschmidt number is now taken as the number of molecules in 1 cm.^{3} of any gas under standard conditions, which is $2.6864 \, (10)^{19}$. To liberate N univalent ions requires the passage of Q units of electricity whatever the substance. Thus, the charge e carried by a single univalent ion is

$$e = \frac{Q}{N}. \tag{216.1}$$

Q is determined directly from electrolytic measurements coupled with the atomic weight of silver. If N had been known in Faraday's time e could have been calculated. However, N was estimated at a later date by use of the kinetic theory of gases. These

estimates, based upon rather uncertain data as to the size of a molecule, placed N anywhere from 2 $(10)^{23}$ to 20 $(10)^{23}$. It was by use of
these uncertain figures that Stoney in 1874 estimated the value of e
to be of the order of 0.3 $(10)^{-10}$ cgse. unit. However, the most accurate
method now of determining N is to use the value of e, obtained from
independent measurements, as known and solve for N in equation
(216.1). The most accurate value of N determined in this manner is,
using the value of e to be 4.8029 $(10)^{-10}$ cgse. unit or 1.6023 $(10)^{-19}$
coulomb, is 6.023 $(10)^{23}$. This value of e is based largely upon the
X-ray spectra produced by calcite crystals.

Using the data obtained from electrolysis we find the ratio e/m as
follows: If m is the mass of one univalent ion, w the mass of a mole,
and N the number of atoms or molecules in a mole, we have

$$m = \frac{w}{N},$$

and therefore,

$$\frac{e}{m} = \frac{Q}{N}\frac{N}{w} = \frac{Q}{w}.$$

If m refers to silver, we have

$$\frac{e}{m} = \frac{96{,}494}{107.88} = 894.45 \text{ coulombs/gm.}$$

If m refers to hydrogen, we have, since the atomic weight of silver is
$107.88/1.0078$ times that of hydrogen,

$$\frac{e}{m} = 894.34 \frac{107.88}{1.0078} = 95{,}744 \text{ coulombs/gm.}$$

$$= 9{,}574.4 \text{ cgsm. units/gm.}$$

Thus, for univalent ions e/m is inversely proportional to the atomic
weight of the ion, and, since hydrogen is the lightest atom, the ratio
of e/m for hydrogen has its greatest value for univalent atoms. For
polyvalent ions the ratio is

$$\frac{2e}{m}, \quad \frac{3e}{m}, \text{ etc.}$$

While e/m varies for the different elements as obtained from electrolytic data, there is one universal constant obtained from electrolysis. This is by equation (216.1)

$$Ne = Q = 96,494 \text{ coulombs/gm. equiv.}$$

$$= 9,649.4 \text{ cgsm. units/gm. equiv.}$$

$$= 28,948(10)^{10} \text{ cgse. units/gm. equiv.}$$

217. The Zeeman Effect. — The electromagnetic theory as developed by Faraday, Maxwell, and Hertz points rather conclusively to the electric nature of matter itself. If light is a harmonic variation of electric and magnetic intensitites, there must be in matter vibrating or revolving electric charges which give birth to electromagnetic waves, and, on the other hand, these vibrating charges should be influenced by magnetic fields, since charges in motion constitute in reality a convection current. As early as 1862 Faraday sought experimental confirmation of this deduction. He placed a sodium flame between the poles of a strong electromagnet and examined the D lines with a spectroscope. He failed, however, to detect any change in the appearance of the lines when the magnetizing current was switched on.

In 1896 Pieter Zeeman, Professor at the University of Amsterdam, repeated Faraday's experiment with a spectroscope of higher resolving power and a more powerful electromagnet. He found, as theory predicted, that spectral lines are split up into components when the source of light, while emitting the lines, is placed in a strong magnetic field. This was a brilliant confirmation of Lorentz's electron theory of matter, and a proof of the electric origin of radiation. In the simplest case a spectral line is split up into two lines when the source is placed in a magnetic field, the two lines being equally spaced on either side of the position of the original line. Further detailed investigation of the Zeeman effect showed that the vibrating electric charge is negative, and, furthermore, measurements on the ratio of charge to mass, e/m, sometimes called *specific charge*, showed it to be about 1,800 times larger than the specific charge for hydrogen in electrolysis. If it is assumed, as seems most likely, that the charge is the same in each case, an elemental quantum of electricity, then we are forced to the conclusion, startling at the time, that the mass of the electrically charged particle giving rise to a spectral line is about 1,800 times smaller than the mass of the hydrogen ion in electrolysis, which up to that time had been considered the smallest possible unit of mass. Here we have evidence that there is a smaller unit of mass than the hydrogen atom, which had been suggested at an earlier date. Within a few years this conclusion was confirmed by more exact measurements made with cathode rays, soon to be considered.

Zeeman found that when a sodium flame is placed between the poles of a powerful electromagnet the lines are split up into components. Holes were bored longitudinally through the pole pieces of the magnet so as to make it possible to view the light in a direction parallel to the magnetic field. When so viewed through the spectroscope there were found to be two lines equally spaced on either side of the position of the original line, the lines being circularly polarized in opposite senses. When the flame was viewed through the spectroscope at right angles to the magnetic field there were three lines, the middle line being in the original position, and those on either side being spaced as when viewed longitudinally. The middle line is plane polarized, the electric vector being parallel to the magnetic field. The two outer lines are also plane polarized but at right angles to the polarization of the central line.

In his original paper, Zeeman gave a simple explanation of this phenomenon based upon Lorentz's electron theory. This explanation is adequate to explain the simple splitting of the D lines of sodium, and was the only explanation possible at the time. Later investigations have revealed more complicated Zeeman effects which cannot be explained in the simple manner of Zeeman's explanation, but they are fully explained by the quantum theory. It is outside the purpose of this book to pursue this subject further.

218. The Faraday Effect. — Even prior to the time that Maxwell brought out his electromagnetic theory of light Faraday had suspected that there might be some relationship between light and magnetism for he had tried many experiments in an effort to detect some relationship. However, the only relationship between light and magnetism which he was able to detect was that the plane of polarization is rotated when plane polarized light is caused to traverse a dense transparent medium, such as dense lead glass, along the tubes of magnetic force. In 1845 he bored holes longitudinally through the pole pieces of an electromagnet, and placed between the poles a piece of dense lead glass. Light, which had been rendered plane polarized by being passed through a Nicol's prism, was caused to traverse the glass and was then analyzed by a second Nicol's prism. When the magnetic field was applied it was found that, in order to produce extinction again, the analyzer had to be rotated through a certain angle from its undisturbed position, the magnitude of the rotation depending upon the nature of the medium, its length, and the strength of the magnetic field.

There is some resemblence between this phenomenon and that of the rotation of the plane of polarization when a plane polarized beam of light is passed through certain crystalline substances, such as quartz, in a direction parallel to the optic axis. However, there is one marked distinction between the two phenomena which serves to place them in different categories. In crystalline substances the rotation of the plane of polarization depends in some manner upon the structure of the crystal as such, since, if, when the beam of light has traversed the substance in one direction, it is reflected back so as to traverse the substance in the reverse direction, an exactly equal rotation in the reverse sense takes place so that the beam emerges in the original plane of polarization. In the Faraday effect, however, the rotation of the plane of polarization is conditioned by the magnetic field, since, when the beam of plane polarized light is reflected back along its path, on emerging the rotation of the plane of polarization is found to be doubled.

In the Faraday effect the rotation of the plane of polarization may be explained as being due to the influence of the magnetic field upon the electrons which are executing orbital motions about fixed positions within the atoms composing the substance. The dispersion of an electromagnetic wave depends, according to the Lorentz theory, upon the resonant or forced vibrations of the electronic vibrators within the atoms, and, in the Zeeman effect, the undisturbed periods of the electronic vibrators are changed by the presence of a magnetic field.

The Faraday effect may be explained in the following manner: In the block of glass the electronic orbits within the atoms may be resolved into components normal and parallel to the magnetic field. Only those components whose planes are normal to the magnetic field will be affected by the field, or will affect an electromagnetic wave traveling parallel to the field. On the average there will be as many clockwise as counter-clockwise electronic vibrators, and, in the absence of a magnetic field, these will all have the same period. We may consider a plane polarized beam of light to be composed of two equal and opposite circularly polarized components. In the absence of a magnetic field these two circularly polarized components will travel through the medium with the same speed, since, the refractive index being the same for both, the electrons of the medium affect each to the same extent, and, on emerging, they are in the same relative phase as when entering, and hence will recombine to form a plane polarized beam which is in the original plane of polarization. If, however, there is a magnetic field the electronic orbital motions are modified, the period of one sense of rotation being increased and of the other sense of rotation being decreased. The refractive indices for the two circularly polarized components of the beam of light will be different; one will be modified by the electronic vibrators in a different manner from the other. Hence, on emerging the phase relations of the two components of the beam will not be the same as on entering; one will have gained on the other by an amount depending upon the length of the path in the medium and the strength of the magnetic field, and they will, therefore, recombine on emerging into a plane polarized beam whose plane of polarization has been rotated relative to the original plane by an amount depending upon the phase shift between the two circularly polarized components.

From various measurements on different substances Verdet arrived at a relationship which expresses the angular rotation θ of the plane of polarization in terms of measureable quantities. The expression is

$$\theta = mlH \frac{n^2}{\lambda} \left(n - \lambda \frac{dn}{d\lambda} \right),$$

where l is the length of the path traversed by the light, H the strength of the field, λ the wavelength of the light, n the index of refraction, and m a constant depending upon the substance. The ratio θ/lH, which may be called the "specific rotation" of the plane of polarization, is called *Verdet's constant*. It is the rotation resulting from the light having traveled unit distance in unit field.

219. The Kerr Effect. — Other effects which show a close relationship between light, magnetism, electricity and the structure of the atoms of matter were discovered by J. Kerr. In 1875 Kerr found that a transparent substance becomes slightly doubly refracting when placed in a strong electric field, and, in 1878, he found that plane polarized light is rendered elliptically polarized when reflected from the surface of magnetized iron. If light is an electromagnetic wave in the Maxwellian sense, and the atoms of magnetized substances have electronic constituents which are executing orbital motions, it is to be expected that anything which will change the planes of the orbits of the electrons will, also, influence light which is incident upon the surface of the substance or traverses it. As we have seen, magnetism finds its most acceptable explanation in the supposition that within the atoms of magnetic substances there are revolving electrons which are equivalent to miniature magnetic shells, each having a definite though very small magnetic moment and, hence, susceptible of being oriented in a magnetic field. When iron, say, is magnetized a majority of the electronic orbits on the pole face have the same sense of revolution, and the planes of the orbits are so oriented as to be parallel to the pole face. Now, if plane polarized light which, according to the electromagnetic theory, consists of vibrating electric and magnetic vectors, normal to the line of propagation, is reflected from the pole face of a magnet it is to be expected that a twist, so to speak, will be given to the electromagnetic wave, or, in other words, that it will be rendered elliptically polarized.

Du Bois [1] used the Faraday and Kerr effects to measure the strength of a strong magnetic field, and also, the intensity of magnetization produced by the field in a piece of iron. The procedure is as follows: On the pole face A of an electromagnet is placed a polished sample S of the ferromagnetic substance under test, Fig. 185. (The glass G is not present at this stage of the operation.) Plane polarized light is passed through a hole

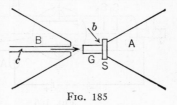

Fig. 185

c in the pole B and is reflected from the polished surface of the sample S. The rotation of the plane of polarization (Kerr effect) is proportional to the intensity of magnetization of S, which may be calculated from the factor of proportionality which must be determined. The strength of the magnetizing field is measured by placing on the pole face A a piece of glass G, the back surface b of which is silvered so as to reflect the light. The plane of polarization is rotated by traversing the glass forward and back (Faraday effect), and, knowing the Verdet constant for the substance, the strength of the field is determined from the measured rotation of the plane of polarization and the thickness of the glass.

220. The Cathode Particle. — The effects we have just considered led to the belief that there are in reality electric charges within the

[1] Du Bois, Phil. Mag. 29, p. 293, 1890.

atoms of matter, each having a definite value and a definite inertial mass. This remarkable conclusion was soon to be confirmed by the results of the more exact measurements made on the so-called *cathode rays*. As early as 1859 Julius Plucker, Professor at the University at Bonn, noticed that the cathode of a Geissler tube emits "rays" of a peculiar nature when the potential difference between the electrodes is sufficiently high and the gas pressure in the tube is sufficiently low, from 0.05 to 0.005 mm. of mercury. This phenomenon led subsequently to numerous investigations by Crookes, Lenard, Perrin, J. J. Thomson, and others.

Under the general heading of the "discharge of electricity through rarefied gases" one will find in most text books on general physics a description of the beautiful effects exhibited when a Geissler tube is gradually exhausted, and, at the same time, subjected to a sufficiently high potential difference. Such a tube is represented diagrammatically

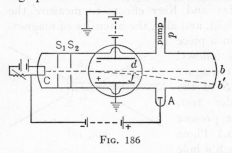

FIG. 186

in Fig. 186. Let the electrodes C (cathode) and A (anode) be connected to an induction coil or electrostatic machine while the tube is being exhausted through the side tube p. At a little below atmospheric pressure a very high potential difference produces a spark discharge between C and A. As the pressure is reduced the spark expands until a soft glow diffuses the whole tube. With still lower pressure the glow is broken up into striations from C to A, and, as the pressure is progressively decreased, the striations recede towards A. At a very low pressure there develops about C a dark space, called the "Crookes's dark space," which with still lower pressure lengthens until finally the distal edge reaches the wall of the tube at b. At this stage of exhaustion the glass at b is observed to glow with a greenish or bluish color, depending upon the kind of glass used in the tube. Clearly, something which emanates from the cathode C travels in straight lines the length of the tube and causes the fluorescence observed on the glass wall. A controversy arose between the German physicists and the English physicists as to the nature of this "something" which emanates from the cathode. The German physicists held the opinion that the emanation from the cathode was of the nature of light waves, hence the name "cathode rays," while the English physicists held to the opinion that the emanation consisted of minute negatively charged particles which were shot off from the cathode with high velocities. Subsequent experiments proved the English opinion to be correct, and as it turned out the negative particles are electrons.

Briefly, we may summarize the properties of the "cathode particles" as follows: They are invisible, but they manifest their existence in various ways. They excite fluorescence in certain bodies or substances upon which they impinge, such as the wall of a glass tube, luminescent calcium tungstate, willemite, or zinc sulphide. When suddenly stopped by a solid, as a target made of a dense metal, they induce a radiation from the target called Roentgen or X-rays. They heat bodies they encounter in their flights, and therefore they must possess energy. The cathode particles are found to leave the surface of the cathode in a direction perpendicular to the surface, and travel in straight lines irrespective of the position of the anode. If the cathode has a plane surface the particles form a bundle of nearly parallel streaming particles, and if the cathode is a spherical concave surface the particles are brought to a focus at a point a little beyond the center of curvature of the surface. This is due to the fact that the streaming particles, being negative charges, repel each other. A screen, such as a lamina of platinum, placed at the focus is heated, even to incandescence or even melted. If an obstacle is placed in the path of the particles (screens S_1 and S_2 not being present) a shadow is cast on the glass at b, or if they impinge upon the blades of a small windmill placed in their path the windmill is turned. If screens S_1 and S_2 are present, each with a small opening exactly at the center, the cathode particles form a narrow pencil which produces a small spot of luminescence at b. If the tube is placed between the poles of an electromagnet (indicated by the circle), so that the field is normal to the direction of projection of the particles, the pencil of projectiles is deflected, as is shown by the change in position of the spot of luminescence on the end of the tube, the direction of the deflection being such as would be produced if the pencil of projectiles were a convection current of negatively charged particles. Direct proof that the cathode particles are negatively charged was given by Perrin who sealed in a side tube a cup, called a Faraday chamber, as at b, Fig. 187, which was connected to an indicating instrument, such as an electroscope or a quadrant electrometer. The particles were deflected by a magnetic field, indicated by the circle *c*, so as to be caught in the cup *b*. The electrometer showed that the cup received a negative charge. A still further proof that the cathode particles are negative charges is furnished by subjecting them to an electric field. Two plates, *f* and *d*, Fig. 186, were sealed in the tube. When one plate is made positive relative to the other the particles are deflected in the direction they should be if negatively charged. The first attempts that were made to produce this effect were unsuccessful owing to the fact that the residual gas in the tube, on becoming ionized, acted as an electric conductor surrounding the cathode beam and so shielded it from the action of the electric field. The effect was observed, however, when the vacuum was sufficiently low. Hertz showed that cathode particles are

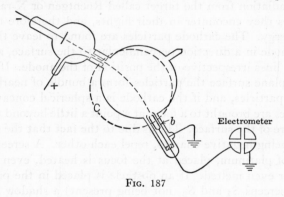

Fig. 187

capable of penetrating very thin sheet of gold leaf placed between the cathode and glass, as they produced fluorescence after passing through the gold leaf. If a thin aluminum sheet closes the end *b* of the tube, Fig. 186, the cathode particles will be found to emerge into the air, and will travel for a distance of several cms. beyond the end of the tube. They are then called "Lenard rays," after their discoverer. These rays are produced in large numbers by the Coolidge cathode-ray tube. The idea that particles, at the time thought to be of molecular size, could penetrate a solid was very startling. These effects led J. J. Thomson to a very careful investigation of cathode rays in order to determine their exact nature. These experiments are fundamental in the history of the electric theory of matter.

221. Measurement of Specific Charge and Velocity of Cathode Particles. — On the assumption that the "cathode rays" consist of negatively charged particles moving with high velocities, J. J. Thomson arranged his experiment so as to measure the velocity and the specific charge of these particles.[1] These measurements were comparatively simple, but the determination of the mass and charge proved to be more difficult. Thomson's apparatus was essentially as shown in Fig. 188, except that he used a cold cathode. Cathode particles emanate from the cathode C, are accelerated between C and A, then travel through the narrow openings in the anode A, and proceed on after emerging from A with constant horizontal velocity and produce at b a small luminescent spot. The screen at b is coated with a fluorescent substance. When, however, the plates a and g are given a difference of potential the spot of light moves in the plane of the

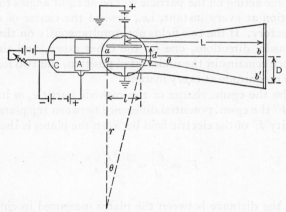

Fig. 188

paper to a point b', say, if the polarity is as shown. Also, if the tube be placed between the poles of an electromagnet giving a field coterminous with the plates, in the position shown by the circle, the spot of light is deflected in the plane of the paper when the magnetic field is applied alone. The magnetic field is normal to the plane of the paper, but, since the deflection is normal to both the magnetic field and the velocity of the cathode particles, it is also in the plane of the paper.

The experiment as performed by Thomson is divided into two parts:

(a) The deflection produced by the electric field is exactly coun-

[1] J. J. Thomson, Phil. Mag., 44, p. 293, 1897.

terbalanced by a reverse magnetic field. This gives the velocity v of the particle.

(*b*) The electric field, or the magnetic field, acts alone and produces a deflection which is measured. This, together with the velocity obtained from the first part of the experiment, yields the specific charge, e'/m.

If a particle of mass m and charge e' moves horizontally between the plates a and g, between which a constant difference of potential is maintained, the trajectory will be a parabola, since there is a constant vertical force acting on the particle, just as in the case of a bullet projected horizontally in the gravitational field of the earth. In case of the magnetic field, when acting alone, the trajectory will be a circle, since the force acting on the particle will be at right angles to its direction of motion at every instant, i.e., toward the center of curvature of the trajectory. If the two fields act simultaneously on the particle, but in opposite directions, one up the other down, and the spot of luminescence remains in the undeviated position, the two forces must be equal in magnitude at every instant.

Let e' be the cgsm. charge of the cathode particle, m its mass in gms., and V' the cgsm. potential difference between the plates a and g. The intensity E' of the electric field between the plates is then

$$E' = \frac{V'}{d} = \frac{10^8 V}{d}, \qquad (221.1)$$

where d is the distance between the plates measured in cms., and V is the potential difference in volts.

(*a*) Let H be the intensity of the magnetic field measured in oersteds, and v the constant horizontal velocity of a cathode particle. If a stream of electrified particles moves with a constant velocity v, it will carry a charge dq' across any section of its path in time dt. But since dq'/dt is a current, this is equivalent to a current i'. This current will have a magnetic field associated with it, and, in turn, will be acted on by an impressed magnetic field. The mechanical force F on a current element $i'ds$ in a magnetic field of H oersteds is $Hi'ds$, when the current element and magnetic field are mutually perpendicular. Then,

$$F = H\frac{dq'}{dt}\, ds = Hdq'v \text{ dynes.}$$

Now let $dq' = e'$, and we have

$$F = He'v \text{ dynes.} \tag{221.2}$$

This is the force on a single particle due to the magnetic field. The force on a single particle due to the electric field is $E'e'$ dynes. If, when both fields act simultaneously, the spot of luminescence remains in the undeviated position these two forces are numerically equal. Therefore, we have

$$He'v = E'e'.$$

Or

$$v = \frac{E'}{H} = \frac{V'}{Hd} = \frac{10^8 V}{Hd} \text{ cms./sec.} \tag{221.3}$$

This velocity turned out to be astonishingly large, of the order of one third the velocity of light.

(*b*) Since when the magnetic field acts alone the cathode particle describes the arc of a circle of radius r, we may equate the centrifugal force to the centripetal force exerted on the particle by the magnetic field. We then have

$$\frac{mv^2}{r} = He'v, \quad \text{or} \quad \frac{e'}{m} = \frac{v}{rH}.$$

And by use of equation (221.3) we have

$$\frac{e'}{m} = \frac{E'}{rH^2} = \frac{V'}{rH^2 d} = \frac{10^8 V}{rH^2 d} \text{ cgsm./gm.} \tag{221.4}$$

The radius of curvature r is obtained from the dimensions of the apparatus as follows:

$$\tan \theta = \frac{l}{r} = \frac{D}{L}, \quad \text{or} \quad r = \frac{lL}{D}.$$

The magnetic field H may be calculated from Ohm's law for the magnetic circuit, or measured directly with a fluxmeter.

In this pioneer work Thomson found the specific charge to be $7.7(10)^6$ cgsm./gm., a value of the same order of magnitude as was found for the specific charge in the Zeeman effect for the particles taking part in the emission of light. It is reasonable to suppose, therefore, that the particles are identical. The most probable value now obtained for this ratio for low velocities is $1.75764(10)^7$. The specific charge for the hydrogen ion in electrolysis was found to be

9,574.4 (Section 216). Thus, the specific charge for cathode particles is 1,836 times that of the hydrogen ion in electrolysis. This large value for the specific charge of cathode particles might result from a large value of e' or a small value of m, or both. All evidence seemed to point to a small value of m. It became a matter of very great importance, therefore, to measure either e' or m by an independent method. e' was later measured by an independent method. m has never been measured independently. See Section 18.

(c) The ratio e'/m may be calculated by other combinations of relationships obtainable by use of the same setup, Fig. 188. Thus, let the potential difference between the cathode C and anode A be V'_1. Then the electric energy, $V'_1 e'$ ergs is equal to the mechanical energy of the particle as it leaves the anode and its velocity v becomes constant. Therefore, we have

$$V'_1 e' = \tfrac{1}{2}mv^2.$$

Or

$$\frac{e'}{m} = \frac{v^2}{2V'_1} \text{ cgsm./gm.} \tag{221.5}$$

By equation (221.3) this may be changed to

$$\frac{e'}{m} = \frac{E'^2}{2V'_1}H^2 = \frac{10^8 V^2}{2V'_1}d^2 H^2 \text{ cgsm./gm.} \tag{221.6}$$

Still another variation is as follows: Let the cathode particle experience a deflection h cms. in traveling the distance l in the electric field when acting alone. The constant deflecting force $E'e'$ dynes acting on the particle will give it a constant acceleration a normal to the plates, given by

$$a = \frac{E'e'}{m} \text{ cms./sec.}^2, \tag{221.7}$$

which will obtain over the length l of the plates in which the electric field is constant. If the electric field were to terminate abruptly at the edges of the plates, a and g, the particle would continue on in a straight line tangent to the trajectory at the point where it emerges from the electric field. The field, however, does not terminate abruptly, but, rather, fades out gradually. This introduces an error which may be corrected. If, however, the fluorescent screen or photographic plate is placed at the edges of the plates a and g no correction is necessary. Let us assume that the deflection h is measured at this place. In the time t that the particle traverses the length l between the plates it will fall a distance h, given by

$$h = \frac{1}{2} at^2 = \frac{1}{2} a \frac{l^2}{v^2},$$

since $t = l/v$. Hence, on combining with equation (221.7), we have

$$\frac{e'}{m} = \frac{a}{E'} = \frac{2hv^2}{E'l^2}.$$

And by equation (221.3)

$$\frac{e'}{m} = \frac{2hV'}{dl^2H^2} = \frac{2(10)^8 hV}{dl^2H^2} \quad \text{cgsm./gm.} \quad (221.8)$$

Thomson found that no matter how the cathode particles were produced in a discharge tube essentially the same value for e'/m was obtained. Thus, by changing the dimensions of the tube and the potential differences considerable change in the velocity of the particles may be obtained, but, unless the velocity becomes so great as to approach the velocity of light, the ratio e'/m remains constant within the limits of experimental error. As we have seen, the mass m increases as the velocity increases, thus causing a change in the ratio e'/m, but this change is inappreciable until the velocity approaches that of light. The specific charge was found to be independent of the substances forming the electrodes and the kind of gas in the tube. Whatever the source of the cathode particles, whether from the atoms composing the cathode or the atoms composing the residual gas in the tube, the specific charge always came out the same. It was concluded, therefore, that these particles, which are some 1,836 times smaller in mass than the hydrogen atom, are constituents of all atoms. Thus it was shown that the hydrogen atom is not the lightest particle of substance which may have an independent existence as was supposed by Prout.

Subsequent investigations have shown that these particles (electrons) are of very general occurrence in nature. We have described a number of phenomena which reveal their existence. Any body when heated emits them to some extent, and some substances emit them very copiously, as, for example, the filaments used in radio tubes. Some substances, such as rubidium and alloys of potassium and sodium, emit them even at room temperature. They are emitted by some metals, especially the alkali metals, when exposed to light, the photoelectric effect. They are emitted by all radioactive substances, and are then called β rays or particles. They are liberated from the atoms of the atmosphere by flames, X-rays, radioactive emanations, and by ultraviolet light, and it is supposed that they reach the earth's atmosphere from the sun in large numbers. But wherever they have been observed and the ratio e'/m has been measured it has always been found to be of the same order of magnitude.

222. The Magnetron Method. — This method of measuring the specific charge, while not very accurate, is of interest and importance since it involves the principle of a tube oscillator which may be made to yield very short electromagnetic waves. A two-electrode vacuum tube is used, which consists of a hot filament stretched along the axis of a cylindrical plate or anode, as shown schematically in Fig. 189.

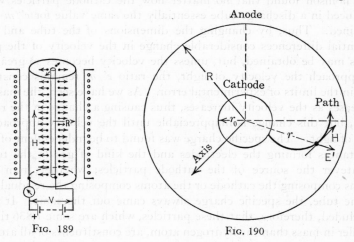

Fig. 189   Fig. 190

The tube is placed inside a solenoid or between the poles of an electromagnet in such a manner that the magnetic field is parallel to the filament. The thermions (electrons) emitted by the filament are acted upon by the electric field E', between cathode and anode, and normal to this field a magnetic field H oersteds. Under the joint action of the two fields the electrons will be caused to describe curved paths, called cycloids, which, when the critical magnetic field is applied, are very nearly circles. The electric field E', and heating current i' must be kept constant, and the filament must be accurately coaxial with the anode. H is varied until the critical value is obtained.

The equation of motion of an electron moving under the influence of the two fields may be derived as follows:[1] The electrons leave the surface of the filament at right angles with a comparatively small velocity. There will be a radial acceleration directed outward due to the electric field, and a radial acceleration directed inward produced by the magnetic field, since the electron is moving in a curved path, Fig. 190. Thus, for the radial motion, we have

$$m \frac{d^2r}{dt^2} = - mr \left(\frac{d\theta}{dt}\right)^2 = E'e' - He'r \frac{d\theta}{dt}.$$

Or

$$\frac{d^2r}{dt^2} - r\left(\frac{d\theta}{dt}\right)^2 = \frac{E'e'}{m} - H \frac{e'}{m} r \frac{d\theta}{dt}. \tag{222.1}$$

For the motion normal to the radius of the anode, we have

$$\frac{1}{r}\frac{d}{dt}\left(r^2 \frac{d\theta}{dt}\right) = H \frac{e'}{m} \frac{dr}{dt}.$$

Or

$$\frac{d}{dt}\left(r^2 \frac{d\theta}{dt}\right) = H \frac{e'}{m} r \frac{dr}{dt}. \tag{222.2}$$

There will be no axial velocity. The integration of (222.2) follows immediately, and is

$$r^2 \frac{d\theta}{dt} = \frac{He'}{2m} r^2 + K.$$

To evaluate the constant of integration K, we have the following boundary conditions: When the electron leaves the filament of radius r_0, the component of its velocity tangent to the filament is

$$r_0 \frac{d\theta}{dt} = v_0, \quad \text{and} \quad r = r_0.$$

Then

$$r_0 r_0 \frac{d\theta}{dt} \equiv r_0 v_0 = \frac{He'}{2m} r_0^2 + K.$$

The solution then is

$$r^2 \frac{d\theta}{dt} = \frac{He'}{2m} r^2 + r_0 v_0 - \frac{He'}{2m} r_0^2. \tag{222.3}$$

[1] Albert W. Hull, Phys. Rev., 18, p. 31, 1921.

To integrate (222.3), first eliminate $d\theta/dt$ between (222.1) and (222.3), and we have

$$\frac{d^2r}{dt^2} = \frac{e'}{m}E' + r\left\{\frac{He'}{2m} + \frac{r_0}{r^2}v_0 - \frac{He'}{2m}\frac{r_0^2}{r^2}\right\}^2$$

$$- \frac{He'}{m}r\left\{\frac{He'}{2m} + \frac{r_0}{r^2}v_0 - \frac{He'}{2m}\frac{r_0^2}{r^2}\right\}.$$

Squaring and collecting terms, there results

$$\frac{d^2r}{dt^2} = \frac{e'}{m}E' - \frac{H^2e'^2}{4m^2}r + \frac{r_0^2v_0^2}{r^3} - \frac{He'}{m}\frac{r_0^3v_0}{r^3} + \frac{H^2e'^2}{4m^2}\frac{r_0^4}{r^3}.$$

Hence

$$\int \frac{d^2r}{dt^2}\frac{dr}{dt}dt = \frac{e'}{m}\int_{r_0}^{r} E'\,dr - \frac{H^2e'^2}{4m^2}\int r\,dr + r_0^2v_0^2\int\frac{dr}{r^3}$$

$$- \frac{He'}{m}r_0^2v_0\int\frac{dr}{r^3} + \frac{H^2e'^2}{4m^2}r_0^4\int\frac{dr}{r^3} + \frac{1}{2}K'.$$

When $r = r_0$, $dr/dt = u_0$, the initial radial velocity. Evaluating K', and rearranging terms, we have, on integrating

$$\left(\frac{dr}{dt}\right)^2 = \frac{2e'}{m}V'_r - H^2\left(\frac{e'}{2m}\right)^2 r^2\left(1 - \frac{r_0^2}{r^2}\right)^2 - H\frac{e'}{m}r_0v_0\left(1 - \frac{r_0^2}{r^2}\right)$$

$$+ v_0^2\left(1 - \frac{r_0^2}{r^2}\right) + u_0^2, \tag{222.4}$$

where $V'_r = \displaystyle\int_{r_0}^{r} E'\,dr$.

The maximum distance the electron can reach from the axis is obtained by putting $dr/dt = 0$. Equating to zero and solving for V'_r,

$$V'_r = \frac{H^2e'}{8m}R^2\left(1 - \frac{r_0^2}{R^2}\right)^2$$

$$+ \left(\frac{Hr_0v_0}{2} - \frac{v_0^2m}{2e'}\right)\left(1 - \frac{r_0^2}{R^2}\right) - \frac{mu_0^2}{2e'}. \tag{222.5}$$

This equation expresses the condition that the electron shall just reach the anode. When this occurs the constant anode current will drop abruptly to zero.

Now, in the actual case v_0 is approximately zero and may be neglected. Also, $u_0 = 0$ when the electron path is tangent to the anode at the critical magnetic field value. Equation (222.5) then becomes

$$V'_r = \frac{H^2 R^2}{8} \frac{e'}{m} \left(1 - \frac{r_0^2}{R^2}\right)^2. \tag{222.6}$$

If, further, $r_0^2/R^2 < < 1$, we have finally

$$\frac{e'}{m} = \frac{8 V'_R}{H^2 R^2} = \frac{8(10)^8 V}{H^2 R^2}. \tag{222.7}$$

A typical characteristic anode-current H curve is shown in Fig. 191 (taken from Hull's paper). It will be seen that the "cut off" is not absolutely sharp, but very abrupt. The fact that the anode current does not drop suddenly to zero at the critical magnetic field is due to approximations to the ideal condition, and because the electrons do not all leave the cathode with exactly the same velocity. The critical value of H was taken, therefore, to be its value when the anode current had dropped to one half its initial steady value.

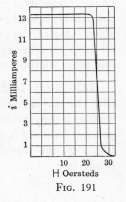

Fig. 191

When the magnetic field is adjusted to this critical value, the circling electrons, possessing central accelerations, will, according to the electromagnetic theory, act as harmonic oscillators and will produce radio waves of very high frequency. Ultra-short radio waves of a length of 6.4 mm. have been produced by this method.[1]

Many other methods for measuring the specific charge of an electron have been devised. For other methods see "Electron and Nuclear Physics" by J. Barton Hoag.

The Charge of the Electron. — While these experiments we have described gave the velocity and specific charge of the cathode particles, they did not answer the moot question as to why the specific charge of the cathode particles, as well as in all other cases, came out about 1,836 times larger than the specific charge of the hydrogen ion in electrolysis. If the charge e' is of the same magnitude as that carried

[1] Cleeton and Williams, Phys. Rev., 50, p. 1019, 1936.

by the hydrogen ion in electrolysis, then the mass m of the cathode particle is about 1,836 times smaller than the hydrogen ion. This means that there is a particle much smaller than the hydrogen atom, but up to the time that J. J. Thomson determined the specific charge of the cathode particles the hydrogen atom was considered to be the smallest particle of matter having an independent existence. On the other hand, the charge e' might be some 1,836 times larger than the charge carried by the hydrogen ion in electrolysis, or both the charge and the mass might be different from the corresponding quantities for the hydrogen ion in electrolysis. These were the alternative explanations advanced at the time when there was no means at hand to choose between them. In order to settle the question definitely it became necessary to determine by independent measurement either e' or m. Methods were soon developed for the measurement of e' independently, and then m was determined immediately from the ratio e'/m. One of the most trustworthy of these methods was Millikan's oil-drop experiment described in Section 18. We will consider only one other method of measuring e, the X-ray method.

223. X-ray Method of Measuring e. — It is a well-known fact that the wavelength of an X-ray may be measured by use of a crystal used as a diffraction grating, such as rock salt, NaCl. When a homogeneous beam of X-rays falls on a crystal C at a small glancing angle θ, Fig. 192, the wavelength of the X-ray is given by the well-known Bragg law

$$\lambda = 2d \sin \theta, \tag{223.1}$$

for first order spectra, where d is the grating constant, or the distance between adjacent atoms in the crystal.

It was discovered by A. H. Compton [1] and Doan [2] that X-rays may be reflected from the surface of metals or glass if the angle that the ray makes with the surface is below the critical angle for total reflection. Since the index of refraction for X-rays is less than unity, total reflection takes place in the rarer medium. This corresponds to total reflection in the denser medium in optics. Fig. 192 is a schematic representation of the setup used by Doan. A collimated beam of X-rays from the target T of an X-ray tube falls upon a crystal C at a small angle θ, by means of which a characteristic line of the target is reflected at a very small angle onto an ordinary ruled diffrac-

[1] Compton, Nat., Research Council Bull., 20, p. 50, 1922.
[2] Doan, Phil. Mag. Vol. 4, p. 100, 1927.

tion grating G.   This will form spectra to the right and left of the central reflected beam, as in optics, which may be photographed with a photographic plate in the position S.   Thus, the wavelength of an X-ray may be measured in exactly the same manner as are optical wavelengths with a diffraction grating.   Recent measurements of X-ray wavelengths by the grating method have been made by Bearden [1] with a precision of the order of a few parts in 100,000.   His gratings were ruled on glass with rulings ranging from 50 to 600 lines per mm.   Thus, the wave-length λ in equation (223.1) may be measured directly and independent of the crystal, and since θ can be measured, this affords

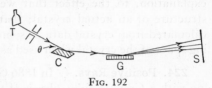

Fig. 192

a means of calculating d, the effective grating space in the crystal, which has been taken to be the distance between adjacent atoms in the crystal, independent of any consideration of the structure of the crystal itself.

In order to obtain a value for e by this method, let us consider a cubic crystal of rock salt, NaCl, which is made up of many small cubes with alternate Na and Cl atoms at the corners.   Let the crystal be a gram-molecular weight $M = 58.454$ gms. (Na = 22.997 gms., Cl = 35.457 gms.).   By the definition of Avogadro's constant there will be, therefore, $2N$ atoms in all, N of each kind.   Thus, along each edge there will be $\sqrt[3]{2N}$ atoms, spaced d cms. apart.   The length of an edge of the cube will be $d \sqrt[3]{2N}$ cms., and hence the volume, of the crystal is $2Nd^3$ cm.^{3} Since density is mass/volume, we have for the density of the crystal

$$\rho = \frac{M}{2Nd^3}, \quad \text{or} \quad N = \frac{M}{2\rho d^3}.$$

But $Ne' = Q = 9{,}649.4$, which is a universal constant, the Faraday constant.   Then

$$Ne' = Q = \frac{Me'}{2\rho d^3}, \quad \text{or} \quad d = \sqrt[3]{\frac{Me'}{2\rho Q}}.$$

Equation (223.1) then becomes

$$\lambda = 2 \sqrt[3]{\frac{Me'}{2\rho Q}} \sin \theta. \tag{223.2}$$

[1] Bearden, Phys. Rev., Vol. 33, p. 1088, 1929.

All quantities in this equation are known or can be measured independently except e', and therefore e' may be calculated.

This method of measuring e' gives consistently higher values than the oil-drop method. The oil-drop method has been critically reexamined, and Millikan's value has been changed slightly, but the discrepancy between the results of the two methods is not entirely accounted for. Zawisky [1] has advanced perhaps the most likely explanation, to the effect that we must revise our picture of the structure of an actual crystal; that the computed grating space, as calculated from crystal data, is somewhat less than the effective grating space of the crystal when used as a grating.

224. Positive Rays.

— In 1886 Goldstein of Germany, while working with a Crookes tube, observed that luminous streamers appeared behind a perforated cathode when the gas pressure was low. He called these "rays" *kanalstrahlen* (canal rays) because of the channels in the cathode through which they passed. Goldstein, in common with all German physicists of that time, thought that the observed effects were due to a radiation of the nature of light, hence the term "ray." Later investigations proved that the canal rays were positively charged particles of atomic or molecular size. J. J. Thomson did most of the early work with these particles, and he called them *positive rays*, the designation now generally used. Following the plan of determining the ratio e'/m for cathode rays, the specific charge of positive rays was determined. It has been seen that the specific charge for cathode rays always came out to be of the same value irrespective of the kind of gas in the discharge tube or the kind of electrodes. On the contrary, the ratio e'/m for positive rays (anode rays) varies with the kind of gas in the tube. For positive rays e'/m is always much smaller than for cathode particles. When the tube contained hydrogen the specific charge had the same value as for the hydrogen ion in electrolysis. In the case of other gases in the tube the value of the ratio e'/m is inversely proportional to the atomic or molecular weight of the gas under observation. Thus, the anode particles are of atomic or molecular mass. *They are the positively charged residues of ionized atoms or molecules*. There are three sources of positive rays generally employed:
(1) The canal rays, which come from the gas in the discharge tube.
(2) The positive ions emitted by heated salts under certain conditions.
(3) The positive ions resulting from vaporization of solids in the dis-

[1] Zawisky, Proc. Nat. Acad. Sci., Vol. 16, p. 211, 1930.

charge tube. These rays have been studied exhaustively, and the study has resulted in the discovery of *isotopes*, a very important contribution to our understanding of atomic structure. J. J. Thomson and Aston have each measured the masses of isotopes, but we will not consider their work as it is not our purpose here to enter into a discussion of modern physics. We will consider only the early mass spectrographs of Dempster and Bainbridge, as these experiments are good examples of the effects we are studying in this chapter.

225. Dempster's Early Mass Spectrograph.[1]—Dempster's arrangement of apparatus is shown diagrammatically in Fig. 193. Electrons emanating from the hot grid g in an evacuated chamber are used to ionize the vapor of a solid which is heated in a small electrically heated cylinder o. The positive ions thus produced move under a small potential gradient to and through slit s_1. They are then accelerated by a potential difference of from 800 to 1,000 volts between slits s_1 and s_2. By this method the ions all have approximately the same velocity. Because of the width of slit s_2 they travel on in slightly different directions, but, after passing through the magnetic field, they are focused on slit s_4. On passing through slit s_2 they enter a nearly uniform magnetic field H, normal to the paper, are bent into a circular arc of radius r, and, with proper values of H and V, pass through s_4 and are collected on plate p which is connected to one pair of quadrants of a quadrant electrometer. Slit s_3 is for the purpose of preventing ions that might be reflected from the walls of the vacuum chamber from reaching slit s_4. The radius r of the circular path in the magnetic field is determined by the velocity v of the ion as it passes through slit s_2, its mass m and charge e'. r is given by the the well-known relation

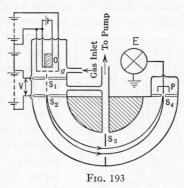

Fig. 193

$$He'v = \frac{mv^2}{r}.$$ (225.1)

[1] Dempster, Phys. Rev., 11, p. 316, 1918; 18, p. 415, 1921; 20, p. 631, 1922.

If V' is the accelerating potential, we have

$$\tfrac{1}{2}mv^2 = V'e'. \qquad (225.2)$$

Combining these two equations, we have

$$\frac{e'}{m} = \frac{2V'}{H^2 r^2}. \qquad (225.3)$$

Positive ions of different specific charges (e'/m) are focused on slit s_4 either by changing the accelerating potential V' or the magnetic field H. The electrometer readings will be proportional to the number of ions reaching plate p, whereas e'/m is proportional to the accelerating potentials when H is constant. The atomic weights are obtained by an empirical method. The method used by Dempster was to obtain the atomic weight of an unknown ion by comparison with that of an ion of known atomic weight, coupled with the known

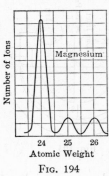

24 25 26
Atomic Weight

Fig. 194

constants of the apparatus. In Fig. 194 is shown Dempster's graph for magnesium, where numbers of ions reaching the electrometer plate are plotted against the atomic weights. It is seen that there are three isotopes of magnesium of atomic weights 24, 25, and 26. The lines are not sharp because the direction focusing is imperfect and the ions do not all have the same velocity. The relative abundance of the isotopes of an element can be determined with fair accuracy by means of Dempster's curves. Thus for magnesium the relative abundance of atoms of atomic weights 24, 25, and 26 are 77.4, 11.5, and 11.1, giving an average atomic weight of 24.34. This is in good agreement with the atomic weight obtained by chemical methods which is 24.32. For details the reader is referred to the original paper.

When a gas is analyzed it is pumped in very slowly through the gas inlet tube shown, and is ionized as explained. A very steep pressure gradient through slit s_1 must be maintained by pumping the gas out very rapidly through the exit tube shown. When solids are being analyzed the gas inlet tube is closed. Dempster has improved this early mass spectrograph so as to give greater resolving power, and hence greater accuracy of mass measurements. For this later work, see Phys. Rev., 33, 1019 (1929) and Proc. Amer. Phil. Soc., 75, 755 (1935).

226. Bainbridge's Early Mass Spectrograph.[1] — Brainbridge's arrangement is shown schematically in Fig. 195. This is a positive ray or mass spectrograph of very high resolving power which has yielded results of great precision. A beam of positive ions, produced by an electric discharge in a spherical or cylindrical chamber (not shown) above slit s_1, is collimated by slits s_1 and s_2. Between slits s_1 and s_2 the ions are accelerated by a potential difference of several thousand volts. Ions of various velocities will pass through slit s_2. Between slits s_2 and s_3 the ions must pass between the plates PP of a charged condenser and through a magnetic field, indicated by the circle. The electric field of intensity E' is horizontal and parallel to the plane of the paper, whereas the magnetic field of intensity H is

normal to the plane of the paper, i.e., E', H, and the velocity v are mutually perpendicular. Thus, only ions of a particular velocity v will pass straight through the "velocity selector," as it is called, and emerge from slit s_3. All other ions will be deflected to one plate or the other of the condenser and thus will be sifted out of the stream. After the ions pass through slit s_3 they enter a uniform magnetic field of intensity H_1,

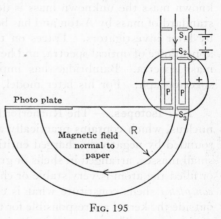

Photo plate

Magnetic field
normal to
paper

R

FIG. 195

normal to the plane of the paper in the camera chamber, which causes them to move in a circular path through an angle of 180° and impinge upon a photographic plate, as shown, where they act upon the plate and leave traces or lines (mass spectrum).

The condition that an ion will pass straight through the velocity selector is

$$E' e' = He'v \quad \text{or} \quad v = \frac{E'}{H}.$$

The ions usually bear but a single charge e' (first order spectrum), but in the case of double ionization they bear a charge $2e'$ (second order

[1] K. T. Bainbridge, Journ. Franklin Inst., Vol. 215, p. 509, 1933.

spectrum). The different order spectra are easily recognized by their positions on the photographic plate.

The radius R of the circular path in the camera chamber is given by the well-known relation

$$He'v = \frac{mv^2}{R},$$

from which we obtain $R = (m/e') \, (v/H_1)$. Thus R is proportional to m/e', with a given value of v/H_1, or, for ions having the same charge e', R is proportional to m, and thus the mass scale on the photographic plate is linear. By comparing the positions of traces produced by ions of unknown masses with the position of a trace produced by an ion of known mass the unknown mass is determined. O^{16} was used as the standard of mass by Aston and has been used as the standard of mass by later investigators. Traces on the photographic plate have the appearance of optical spectra, and hence these traces have been called mass spectra. Bainbridge has improved this early type of mass spectrograph. For his later model, see Phys. Rev. 50, 282 (1936).

227. Isotopes. — The Rutherford-Bohr atom consists of a central nucleus, which contains practically all of the mass of the atom, surrounded by negatively charged entities (electrons), of relatively very small masses, arranged in shells or groups. When a shell is completed or filled the atom is very stable or chemically inert. The nucleus and *completed* shells constitute what is called the *kernel*. Unfilled shells outside the kernel are responsible for the chemical and optical behavior of the atom. Thus, any variation in the mass of the nucleus cannot be detected by chemical or spectroscopic methods. All that is required of the nucleus, from the standpoint of chemistry and spectroscopy, is that it possesses a positive charge equal in amount to the combined negative charge of the electrons outside the nucleus in the normal atom. The mass of the nucleus in no way influences the number and arrangement of the electrons outside the nucleus; it is only the magnitude of the positive charge in the nucleus that has any influence in this respect. Hence the masses of individual atoms of a given element may vary through wide ranges, theoretically, and still possess the same chemical and optical properties. Ionization, chemical affinity, and optical spectra are due to the electrons in the outermost, unfilled shell of the atom (valence electrons). Atomic weights, as determined by chemical methods, are averages of a very great number of atoms, and, with few exceptions, the atomic weights of the elements come out the same no matter from what source the sample is taken, thus showing that the atoms of the universe have been thoroughly mixed during past eons.

As a first step in the development of nucleur theory, chemists discovered as early as 1906 that elements of the radioactivity class might differ in the physical property of mass though having the same chemical property. In 1913 Sir Frederick Soddy suggested the name "isotope" to denote atoms differing in mass but occupying the same place in the periodic table of the elements. As we have seen, the researches of Thomson, Aston, Dempster, and Bainbridge extended our knowledge in this phase of nucleur physics very greatly and showed that isotopy is a general property of all elements, not alone those of the radioactivity class.

In the early part of the last century Dalton advanced the idea that the atoms of any given element are similar in all respects and equal in mass. Dalton's hypothesis was accepted, tentatively at least as a working basis, and atomic weights (combining weights) were henceforth looked upon as the weights of the individual atoms themselves, until in 1912 Thomson showed that all neon atoms did not have masses of 20.2 referred to oxygen as 16, but that at least two atomic species exist, one having an atomic mass of 20 and the other a mass of 22, occurring in the abundance ratio of approximately 10 to 1. Prout (1915) had advanced the suggestion that the elements are aggregates of a single fundamental building unit which is identical with hydrogen. On this hypothesis the masses of all the elements would be integral multiples of the mass of hydrogen. This, however, as we have seen, is not the case, and so Prout's hypothesis was abandoned, though it contained an element of truth. The extensive researches on isotopes have shown that the weights of all the atoms examined, with the exception of hydrogen, are to a very close approximation whole numbers when referred to a hypothetical unit which is one 16th the mass of O^{16}. The reason hydrogen is not this hypothetical unit is, according to theory, that in the formation of the nuclei of higher atomic weights there has been a transformation of a small amount of mass into energy, which is known as the "packing effect."

But, what are the building blocks of the atoms? Since the nuclei of radioactive elements eject α and β particles, it was first supposed that electrons and protons were the building blocks, that the α particle (nucleus of a helim atom) was composed of 4 protons and 2 electrons in very close union, the 2 electrons acting as binders and in some manner neutralizing the positive charges of 2 protons, thus leaving a "free" charge of $+2e$ in the nucleus. However, later investigations go to show that we are not justified in using the terms electrons and protons with the same connotation when speaking of the structures of atomic nuclei as when speaking of free electrons and protons outside the nucleus. "From experimental and theoretical considerations it appears that the electrons lose their identity in nuclei and that what we once knew as an electron has vanished for all intents and purposes except that it appears to have neutralized one positive charge" (Bainbridge). When an electron enters a nucleus it loses its identity, much as does a photon lose its identity when radiant energy is absorbed by an atom, or, conversely, a photon is born or comes into existence as such at the instant an electron changes from a higher to a lower energy state. The photon does not exist, as such, in the atom during the normal, unchanging existence of the atom; it makes its appearance, or enters the stage of action, at the instant of a catastrophic change in the atom. The conception that now seems most prevalent is that the nuclei are composed of protons and neutrons, the neutron being a close union of a proton and an electron, wherein each has lost its identity. Neutrons are ejected from some nuclei as such, thus showing that, in some cases at least, the proton and electron composing the neutron do not exist in their own rights outside the nucleus, but that in other cases electrons and protons emerge as such from neutrons at the instant of nuclear disintegration. Thus, on this hypothesis, there are as many protons in the nucleus as there are positive charges in the nucleus, which is equal to the ordinal number of the element in the periodic table of elements. The additional mass of the nucleus is made up of neutrons, which in many cases are more numerous than the protons. In view of this nuclear structure, the question arises, how can electrons be emitted from the nucleus, as is known to be the case. The answer is, they are manufactured, so to speak, at the moment of emission. Heisenberg has advanced the idea that a neutron may at times be transformed into a proton and an electron while still within the nucleus, after which the electron escapes. In dealing with the nucleus it is, for clarity of thinking, conceived of as composed of separate units, protons and neutrons, whereas in reality it may be a melting pot in which the various particles lose all semblance of their identities. With this understanding as to the inadequacy of our knowledge of the actual structure of the nucleus,

TABLE RECORDING DATA PERTAINING TO THE ISOTOPES OF THE FIRST EIGHTEEN ELEMENTS (*Hoog*)

Isotope of	Atomic Number	Symbol	Isotopic Mass	Relative Abundance
(Neutron)...................		n^1	1.0090	
Hydrogen..................	1	H^1 H^2 H^3	1.0081 2.0147 3.0171	99.98 0.02 7×10^{-8}
Helium......................	2	He^4	4.0039	100.
Lithium....................	3	Li^6 Li^7	6.0167 7.0180	7.9 92.1
Beryllium..................	4	Be^8 Be^9 Be^{10}	8.0078 9.0149 10.0164	0.05 99.95 .....
Boron......................	5	B^{10} B^{11}	10.0161 11.0128	20. 80.
Carbon.....................	6	C^{12} C^{13}	12.0036 13.0073	99.3 0.7
Nitrogen...................	7	N^{14} N^{15}	14.0073 15.0048	99.62 0.38
Oxygen....................	8	O^{16} O^{17} O^{18}	16.0000 17.0046 18.0057	99.76 0.04 0.20
Fluorine....................	9	F^{19}	19.0049	100.
Neon......................	10	Ne^{20} Ne^{21} Ne^{22}	19.9986 21.00(07) 21.9985	90.00 0.27 9.73
Sodium....................	11	Na^{23}	22.9972	100.
Magnesium.................	12	Mg^{24} Mg^{25} Mg^{26}	23.9938 24.99(46) 25.99(09)	77.4 11.5 11.1
Aluminum..................	13	Al^{27}	26.9911	100.
Silicon.....................	14	Si^{28} Si^{29} Si^{30}	27.9860 28.9864 29.9845	89.6 6.2 4.2
Phosphorus.................	15	P^{31}	30.9844	100.
Sulphur....................	16	S^{32} S^{33} S^{34}	31.9812 .... 33.9799	96. 1. 3.
Chlorine....................	17	Cl^{35} Cl^{37}	34.9796 36.9777	76. 24.
Argon......................	18	A^{36} A^{38} A^{40}	35.978 37.9753 39.9754	0.33 0.05 99.62

while existing as a nucleus, we may consider it to be an aggregation of protons and neutrons.

Oxygen was long thought to be composed of atoms all of the same mass. However, it has now been proved that oxygen is a mixture of O^{16}, O^{17}, and O^{18}. The relative abundance of the respective isotopes is 99.76% of O^{16}, 0.04% of O^{17}, and 0.20% of O^{18}. When $O^{16} = 16$ is taken as the standard of reference, the *mass unit* is called the *atomic mass unit* (amu.). On this mass scale the average mass of the oxygen atom is 16.002. The mass unit, on the scale such that the average atomic mass of oxygen is 16, is called the *chemical mass unit* (cmu.). The weights of all the atoms that have been measured, excepting hydrogen, are to a very close approximation whole numbers on the atomic mass scale.

CHAPTER XVII

TRANSIENT CURRENTS

228. When an emf. is impressed upon a circuit, by closing a switch, *in which there is only ohmic resistance*, the current rises instantly to its full value, which is given by Ohm's law. If, however, the circuit contains, in addition to ohmic resistance, either capacitance or inductance or both such is not the case, for within the circuit there are developed counter emfs. which prevent the current from rising to its full value instantly. Like conditions obtain when the impressed emf. is removed, and at the same instant the circuit is closed, for then the current does not cease instantly. In this Chapter we shall consider such cases, which are called transient phenomena.[1]

229. Circuit Containing Resistance and Inductance. *Decaying Current.* — Let us say we have a circuit containing a coil of inductance L, a resistance R, and a battery of emf. $\mathcal{E}$ connected in series, as shown in Fig. 196. R includes the resistance in the coil as well as any resistance outside the coil.

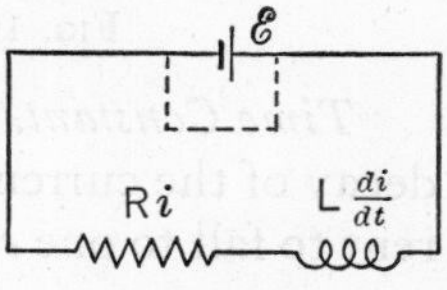

By Kirchhoff's law the instantaneous p.d.'s. add up to zero. Therefore, we have

FIG. 196

$$L\frac{di}{dt} + Ri - \mathcal{E} = 0. \qquad (229.1)$$

Now suppose we short circuit the battery, as indicated by the broken line, and, at the same time, cut out the battery. Then $\mathcal{E} = 0$, and we have

$$L\frac{di}{dt} + Ri = 0. \qquad (229.2)$$

This is a linear differential equation. To solve put $i = e^{mt}$, where e is the base of the Naperian logarithms and m is a constant to be deter-

---

[1] Bedell and Crehore, Alternating Currents, Pierce, Electric Oscillations and Electric Waves, Steinmetz, Transient Phenomena.

mined.[1] Differentiating and setting in (229.2), we have

$$Lm + R = 0, \quad \text{and hence} \quad m = -\frac{R}{L}.$$

The solution is

$$i = Ae^{-\frac{R}{L}t}, \tag{229.3}$$

where A is a constant to be evaluated from boundary conditions. At time $t = 0$, $i = I$, the initial current. Therefore, $A = I$, and the complete solution is

$$i = Ie^{-\frac{R}{L}t} = \frac{\mathcal{E}}{R} e^{-\frac{R}{L}t}. \tag{229.4}$$

The current dies away from the value I at time $t = 0$ to 0 at time

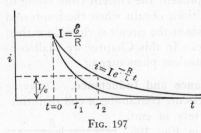

$t = \infty$ according to equation (229.4). If we assign values to $\mathcal{E}$, R, and L and plot equation (229.4) the curves shown in Fig. 197 are obtained. The rate at which the current dies away will depend upon the values of R and L. This rate is expressed by a quantity called the *time constant*.

Fig. 197

Time Constant. — The time τ, which is a measure of the rate of decay of the current, may be defined as the time required for the current to fall to one eth (0.368) of its initial value. To obtain τ, we have

$$\frac{I}{e} = i_\tau = Ie^{-\frac{R}{L}\tau},$$

from which we have $\tau = L/R$ sec. Increasing L or decreasing R increases the time of decay.

Another way of looking at the time constant is as follows: The rate of decay of the current at any instant is

$$-\frac{di}{dt} = I\frac{R}{L} e^{-\frac{R}{L}t}.$$

At time $t = 0$, the rate at which the current starts to decay is $I(R/L)$.

---

[1] Differential equations will be solved by the differential equations methods in order to acquaint the student with such methods. Where possible all equations should be solved also by integration.

The time required for the current to decrease to zero, if it continues to decrease at the same rate as at the beginning, is, therefore,

$$\tau = \frac{I}{I(R/L)} = \frac{L}{R} \text{ sec.} \qquad (229.5)$$

To obtain the quantity Q of electricity discharged in the circuit while the current dies away to zero, we have

$$i = \frac{dq}{dt} = Ie^{-\frac{R}{L}t}.$$

Therefore,

$$Q = \int_0^Q dq = I \int_0^\infty e^{-\frac{R}{L}t} dt = \frac{L}{R} I. \qquad (229.6)$$

Q is represented by the area under the curve of Fig. 197. Further,

$$Q = \frac{L}{R} I = \tau I. \qquad (229.7)$$

Hence Q is the quantity of electricity which will be discharged in the circuit in time τ with constant current I. *It is left as an exercise for the student to solve equation* (229.2) *by the method of the integral calculus.*

230. Circuit Containing Resistance and Inductance. *Rising Current.* — Let there be a simple circuit as shown in Fig. 196, without the broken line, in which there is a key. Let the key be suddenly closed. The current will rise to its final value exponentially. The differential equation in this case is

$$L\frac{di}{dt} + Ri - \mathscr{E} = 0. \qquad (230.1)$$

To solve this differential equation we first differentiate, and then have

$$L\frac{d^2i}{dt^2} + R\frac{di}{dt} = 0. \qquad (230.2)$$

To solve, put $i = e^{mt}$, as before, and therefore

$$Lm^2 + Rm = 0, \quad \text{and hence} \quad m_2 = 0, \quad m_1 = -\frac{R}{L}.$$

Therefore,

$$i = Ae^{-\frac{R}{L}t} + B. \qquad (230.3)$$

When $t = 0$, $i = 0$, and therefore, $B = -A$. When $t = \infty$, $i = I = \mathscr{E}/R$, and $I = B = \mathscr{E}/R$. Hence

$$i = I(1 - e^{-\frac{R}{L}t}). \qquad (230.4)$$

Assigning values to $\mathscr{E}$, R, and L and plotting, we have the curves of Fig. 198, which show how currents grow. The time constant is here defined as the time required for the current ro rise to within one eth of its final value. That is

$$\left(1 - \frac{1}{e}\right)I = I(1 - e^{-\frac{R}{L}\tau}), \text{ or } \frac{1}{e} = e^{-\frac{R}{L}\tau}, \text{ and } \tau = \frac{L}{R}. \qquad (230.5)$$

It is left as an exercise to show that the time constant is, also given by the time in which the current would reach full value, if it continued to rise at the same rate as at the beginning. Solve equation (230.1) by integration.

The curves of Fig. 198 are the curves of Fig. 197 inverted for corresponding values of R, L, and $\mathscr{E}$. Or, to state it in another way, if the ordinates of the corresponding curves in Figs. 197 and 198 are added the sum equals I in each case. In calculations, L and R must be expressed in cgsm. units if t is in seconds. However, since 1 ohm = 10^9 cgsm. units and 1 henry = 10^9 cgsm. units, R and L may be expressed in ohms and henrys in this case.

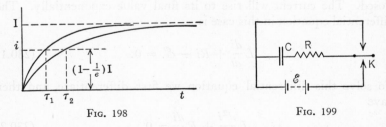

Fig. 198

Fig. 199

231. Circuit Containing Resistance and Capacitance. *Discharge of a Condenser.* — The wiring diagram of the circuit is shown in Fig. 199. Suppose key K is thrown so as to include the battery, of constant emf. $\mathscr{E}$, thus charging the condenser.[1] Then let key K be thrown to the discharge position. The condenser will be discharged through

---

[1] Polarization and thermal emfs. are assumed not to exist in the circuits.

the resistance R. Equating the instantaneous p.d.'s. in the circuit to zero, we have

$$Ri + \frac{q}{C} = 0. \tag{231.1}$$

Or

$$R\frac{dq}{dt} + \frac{q}{C} = 0. \tag{231.2}$$

Let $q = e^{mt}$, and then $Rm + 1/C = 0$. Therefore, $m = -1/RC$. Hence, the solution is

$$q = Ae^{-\frac{t}{RC}} \tag{231.3}$$

To obtain the constant A we have the boundary conditions: At time $t = 0$, $q = Q$, the initial charge. Therefore, $A = Q$. The complete solution is

$$q = Qe^{-\frac{t}{RC}} = \mathscr{E}Ce^{-\frac{t}{RC}} \tag{231.4}$$

The charge decreases exponentially from Q to 0. The curves are of the same form as those shown in Fig. 197. In this case the time constant $\tau = RC$. As a specific application of this case we have the discharge of a condenser in the grid circuit of the detector tube in a radio set. The resistance R is here called a *grid leak*.

The current equation is obtained by differentiating (231.4). This gives

$$i = -\frac{Q}{RC}e^{-\frac{t}{RC}} = -\frac{\mathscr{E}}{R}e^{-\frac{t}{RC}} = -Ie^{-\frac{t}{RC}}. \tag{231.5}$$

The current decreases exponentially from $q = \mathscr{E}/R$ to 0.

Solve equation (231.2) by integration.

232. Circuit Containing Resistance and Capacitance. *Charging a Condenser.* — With the condenser fully discharged, throw key K to the charging position, Fig. 199. The charge in the condenser will grow to its full value in accordance with the equation

$$Ri + \frac{q}{C} - \mathscr{E} = 0. \tag{232.1}$$

Or

$$R\frac{dq}{dt} + \frac{q}{C} - \mathscr{E} = 0. \tag{232.2}$$

To solve, differentiate (232.2), and we have

$$\frac{d^2q}{dt^2} + \frac{1}{RC}\frac{dq}{dt} = 0.\tag{232.3}$$

Let $q = e^{mt}$, and $m^2 + m/RC = 0$. Hence, $m_1 = -1/RC$, $m_2 = 0$. Therefore, the solution is

$$q = Ae^{-\frac{t}{RC}} + B.\tag{232.4}$$

When $t = 0$, $q = 0$, and therefore, $A = -B$. When $t = \infty$, $q = Q = B$. Therefore,

$$q = Q(1 - e^{-\frac{t}{RC}}) = C\mathscr{E}(1 - e^{-\frac{t}{RC}}).\tag{232.5}$$

The curves obtained from this equation are of the same general form as those shown in Fig. 198. The charge rises exponentially from zero to full charge Q at potential $\mathscr{E}$. These curves, for the same values of R, C, and $\mathscr{E}$ are the images of the curves obtained on discharge of the same condenser.

The current equation is obtained by differentiating (232.5), and is

$$i = \frac{Q}{RC}e^{-\frac{t}{RC}} = \frac{\mathscr{E}}{R}e^{-\frac{t}{RC}} = Ie^{-\frac{t}{RC}}.\tag{232.6}$$

The current decreases exponentially from $i = \mathscr{E}/R$ to 0. The time constant is obtained as before, and is $\tau = RC$. Solve equation (232.2) by integration.

The energy expended by the battery in charging the condenser is obtained as follows: The energy expended in the resistance is

$$W = \int_0^\infty Ri^2 dt = RI^2\int_0^\infty e^{-\frac{2t}{RC}}dt = \tfrac{1}{2}R^2I^2C.\tag{232.7}$$

But $R^2I^2 = \mathscr{E}^2$, and therefore, $W = \tfrac{1}{2}C\mathscr{E}^2$. The energy stored in the condenser is also $\tfrac{1}{2}C\mathscr{E}^2$. Thus, half of the energy expended by the battery is stored in the condenser and half is turned into heat in the resistance.

233. Capacitance and Inductance in Parallel. — Let a circuit be arranged as shown in Fig. 200. By properly selecting R, L, and C the parallel branch may be made to behave as pure ohmic resistance on rising and falling currents, i.e., the current rises to its full value instantly and falls to zero instantly. Let the total resistance in one branch of the parallel circuit equal the total resistance in the other branch. Then on rising current, we have

$$i_1 = I_1(1 - e^{-\frac{R}{L}t}), \\ i_2 = I_2 e^{-\frac{t}{RC}}.$$ (233.1)

and

Since the resistances are equal $I_1 = I_2 = I$. Hence the current in the main branch at any instant is

$$i = I + I(e^{-\frac{t}{RC}} - e^{-\frac{R}{L}t}).$$ (233.2)

If the time constants of the two branches are the same, $i.e.$, $RC = L/R$, then $i = I$, and the current rises instantly to its full value.

For falling current, we have

$$i_1 = Ie^{-\frac{R}{L}t}, \\ i_2 = -Ie^{-\frac{t}{RC}}.$$ (233.3)

and

Thus, when $RC = L/R$, $i_1 = -i_2$, and the sum of the currents in the two branches is zero at every instant.

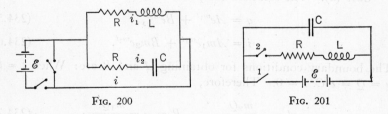

Fig. 200   Fig. 201

234. Discharge of a Condenser through Resistance and Induc-tance. — Let a circuit be arranged as shown in Fig. 201. With key 2 open, close key 1, thus charging the condenser to a potential $\mathcal{E}$. Then if key 1 is opened, and, an instant later, key 2 is closed the condenser will discharge through the resistance R and the inductance L. Equat-ing the sum of the instantaneous p.d.'s. in the circuit to zero, we obtain the following differential equations:

$$L\frac{di}{dt} + Ri + \frac{q}{C} = 0,$$

$$L\frac{d^2i}{dt^2} + R\frac{di}{dt} + \frac{i}{C} = 0.$$ \quad (234.1)

$$L\frac{d^2q}{dt^2} + R\frac{dq}{dt} + \frac{q}{C} = 0. \quad (234.2)$$

Let $q = e^{mt}$ in equation (234.2), and we have as auxiliary equation

$$Lm^2 + Rm + \frac{1}{C} = 0.$$

Solving, we have

$$m_{1-2} = \frac{-RC \pm \sqrt{R^2C^2 - 4LC}}{2LC}. \quad (234.3)$$

The complete solution of the equation is

$$q = Ae^{m_1 t} + Be^{m_2 t}, \quad (234.4)$$

where m_1 and m_2 are given by (234.3).

There are three cases to be considered, as follows:

(a) $R^2C^2 > 4LC$ Nonoscillatory or over damped discharge.
(b) $R^2C^2 = 4LC$ Critically damped discharge.
(c) $R^2C^2 < 4LC$ Oscillatory discharge.

Case (*a*).   The solutions for q and i are

$$q = Ae^{m_1 t} + Be^{m_2 t}, \quad (234.5)$$

$$i = Am_1 e^{m_1 t} + Bm_2 e^{m_2 t}. \quad (234.6)$$

The boundary conditions for obtaining A and B are: When $t = 0$, $q = Q = \mathscr{E}C$, $i = 0$. Therefore,

$$A = \frac{m_2 Q}{m_2 - m_1}, \qquad B = -\frac{m_1 Q}{m_2 - m_1}. \quad (234.7)$$

Substituting in equations (234.5) and (234.6), we have

$$q = \frac{Q}{m_2 - m_1}\{m_2 e^{m_1 t} - m_1 e^{m_2 t}\}. \quad (234.8)$$

$$i = \frac{Qm_1 m_2}{m_2 - m_1}\{e^{m_1 t} - e^{m_2 t}\}. \quad (234.9)$$

Since m_1 and m_2 are both negative, equation (234.8) shows that q is the difference of two charges which decrease to zero at different rates owing to the fact that the time constants are different. The resultant curve is shown in Fig. 202.

Equation (234.9) shows that when $t = 0$, $i = 0$, and also when $t = \infty$, $i = 0$. Therefore, the current must increase to a maximum and then decrease to zero. To obtain the time at which i is a maximum, differentiate equation (234.9) and equate to 0. We then have

$$t_{\text{max.}} = \frac{1}{m_1 - m_2} \log_e \frac{m_2}{m_1}. \tag{234.10}$$

The current curve is, also, the resultant of two exponential curves which start with the same absolute value, but opposite in sense, and decrease to zero at different rates owing to different time constants. The resultant current curve is shown in Fig. 202.

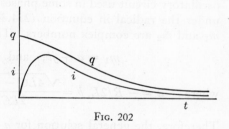

FIG. 202

Case (b). In this case, $m_1 = m_2 = - R/2L$. The two terms of equations (234.5) and (234.6) are the same. Since the linear differential equations are of the second order, there must be two constants of integration. In order to obtain the two constants it is assumed that $m_1 \neq m_2$, but that $m_2 = m_1 + h$, where h is a very small quantity. The solution of equation (234.2) then becomes

$$q = Ae^{mt} + Be^{(m+h)t} = e^{mt}(A + Be^{ht}). \tag{234.11}$$

Expanding e^{ht} by Maclaurin's theorem, we have

$$e^{ht} = 1 + ht + \frac{h^2 t^2}{\lfloor 2} + \cdots = 1 + ht \text{ approximately.}$$

Substituting in (234.11), we have

$$q = e^{mt}\{A + B(1 + ht)\} = e^{mt}(K_1 + K_2 t). \tag{234.12}$$

When $t = 0$, $q = Q = \mathscr{E}C$, $i = 0$. Therefore, $Q = K_1$.
Further,

$$i = K_1 m e^{mt} + K_2 m t e^{mt} + K_2 e^{mt}.$$

Therefore, $K_1m + K_2 = 0$. Hence $K_2 = -Qm$. We then have

$$q = Qe^{mt}(1 - mt) = \mathscr{E}Ce^{-\frac{R}{2L}t}\left(1 + \frac{R}{2L}t\right). \qquad (234.13)$$

Differentiating, we obtain

$$i = -\frac{\mathscr{E}}{L}\, te^{-\frac{R}{2L}t}. \qquad (234.14)$$

The resultant curves for q and i are of the same general form as those shown in Fig. 202. In this case the time for the maximum current is

$$t_{\max.} = \frac{2L}{R}.$$

Case (*c*). This is a very important and interesting case. It is the oscillatory circuit used in some phases of radio work. The expression under the radical in equation (234.3) is imaginary, and, therefore, m_1 and m_2 are complex numbers. They are

$$m_1 = a + jb, \quad \text{and} \quad m_2 = a - jb,$$

where $\quad a = -R/2L, \ b = \dfrac{\sqrt{4LC - R^2C^2}}{2LC}$, and $j = \sqrt{-1}$.

Therefore, the general solution for q is of the form

or,
$$\left.\begin{array}{l} q = Ae^{(a+jb)t} + Be^{(a-jb)t} \\[2mm] q = e^{at}(Ae^{jbt} + Be^{-jbt}). \end{array}\right\} \qquad (234.15)$$

When equation (234.15) is treated in the same manner as was equation (186.3) in Section 186, Chap. XIII, it reduces to

$$q = Ke^{at}\sin(bt + \phi). \qquad (234.16)$$

When $t = 0$, $q = Q = \mathscr{E}C$, $i = 0$. Therefore, $Q = K\sin\phi$. Differentiating (234.16), and then setting $t = 0$, we have

$$i = Ka\sin\phi + Kb\cos\phi = 0.$$

Therefore,
$$\tan\phi = -\frac{b}{a}, \qquad (234.17)$$

and hence

$$\sin\phi = \frac{\sqrt{4LC - R^2C^2}}{\sqrt{4LC}}, \quad \text{and} \quad K = \frac{Q\sqrt{4LC}}{\sqrt{4LC - R^2C^2}}.$$

Therefore, the final solution for the current is

$$i = -\frac{2Q}{\sqrt{4LC - R^2C^2}} e^{-\frac{R}{2L}t} \sin\left(\frac{\sqrt{4LC - R^2C^2}}{2LC} t\right). \quad (234.18)$$

The equations for q and i are sine functions, and, therefore, are the equations of an oscillatory motion. The curves are sine curves, the amplitudes of which gradually decrease, since each function is multiplied by the *damping factor* $e^{-\frac{R}{2L}t}$. Such a curve as is represented by either (234.16) or (234.18) is called a *damped sine curve*. The curve is shown in Fig. 159. The sine curve for the charge is ahead of the curve for the current i by the phase angle ϕ. It is seen from (234.17) that when $R = 0$, the phase angle ϕ is $\pi/2$. This can never actually occur, however, since an inductance coil must always have some resistance. The period of the oscillation is given by

$$T = 2\pi \frac{2LC}{\sqrt{4LC - R^2C^2}}. \quad (234.19)$$

Therefore, $b = \omega = 2\pi/T$, is the angular velocity. If R is negligibly small, and hence may be placed equal to zero, the expression for the period reduces to

$$T = 2\pi\sqrt{LC} \text{ sec.,} \quad \text{and} \quad f = \frac{1}{2\pi\sqrt{LC}} \text{ cycles/sec.} \quad (234.20)$$

omit

235. Logarithmic Decrement. — The physical interpretation of equation (234.18) is as follows: When the condenser is charged to a potential $\mathscr{E}$ it contains an amount of energy $\frac{1}{2}C\mathscr{E}^2$. On the first discharge a current flows in the circuit, and, when it reaches its first maximum (times $T/4$ sec.), there is stored in the magnetic field an amount of energy equal to $\frac{1}{2}Li^2$. $\frac{1}{2}Li^2$ is less than $\frac{1}{2}C\mathscr{E}^2$ by the amount of energy which has been transformed into heat in the ohmic resistance. As the current decreases to zero the condenser is charged in the reverse sense, the amount of energy it now contains, $\frac{1}{2}C\mathscr{E}_1^2$, being less than its initial energy by the amount of energy that has been dissipated as heat in the ohmic resistance during the first half period. The condenser then discharges in the reverse sense, and the process is repeated. Each succeeding value of $\frac{1}{2}Li^2$ and $\frac{1}{2}C\mathscr{E}^2$ is smaller than the preceding value. The initial store of energy is gradually dissipated, and the amplitudes of the sine curve gradually decrease to zero. If there were no ohmic resistance the oscillations, once started, would continue indefinitely at constant amplitude, i.e., the damping factor would be 1. This would be approximately true if the circuit were at the absolute zero of temperature and composed of a metal which exhibits the phenomenon of superconductivity. Clearly, the greater the rate of energy dissipation the sooner will the oscillations cease. In order to obtain an expression which will serve as a measure of the rate of energy dissipation, and hence decay of amplitude of oscillation, we proceed as follows: Let us write equation (234.18) in the form

$$i = Ie^{at} \sin bt. \tag{235.1}$$

Let I_1, I_3, I_5, etc., be the successive current maxima in the same sense, corresponding to θ_1, θ_3, θ_5, etc., as indicated in Fig. 159. The times at which maxima occur are $t_1 = \frac{1}{4}T$, $t_3 = \frac{5}{4}T$, etc. Then $bt_1 = \pi/2$, and $\sin bt_1 = 1$. $bt_3 = \frac{5}{2}\pi$, and $\sin bt_3 = 1$, etc. Hence

$$\sin bt_1 = \sin bt_3 = \sin bt_5 = \cdots = 1.$$

Then $I_1 = Ie^{at_1}$, $I_3 = Ie^{a(t_1+T)}$, $I_5 = Ie^{a(t_1+2T)}$, etc. Taking ratios, we have $I_1/I_3 = I_3/I_5 = \cdots = e^{-aT} = $ a constant. Taking the logarithms of these ratios, we have the *logarithmic decrement*

$$\delta = \log_e\left(\frac{I_{2n-1}}{I_{2n+1}}\right) = -aT = \frac{2\pi RC}{\sqrt{4LC - R^2C^2}}. \tag{235.2}$$

If the resistance of the circuit is so small that (234.20) is approximately true,

$$\delta = \pi R\sqrt{\frac{C}{L}}. \tag{235.3}$$

This is the expression for the logarithmic decrement usually used in radio work. δ may be obtained, also, by substituting in equation (186.10). Whence

$$\delta = K\frac{\pi}{\omega_1}.$$

The value of δ obtained here is twice the value obtained in Section 186.

In radio work a quantity Q is used sometimes instead of δ, which is called a "figure of merit" for an oscillatory circuit. It is defined as the ratio between the inductive reactance of the circuit and its ohmic resistance, i.e.,

$$Q = \frac{L\omega}{R}.$$

But since

$$\delta = \frac{R}{2L} T = \frac{\pi R}{L\omega}, \quad Q = \frac{\pi}{\delta} = \frac{1}{R}\sqrt{\frac{L}{C}}.$$

Thus, an efficient periodic circuit has a small resistance R or a large Q.

The damped wave radio transmitting circuit is essentially the circuit here considered. A simple circuit arrangement for sending damped radio waves is shown in Fig. 203. I is an induction coil, the secondary of which is connected to an oscillatory circuit consisting of a condenser C_1, an induction coil L_1, and a spark gap S. When the key K is depressed the induction coil is put into action, and the vibra-

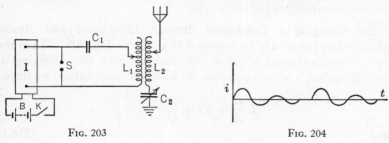

FIG. 203   FIG. 204

tions of the armature produce high-tension currents in the secondary. At each break of the interrupter the potential in the secondary mounts sufficiently to break down the air gap S. The first discharge ionizes the air in the gap and the resistance becomes so low that high-frequency oscillations are set up in the closed circuit consisting of the condenser C_1 and the inductance L_1. These oscillations are damped, as shown in Fig. 204. Each time the primary circuit of the induction coil is broken an alternating current of high frequency is set up in the oscillatory circuit which is damped out before the next break of the primary circuit. Thus, we have a broken series of high-frequency damped currents. The group frequency of the damped currents is the frequency of the interrupter of the induction coil which is low, whereas the frequency of the alternating current in the oscillator is very high (frequency within a group of waves). This frequency will depend upon the constants of the oscillatory circuit, and is given very approximately by (234.20). The impedance of the secondary of the induction coil is so large that no appreciable part of the high-frequency current passes through it.

Coil L_1 is coupled with coil L_2 which is in the antenna circuit, and hence high-frequency currents will be set up in the antenna circuit, which will have their maximum strength when resonance obtains

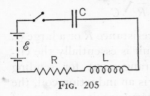

FIG. 205

between the two circuits, i.e., when equation (234.20) gives the same value for the frequency in the two circuits. Since the antenna circuit is an open circuit electromagnetic waves will be radiated out into space. The oscillator used by Hertz in his classic experiments in 1888 was essentially of the same circuit form as considered here. The Lodge oscillator, an early type of oscillator used for generating electromagnetic waves, also was essentially of the same type.

236. Charging a Condenser through Inductance and Resistance. — Let the circuit be arranged as shown in Fig. 205. When the key is closed a current will flow into the condenser, thus charging it. From Kirchhoff's second equation for instantaneous values, we have

Or

$$\left. \begin{array}{c} L\dfrac{di}{dt} + Ri + \dfrac{q}{C} = \mathscr{E}. \\[2mm] L\dfrac{d^2q}{dt^2} + R\dfrac{dq}{dt} + \dfrac{q}{C} = \mathscr{E}. \end{array} \right\} \tag{236.1}$$

In order to eliminate the constant $\mathscr{E}$, let $q = x + C\mathscr{E}$. Then

$$L\frac{d^2x}{dt^2} + R\frac{dx}{dt} + \frac{x}{C} = 0. \tag{236.2}$$

Let $x = e^{mt}$. Then $Lm^2 + Rm + 1/C = 0$. Therefore,

$$m_{1-2} = \frac{-RC \pm \sqrt{R^2C^2 - 4LC}}{2LC}.$$

The solution is, accordingly,

$$x = Ae^{m_1 t} + Be^{m_2 t}.$$

Or

$$q = C\mathscr{E} + Ae^{m_1 t} + Be^{m_2 t}. \tag{236.3}$$

And
$$i = Am_1 e^{m_1 t} + Bm_2 e^{m_2 t}. \tag{236.4}$$

There are three cases here as in Section 234.

Case (*a*). The final solutions are

$$q = C\mathscr{E} + \frac{C\mathscr{E}}{m_1 - m_2}(m_2 e^{m_1 t} - m_1 e^{m_2 t}), \tag{236.5}$$

$$i = C\mathscr{E}\frac{m_1 m_2}{m_1 - m_2}(e^{m_1 t} - e^{m_2 t}). \tag{236.6}$$

q rises exponentially from 0 to the final value $C\mathscr{E}$. i rises from 0 to a maximum and then gradually decreases to 0 as the condenser takes its full charge. The time at which the maximum occurs is found as in Section 234.

Case (*b*). Since $m_1 = m_2 = m$, in this case, we have, as before,

$$q = C\mathscr{E} + e^{mt}(K_1 + K_2 t).$$

Therefore, the complete solutions are

$$q = C\mathscr{E}(1 - e^{mt} + mt\,e^{mt}). \tag{236.7}$$

$$i = C\mathscr{E}\,m^2 t\,e^{mt}. \tag{236.8}$$

The maximum value of i occurs at time $t_1 = 2L/R$ seconds after the key is closed.

Case (*c*). Except for the constant term $\mathscr{E}$, the solution is the same as in Section 234. Thus,

$$x = K'e^{at}\sin(bt + \phi),$$

or

$$q = C\mathscr{E} + K'e^{at}\sin(bt + \phi). \tag{236.9}$$

When $t = 0$, $q = 0$, $i = 0$, we have

$$\tan\phi = -\frac{b}{a} = \frac{\sqrt{4LC - R^2 C^2}}{RC}, \tag{236.10}$$

$$K' = -\frac{2C\mathscr{E}\sqrt{LC}}{\sqrt{4LC - R^2 C^2}}.$$

Therefore, the complete solutions are

$$q = C\mathscr{E} - \frac{2C\mathscr{E}\sqrt{LC}}{\sqrt{4LC - R^2C^2}} e^{at} \sin (bt + \phi), \qquad (236.11)$$

$$i = \frac{2C\mathscr{E}}{\sqrt{4LC - R^2C^2}} e^{at} \sin bt. \qquad (236.12)$$

In cases (a) and (b) q rises exponentially to its final value $C\mathscr{E}$, as shown by the broken line in Fig. 206. The curves for i in these two cases are, in general, of the same form as the curve for i shown in Fig. 202. The curve for equation (236.11) is the solid line curve shown in Fig. 206. The charge oscillates about the constant value $C\mathscr{E}$, until

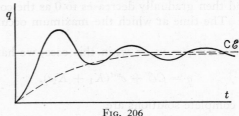

FIG. 206

damped out owing to the damping factor e^{at}. The logarithmic decrement has the same value as was obtained in Section 234. Since the charge in the condenser rises above the value $C\mathscr{E}$, the potential across the condenser rises above the potential of the source—battery or dynamo—and there is danger of breaking down the dielectric of the condenser, and hence its destruction. For this reason, if the potential of the source is near the breakdown potential of the condenser, enough resistance should be inserted in the circuit to make the charging aperiodic. The curve for i, equation (236.12), is of the general form of the curve for q except that i oscillates about the value $i = 0$, i.e., about the t axis in Fig. 206.

PROBLEMS

1. An emf. of 50 volts is applied to a circuit containing 5 ohms and an inductance of 0.3 henry. (a) What is the final value of the current? (b) What is the time constant of the circuit? (c) What is the rate at which the current begins to rise? (d) At what rate is the current rising τ seconds after the circuit is closed? (e) Plot the curve, current against time.

2. (a) At what rate is the battery supplying energy to the circuit τ seconds after closing the switch in Problem 1?

(b) How much energy is stored in the magnetic field when the current of Problem 1 has reached its final value?

(c) How much energy is stored in the magnetic field of Problem 1 τ seconds after closing the switch?

3. A condenser having a capacitance of 50 mf. is charged to a potential of 120 volts. It is then discharged through a resistance of 1000 ohms. (a) What is the maximum charge in the condenser? (b) What is the maximum energy in the condenser? (c) What is the magnitude of the current at the instant discharge begins? (d) At what rate does the discharge begin? (e) What is the time constant? (f) Plot the current-time curve.

4. Suppose that the condenser of Problem 3 had been discharged through a resistance of 1000 ohms and an inductance of 0.3 henry. (a) Is the discharge oscillatory or aperiodic? (b) What resistance would be required to make the circuit critically damped?

5. Let $m_1 = -\dfrac{1}{\tau_1}$ and $m_2 = -\dfrac{1}{\tau_2}$. Then show that equations (234.8) and (234.9) reduce to

$$q = \frac{Q}{\tau_1 - \tau_2}\left\{\tau_1 e^{-\frac{t}{\tau_1}} - \tau_2 e^{-\frac{t}{\tau_2}}\right\},$$

$$i = \frac{Q}{\tau_2 - \tau_1}\left\{e^{-\frac{t}{\tau_1}} - e^{-\frac{t}{\tau_2}}\right\},$$

where τ_1 is the time constant of the first exponential curve and τ_2 is the time constant of the second exponential curve.

6. (a) Show that equation (234.10) reduces to

$$t_{\text{max.}} = \frac{LC}{\sqrt{R^2C^2 - 4LC}} \log_e \frac{\tau_1}{\tau_2}.$$

(b) Calculate $t_{\text{max.}}$ using the data of Problem 4. (c) What is $t_{\text{max.}}$ when the circuit is critically damped?

7. Using the data $R = 1000$ ohms, $C = 50$ mfs., $\mathscr{E} = 120$ volts, $L = 0.3$ henry, calculate the maximum current.

8. The resistance in Problem 7 is 100 ohms, the other data remaining the same. (a) What is the frequency of the oscillatory current? (b) What is the logarithmic decrement?

9. A condenser of 1 mf. charged to a potential of 2000 volts is discharged through an inductance of 0.012 henry and a resistance of 5 ohms. (a) Calculate the frequency. (b) Calculate the logarithmic decrement. (c) What is the phase angle ϕ? (d) What is the value of the current at the first maximum? (e) How much energy has been turned into heat during the first quarter period?

10. A solenoid is 100 cms. in length and has a single layer of 1000 turns of wire. If the mean radius is 3 cms. what is the coefficient of self inductance in henrys if the core is air?

11. If the solenoid of Problem 10 is wound with No. 21 B&S gauge copper wire at 20° C., what is the time constant of the solenoid? If the coil has an iron core of permeability 2000 what is the time constant?

12. A condenser of 25 mfs. is charged to a potential of 2000 volts, and then discharged through a resistance of 200 ohms and an inductance of 0.1 henry. (a) What is the initial energy in the condenser? (b) What is the time of maximum current, $t_{\text{max.}}$? (c) What is the value of the maximum current? (d) What is the energy in the magnetic field at this instant? (e) How much energy remains in the condenser at this instant? (f) How much energy has been turned into heat in the resistance at this instant? (g) What is the difference of potential across the condenser at this instant?

CHAPTER XVIII

ALTERNATING CURRENTS

237) Alternating currents are of paramount importance in the utilization of electricity today. A dynamo, in which a coil of wire revolves in a magnetic field of force, generates an induced alternating emf. which, under suitable conditions, produces an alternating current in a circuit. Alternating emfs. are readily stepped up or down by transformers to any extent desired. The extensive industrial use of alternating currents, which vary harmonically with the impressed emf., has rendered a study of such currents of very great interest and value. In the field of radio high-frequency alternating currents generated by electron tube circuits have ushered in an entirely new class of phenomena with their industrial applications. We shall, therefore, develop the fundamental equations used in alternating currents in this Chapter, and show their meanings and applications. In all cases it will be assumed that the emf., and also the current, vary harmonically, and that they are of the form $\mathscr{E} \sin \omega t$ and $I \sin \omega t$. In most cases there are harmonics present, but these harmonics will be considered as negligible, i.e., emfs., and currents will be treated as pure sine functions. The emf. developed by a dynamo is, when accurately represented, given by

$$\mathscr{E} = \mathscr{E} \sin \omega t + \mathscr{E} \sin 3\omega t + \mathscr{E} \sin 5\omega t + \cdots.$$

We shall consider that the first term alone is present, as this term is always by far the strongest. We shall, also, assume that the wave is sinusoidal.

238) **Circuit Containing Inductance and Resistance.** — In many circuits capacitance plays a relatively unimportant role. We shall, therefore, first consider a circuit containing inductance and resistance upon which there is impressed a harmonically varying emf. of the form

$$\mathscr{E} = \mathscr{E} \sin \omega t. \tag{238.1}$$

494

The differential equation representing the electric performance of such a circuit, as is shown in Fig. 207, is

$$L \frac{di}{dt} + Ri = \mathcal{E} \sin \omega t, \qquad (238.2)$$

where $\mathcal{E}$ is the maximum impressed emf., $\omega = 2\pi f$, f being the frequency in cycles/sec., and t the time in seconds. This equation may be put in the form

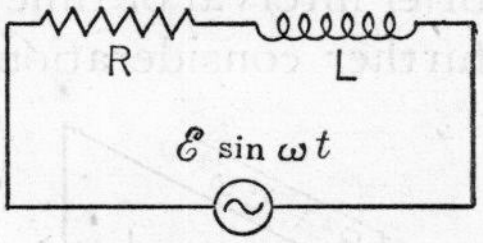

$$\frac{di}{dt} + \frac{R}{L} i = \frac{\mathcal{E}}{L} \sin \omega t.$$

FIG. 207

An integrating factor is $e^{\frac{R}{L} t} dt$. We than have

$$\left(\frac{di}{dt} + \frac{R}{L} i \right) e^{\frac{R}{L} t} = \frac{\mathcal{E}}{L} \int e^{\frac{R}{L} t} \sin \omega t \, dt + A.$$

Or

$$i e^{\frac{R}{L} t} = \frac{\mathcal{E}}{L} \int e^{\frac{R}{L} t} \sin \omega t \, dt + A, \qquad (238.3)$$

since the left-hand member is readily integrated. The right-hand member may be integrated by parts, the general formula for which is

$$\int u \, dv = uv - \int v \, du.$$

Let $R/L = a$. We have to integrate, therefore, $e^{at} \sin \omega t \, dt$. On applying the general formula, we have

$$\int e^{at} \sin \omega t \, dt = \frac{1}{a} e^{at} \sin \omega t - \frac{\omega}{a} \int e^{at} \cos \omega t \, dt. \qquad (238.4)$$

Then, integrating the last integral by parts, we have

$$\int e^{at} \cos \omega t \, dt = \frac{1}{a} e^{at} \cos \omega t + \frac{\omega}{a} \int e^{at} \sin \omega t \, dt. \qquad (238.5)$$

Substituting (238.5) in (238.4) and reducing, there results

$$\int e^{at} \sin \omega t \, dt = \frac{e^{at}}{\omega^2 + a^2} (a \sin \omega t - \omega \cos \omega t). \qquad (238.6)$$

Substituting this solution in equation (238.3), and remembering that $a = R/L$, we have

$$i = \frac{\mathscr{E}}{R^2 + L^2\omega^2} (R \sin \omega t - L\omega \cos \omega t) + Ae^{-\frac{R}{L}t}. \qquad (238.7)$$

The term $Ae^{-\frac{R}{L}t}$ represents a transient current which exists for but a brief interval of time after closing the circuit, and so may be given no further consideration. It is superposed upon the regular sinusoidal current, and its existence is recognizable in oscillograms which show the currents from the instant of closing the switch.

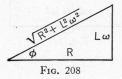

FIG. 208

In order to transform this equation into a single sine function, let R and $L\omega$ represent the sides of a right angle triangle as shown in Fig. 208. Multiply and divide (238.7) by the hypothenuse of this triangle, we have

$$i = \frac{\mathscr{E}}{\sqrt{R^2 + L^2\omega^2}} (\cos \phi \sin \omega t - \sin \phi \cos \omega t).$$

Or

$$i = \frac{\mathscr{E}}{\sqrt{R^2 + L^2\omega^2}} \sin (\omega t - \phi). \qquad (238.8)$$

This is the complete solution of (238.2). It shows that the current is a harmonic function of the time. It has its maximum value,

$$I = \frac{\mathscr{E}}{\sqrt{R^2 + L^2\omega^2}}, \qquad (238.9)$$

when $(\omega t - \phi) = n(\pi/2)$, where n takes the values 1, 3, 5, etc. The current lags behind the impressed emf. by the phase angle ϕ, where

$$\phi = \text{arc tan} \frac{L\omega}{R}. \qquad (238.10)$$

In the special case when $L = 0$, $\phi = 0$, and

$$i = \frac{\mathscr{E}}{R} \sin \omega t. \qquad (238.11)$$

The current is then in phase with the impressed emf. The maximum value of the current is then

$$I = \frac{\mathscr{E}}{R}.$$

Read.

239. Cause of the Phase Angle ϕ. — In the circuit just considered, where there is only resistance and inductance, ϕ is the angle by which the current *lags* behind the emf. This is due to the emf. of self inductance. As is seen from equation (238.10) ϕ depends upon the relative values of the resistance and inductance, with the angular velocity ω a contributing factor. Now the emf. $\mathcal{E}_s$ of self inductance will always lag $\pi/2$ radians behind the current (when no ferromagnetic substance is present in the circuit), because $\mathcal{E}_s$ has its maximum value when the flux is varying most rapidly. That will be when the current passes through zero and changes sign, Fig. 209. The flux is in step with the

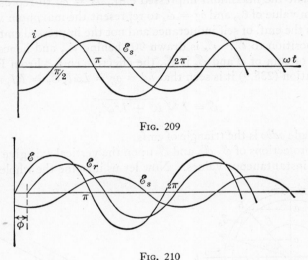

FIG. 209

FIG. 210

current, since it is created by the current, but the magnitude of $\mathcal{E}_s$ depends upon the rate of change of flux, and the sense of $\mathcal{E}_s$ depends upon whether i is increasing or decreasing. When the current i reaches its maximum (in either sense) and begins to decrease $\mathcal{E}_s$ passes through zero and changes sign. When the current is decreasing in magnitude $\mathcal{E}_s$ is in the same sense as i and hence positive relative to i, but when the current is increasing in magnitude $\mathcal{E}_s$ is in the opposite sense and hence negative relative to i, as is seen by an inspection of the curves in Fig. 209.

Now, the resultant emf. at any instant is the scalar sum of the impressed emf. $\mathcal{E}$ and the emf. of self inductance $\mathcal{E}_s$, or $\mathcal{E}_r$, Fig. 210. The current i is in phase with the resultant emf. $\mathcal{E}_r$, and hence lags behind the impressed emf. $\mathcal{E}$ by the phase angle ϕ. The resultant emf. $\mathcal{E}_r$ drives the current through the ohmic resistance R, the instantaneous current being determined by Ohm's law. Hence, we have: (1) $\mathcal{E}_s$ lags more than 90° behind $\mathcal{E}$. (2) $\mathcal{E}_r$, and hence also i, lags behind $\mathcal{E}$ from 0° to 90°, and $\mathcal{E}_r$ is smaller than $\mathcal{E}$. (3) The current is in phase with $\mathcal{E}_r$ and is equal to $\mathcal{E}_r/R$.

240. The Vector Diagram. — emfs. and currents are not, strictly speaking, vector quantities, but they are conveniently so represented as they follow a sine law. Let the line ob (Fig. 211) be drawn to scale to represent the maximum impressed emf., $od = \mathcal{E}_r$ to represent the maximum value of $\mathcal{E}_r$, and $og = \mathcal{E}_s$ to represent the maximum value of $\mathcal{E}_s$. $\mathcal{E}_s$ is the emf. of self inductance and not the impressed emf. which is in opposition to $\mathcal{E}_s$. $\mathcal{E}_s$ is drawn 90° behind $\mathcal{E}_r$, and hence also i. The vector sum of $\mathcal{E}$ and $\mathcal{E}_s$ is $\mathcal{E}_r$, the effective emf. From Fig. 208 and equation (238.9) it is seen that $bd = og = L\omega I$, $\mathcal{E}_r = RI$, and

$$\mathcal{E} = I \sqrt{R^2 + L^2\omega^2}.$$

The triangle $odbo$ is the triangle of emfs.

The projections of $\mathcal{E}$, $\mathcal{E}_s$, and $\mathcal{E}_r$ upon the vertical axis give the respective instantaneous values. Now let us imagine the whole vector

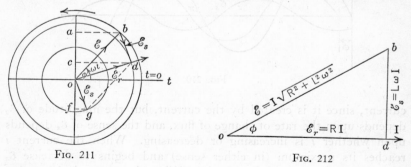

FIG. 211   FIG. 212

diagram to revolve in the counterclockwise sense at an angular speed of $\omega = 2\pi f$. If we let the axis ot be the time axis, then the projections of $\mathcal{E}$, $\mathcal{E}_s$, and $\mathcal{E}_r$ upon the vertical axis, giving the instantaneous values, will trace out curves when combined with a uniform transverse motion. The curves so formed are those of Fig. 210.

The vector triangle $odbo$ is usually drawn detached from the clock diagram of Fig. 211, as shown in Fig. 212. It is then called the triangle of emfs.   The hypothenuse represents the maximum value of the impressed emf., the vertical line the maximum value of the induced emf., and the base line the maximum effective emf.   Therefore,

$$\mathscr{E}^2 = \mathscr{E}_r^2 + \mathscr{E}_s^2. \qquad (240.1)$$

This relationship does not hold for instantaneous values.   It holds only for maximum values or *effective* (virtual) values, which add geometrically.   Instantaneous values add algebraically, and, therefore, we have

$$\mathscr{E}_r \sin (\omega t - \phi) = \mathscr{E} \sin \omega t + \mathscr{E}_s \sin \left(\omega t - \phi - \frac{\pi}{2} \right),$$

or $oc = oa - of$.

The triangle of Fig. 208 is similar to the triangle of Fig. 212.   In the triangle (Fig. 208) the hypothenuse is

$$\sqrt{R^2 + L^2\omega^2},$$

which is called the *impedance* of the circuit.   Impedance is the effective resistance of the circuit and is measured in ohms.   The vertical line is $L\omega$, which is called *inductive reactance*, and is also measured in ohms. The base line is the ohmic resistance of the circuit.

From equation (238.9) it is seen that the impedance plays the role of the total resistance in the circuit.   The limiting value of the impedance for decreasing L or ω is simply the ohmic resistance R.   If, on the other hand, R decreases practically to zero, or ω increases out of all proportion to R, as is the case in radio-frequency circuits, the term $L\omega$ is the dominant term.   The impedance is then practically all inductive reactance, and ϕ approaches 90°.

Since, in Fig. 212, $\mathscr{E}_r$ is the emf. which is effective in driving the current i through the ohmic resistance, it has been called the *working* or *active* component of the emf.   It is

$$\mathscr{E}_r = \mathscr{E} \cos \phi. \qquad (240.2)$$

Multiplying the maximum value of $\mathscr{E}$ or I by 0.707 gives the effective value, to be explained in the following Section.   Multiplying the sides of the triangle in Fig. 212 by 0.707 changes to effective values.   Then using effective values, we have, on multiplying (240.2) by I

$$P = \mathscr{E} I \cos \phi \text{ watts.} \qquad (240.3)$$

This expression gives the true or active power expended in the circuit. cos φ is called the *power factor*, where

$$\phi = \text{arc tan } \frac{L\omega}{R}.$$

The vertical component of the apparent power is

$$P = \mathscr{E}I \sin\phi \text{ watts.} \qquad (240.4)$$

This is called the *wattless* component of the power.

241. **Effective Currents and emfs.** — An ordinary ammeter or voltmeter of the D'Arsonval type, whose moving parts are massive and strongly damped, will indicate the mean value of the quantity to be measured if the frequency of variation is rapid. Now the mean value of the emf. for the first half period is

$$\mathscr{E}_{\text{av.}} = \frac{\mathscr{E}}{\frac{1}{2}T} \int_0^{\frac{1}{2}T} \sin\omega t \, dt = \frac{2\mathscr{E}}{\pi}, \qquad (241.1)$$

where $\omega = 2\pi/T$. And for the second half period

$$\mathscr{E}_{\text{av.}} = \frac{\mathscr{E}}{\frac{1}{2}T} \int_{\frac{1}{2}T}^{T} \sin\omega t \, dt = -\frac{2\mathscr{E}}{\pi}. \qquad (241.2)$$

For the whole period, we have

$$\mathscr{E}_{\text{av.}} = \frac{2\mathscr{E}}{\pi} - \frac{2\mathscr{E}}{\pi} = 0.$$

Thus the mean values for the half periods are equal and alternately positive and negative, and, therefore, the sum for any period is zero. The moving system receives successive equal and opposite impulses during a complete cycle, and, as the impulses are too rapid for response, the moving system remains essentially at rest. For this reason measuring instruments used on alternating currents must be so constructed as to give deflections always in the same direction no matter what the direction of the current. This condition is fulfilled with all instruments whose deflections depend upon the square of the current or emf. Instruments employing this principle are hot wire instruments, thermocouple instruments, and dynamometer instruments.

In reality it is not the average we are concerned with. Measuring instruments are so calibrated that an alternating current gives the same heating effect as a direct current, and the heating effect varies as the square of the current (RI^2) or the square of the emf. $(\mathscr{E}^2/R)$. Hence, the expression required is the square root of the mean square value, which is called the *effective* value. This is for the emf.

$$\mathscr{E}_{ef.}^2 = \frac{\mathscr{E}^2}{T} \int_0^T \sin^2 \omega t \, dt = \frac{\mathscr{E}^2}{2} .$$

Therefore,

$$\mathscr{E}_{ef.} = \left(\frac{\mathscr{E}^2}{2}\right)^{\frac{1}{2}} = \frac{\mathscr{E}}{\sqrt{2}} = 0.707\mathscr{E} . \qquad (241.3)$$

Likewise for the current, we have

$$I_{ef.}^2 = \frac{I^2}{T} \int_0^T \sin \omega t \, dt = \frac{I^2}{2} .$$

Therefore,

$$I_{ef.} = 0.707 I. \qquad (241.4)$$

Thus, alternating current ammeters and voltmeters measure effective amperes and effective volts. In equation (238.9) we may use effective values as well as in the vector diagram, Fig. 212, and then the results will agree with our measuring instruments.

242. Power in the Alternating Current Circuit. — In order to derive an expression for the power in the alternating current circuit, we have

$$dP = \mathscr{E}i \, dt, \quad \text{or} \quad P_{av.} = \frac{1}{T} \int_0^T \mathscr{E}i \, dt.$$

But since

$$\mathscr{E} = \mathscr{E} \sin \omega t \quad \text{and} \quad i = I \sin (\omega t \pm \phi),$$

$$P_{av.} = \frac{\mathscr{E} I}{T} \int_0^T \sin \omega t \sin (\phi t \pm \phi) \, dt.$$

And on expanding $\sin (\omega t \pm \phi)$, we have

$$P_{av.} = \frac{\mathscr{E} I}{T} \int_0^T (\sin^2 \omega t \cos \phi \pm \sin \omega t \cos \omega t \sin \phi) \, dt. \quad (242.1)$$

On integrating, we have

$$P_{av.} = \frac{\mathscr{E} I}{2} \cos \phi = \mathscr{E}_{ef.} I_{ef.} \cos \phi \text{ watts.} \qquad (242.2)$$

This is the expression for the power in watts, where $\mathscr{E}_{\text{ef.}}$ and $I_{\text{ef.}}$ are the effective emf. and current as measured with alternating current instruments. $\cos \phi$ is the *power factor*, and $\phi = $ arc tan $L\omega/R$ is the *phase angle* between emf. and current. The power factor and phase angle are easily measured if an indicating wattmeter, an a.c. voltmeter, and a.c. ammeter are available. From the readings obtained by substitution in equation (242.4), $\cos \phi$ and also ϕ are readily obtained.

We shall no longer retain the subscript ef. as effective values will be understood henceforth, unless otherwise indicated.

243 **Circuit Containing Resistance and Capacitance.** *Harmonic Impressed emf.* — Let us consider a circuit as shown in Fig. 213. The resistance R may be in part the fictitious resistance of a defective dielectric in the condenser. Applying the condition that the instantaneous impressed emf. is equal to the counter potential differences, we have

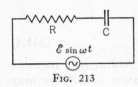

Fig. 213

$$R \frac{dq}{dt} + \frac{q}{C} = \mathscr{E} \sin \omega t. \qquad (243.1)$$

Or

$$\frac{dq}{dt} + \frac{q}{RC} = \frac{\mathscr{E}}{R} \sin \omega t. \qquad (243.2)$$

As with the similar equation for resistance and inductance, we may write

$$\left(\frac{dq}{dt} + \frac{q}{RC} \right) e^{\frac{t}{RC}} = \frac{\mathscr{E}}{R} \int e^{\frac{t}{RC}} \sin \omega t \, dt + A. \qquad (243.3)$$

And

$$q e^{\frac{t}{RC}} = \frac{\mathscr{E}}{R} \int e^{\frac{t}{RC}} \sin \omega t \, dt + A.$$

Integrating by parts, we have

$$q = \frac{\mathscr{E}}{\omega(R^2 + 1/C^2\omega^2)} \left(\frac{1}{C\omega} \sin \omega t - R \cos \omega t \right) + A e^{-\frac{t}{RC}}. \qquad (243.4)$$

The last term is quickly reduced to zero, and, therefore, will not be considered further. Multiplying and dividing by the hypotenuse of the triangle of Fig. 214, $\sqrt{R^2 + 1/C^2\omega^2}$, we have as the complete solution

$$q = \frac{-\mathscr{E}}{\omega\sqrt{R^2 + 1/C^2\omega^2}} \cos(\omega t + \phi). \tag{243.5}$$

And

$$i = \frac{\mathscr{E}}{\sqrt{R^2 + 1/C^2\omega^2}} \sin(\omega t + \phi), \tag{243.6}$$

where $\phi = $ arc tan $1/RC\omega$ is the phase angle between current and emf., which, in this case, is an advance angle. When $\omega t + \phi = n(\pi/2)$, where $n = 1, 3, 5$, etc., we have

$$I = \frac{\mathscr{E}}{\sqrt{R^2 + 1/C^2\omega^2}}. \tag{243.7}$$

In this equation I and $\mathscr{E}$ may be taken as effective values, as previously explained.

In the limiting case when $C = \infty$, i.e., when the plates of the condenser are brought into contact, or when $\omega = \infty$, i.e., very high frequency, $I = \mathscr{E}/R$. However, in the case of very high frequencies, R will increase due to the "skin effect," i.e., the current is confined to the surface of the conductor, for the most part, thus decreasing the effective cross section. When $R = 0$,

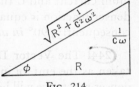

Fig. 214

$I = \mathscr{E}C\omega$, and there is only capacitive reactance in the circuit. The expression for the impedance is

$$\sqrt{R^2 + \frac{1}{C^2\omega^2}},$$

where $1/C\omega$ is the *capacitive reactance*.

In the equation (243.1) the term q/C is the instantaneous p.d. across the condenser. In equation (243.6) the phase angle $+\phi$ shows that the current leads the impressed emf. Equation (243.5) may be written

$$q = \frac{\mathscr{E}}{\omega\sqrt{R^2 + 1/C^2\omega^2}} \sin\left(\omega t + \phi - \frac{\pi}{2}\right). \tag{243.8}$$

On comparing (243.6) and (243.8) it is seen that the charge in the condenser is 90° behind the current. That is, the charge is zero when the current reaches its maximum value, and, as the current decreases to zero, the charge increases to a maximum. Then, as the current changes sign and increases to a maximum in the reverse sense the charge decreases to zero. The polarity of the condenser reverses with each successive charge.

The impressed emf. which is in opposition to the condenser reaction is, at any instant, equal to q/C. This emf. is 90° out of phase with the current, and lagging. Thus,

$$\mathcal{E}_c = \frac{q}{C} = \frac{\int i\,dt}{C} = \frac{\mathcal{E}}{C\omega\sqrt{R^2 + 1/C^2\omega^2}} \sin\left(\omega t + \phi - \frac{\pi}{2}\right). \quad (243.9)$$

Combining with (243.7), we have

$$\mathcal{E}_c = \frac{q}{C} = \left(\frac{I}{C\omega}\right) \sin\left(\omega t + \phi - \frac{\pi}{2}\right). \quad (243.10)$$

Thus, comparing (243.10) and (243.6), it is seen that $\mathcal{E}_c$ is 90° behind the current, and that its maximum value is $I/C\omega$, where I is the maximum current and C the capacitance of the condenser. Now the condenser reaction is equal in magnitude to $\mathcal{E}_c$ but opposite in sense, and, consequently, 90° *in advance* of the current.

244. The Vector Diagram. — In the case of inductance, $\mathcal{E}_s$ was taken as the emf. of inductance. Likewise, in this diagram, the condenser reactance will be taken and drawn 90° *in advance* of the current. Thus, in Fig. 215, *oa* is the maximum impressed emf. $\mathcal{E}$, *ob* is the maximum resultant $\mathcal{E}_r$, and *oc* is the maximum condenser reactance $\mathcal{E}_c$. $\mathcal{E}_r$ is the vector sum of $\mathcal{E}$ and $\mathcal{E}_c$. In absolute value it is

$$\mathcal{E}^2 = \mathcal{E}_r^2 + \mathcal{E}_c^2. \quad (244.1)$$

$\mathcal{E}_r = RI$ and $\mathcal{E}_c = I/C\omega$. The triangle *oabo* is the triangle of emfs. Equation (244.1) holds only for maximum or effective values, which may be treated as vector quantities. For instantaneous values algebraic addition must be used, and therefore,

$$\mathcal{E}_r \sin(\omega t + \phi) = \mathcal{E} \sin \omega t + \mathcal{E}_c \sin\left(\omega t + \phi + \frac{\pi}{2}\right) \quad (244.2)$$

That is, the sum of the projections of $\mathcal{E}$ and $\mathcal{E}_c$ upon the vertical axis equals the projection of $\mathcal{E}_r$ upon the vertical axis at any instant. Now, let us imagine the whole vector diagram to revolve in a counterclockwise sense at a constant angular speed of ω radians per second. If we let the axis *ot* be the time axis, then the projections of $\mathcal{E}$, $\mathcal{E}_r$, and $\mathcal{E}_c$ upon the vertical axis, giving the instantaneous values, will trace out curves when combined with a uniform transverse motion. The curves thus traced out will be of the same type as those shown in Fig. 210, except that the $\mathcal{E}_r$ and $\mathcal{E}_s$ curves will be shifted to the left relative to the $\mathcal{E}$ curve, thus giving a lead angle instead of a lag angle.

The triangle *oabo* is usually drawn detached from Fig. 215, as is shown in Fig. 216. It is the triangle of emfs. This triangle is drawn inverted as compared with the triangle shown in Fig. 212. The reason for this is that $\mathcal{E}_c$ and $\mathcal{E}_s$ are in opposition when in the same circuit, as

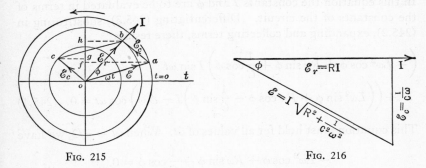

Fig. 215   Fig. 216

will be seen later. If, in Fig. 216, the emfs. are effective, the active component is $\mathcal{E}_r = RI = \mathcal{E} \cos \phi$. The wattless component is $\mathcal{E}_c = I/C\omega = \mathcal{E} \sin \phi$. The active component of the power is $\mathcal{E}I \cos \phi$, and the wattless component is $\mathcal{E}I \sin \phi$.

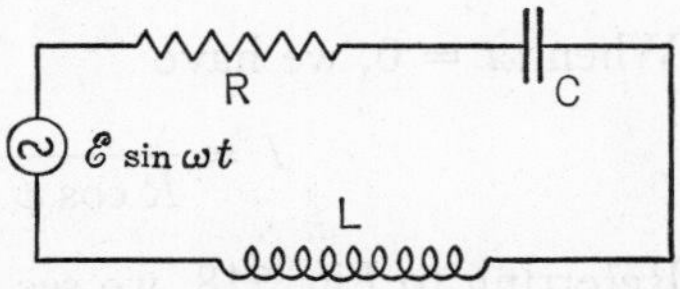

(245.) Circuit Containing Inductance, Capacitance and Resistance. *Harmonic Impressed emf.* — We shall now

Fig. 217

consider the most general case, a circuit such as is shown in Fig. 217, containing inductance, capacitance, and resistance connected in series with a source of a.c. supply. The differential equation in this case is

$$L \frac{di}{dt} + Ri + \frac{q}{C} = \mathcal{E} \sin \omega t. \qquad (245.1)$$

Or

$$L \frac{d^2i}{dt^2} + R \frac{di}{dt} + \frac{i}{C} = \mathcal{E} \omega \cos \omega t. \qquad (245.2)$$

The solution of this differential equation by the method used in the subject of Differential Equations is somewhat involved. (See Johnson's "Differential Equations", p. 101, or "Alternating Currents" by Bedell and Crehore.) Therefore, we will use a simpler method of solution, one which assumes the form the solution will take. Since the impressed emf. is harmonic, it is reasonable to expect that the current also will be harmonic, but, in general, out of phase with the impressed emf. by an angle ϕ. Therefore, let the solution be of the form

$$i = I \sin(\omega t - \phi). \tag{245.3}$$

In this equation the constants I and ϕ are to be evaluated in terms of the constants of the circuit. Differentiating (245.3), substituting in (245.2), expanding and collecting terms, there results

$$\left(- L\omega^2 \cos \phi + R\omega \sin \phi + \frac{1}{C} \cos \phi\right) I \sin \omega t$$

$$+ \left(\left(L\omega^2 \sin \phi + R\omega \cos \phi - \frac{1}{C} \sin \phi\right) I - \mathcal{E}\omega\right) \cos \omega t = 0. \tag{245.4}$$

This equation must hold for all values of ωt. When $\omega t = \pi/2$, we have

$$- L\omega^2 \cos \phi + R\omega \sin \phi + \frac{1}{C} \cos \phi = 0.$$

Therefore,

$$\tan \phi = \frac{L\omega - 1/C\omega}{R}. \tag{245.5}$$

When $\omega t = 0$, we have

$$I = \frac{\mathcal{E}}{R \cos \phi + (L\omega - 1/C\omega) \sin \phi}. \tag{245.6}$$

Referring to Fig. 218, we see that

$$\sin \phi = \frac{L\omega - 1/C\omega}{\sqrt{R^2 + (L\omega - 1/C\omega)^2}}, \text{ and } \cos \phi = \frac{R}{\sqrt{R^2 + (L\omega - 1/C\omega)^2}}.$$

Setting these expressions in (245.6) and reducing, there results

$$I = \frac{\mathcal{E}}{\sqrt{R^2 + (L\omega - 1/C\omega)^2}}. \tag{245.7}$$

And, therefore,

$$i = \frac{\mathcal{E}}{\sqrt{R^2 + (L\omega - 1/C\omega)^2}} \sin (\omega t - \phi). \tag{245.8}$$

The sign of ϕ will be positive if $L\omega > 1/C\omega$, and the current will lag behind the impressed emf. If $1/C\omega > L\omega$, ϕ is negative and the current leads the impressed emf. When $L\omega = 1/C\omega$, $\phi = 0$, and the current is in phase with the impressed emf. When $(\omega t - \phi) = n\pi/2$, where $n = 1, 3, 5$, etc., i is a maximum and equation (245.7) obtains. In practical use the values of $\mathscr{E}$ and I in this equation are effective.

The term $(L\omega - 1/C\omega)$ is called the *reactance*, and the expression $\sqrt{R^2 + (L\omega - 1/C\omega)^2}$ is called the *impedance*. In Fig. 219 is shown the clock diagram for this circuit. $\mathscr{E}_r$ is the vector sum of $\mathscr{E}$, $\mathscr{E}_c$, and $\mathscr{E}_L$.

There are two methods of drawing these vector diagrams. In the one case, the reactive emf. vector is drawn, and then the effective emf.

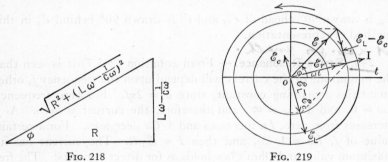

FIG. 218   FIG. 219

vector, in the direction of the current, is regarded as the resultant of the impressed emf. and the reactive emf. This method has been used here in all of the clock diagrams and sinusoidal curves. With the other method, the impressed emf. in opposition to the reactive emf. is used. This emf. is equal to but opposite in sense to the reactive emf. In this method of drawing the vector diagrams, the impressed emf. is regarded as the resultant of the effective emf., in the direction of the current, and the emf. in opposition to the reactive emf. This method is used here in all of the vector diagrams which are drawn apart from the clock diagrams, as it is the more usual representation. Either of these methods, if carried consistently throughout a drawing, is correct and will give the required results.

The vector diagrams of this Section are similar to those already worked out, except that account must be taken of the predominance of either $L\omega$ or $1/C\omega$, as the case may be. If $L\omega > 1/C\omega$ the vector diagram is as shown in Fig. 220. If $1/C\omega > L\omega$ the vector diagram is as shown in Fig. 221. In all cases the current I is in phase with the effective emf., $\mathscr{E}_r = RI$, and, therefore, the I vector is drawn along the $\mathscr{E}_r$ vector, which is usually drawn in a horizontal position.

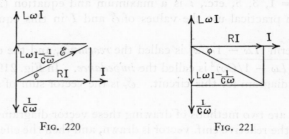

FIG. 220   FIG. 221

$\mathscr{E}_L$ is drawn 90° ahead of $\mathscr{E}_r$, and $\mathscr{E}_c$ is drawn 90° behind $\mathscr{E}_r$ in this method of representation.

not rep. for math.

246. Series Resonance. — From equation (245.7) it is seen that the magnitude of the current will depend upon the frequency f, other quantities remaining constant, since $\omega = 2\pi f$. For zero frequency $L\omega = 0$, and $1/C\omega = \infty$, and therefore, the current is zero. As f increases from zero, $L\omega$ increases and $1/C\omega$ decreases. For a certain value of f, $L\omega = 1/C\omega$, and then $I = \mathscr{E}/R$. The current has its maximum value and Ohm's law holds as for direct currents. The frequency for which $L\omega = 1/C\omega$ is called the *frequency of resonance*, since for this frequency, the frequency of the generator is equal to the natural frequency of the circuit which was considered in Section 234, assuming the resistance of the circuit to be negligible. Considering this as the natural frequency of the circuit, we see that at any other frequency the impressed emf., forces the circuit to oscillate at a frequency which is unnatural to it, i.e., the oscillations are forced. The circuit then behaves as though it has a resistance greater than its ohmic resistance. For values of f such that $1/C\omega < L\omega$ the current decreases, approaching zero asymptotically as f approaches ∞. The variation of current with frequency in a circuit containing resistance, inductance, and capacitance is shown for two different resistances by the curves of Fig. 222. If R is large the maximum current is small, and the peak is broad. If R is small the maximum current is large, and the peak is sharp. Two curves are shown, one for resistance R_1 and the other for resistance R_2, where $R_1 > R_2$, $\mathscr{E}$ being constant.

At the frequency of resonance, we have $L\omega = 1/C\omega$, and since $\omega = 2\pi f$,

$$f = \frac{1}{2\pi\sqrt{LC}}, \qquad (246.1)$$

and

$$T = 2\pi\sqrt{LC}, \qquad (246.2)$$

where L is expressed in henrys and C in farads.

For radio transmission, we have the well-known wave equation $f\lambda = 3(10)^8$ meters/sec., which, when combined with (246.1), gives

$$\lambda = 1,885(10)^6\sqrt{LC} \text{ meters.} \qquad (246.3)$$

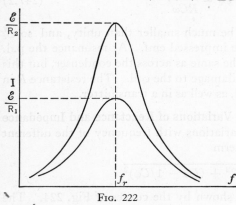

Fig. 222

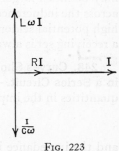

Fig. 223

247. Applications in Radio. — In the ordinary applications of the resonant condition in radio circuits the frequency is fixed and either the inductance or capacitance, or both, must be varied, in such a manner as to give the frequency of resonance. This cannot be done in power circuits with very great accuracy, although an effort is made to balance capacitance against inductance so as to make the power factor, $\cos\phi$, as near unity as possible. In radio receiving sets the inductance and capacitance are varied so as to make the natural frequency of the circuit equal to the frequency of the station being received. The receiving set is brought into resonance with, or tuned to, the frequency of the transmitting station. In the transmitting station itself the oscillating circuit, which is coupled with the tubes, is brought into resonance with the antenna circuit. In the case of series resonance the vector diagrams shown in Figs. 220 and 221 reduce to that shown in Fig. 223.

It frequently happens that the dielectric of the condenser breaks down, or is punctured, at the frequency of resonance. This is because the potential across the condenser may rise to a value many times the potential of the impressed emf. For any frequency the difference of potential across the condenser is given by

$$\mathscr{E}_c = \frac{I}{C\omega}. \tag{247.1}$$

But, at resonance, $I = \mathscr{E}/R$, and therefore,

$$\mathscr{E}_c = \frac{\mathscr{E}}{RC\omega}. \tag{247.2}$$

Now the value of $RC\omega$ may be much smaller than unity, and so $\mathscr{E}_c$ may be much larger than the impressed emf. At resonance the p.d. across the inductance coil is the same as across the condenser, but this high potential seldom causes damage to the coil. The resistance R in a receiving set is always small, as well as in a transmitter.

248. Curves Showing the Variations of Reactance and Impedance in a Series Circuit. — The variations with frequency of the different quantities in the impedance term

$$Z = \sqrt{R^2 + (L\omega - 1/C\omega)^2},$$

and the impedance itself are shown by the curves of Fig. 224. The term $1/C\omega$ is drawn as a negative quantity and the term $L\omega$ as a positive quantity, since these terms have opposite effects in the circuit. At zero frequency $L\omega = 0$, and $1/C\omega = -\infty$. As the frequency increases from zero, $L\omega$ increases linearly from zero, and $1/C\omega$ decreases in absolute value from ∞, as shown in Fig. 224. The effective reactance X is obtained by adding the ordinates of the two reactance terms. The X curve crosses the frequency axis at the

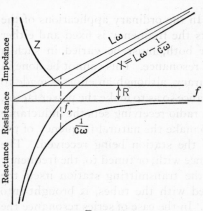

FIG. 224

frequency of resonance f_r. For frequencies lower than the frequency of resonance the capacitive reactance predominates and the current leads the impressed emf. For frequencies greater than the frequency of resonance the inductive reactance predominates and the current lags the impressed emf. The impedance Z is positive for all frequencies, and hence the impedance curve is wholly above the frequency axis. For zero frequency Z is infinite. As the frequency increases from zero the impedance decreases to a minimum at the frequency of resonance, where it is equal to the ohmic resistance R in the circuit. It then increases for higher frequencies, becoming very large for very high frequencies.[1]

249. Parallel Resonance. — When the impressed emf. is applied to a circuit containing resistance, inductance, and capacitance, as shown in Fig. 225, the capacitance and inductance are in parallel. The electric behavior of this circuit is markedly different from that of the series circuit considered in Sections 247 and 248, Fig. 217. It will be assumed in this discussion that the condenser is free from absorption, and therefore, the current leads the impressed emf. by 90°. Because of resistance in

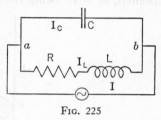

FIG. 225

the inductive branch the current in that branch lags by an angle less than 90°.

In the investigation for series connection it was found that the impressed emf. is the vector sum of the p.d.'s across the capacitance, the inductance, and the resistance, Figs. 220 and 221. In the case of parallel connection, on the other hand, the current I in the main line is the vector sum of the currents I_c and I_L in the branch lines. The currents in the branch lines are obtained from the condition that the p.d. $\mathscr{E}$ from a to b is the same for either branch, and the currents are, therefore, equal to this p.d. divided by the impedance in the respective branches. We have, therefore,

$$I_c = \mathscr{E}C\omega, \quad \text{and} \quad I_L = \frac{\mathscr{E}}{\sqrt{R^2 + L^2\omega^2}}. \tag{249.1}$$

The vector diagram for currents is shown in Fig. 226. The vector $\mathscr{E}$ of the impressed emf. is drawn horizontally. The vector for I_c

[1] See Principles of Radio Communication by J. H. Morecroft.

is 90° in advance of this vector, and the vector for I_L is behind $\mathscr{E}$ by the angle

$$\phi_L = \text{arc tan } \frac{L\omega}{R}.$$

The current I in the main line is the vector sum of I_c and I_L, and is, therefore,

$$I^2 = I_c{}^2 + I_L{}^2 - 2I_cI_L \cos \theta, \qquad (249.2)$$

where

$$\theta = \text{arc cos } \frac{L\omega I}{\mathscr{E}} = \text{arc cos } \frac{L\omega}{\sqrt{R^2 + L^2\omega^2}}. \qquad (249.3)$$

The triangle abc is the vector triangle for the p.d.'s in the inductive branch, $ab = \mathscr{E}$ being the p.d. from a to b, Fig. 226.

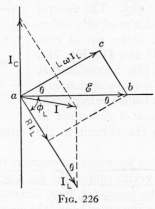

Fig. 226.

Substituting from equations (249.1) and (249.3) in equation (249.2), we have

$$I^2 = \mathscr{E}^2 \left\{ C^2\omega^2 + \frac{1}{R^2 + L^2\omega^2} - \frac{2CL\omega^2}{R^2 + L^2\omega^2} \right\}. \qquad (249.4)$$

Adding and subtracting $\dfrac{L^2\omega^2}{(R^2 + L^2\omega^2)^2}$, and rearranging terms, equation (249.4) becomes

$$I = \mathscr{E} \sqrt{\left(C\omega - \frac{L\omega}{R^2 + L^2\omega^2} \right)^2 + \frac{R^2}{(R^2 + L^2\omega^2)^2}}. \qquad (249.5)$$

This equation gives the numerical value of the current in the main line for all variations of R, L and C. The condition that I shall be in phase with the impressed emf. is

$$I^2 = I_L^2 - I_c^2, \qquad (249.6)$$

as can be seen from the vector diagram, Fig. 226. Substituting equations (249.1) and (249.4) in equation (249.6), there results

$$\omega = \frac{\sqrt{4LC - R^2C^2}}{LC}. \qquad (249.7)$$

The value of ω corresponding to the natural frequency of the parallel circuit when acting as a series circuit, is

$$\omega = \frac{\sqrt{4LC - R^2C^2}}{2LC}, \quad \text{equation (234.19)}.$$

Thus the frequency of resonance for parallel connection is not exactly that of the natural frequency of the parallel circuit, when acting as a series circuit, but approximates it very closely. However, when $R = 0$, equations (234.19) and (249.7) are identical, and give

$$f = \frac{1}{2\pi\sqrt{LC}}.$$

From equation (249.5) we see that I_r for the condition of resonance is given by

$$I_r = \frac{\mathscr{E}R}{R^2 + L^2\omega^2}. \qquad (249.8)$$

If R is small as compared with $L\omega$ we may write for the approximate value of I_r,

$$I_r = \left(\frac{\mathscr{E}}{L^2\omega^2}\right)R = KR. \qquad (249.9)$$

Thus, for small values of R, the current is very nearly proportional to R. Hence we have the anomalous condition that the line current *increases* as the resistance *increases*. When $R = 0$, $I_r = 0$. Thus, the only cause for current to flow in the main line is that the parallel circuit possesses resistance, and hence dissipates energy. The magnitude of I will be just sufficient to compensate for the natural decrement of the parallel branches. The variation of I in the vicinity of the frequency of resonance is shown in Fig. 227.

It was shown in the case of series resonance that the potential drop across the capacitance and also across the inductance was greater than the impressed emf. However, in the case of parallel resonance, the current in each branch is greater than the current in the main line. In series connection the impedance is a minimum at the frequency of resonance, whereas in parallel connection the impedance is a maximum at the frequency of resonance. It is for this reason that a parallel circuit is sometimes inserted in a line and tuned to a particular frequency which it is desired to suppress. When so used it is called a *frequency choke* or *wave trap*. In radio circuits wave traps are frequently used to suppress interfering radio waves or disturbing harmonics.[1]

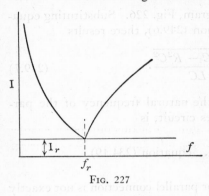

FIG. 227

250. The Oscillograph.

250. **The Oscillograph.** — The moving system of an ordinary galvanometer, of the D'Arsonval type say, is too heavy to follow rapidly fluctuating currents. As was stated in Section 241, the moving system either cannot respond or, if not too heavy, the deflection is an average of some sort. If the moving system is so constructed as to have an extremely low moment of inertia and high free frequency of oscillation it may follow varying currents with considerable fidelity, if the variations are not too rapid. A number of galvanometers have been designed to meet these requirements. When a photographic record is required, a spot of light is reflected from a tiny mirror attached to the moving system and allowed to fall on a moving photographic film, the motion of the film being normal to the direction of fluctuations of the spot of light. If to be observed visually, the spot of light is permitted to fall on a revolving, multisided mirror from which it is reflected to a screen. Such an instrument when used in the manner described is called an *oscillograph*.

One of the very sensitive galvanometers, having a moving system

---

[1] See Circular 74, U. S. Bureau of Standards, p. 39; Advanced Laboratory Practice in Electricity and Magnetism by E. M. Terry, 3rd ed.; Radio Engineering Principles by Lauer and Brown, p. 32; 2nd ed.; Radio Communication by J. H. Morecroft, pp. 77–84.

of low moment of inertia and short free period, is the Einthoven string galvanometer. The moving system in this instrument is a single fine wire or a silvered quartz fiber, stretched between the pole pieces of a powerful electromagnet. The tension of the fiber is controlled by an adjustable spring, which may be used to vary the free period of oscillation. The pole pieces of the electromagnet are wedge shaped and the fiber is placed between them where the field is strongest. When a current flows through the fiber it is pushed sideways by the magnetic field. Holes are drilled through the pole pieces parallel to the field, through which the position of the fiber is viewed by means of a telescope and scale, or suitable optical system. A permanent record may be made on a moving photographic film. For this purpose a narrow slit is placed immediately in front of the film and behind a cylindrical lens so that the image of the fiber appears on the film as a shadow which prevents the exposure of that part of the film on which it falls.[1]

251. The Cathode-Ray Oscillograph. — The cathode-ray tube, "electron gun," is a specially designed thermionic tube which is used for the study of electric phenomena. The action of the tube depends upon the projection of an electron beam, from a heated filament, on a fluorescent screen at the end of a long tube. Certain substances when bombarded by electrons fluoresce. The color of the fluorescent light depends upon the fluorescent material used. The substance used and the method of preparation determine the duration of the fluorescent light. For a cathode-ray oscillograph the use of a fluorescent substance is required that ceases fluorescing almost as soon as the electron bombardment ceases. Electrons shot from the cathode, and possessing sufficient energy, will penetrate the crystal lattice of the fluorescent substance and disrupt the electron structure of atoms composing the crystal lattice. With a return to the normal electronic configuration energy is liberated in the form of radiation.

A cathode-ray tube is shown in Fig. 228a. The electron beam is focused by an electric or magnetic field before passing through the cylindrical anode. It then passes between two pairs of condenser plates (deflecting plates) set at right angles to each other. The tube is mounted so that one pair of plates is horizontal, electric intensity E_y between them vertical. The other pair of plates is vertical, electric intensity E_z between them horizontal. Let us say that the electron beam is along the x axis, passing centrally between the two pairs of

[1] See Electrical Instruments by Frank A. Laws.

plates. Suppose a difference of potential is impressed upon the horizontal plates. The electron beam will then be deflected either up or down depending upon the polarity. It can be shown that the magnitude y of the deflection on the fluorescent screen at the end of the tube is given by

$$y = \frac{Ll}{2\mathscr{E}} E_y, \text{ approximately,}$$

where L is the distance from the center of the plates to the fluorescent screen, l the horizontal breadth of the plates, E_y the electric

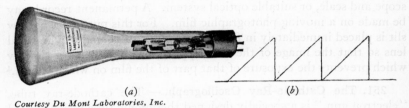

(a)   *(b)*

Courtesy Du Mont Laboratories, Inc.

FIG. 228

intensity between them, and $\mathscr{E}$ the anode-cathode difference of potential which gives velocity to the electrons, according to the equation $\frac{1}{2}mv^2 = e\mathscr{E}$. Thus the deflection on the screen is directly proportional to the intensity E_y, and inversely proportional to the anode-cathode difference of potential.

The cathode-ray tube may be used in a variety of ways, and hence has many applications. $\mathscr{E}$, E_y, and E_z may all be varied to suit conditions. There are two general methods of using the tube: (1) that in which sinusoidal potential differences are impressed simultaneously upon both sets of deflecting plates, and (2) that in which a saw-tooth potential difference or linear time axis is impressed on one pair of plates and the potential difference to be analyzed is impressed on the other pair of plates.

The first method is applicable to the study of sinusoidal potentials which are in quadrature. Let us say that the sinusoidal potentials are of the same frequency but differ in phase. Then the deflections are given by

$$y = Y \cos \omega t,$$

$$z = Z \cos (\omega t - \phi),$$

where Y and Z are the amplitudes of the potential waves. If there is no phase difference ϕ between the potential waves, which would be the case if both circuits were noninductive,

$$y = \frac{Y}{Z} z.$$

The spot of light would then move on the straight line making an angle arc tan $\frac{Y}{Z}$ with the z axis. If $\phi = \pi$, or the leads to one set of terminals are interchanged, there will be a straight line of the same amplitude but with a negative slope. If $\phi = \pi/2$, which would be the case if one pair of terminals gives the potentials across a noninductive resistance and the other the potentials across a perfect condenser, we will have

$$y = Y \cos \omega t,$$

$$z = Z \sin \omega t.$$

Then the equation of the path of the spot of light is

$$\frac{y^2}{Y^2} + \frac{z^2}{Z^2} = 1,$$

which is the equation of an ellipse. In general we have

$$y = Y \cos \omega_1 t,$$

$$z = Z \cos (\omega_2 t - \phi).$$

If ω_1 and ω_2 are incommensurate the spot of light will sweep out the whole rectangle of sides Y and Z if given sufficient time. If $n_1\omega_1 = n_2\omega_2$, where n_1 and n_2 are small integers, the spot of light will trace out a closed curve giving what is known as a Lissajous figure.

The second method of using the cathode-ray oscillograph is to impress the harmonic potential to be analyzed on the pair of horizontal plates (y deflections). Since a wave motion is the resultant of a harmonic motion and a uniform linear motion, there must be a uniform linear motion in the z direction. For this purpose a circuit called a "sweep circuit" is required, which gives a saw-tooth voltage output as shown in Fig. 228b. The spot of light is moved across the screen at a constant rate in the z direction in time T, say, and then returns to the starting point almost instantly, the time being so short that the illumination is not noticeable. If this occurs once per cycle of the harmonic potential in the y direction, one complete wave will be seen on the screen. If the period of the harmonic potential in the

y direction is T/n, n waves will be seen on the screen. If there is perfect synchronism between the two circuits the waves will appear to be stationary, owing to persistence of vision and a small retentivity of the fluorescent material. The saw-tooth voltage output curve is never as regular as indicated in Fig. 228b. This is the ideal. The sloping part of the wave is slightly convex, and the return is not as abrupt as indicated.

The linear axis is obtained by charging a condenser at a constant rate, and, when a certain limiting potential is reached, the condenser is suddenly discharged owing to the breakdown of a gas-filled discharge tube. The potential across the condenser is impressed on the sweep-circuit deflecting plates. Some special arrangement must be provided for charging the condenser at a constant rate. One such device is shown in Fig. 229. In this device the condenser C is charged through the resistance R by the potential drop across the resistance R_1. This potential is applied to the deflecting plates through the condenser C'_1, the terminals a and b being connected to the sweep circuit plates. The discharge is brought about by the gas-filled tube t (thyratron), which breaks down suddenly when a certain critical potential $\mathscr{E}_1$ is reached, thus furnishing a low-resistance path for the discharge.

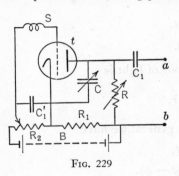

Fig. 229

The potential $\mathscr{E}_1$ is controlled by the grid bias R_2, and this determines the amplitude of the saw-tooth wave. The period of the saw-tooth wave is proportional to the product RC. Thus the amplitude and period may be controlled. The coupling coil S is for the purpose of synchonizing the sweep-circuit frequency and the potential frequency which is being analyzed. This is necessary in order that the wave form on the fluorescent screen may remain stationary. The synchronization is accomplished by inductive coupling between the two circuits so that the grid of the thyratron receives small positive impulses of frequency equal to that of the potential being analyzed. Thus, the time of the breakdown is controlled, within certain limits, by the period of the circuit being examined.

The cathode-ray oscillograph is not restricted to the study of a sinusoidal wave form. Any wave form may be analyzed. If a permanent record is required the wave form is recorded on a photographic film. Thus transient and rapidly alternating potentials may be photographed and studied or observed visually. The inertia of the electron beam is negligibly small, and therefore it responds accurately to high-frequency variations of potential. It can follow oscillations up to a frequency of the order of a megacycle.[1]

PROBLEMS

1. A noninductive resistance of 80 ohms is connected to a line in which there is a 60-cycle, harmonic emf. of 300 volts maximum. (a) What is the effective emf.? What is the average emf.? (b) What is the effective current? The maximum current? (c) What is the active power? The wattless power? (d) Plot the sinusoidal emf. curve for one cycle.

2. Let the coil of Problem 1 be inductive having a coefficient of self inductance of 0.2 henry, data otherwise the same. (a) Calculate the effective current. The maximum current. (b) What is the phase angle? (c) What is the active power? The wattless power? (d) Plot the sinusoidal curves for the current and emf. for one cycle in their relative positions. Repeat all of the calculations for a 25-cycle, harmonic emf.

3. A condenser having a capacitance of 50 mfs. is connected in series with the resistance of Problem 1, data otherwise the same. (a) What is the effective current? (b) What is the phase angle? Lag or lead? (c) What is the active power? The wattless power? (d) Plot the sinusoidal curves for the emf. and current in their relative positions.

4. The coil of Problem 2 is placed in series with the condenser of Problem 3, data otherwise the same. (a) What is the effective current? (b) What is the phase angle? Lag or lead? (c) What is the active power?

5. What capacitance placed in series with the inductance coil of Problem 2 will produce resonance?

6. Solve Problems 4 and 5 using a frequency of 25-cycles per sec.

7. An inductance coil having an inductance of 0.1 henry and a resistance of 20 ohms is placed in parallel with a perfect condenser having a capacitance of 40 mfs. This parallel group is then connected across a 110-volt, 60-cycle transmission line. (a) What is the current in each branch of the parallel circuit? (b) What current is drawn from the main line? (c) What is the phase angle in each branch? What is the phase angle for the resultant current? Lag or lead? (d) Draw the vector diagram to scale.

8. What frequency in Problem 7 will produce resonance? What will the current then be?

9. In Problem 7 keep f and L constant and allow C to vary. Calculate the value of C which will produce resonance. What will the current then be?

[1] See Principles of Electricity and Electromagnetism by G. P. Harnwell and the Cathode-Ray Tube at Work by John F. Rider.

CHAPTER XIX

VECTOR TREATMENT OF ALTERNATING CURRENTS

252. In calculations involving networks of conductors where direct currents are used Ohm's law and Kirchhoff's two laws are entirely adequate; the quantities involved are scalar quantities and the rules of algebra suffice. Ohmic resistance is the only type of resistance met with, and phase relations do not exist. The conditions are quite different, however, when dealing with alternating currents. Reactances as well as ohmic resistance are present, and there are phase displacements. The currents and emfs. are harmonic, and hence obey the laws of vectors.

In alternating currents the electric principles are essentially the same as in direct currents, except that the quantities involved must be treated as vector quantities instead of scalar quantities. For instance, when resistances are connected in series the current is constant and the scalar sum of the potential drops across the separate resistances is equal to the total potential drop. Or, in any closed circuit, the scalar sum of the potential drops is equal to zero. In the case of alternating currents the same general law holds, except that in addition to ohmic resistance there are usually present inductive and capacitive reactances, and hence the total potential drop is the vector sum of the separate potential drops. Or, in any closed circuit, the vector sum of the separate potential drops is equal to zero.

In a parallel circuit the potential drop is constant for the several branches for alternating currents as well as for direct currents. In the case of direct currents, the current in the main line is the scalar sum of the currents in the branch lines. Or the scalar sum of the currents at a junction is equal to zero. In alternating currents the current in the main line is equal to the vector sum of the currents in the branch lines. Or the vector sum of the currents at a junction is equal to zero.

The preceding Chapter laid the foundations for the vector treatment of alternating currents. In the present Chapter the principles thus far developed will be used in the solutions of problems involving networks of conductors in which there are alternating currents. A few typical cases will serve to elucidate the fundamental principles involved.

253. Three-Voltmeter Method of Measuring Power. —

As a first simple case of the use of vector diagrams let us consider a method of measuring the power expended in any appliance containing inductance L and resistance R_2. This was a practical method of measuring power before the advent of the indicating wattmeter. Let the circuit be as shown schematically in Fig. 230. There is

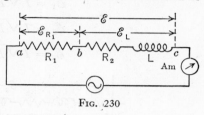

FIG. 230

connected in series with the appliance considered a noninductive resistance R_1. The three potential drops $\mathscr{E}$, $\mathscr{E}_r$, and $\mathscr{E}_L$, as shown,

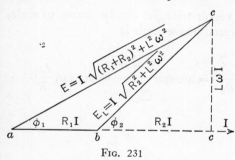

FIG. 231

and the current I are measured. The three emf. vectors form the closed triangle abc, Fig. 231. The potential drops across the resistances are in phase with the current I, and so form the base line abe. The vector diagram gives the true phase relations, and therefore, ϕ_2 is easily obtained from the construction by obvious methods. The power expended in the appliance is

$$P = \mathscr{E}_L I \cos \phi_2. \qquad (253.1)$$

If R_1 is known it is not necessary to measure I, since $I = \mathscr{E}_{R_1}/R_1$. R_2 may be obtained from the construction, and then L is easily calculated. ϕ_1 is easily obtained, and hence, the overall power factor, $\cos \phi_1$.

254. Inductances in Series. —

Let there be connected in series three inductances L_1, L_2, and L_3, having resistances R_1, R_2, and R_3, as indicated in Fig. 232. Let the frequency be f cycles/sec. The overall emf. $\mathscr{E}$ is the vector sum of the potential drops over the separate units, $\mathscr{E}_1$, $\mathscr{E}_2$, and $\mathscr{E}_3$, as shown in Fig. 233. The phase angles are

$$\phi_1 = \text{arc tan } \frac{L_1\omega}{R_1}, \quad \phi_2 = \text{arc tan } \frac{L_2\omega}{R_2}, \quad \phi_3 = \text{arc tan } \frac{L_3\omega}{R_3}.$$

The potential drops are

$$\mathscr{E}_1 = I\sqrt{R_1{}^2 + L_1{}^2\omega^2},$$

$$\mathscr{E}_2 = I\sqrt{R_2{}^2 + L_2{}^2\omega^2},$$

$$\mathscr{E}_3 = I\sqrt{R_3{}^2 + L_3{}^2\omega^2}.$$

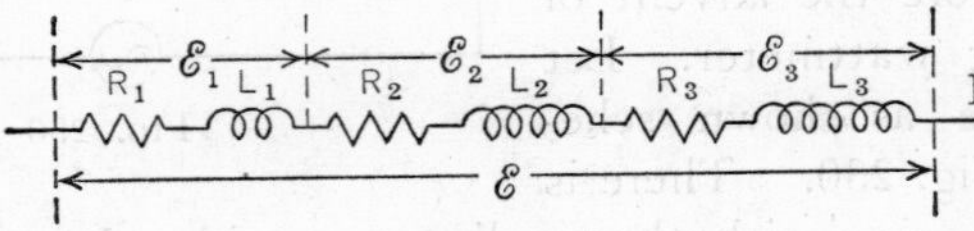

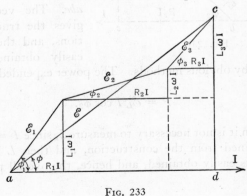

FIG. 232

If the current I is known the vector triangles can be drawn to scale, as shown in Fig. 233. The overall phase angle is

$$\phi = \text{arc tan } \frac{(L_1 + L_2 + L_3)\omega}{R_1 + R_2 + R_3} = \text{arc tan } \frac{\omega \sum\limits_1^n L}{\sum\limits_1^n R} = \text{arc tan } \frac{L\omega}{R}.$$

FIG. 233

Thus, when inductances are connected in series the total effective inductance is the scalar sum of the inductances, i.e., $L = L_1 + L_2$

$+ L_3 + \cdots L_n$. The total resistance $R = R_1 + R_2 + R_3 + \cdots R_n$. The active power is

$$P = \mathscr{E}I \cos \phi = \mathscr{E}_1 I \cos \phi_1 + \mathscr{E}_2 I \cos \phi_2 + \mathscr{E}_3 I \cos \phi_3.$$

The power factors and wattless components of the power are obtained in the usual manner. The total current is

$$I = \frac{\mathscr{E}}{\sqrt{R^2 + L^2 \omega^2}}.$$

Any number of inductances in series may be handled in the same manner, and with sufficient data the various unknown quantities may be obtained.

254. Inductances in Parallel. — Let us consider a divided circuit of two branches, as indicated in Fig. 234. The potential drop from a to b is the same by either branch, but the current in the main line is the vector sum of the currents in the branches. Let the impressed emf. between a and b be $\mathscr{E}$ volts and the frequency f cycles/sec. It is required to find the currents.

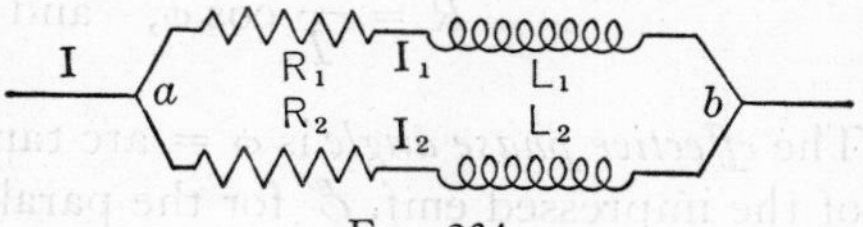

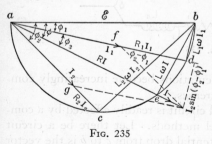

FIG. 234

Since the potential drop is the same by either branch, it may be made common to the vector triangles for the two branches. It is represented by the line ab, Fig. 235. The triangle adb is the potential triangle for branch 1, and acb is the potential triangle for branch 2. These triangles are inscribed in a semicircle, the diameter of which is the potential drop ab, since each triangle is a right-angle triangle.

FIG. 235

Let af be the current vector in branch 1, which is in phase with the active component of the impressed emf. ad. Let ag be the current vector in branch 2, which is in phase with the active component of the emf. ac. The current I in the main line is the vector sum of the currents in the branch lines, or in absolute value

$$I^2 = I_1{}^2 + I_2{}^2 + 2I_1 I_2 \cos (\phi_2 - \phi_1), \qquad (254.1)$$

where $\phi_1 = \text{arc tan } L_1\omega/R_1$, and $\phi_2 = \text{arc tan } L_2\omega/R_2$. Also, $R_1I_1 = \mathscr{E} \cos \phi_1$, and $R_2I_2 = \mathscr{E} \cos \phi_2$. Since the emf. triangles all lie in the same semicircle, we have

$$\mathscr{E} = I_1\sqrt{R_1{}^2 + L_1{}^2\omega^2} = I_2\sqrt{R_2{}^2 + L_2{}^2\omega^2} = I\sqrt{R^2 + L^2\omega^2}. \quad (254.2)$$

R is the *equivalent resistance* of the parallel branches, and L is the *equivalent inductance*, both of which are readily obtained from the vector diagram. This may be done by drawing vectors to scale and measuring the lines ae and eb, from which R and L may be obtained, or it may be accomplished mathematically as follows:

$$\tan \phi_3 = \frac{I_2 \sin (\phi_2 - \phi_1)}{I_1 + I_2 \cos (\phi_2 - \phi_1)}, \quad \text{and} \quad \phi = \phi_1 + \phi_3. \quad (254.3)$$

Then

$$R = \frac{\mathscr{E}}{I} \cos \phi, \quad \text{and} \quad L = \frac{\mathscr{E}}{I\omega} \sin \phi. \quad (254.4)$$

The *effective phase angle* is $\phi = \text{arc tan } L\omega/R$. The active component of the impressed emf. $\mathscr{E}$ for the parallel circuit is $ae = RI = \mathscr{E} \cos \phi$, and the total active power is $\mathscr{E}I \cos \phi$. The wattless component of the impressed emf. $\mathscr{E}$ is $eb = L\omega I = \mathscr{E} \sin \phi$, and the wattless power is $L\omega I^2 = \mathscr{E}I \sin \phi$. This vector construction enables one to effect a complete solution of a parallel circuit of two or more branches. How-

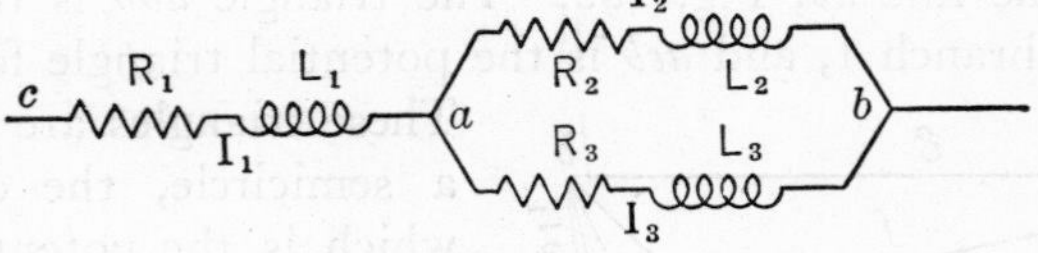

Fig. 236

ever, the vector diagrams and calculations become increasingly complex as the number of branches increases.

The solution of a series-parallel circuit is readily effected by a combination of the series and parallel methods. Let there be a circuit as indicated in Fig. 236. The potential drop from c to b is the vector sum of the potential drops ca and ab. The current I_1 is the vector sum of the currents I_2 and I_3. The parallel branch is first handled separately in order to obtain the equivalent inductance and equivalent resistance. There is then a simple series circuit to solve. In solving the parallel circuit, any potential drop ab may be assumed, since the potential drop does not affect the values of the equivalent inductance and resistance. Thus, any circuit consisting of series and parallel groupings may be reduced to a series circuit, and then solved by the series method as shown.

255. Resistances and Capacitances in Series. — Let there be a circuit as shown in part in Fig. 237. The resistances may be for the

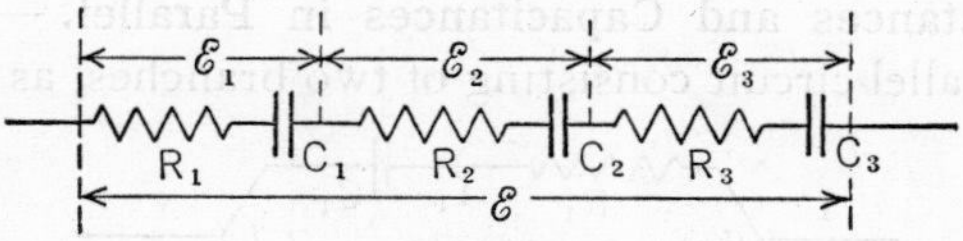

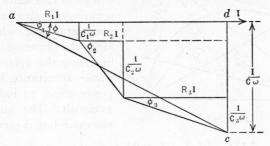

FIG. 237

most part outside the condensers, but include, also, the fictitious resistances due to imperfect dielectrics. Since this is a series circuit, the current is constant and the vector representing it is drawn in the horizontal line in phase with the potential drop over the ohmic resistance, Fig. 238. The potential drop over the capacitive reactances are

FIG. 238

drawn as though negative, since capacitance has the opposite effect in a circuit to inductance. Otherwise the vector construction is the same as for inductances in series. The phase angles are

$$\phi_1 = \text{arc tan} \frac{1}{R_1 C_1 \omega}, \quad \phi_2 = \text{arc tan} \frac{1}{R_2 C_2 \omega}, \quad \phi_3 = \text{arc tan} \frac{1}{R_3 C_3 \omega}.$$

The equivalent resistance is $R = R_1 + R_2 + R_3$, and the equivalent capacitance is obtained from the relation

$$\frac{1}{C\omega} = \frac{1}{C_1\omega} + \frac{1}{C_2\omega} + \frac{1}{C_3\omega},$$

and therefore

$$C = \frac{1}{\sum_{1}^{n} \dfrac{1}{C}}. \tag{255.1}$$

The final phase angle is $\phi = \arctan 1/RC\omega$, and the active power is $\mathscr{E}I \cos \phi$.

256. Resistances and Capacitances in Parallel. — Let us next consider a parallel circuit consisting of two branches, as shown in Fig.

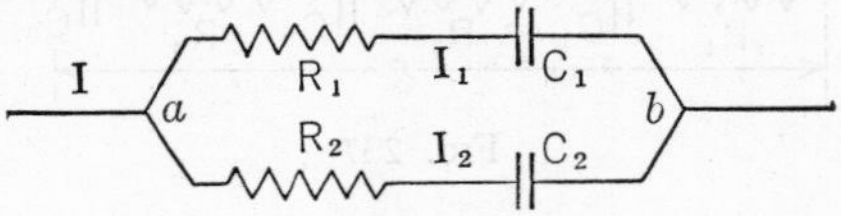

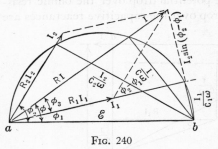

FIG. 239

239. The potential drop from a to b is the same by either branch. Therefore, $ab = \mathscr{E}$ is drawn, upon which a semicircle is erected, Fig. 240. The emf. vector triangles will lie in this semicircle. The semicircle is drawn above the horizontal line which represents the impressed emf., thus inverting the vector triangles, since capacitance has the opposite effect to inductance in a circuit. The current I in the main line is given by

FIG. 240

$$I^2 = I_1{}^2 + I_2{}^2 + 2I_1I_2 \cos(\phi_2 - \phi_1). \tag{256.1}$$

ϕ_1 and ϕ_2 are obtained in the usual manner. From the diagram we obtain ϕ_3 and hence ϕ by the same mathematical expressions as in (254.3). Further

$$\mathscr{E} = I_1\sqrt{R_1{}^2 + \frac{1}{C_1{}^2\omega^2}} = I_2\sqrt{R_2{}^2 + \frac{1}{C_2{}^2\omega^2}} = I\sqrt{R^2 + \frac{1}{C^2\omega^2}}. \tag{256.2}$$

And

$$R = \frac{\mathscr{E}}{I} \cos \phi, \quad C = \frac{I}{\mathscr{E} \omega \sin \phi}. \tag{256.3}$$

The unknown quantities may be obtained from the trigonometric relations, or by a graphical method.

A series-parallel circuit is handled as with a similar circuit involving inductances and resistances, which was outlined in Section 254.

257. Inductances, Capacitances, and Resistances in Series. — Let there be a circuit as indicated in part in Fig. 241. The current I is constant but the potential drops add vectorially. The vector diagram for the potential drops is shown in Fig. 242. Let us assume that $L\omega I > I/C\omega$. The current vector is drawn horizontally, and in phase

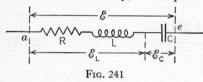

FIG. 241   FIG. 242

with the active potential drop RI. The potential drop across the resistance and inductance is

$$ac = \mathscr{E}_L = I\sqrt{R^2 + L^2\omega^2}, \qquad (257.1)$$

where R is the combined resistance in series with the inductance and within it. The potential drop across the capacitance is

$$bd = \mathscr{E}_c = \frac{I}{C\omega}, \qquad (257.2)$$

and is in quadrature with the current vector, if we assume no absorption in the condenser. The impressed emf. is

$$ae = \mathscr{E} = I\sqrt{R^2 + \left(L\omega - \frac{1}{C\omega}\right)^2}. \qquad (257.3)$$

The active power is $\mathscr{E}I \cos \phi$, and the wattless power is $\mathscr{E}I \sin \phi$, where

$$\phi = \text{arc tan} \frac{L\omega - 1/C\omega}{R}. \qquad (257.4)$$

If resonance obtains, $L\omega = 1/C\omega$, and the impressed emf. is represented by the line ab and is in phase with the current. When $L\omega > 1/C\omega$, ϕ is a lag angle, and when $L\omega < 1/C\omega$, ϕ is an advance angle.

This construction may be extended to any number of inductances, capacitances, and resistances when connected in series. The vector diagrams may be constructed for the several parts of the circuit, and then the impressed emf. is the vector sum of the potential drops. If only the resultant vector diagram is required it may be constructed singly from the fact, as we have seen, that, when connected in series, resistances, inductances, and the reciprocals of the capacitances add algebraically. Then the base line of the potential triangle is $I\sum_{1}^{n} R$, and normal to this, we have $I(\omega \sum_{1}^{n} L - \sum_{1}^{n} 1/C\omega)$. Thus the resultant vector diagram is a single triangle. The effective phase angle is

$$\phi = \arctan \frac{\omega \sum_{1}^{n} L - \sum_{1}^{n} 1/C\omega}{\sum_{1}^{n} R}, \tag{257.5}$$

and the current is

$$I = \frac{\mathscr{E}}{\sqrt{\left(\sum_{1}^{n} R\right)^2 + \left(\sum_{1}^{n} L - \sum_{1}^{n} 1/C\omega\right)^2}}. \tag{257.6}$$

258. Parallel Circuit Containing Inductance, Resistance, and Capacitance in each Branch. — Let there be a parallel circuit as indicated in Fig. 243. Each branch is a series circuit and can be solved as such by methods already indicated. In branch 1 let us assume that $1/C_1\omega > L_1\omega$. Then the resultant triangle is

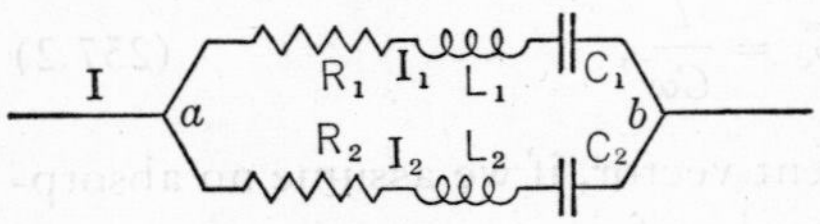

Fig. 243

acb, Fig. 244. In branch 2 let us assume that $L_2\omega > 1/C_2\omega$. The resultant vector triangle is adb. The phase angles in the two branches are obtained in the usual manner. The impressed emf. is

$$ab = \mathscr{E} = I_1 \sqrt{R_1{}^2 + \left(L_1\omega - \frac{1}{C_1\omega}\right)^2} = I_2 \sqrt{R_2{}^2 + \left(L_2\omega - \frac{1}{C_2\omega}\right)^2}$$

$$= I \sqrt{R^2 + L^2\omega^2}. \tag{258.1}$$

Let $af = I_1$ be the current vector in branch 1, and $ag = I_2$ be the current vector in branch 2. We then have for the current in the main line

$$I^2 = I_1{}^2 + I_2{}^2 + 2I_1I_2 \cos(\phi_1 + \phi_2). \tag{258.2}$$

The equivalent reactance is $hb/I = L\omega = (\mathscr{E}/I)\sin\phi$, if inductance predominates. The equivalent resistance is $R = (\mathscr{E}/I)\cos\phi$. The effective phase angle is obtained from the relations

$$\tan\phi_3 = \frac{I_1\sin(\phi_1+\phi_2)}{I_2 + I_1\cos(\phi_1+\phi_2)}, \quad \text{and} \quad \phi = \phi_2 = \phi_3. \quad (258.3)$$

If capacitance predominates, $1/C\omega = (\mathscr{E}/I)\sin\phi$, from which C may

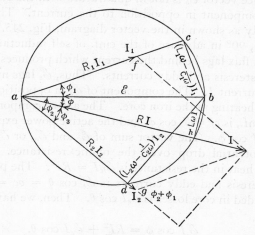

Fig. 244

be calculated. When $L_1\omega - 1/C_1\omega = L_2\omega - 1/C_2\omega = 0, \phi_2 = \phi_1 = 0$, and $I = I_1 + I_2$, as in direct currents. Then $1/R = 1/R_1 + 1/R_2$.

See "Alternating Currents," by Bedell and Crehore for more complete discussion.

259. Effect of Ferromagnetic Material in a Circuit. — In the foregoing discussion it has been assumed that all of the inductances were air-core coils, and that no ferromagnetic material was anywhere present which would in any manner influence the flux magnitude or its distribution. The results we have thus far obtained are valid only in the absence of ferromagnetic substance. When ferromagnetic substance is present the vector diagram must be modified so as to take account of it.

We have seen that the permeability μ is a variable depending upon the current strength and quality of the magnetic substance. Therefore, the inductance L is not constant but varies in some manner with the current strength, or magnetizing field. The consequence of this is to cause the current curve to be nonsinusoidal, even though the impressed emf. is sinusoidal.

Heat, due to hysteresis and eddy currents, is developed *outside* the circuit, but this energy is drawn *from* the circuit. As we have seen, energy can be expended only when there is opposition. Therefore, the current must be flowing against an induced emf., i.e., the emf. of self inductance vector $\mathscr{E}_s$ is not in quadrature with the current vector, but has a component in opposition to the current. The conditions are essentially as shown in the vector diagram, Fig. 245. The flux Φ is, as always, 90° in advance of the emf. of self inductance $\mathscr{E}_s$. But the resultant flux lags behind the current which produces it due to the effects of hysteresis and eddy currents. Thus, $\mathscr{E}_s$ lags more than 90° behind the current I. The component of $\mathscr{E}_s$ in opposition to I (oc) is the result of heating in the iron core. The active component of $\mathscr{E}$, the impressed emf., is $of = \mathscr{E} \cos \phi$, and the active power expended in the circuit is $\mathscr{E} I \cos \phi$. The vector sum of $\mathscr{E}$ and $\mathscr{E}_s$, or $\mathscr{E}_R = og$, represents the potential drop over the ohmic resistance. The power expended as heat in the resistance is $\mathscr{E}_R I = RI^2$. The potential drop due to hysteresis and eddy currents is $\mathscr{E}_s \cos \theta = oc = gf$, and the power expended in core losses is $\mathscr{E}_s I \cos \theta$. Then, we have

$$\mathscr{E} I \cos \phi = RI^2 + \mathscr{E}_s I \cos \theta. \tag{259.1}$$

Since the flux lags behind the current which produces it, the current I may be thought of, conveniently, as the resultant of two currents: I_m in phase with the flux, and I_h in phase with the impressed emf. $\mathscr{E}$. I_m is the magnetizing current, or the current which produces the usual magnetic flux, but, as it is in quadrature with $\mathscr{E}_s$, it does not represent *external power*. I_h is the *core loss* current which represents external power, i.e., the power expended *outside* the circuit, but drawn from it. This power is $\mathscr{E} I_h$ watts.

In order to better understand the construction of Fig. 245 we may take limiting cases. First, let us consider the case of a coil which has neither magnetic substance nor resistance. Such a case is approximately that of a coil of wire with very low resistance. In this limiting case the current lags 90° behind the impressed emf. $\mathscr{E}$, and the emf. $\mathscr{E}_s$ is 90° behind the current, and hence 180° behind $\mathscr{E}$, Fig. 246. $\mathscr{E}_s$ is equal and opposite to $\mathscr{E}$. The current I is given by $\mathscr{E} = \mathscr{E}_s = L\omega I$. I is all magnetizing current and hence has no active component.

Thus, no power is expended even though I may be of considerable magnitude.

If the resistance is zero, but the core of the coil is ferromagnetic, power will be expended, all of which will be *outside* the circuit, i.e., core loss. Fig. 245 is changed to meet this condition by keeping the vector $\mathscr{E}$ fixed in position and rotating the rest of the vector diagram in the clockwise sense until g coincides with o. Then $\theta = \phi$, and $\mathscr{E}_R = 0$, Fig. 247. $\mathscr{E}$ and $\mathscr{E}_s$ are equal and opposite, but there is a phase angle between the current I and the flux Φ. The power expended is $\mathscr{E} I \cos \phi = \mathscr{E}_s I \cos \theta$. All of the energy drawn from the circuit is expended in core losses outside the circuit. This is approximately the case of so-called choke coils used to regulate current, as in theater dimmers, or a transformer operating with secondary open. Choke coils and transformers with secondaries open are sometimes said to

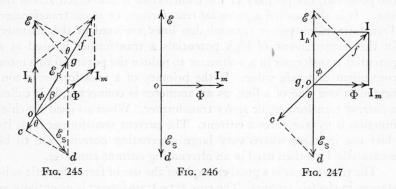

FIG. 245   FIG. 246   FIG. 247

waste no power. It is seen, however, that power is wasted, although a choke coil is less wasteful as a theater dimmer than a rheostat.

The case of a circuit containing no ferromagnetic substance, but inductance and resistance, has been considered. It was the first case discussed in building up vector diagrams. In that case the current is in phase with the flux Φ, and $\mathscr{E}_s$ is normal to I. The core loss is $\mathscr{E}_s I \cos \theta = 0$, since $\theta = 90°$. Thus the vector diagram in Fig. 245 reduces to Fig. 212.

As has been stated, the presence of ferromagnetic substance in the core of a coil causes the current curve to be nonsinusoidal even though the impressed emf. curve is sinusoidal. This is because of the hysteresis effect in the ferromagnetic substance, which causes the flux to lag behind the current, and, since the flux Φ follows the hysteresis curve, the $\mathcal{E}_s$ curve is nonsinusoidal. $\mathcal{E}_R$ is the resultant of $\mathcal{E}$ and $\mathcal{E}_s$, and therefore, $\mathcal{E}_R$ is nonsinusoidal.   But i is in phase with $\mathcal{E}_R$ at all times, and consequently, is also nonsinusoidal.   Since $\mathcal{E}_s$, i, and Φ are nonsinusoidal, they cannot, strictly considered, be represented by vectors in a clock diagram.   However, they may be used as vectors if we consider an average effect, or the *equivalent harmonic function* which would produce the same effect.   Thus, when these quantities are represented as vectors, it is understood that they are equivalent vectors.

260. The Transformer. — The extensive use of electricity today depends very largely upon the transformer, because it permits the easy transformation of potentials and currents from high to low or vice versa, and in any desired ratio.   There are two general ways in which a transformer is used.   When the primary purpose is to change the potential, the primary of the transformer is connected across the line.   It is then called a *potential* transformer, or *shunt* transformer. Transformers on power transmission lines are used in this manner. In the measurement of high potentials a transformer is used as a potential transformer in a voltmeter to reduce the potential to a more convenient and safe value.   If the primary of a transformer is connected in one side of a line, as an ammeter is connected, it is called a *current* transformer, or *series* transformer.   When so used its chief function is to transform a current.   The current transformer finds its chief use in cases where very large alternating currents are to be measured.   It is then used in an alternating current ammeter.

The transformer is a good example of the use of ferromagnetic substances in electric circuits.   The core type transformer is essentially as shown diagrammatically in Fig. 248.   It consists of a core made of laminated, silicon iron which has low hysteresis loss but high ohmic resistance and permeability.   The primary side of the transformer is the side which receives current from some source, usually directly from an a.c. dynamo or power line.   The p.d. of the primary side may be transformed upward or downward depending upon the ratio of turns on the primary side to turns on the secondary side.   If direct current is supplied to the primary side there is no emf. across the secondary except, at the time of make and break of the current, when the current is varying.   An ordinary induction coil is a type of transformer which transforms the emf. upward to a relatively high value, the variation of the current in the primary being brought about by an automatic make and break contactor.   Thus, if an a.c. flows in the primary windings an induced a.c. of the same frequency flows in the secondary, if it is closed. The iron core affords a path of low reluctance for the magnetic flux, and so the flux linked with the primary and secondary is large. Practically all of the flux linked with the primary current is also linked with the secondary winding. The coupling is nearly unity. There is, however, always a slight amount of leakage which cannot be avoided.

There is always a small loss of energy in the transformer itself which causes the energy output on the secondary side to be less than the energy input on the primary side. The loss is due to hysteresis and eddy currents in the laminated iron core, and to Joule loss in the transformer windings. The principal loss, however, is the core loss as the ohmic resistance of the windings is always small. For a complete discussion of transformers of various types and their characteristics the

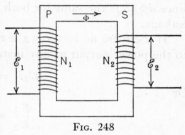

Fig. 248

reader is referred to books on electric engineering. The fundamental principles alone will be discussed here.

A transformer that has no losses would be an ideal transformer. No such transformer exists. However, a good, modern transformer has a very high efficiency. Therefore, in the preliminary discussion of the transformer, considered in the next Section, energy losses within the transformer itself and magnetic leakage will be neglected. The results obtained will be very approximately correct.

261. The Ideal Transformer. — When a transformer is operated, with its secondary open, it is merely a choke coil. The emf. of self inductance is very nearly equal to the impressed emf. and nearly 180° out of phase with it, the current is small, and the lag angle is large. When an alternating emf. $\mathscr{E}_1$ is impressed upon the primary a current I_1 flows in its winding. This develops an effective magnetic flux Φ in the iron core. This, in turn, induces an emf. of self inductance in the primary winding, which, under ideal conditions, would be equal and opposite to the impressed emf. We have for the instantaneous induced emf. in the primary

$$\mathscr{E}'_1 = - N_1 \frac{d\Phi}{dt}.$$

At the same instant the secondary induced emf. is

$$\mathcal{E}'_2 = - N_2 \frac{d\Phi}{dt}.$$

Since these relations hold at every instant, they hold for maximum and for effective values. Therefore, on dividing, we have

$$\frac{\mathcal{E}'_1}{\mathcal{E}'_2} = \frac{N_1}{N_2}, \qquad (261.1)$$

since $d\Phi/dt$ is the same for both primary and secondary, assuming no leakage.

If there are no losses in the transformer, the power input is equal to the power output at any instant, and therefore

$$\mathcal{E}'_1 i_1 = \mathcal{E}'_2 i_2.$$

Or

$$\frac{\mathcal{E}'_1}{\mathcal{E}'_2} = \frac{i_2}{i_1} = \frac{N_1}{N_2}. \qquad (261.2)$$

This relation holds for all values, and hence for effective values. Hence,

$$\frac{\mathcal{E}'_1}{\mathcal{E}'_2} = \frac{I_2}{I_1} = \frac{N_1}{N_2}. \qquad (261.3)$$

The effective power input is

$$P_1 = \mathcal{E}_1 I_1 \cos \phi_1. \qquad (261.4)$$

The effective power output is

$$P_2 = \mathcal{E}_2 I_2 \cos \phi_2. \qquad (261.5)$$

ϕ_1 and ϕ_2 are the primary and secondary phase angles. Since we have assumed $P_1 = P_2$, by equation (261.3) we see that

$$\cos \phi_1 = \cos \phi_2.$$

262. Calculation of Flux Φ. — The primary *induced* emf. is $\mathcal{E}_1 = L\omega I_1$. But $\omega = 2\pi f$, and $LI_1 = \Phi N$ cgsm. units (203.4). Therefore,

$$\mathcal{E}'_1 = 2\pi f \, \Phi N.$$

Or

$$\mathcal{E}'_1 = \frac{2\pi f \, \Phi N_1}{\sqrt{2}\,(10)^8} \text{ effective volts.} \qquad (262.1)$$

The same flux Φ is linked with the secondary, and hence

$$\mathscr{E}'_2 = \frac{2\pi f\, \Phi\, N_2}{\sqrt{2}\,(10)^8} \text{ effective volts.} \qquad (262.2)$$

The induced emfs. $\mathscr{E}'_1$ and $\mathscr{E}'_2$ must be in the same sense and phase since the primary winding and secondary winding are cut by the same flux.

Dividing (262.1) by (262.2), we have

$$\frac{\mathscr{E}'_1}{\mathscr{E}'_2} = \frac{N_1}{N_2}. \qquad (262.3)$$

In the actual transformer $\mathscr{E}'_1$ is a little smaller than the impressed emf. $\mathscr{E}_1$, and $\mathscr{E}'_2$ is a little greater than the secondary terminal emf. $\mathscr{E}_2$. Therefore, in calculations, impressed and terminal emfs. may be used with small error.

By measuring the primary terminal voltage $\mathscr{E}_1$ or the secondary terminal voltage $\mathscr{E}_2$, we may calculate the flux Φ, approximately, from either of the equations (262.1) or (262.2) if the Ns are known. Thus

$$\Phi = \frac{\mathscr{E}_1 \sqrt{2}\,(10)^8}{2\pi f N_1} = \frac{\mathscr{E}_2 \sqrt{2}\,(10)^8}{2\pi f N_2} \text{ maxwells.} \qquad (262.4)$$

If the area of cross section of the iron core is known, we have

$$B = \frac{\mathscr{E}_1 \sqrt{2}(10)^8}{2\pi f N_1 A} = \frac{\mathscr{E}_2 \sqrt{2}(10)^8}{2\pi f N_2 A} \text{ maxwells/cm.}^2, \qquad (262.5)$$

since $\Phi = BA$. The effective flux is

$$\frac{\mathscr{E}_1 (10)^8}{2\pi f N_1} = \frac{\mathscr{E}_2 (10)^8}{2\pi f N_2}. \qquad (262.6)$$

263. Calculation of the Currents I_m and I_h. — With secondary open, the current I is the resultant of the magnetizing current and the core loss current. I_m may be calculated approximately by use of the equation (158.3) which obtains for direct currents when multiplied by the permeability,

$$B = \frac{4\pi \mu N I_m}{10 l}.$$

Therefore,

$$I_m = \frac{10 B l}{4\pi \mu N}. \qquad (263.1)$$

If we apply this equation to an alternating current circuit, B is the maximum flux density, and I_m is the maximum magnetizing current. But the effective value is required. Therefore,

$$I_m = \frac{10Bl}{4\pi\sqrt{2}\mu N}.$$ (263.2)

To obtain I_h we observe that I_h is the component of the current in phase with the impressed emf. $\mathscr{E}_1$, and that the total power expended is core loss plus the RI^2 loss. Thus, neglecting the RI^2 loss which is small, the core loss is given by

$$P = \mathscr{E}_1 I_h \text{ watts, } \quad \text{or} \quad I_h = \frac{P}{\mathscr{E}_1} \text{ amperes.}$$ (263.3)

P may be measured with an indicating wattmeter and $\mathscr{E}_1$ with an a.c. voltmeter.

264. Transformer on Noninductive Load. — As we have seen, a transformer operating with secondary open is a choke coil of very high impedance. Neglecting core and Joule losses, the current is all magnetizing current which is just large enough to maintain the flux which is necessary to develop the emf. of self inductance. See Fig. 246.

However, when current is being drawn from the secondary, the opposing ampere turns of the secondary reduce the flux, and, consequently, the current in the primary immediately increases until a balance obtains, or until the magnetizing current I_m has its former value. Or, looking at it from another angle, the induced emf. $\mathscr{E}_2$ in the secondary drives a current through the load in accordance with Ohm's law. This current flows in such a direction as to develop a flux which is in opposition to the flux developed by the primary current (Lenz's law). This reduces the flux, and, hence, decreases the emf. of self inductance $\mathscr{E}'_1$ in the primary and hence increases the resultant emf., $\mathscr{E}_1 - \mathscr{E}'_1$, in the primary. The current then increases in the primary until $\mathscr{E}'_1$ has its former value, and the flux density is the same as before. Hence, *the flux density is practically the same on all loads, and, also, the magnetizing current.* Therefore, the core losses remain practically constant on all loads if the primary emf. remains constant. Of course, as the current increases in both primary and secondary, the Joule losses increase. Thus, as the current in the secondary increases, the flux created by it increases also. Since this flux is in opposition to the flux created by the primary current, the primary current must increase also, and sufficiently so that the difference between the flux created by the primary current and that created by the secondary current will be the flux due to the magnetizing or exciting current I_m. The magnetizing current is, therefore, that component of the primary current which maintains the actual magnetic flux in the core of the transformer.

With noninductive load the secondary current is in phase with the secondary terminal emf. The secondary terminal emf. is smaller than the induced emf. $\mathscr{E}'_2$ and slightly out of phase with it owing to resistance and reactance in the secondary winding. The primary current is nearly in phase with the primary impressed emf. $\mathscr{E}_1$. There is a small phase angle between the primary current and the impressed emf. owing to resistance and reactance in the primary winding. The primary and secondary currents are nearly 180° out of phase. The excess ampere turns in the primary are only sufficient to maintain the actual or useful flux, which is practically constant on all loads.

The relations of the potentials in an actual, loaded, constant-potential transformer may be made clear by a vector diagram, Fig. 249.[1] The currents are merely indicated. They are shown in detail in Fig. 250. The horizontal line in Fig. 249 is the vector for the useful flux, which, as we have seen, remain practically constant under all conditions of loading. The

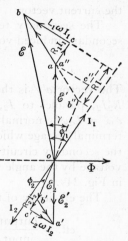

FIG. 249

vector oa, which represents the primary induced emf. $\mathscr{E}'_1$, and the vector oa', representing the secondary induced emf. $\mathscr{E}'_2$, are normal to the flux vector and in opposition. Also, $\mathscr{E}'_1/\mathscr{E}'_2 = N_1/N_2$. The current vector I_2 lags behind the emf. vector $\mathscr{E}_2$ by an angle ϕ_2, which depends upon the load. For a noninductive load $\phi_2 = 0$, and the secondary terminal voltage is in phase with the secondary current. The primary

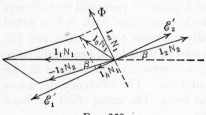

FIG. 250

[1] Karapetoff's Exp. Elec. Eng., Vol. II, p. 79, 2nd Ed.

current I_1 is $180° - \beta$ out of phase with the secondary current I_2 (Fig. 250), and lags behind the primary terminal voltage by a phase angle ϕ_1, which also depends upon the character of the load. The voltage $\mathscr{E}'_1$ is smaller than the primary terminal voltage $\mathscr{E}_1$, due to the primary potential drop ab. The vector

$$ab = I_1 \sqrt{R_1{}^2 + L_1{}^2 \omega^2}$$

is the vector sum of the ohmic resistance drop, $ac = R_1 I_1$, parallel to the current vector I_1, and the inductive drop $cb = L_1 \omega I_1$, normal to the current vector.

The secondary terminal voltage, $ob' = \mathscr{E}_2$, is smaller than the secondary induced voltage $\mathscr{E}'_2$ due to the secondary potential drop

$$a'b' = I_2 \sqrt{R_2{}^2 + L_2{}^2 \omega^2}.$$

The vector $a'b'$ is the resultant of the ohmic resistance drop, $c'b' = R_2 I_2$, parallel to I_2, and the secondary inductive potential drop, $c'a' = L_2 \omega I_2$, normal to the vector I_2. The vector $\mathscr{E}_2$ is the secondary terminal voltage which is available for driving the current I_2 through the secondary circuit, and differs in phase from the primary terminal voltage by the angle γ. The current I_0 of Fig. 250 is not represented in Fig. 249.

The efficiency of the transformer is

$$\text{eff.} = \frac{\text{output}}{\text{input}} = \frac{\mathscr{E}_1 I_1 \cos \phi_1 - R_1 I_1{}^2 - R_2 I_2{}^2 - \text{core loss}}{\mathscr{E}_1 I_1 \cos \phi_1}$$

$$= \frac{\mathscr{E}_2 I_2 \cos \phi_2}{\mathscr{E}_1 I_1 \cos \phi_1}.$$

It will be seen that the efficiency of a constant potential transformer varies with the load, being less with small than with full or rated load, since the core loss is practically constant for all loads, and the terms $R_1 I_1{}^2$ and $R_2 I_2{}^2$, though increasing with load, are small, since R_1 and R_2 are both small. A modern commercial transformer has an efficiency of 95% to 98% at rated load. The efficiency decreases slightly with use due to aging of the core. The aging effect has been lessened but not yet fully overcome.

The vector diagram for the currents is shown in Fig. 250. In this diagram the vectors represent ampere turns. $I_0 N_1$ represents the ampere turns which are required to operate the transformer itself. It is resolved into two components: (1) $I_m N_1$ ampere turns which are required to develop the exciting flux. (2) $I_h N_1$ ampere turns which are required to supply the core losses. $I_0 N_1$ remains practically constant with a constant potential transformer under all loading conditions, but when a transformer is used as a current transformer I_0 varies with the degree of saturation of the core, i.e., with the load current. Thus, both I_m and I_h vary with the load in a current transformer. The vector $I_1 N_1$ represents the total primary ampere turns. It is the vector sum of the secondary ampere turns, $- I_2 N_2$ and the exciting turns $I_0 N_1$. The primary and secondary currents are out of phase by $180° - \beta$, the angle β depending upon the load. The vector diagrams for the transformer are not drawn to scale, and hence they give no idea of relative numerical magnitudes.

265. Transmission Lines. — A transmission line has capacitance, inductance, and resistance. These quantities are said to be distributed when applied to an electric line. In many cases the distributed capacitance is small as compared with the distributed inductance. We shall consider the case where the distributed inductance predominates,

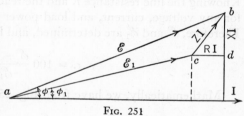

FIG. 251

thus giving a lagging current so far as the line is concerned. Inductance in a transmission line is due to the magnetic flux linked with the loop forming the line conductors. Distributed inductance is noticeable in long, high-voltage lines with considerable spacing between the wires. The voltage relations in a loaded line, where the load is inductive, may be shown by a vector diagram, as in Fig. 251. $\mathscr{E}$ is the generator voltage, $\mathscr{E}_1$ the load voltage, and I the current. The potential drop in the line is, $cb = I \sqrt{R^2 + L^2 \omega^2}$. ϕ_1 is the load phase angle, and ϕ is the overall phase angle at the generator.

Voltage Regulation. — When a transmission line is loaded there is a drop in potential in the line due to the load current flowing through the resistance and inductance of the line. It is important to keep the line drop as small as possible. The percentage line potential drop, under different load conditions, is called the *voltage regulation* of the line. Or, as commonly used, it is the percentage change in voltage between no load and rated load. It will be seen from the vector diagram that the difference between $\mathscr{E}$ and $\mathscr{E}_1$, and hence the voltage regulation, depends upon both the current and power factor of the load.

In order to determine the regulation of the line, the constants of the line must be determined, and then the vector diagram is drawn under actual load conditions. The constants of a transmission line and hence also its regulation at rated load, may be obtained as follows: Short circuit the load end of the line and measure its ohmic resistance R by any d.c. method, as by use of a box bridge. Now send an alternating current through the short-circuited line at low voltage, and measure the voltage and current. Then the radio between $\mathscr{E}$ and I is the line impedance Z. Hence,

$$x = L\omega = \sqrt{Z^2 - R^2}. \tag{265.1}$$

Knowing the line resistance R and the reactance x, the vector diagram for any voltage, current, and load power factor may be constructed. Therefore, $\mathscr{E}$ and $\mathscr{E}_1$ are determined, and hence the voltage regulation

$$\text{v. r.} = 100 \frac{\mathscr{E} - \mathscr{E}_1}{\mathscr{E}_1}. \tag{265.2}$$

Mathematically, we have from Fig. 251

$$\left. \begin{array}{l} \mathscr{E} \cos\phi = \mathscr{E}_1 \cos\phi_1 + RI, \\ \mathscr{E} \sin\phi = \mathscr{E}_1 \sin\phi_1 + RI. \end{array} \right\} \tag{265.3}$$

Squaring and adding, there results

$$\mathscr{E}_2 = (\mathscr{E}_1 \cos\phi_1 + RI)^2 + (\mathscr{E}_1 \sin\phi_1 + xI)^2. \tag{265.4}$$

These relations are sufficient for calculations. If both $\mathscr{E}$ and $\mathscr{E}_1$ are known, the load and overall power factors may be calculated, as well as the voltage regulation. If the load power factor is known, $\mathscr{E}_1$ and the overall power factor, as well as the voltage regulation, may be calculated.

266. Regulation of a Transformer. — The voltage regulation of a transformer is the percentage rise in secondary voltage when the rated load is suddenly thrown off, the primary voltage remaining constant. The regulation of a transformer is of great practical importance in the case of a lighting transformer where a difference in voltage of 2% to 3% between very light load and full load is quite noticeable in the illumination given out by incandescent lamps. For power purposes, however, strict regulation is not so important, except when incandescent lamps are supplied from the same transformer. In this case, if the power load is inductive, as is usually the case, the regulation is worse than on noninductive load.

The voltage drop in a transformer is caused by the inductance and resistance of the windings. Inductance is due to leakage flux which links one of the windings but not the other. The resistance of the windings can be measured, but it is impossible to measure the inductance of the primary apart from the secondary. However, this is not necessary since the inductance of the primary is merged with that of the secondary into an *equivalent* inductance which can be measured. The leakage flux, and hence the inductance, in a transformer varies with the character of the load, being greater with an inductive than with a noninductive load. With a capacitive load the inductance in the transformer is neutralized more or less and the voltage drop is not so great.

The voltage drop in a transformer may be determined in much the same manner as for a transmission line. The difference is that

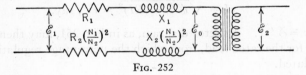

Fig. 252

the transformer circuit, instead of being continuous is made up of two parts, primary and secondary, connected by the useful flux when in operation. However, this affects the problem only in so far as the voltages in primary and secondary are different. In order to obviate the difference in voltage the secondary impedance is imagined transferred to the primary circuit. The transfer of resistance and reactance from secondary to primary consists in multiplying each by the square of the ratio of the number of turns, $(N_1/N_2)^2$. This may be represented schematically by Fig. 252. This scheme is equivalent to transferring the resistance and reactance of the transformer to the primary line, which is then connected to an ideal transformer having no potential drop. The voltage $\mathcal{E}_1$ is then the primary input voltage, and $\mathcal{E}_0$ is the primary voltage which would be effective if the transformer had no potential drop.

The vector diagram for the quantities transferred from secondary to primary is shown by broken lines in Fig. 249. $\mathscr{E}_0 = ob'' = \mathscr{E}_2(N_1/N_2)$, $b''c'' = R_2(N_1/N_2)^2 I_1$, $c''a'' = x_2(N_1/N_2)^2 I_1$. The equivalent p.d., reduced to primary, is $b''b = I_1 \sqrt{R^2 + x^2}$.

The problem of determining the regulation is then the same as for a transmission line, Section 265. The ratio N_1/N_2 is easily obtained, very approximately, since it is almost exactly equal to the ratio between the primary and secondary voltages at no load. The resistances of the windings are first measured. Then, the equivalent resistance is

$$R = R_1 + R_2 \left(\frac{N_1}{N_2}\right)^2.$$

The combined or equivalent impedance of the transformer is obtained by short circuiting the secondary and applying a known, low voltage $\mathscr{E}$ to the primary and measuring the primary current I. The impedance Z of the transformer is then obtained as follows:

$$x = x_1 + x_2 \left(\frac{N_1}{N_2}\right)^2.$$

Then

$$xI = \sqrt{\mathscr{E}^2 - (RI)^2} = \mathscr{E}', \text{ say.}$$

Hence, $x = \mathscr{E}'/I$. A vector diagram, as in Fig. 251, may then be constructed for the rated load, from which the percentage regulation may be calculated.

267. The Autotransformer.

— We have considered the two-windings transformer. Another device that accomplishes the same end is the one-winding transformer, called an *autotransformer*, shown schematically in Fig. 253. In the two-windings transformer, the primary and secondary currents are entirely separate and distinct, and,

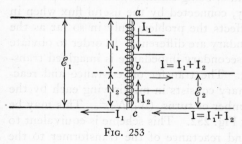

Fig. 253

on noninductive loads, very nearly in opposition. With the autotransformer the same winding carries both primary and secondary currents. In this case there are three different currents: The current I_1 in the part ab, which is the line current; the current I_2 in the part *bc*, and the load current $I = I_1 + I_2$. The currents I_1 and I_2 are in opposition, since the secondary current always opposes the primary current by its magnetic action. If there are N_1 turns in the part *ab* and N_2 turns in the part *bc*, we have

$$N_1 I_1 = N_2 I_2 \qquad (267.1)$$

If $\mathscr{E}_1$ and $\mathscr{E}_2$ are the line and load voltages respectively, there are three other equations that may be written:

$$\frac{\mathscr{E}_1}{\mathscr{E}_2} = \frac{N_1 + N_2}{N_2}, \qquad (267.2)$$

$$I = I_1 + I_2, \qquad (267.3)$$

$$\mathscr{E}_1 I_1 = \mathscr{E}_2 I. \qquad (267.4)$$

Neglecting losses in the transformer itself, the same energy is delivered to the secondary as is supplied to the primary. This transformer may be used, also, as either a step-up or a step-down transformer. Autotransformers are not used as ordinary service or lighting transformers, because of the danger attending such usage. The high voltage and low voltage windings are not insulated from each other. Therefore, if one side of the high voltage line is partly or completely grounded and a person were to touch one of the low voltage wires while in contact with the ground he would receive the full voltage of the line. However, autotransformers are used extensively for starting induction motors and for regulators.

268. Efficiency of a Transformer. — The expression for the efficiency of a transformer was given in Section 264. In the case of a constant potential transformer, the core loss remains practically constant under all conditions of loading. As the load increases the efficiency increases to a maximum at about full load, but falls off rapidly for overloads due to excessive copper losses. Since a transformer is connected to the mains continually the core losses are continuous, but on open secondary the Joule loss is negligible. The effective efficiency, or all day efficiency, will be much less than the efficiency at rated load, because the core loss is continuous, and, for the most part, a transformer is loaded below capacity.

The efficiency of a transformer may be determined *directly* by measuring the watt input and watt output at any given load and then by taking the ratio. However, except with small transformers, this is not feasible. It is customary, therefore, to measure the core losses in a transformer at no load, and then *calculate* the efficiency at any desired load. This method is simpler, and usually more accurate than the direct method. The procedure is as follows: Measure the core losses with an indicating wattmeter at no load, and also the primary and secondary resistances. Knowing the primary and secondary terminal voltages from the transformer rating or actual measurements, the currents at any desired load may be calculated, and hence the RI losses.

269. The Constant-Current Transformer.

— Commercial transformers are generally used as constant-potential transformers. In some cases, however, as in feeding arc lamps connected in series, con-

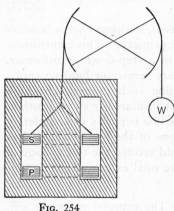

FIG. 254

stant current is required. A transformer designed to supply energy at constant current is called a constant-current transformer. The construction of such a transformer is shown schematically in section in Fig. 254. In the constant-potential transformer the primary and secondary coils are fixed relative to each other. In the constant-current transformer one coil, the secondary coil S, is so arranged as to be capable of moving freely relative to the primary coil P, which is fixed in position at the bottom of the two slots of the transformer. The secondary coil is suspended by a counterweight W, which is a little lighter than the secondary coil, and adjustable, so that when there is no current flowing in the secondary coil it rests upon the primary coil. When current is being drawn from the secondary the secondary coil is repelled upward, since the currents in primary and secondary are in opposition. As the secondary coil moves upward the secondary induced emf. decreases due to increased flux leakage. By adjusting the magnitude of the counterweight the secondary current may be adjusted to the desired strength. Should one of the lamps fail it is automatically short-circuited, thus decreasing the resistance of the circuit and increasing the current, secondary emf. remaining unchanged. However, the increased current causes the secondary coil to move upward until the induced emf. decreases, due to increased leakage, to the proper value to drive the constant current through the decreased resistance of the circuit. In this manner the current is maintained practically constant.

270. Polyphase Systems. — The discussion thus far has had to do with *single-phase* systems. A single-phase current is entirely satisfactory for lighting purposes, but single-phase motors are not generally satisfactory. The single-phase commutator motor has been quite satisfactory for railway work, but single-phase induction motors are not satisfactory, except in small sizes. However, if two or more alternating currents differing in phase by a constant amount are combined in a motor it operates better, since at no time is the power equal to zero in all phases at once. The result is a revolving magnetic field which cuts across the conductors of the rotor of the motor, thus causing it to revolve in the direction of the revolving field.

Such combinations of interlinking, single-phase currents into one system are called *polyphase currents*, and the systems are called *polyphase systems*. There are several ways in which this may be accomplished. However, only two polyphase systems have been used to any extent: the two-phase, three-wire system, and the three-phase, three-wire system.

271. The Two-Phase System. — The two-phase system consists of two current circuits differing in phase by 90°. The electric relations

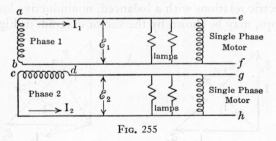

Fig. 255

in the two-phase system are simpler than in the three-phase system. The two-phase currents, differing in phase by 90°, are obtained by winding on the armature of a dynamo two coils so spaced that when the emf. in one is at a maximum it is passing through zero in the other. The generator may be provided with four slip rings, two for each of the windings. Thus two independent, single-phase current-circuits may be taken from the same generator. However, the circuits differ in this one respect that when the current passes through its maximum in one circuit it passes through zero in the other circuit, i.e., the currents are out of phase by 90°. This may be represented as in Fig. 255.

These two independent, single-phase circuits are converted into a two-phase, three-wire system by joining the two generator windings at the points b and c, and using a single, common-return wire for the

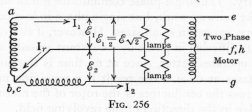

Fig. 256

two circuits, as shown in Fig. 256. The windings are drawn normal to each other to indicate that they differ in phase by 90°. The connection b to c may be made by joining the two slip rings, or the connection may be made inside the armature, in which case there are three slip rings. The loads on the two circuits may be separate and unlike, in which case the system is said to be *unbalanced*, or the loads may be identical in every respect, in which case the system is said to be *balanced*.

The electric relations with a balanced, noninductive load, neglecting line drops, may be shown by the vector diagram in Fig. 257. The

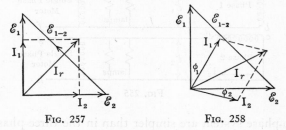

Fig. 257   Fig. 258

current I_r in the return wire bf is the vector sum of the currents I_1 and I_2 in the phase wires ae and cg, which are in phase with the phase emfs. $\mathscr{E}_1$ and $\mathscr{E}_2$, and is equal to $I_1\sqrt{2} = I_2\sqrt{2}$. The voltage $\mathscr{E}_{1-2}$, between the two outside or phase wires, is the vector difference between the voltages $\mathscr{E}_1$ and $\mathscr{E}_2$, and is equal to $\mathscr{E}_1\sqrt{2} = \mathscr{E}_2\sqrt{2}$.

This may be seen by considering instantaneous values. The return wire bf is grounded. Suppose that at a certain instant the potential of wire ae is ε_1 volts above ground, and that wire cg is ε_2 volts above ground, $\varepsilon_1 > \varepsilon_2$, then the instantaneous p.d. between wires ae and cg is $\varepsilon_1 - \varepsilon_2$. In the case of the currents, however, if at a certain instant a current i_1 is flowing in wire ae and a current i_2 in wire cg, the current in the wire bf is $i_1 + i_2$. Relations that hold algebraically for instantaneous values hold geometrically for effective values.

When the load is unbalanced and inductive, the vector diagram is as shown in Fig. 258, neglecting line drops. ϕ_1 and ϕ_2 are the lag angles in the two phases. The loads are assumed to be different in the two phases.

The resistances of the line wires cannot always be neglected. It will be seen that if the p.d. in the return wire bf is to be the same as in a phase wire it must have a cross-sectional area $\sqrt{2}$ times that of a phase wire. The effect of the potential drops in the line wires, at the re-
ceiving end, may be shown by the
vector diagram in Fig. 259. $\mathscr{E}_1$ and
$\mathscr{E}_2$ represent the emfs. at the generator. The current vectors are shown
as out of phase with the emfs., and
lagging. The vectors for the potential
drops in the phase wires, $c'b'$ and cb,
are parallel to the corresponding current vectors, I_2 and I_1. The vectors
for the potential drops in the return

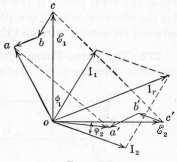

Fig. 259

wire, $b'a'$ and ba, are parallel to the current I_r. The receiving potential vectors are seen to be neither equal nor 90° apart in phase. This distortion may be a serious defect at times.

The electric power is measured with two wattmeters, one in each phase, and then added, the ammeter terminals of the wattmeters being connected in the phase wires. This obtains for unbalanced as well as for balanced loads. Take the case of a balanced load. If ε and i are the instantaneous values of the potential drop and current in one phase, and ε' and i' corresponding values in the other phase, we have

$$\varepsilon = \mathscr{E}' \sin \omega t, \tag{271.1}$$

$$i = I' \sin (\omega t - \phi).$$

Or
$$p = \mathcal{E}i = \mathcal{E}'I' \cos \phi \sin^2 \omega t - \mathcal{E}'I' \sin \phi \sin \omega t \cos \omega t. \quad (271.2)$$

For the other circuit, which differs in phase by 90° from the first, we have

$$\left.\begin{array}{c} \mathcal{E}' = \mathcal{E}' \cos \omega t, \\ i' = I' \cos (\omega t - \phi). \end{array}\right\} \quad (271.3)$$

Or
$$p = \mathcal{E}'i' = \mathcal{E}'I' \cos \phi \cos^2 \omega t + \mathcal{E}'I' \sin \phi \sin \omega t \cos \omega t. \quad (271.4)$$

Adding (271.2) and (271.4), we have

$$P = \mathcal{E}i + \mathcal{E}'i' = \mathcal{E}'I' \cos \phi, \quad (271.5)$$

where $\mathcal{E}'$ and I' are maximum values. For effective values

$$P = 2\mathcal{E}I \cos \phi. \quad (271.6)$$

Thus, the total power is the sum of the powers in the two circuits. I is the effective current in a phase wire and $\mathcal{E}$ is the effective voltage between an outside wire and the return wire.

272. The Three-Phase System. — In the case of the three-phase generator there are three windings on the armature so spaced that the

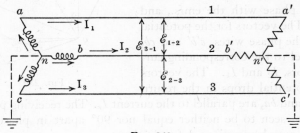

Fig. 260

emfs. differ in phase by 120°. Thus, we might have six slip rings (collector rings) and three independent circuits. These would be single-phase circuits, but the currents would be simultaneously out of phase by 120°. This is not done in case of commercial generators. The three windings are joined and brought out to three slip rings, and then we have a three-wire system. There are two ways in which the windings on the armature of the generator are joined; the Y connection, shown in Fig. 260, and the delta connection, shown in Fig. 264.

273. The Y-Connected System. — The windings of the armature are connected as shown schematically in Fig. 260, the currents at a particular instant flowing as indicated by arrows. The load in Fig. 260 is assumed to be noninductive and balanced. The point *n*, where the three ends of the windings are joined, is called the *neutral point*. If the system is out of balance a fourth-wire return to the neutral point may be used to carry the unbalanced part of the current, or the ground may be used as the return conductor, as indicated. The neutral point connections are usually soldered, taped, and concealed within the armature.

Voltage Relations. — With the Y-connected armature there are two kinds of voltages to be considered: phase voltages $\mathscr{E}'$, *n* to *a*, *n* to *b*, and *n* to *c*, and line voltages $\mathscr{E}_{1-2}$, $\mathscr{E}_{2-3}$, and $\mathscr{E}_{3-1}$. The line voltages are equal, as is clear from Fig. 260. The relationship between phase voltages and line voltages is shown by the vector diagram in Fig. 261. The line voltages $\mathscr{E}$ are the geometric differences of the phase voltages. It is clear from the vector diagram that $\mathscr{E} = \mathscr{E}' \sqrt{3}$.

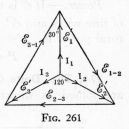

FIG. 261

Current Relations. — It is clear from Fig. 260 that, in case of a balanced load, the current in each line wire is at every instant equal to the current in the corresponding armature winding. If the load is

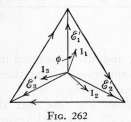

FIG. 262

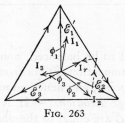

FIG. 263

balanced and noninductive, as shown, the currents in the mains are equal and 120° out of phase, and in phase with the corresponding phase voltages. Since the currents are separated in phase by 120°, and equal, they sum up to zero at every instant or the vector polygon for the currents closes. There is then no current in the return conductor, ground as here shown. This is a direct result of the trigonometric proposition that the sum of the sines of any three angles differing by 120° is zero. Thus,

$$i = I \sin \omega t + I \sin(\omega t + 120°) + I \sin(\omega t - 120°) = 0. \quad (273.1)$$

If the load is balanced and inductive the currents lag behind the corresponding phase voltages by a phase angle ϕ, as shown in Fig. 262, but the geometric sum of the currents is still zero, as well as the algebraic sum of the instantaneous values. If the load is unbalanced and inductive the vector diagram is as shown in Fig. 263. The vector polygon does not close. There is a resultant current I_r which flows in the return conductor, if provided.

Power. — If $\mathcal{E}$ is the effective voltage between any two conductors of line wires and $\mathcal{E}'$ the phase voltage $\mathcal{E}' = \mathcal{E}/\sqrt{3}$. Therefore, the total power is

$$P = 3\mathcal{E}'I \cos \phi = \sqrt{3}\,\mathcal{E}I \cos \phi. \quad (273.2)$$

274. The Delta-Connected System. — The armature windings are joined as shown diagrammatically in Fig. 264. The load is

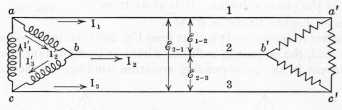

FIG. 264

indicated to be balanced, noninductive, and also connected in delta. The Δ connection differs from the Y connection in that there is no neutral point, and hence no need for a return wire.

Voltage Relations. — It is evident from Fig. 264 that the line voltages $\mathcal{E}$ are equal to the phase voltages $\mathcal{E}'$, both for instantaneous and effective values, the vector diagram being as shown in Fig. 265 (*a*).

Current Relations. — It is evident from Fig. 264 that the instantaneous current in each line wire is equal to the difference between the instantaneous currents in the corresponding armature windings. Therefore, also, the effective current in each line wire is the geometric difference between the effective currents in the corresponding armature windings. The three line voltages $\mathcal{E}$ are represented by the sides of the triangle *abc*, in magnitude and phase relations, in Fig.

265(*a*).   When the load is balanced and noninductive, the winding currents *kl*, *km*, and *kn*, Fig. 265(*b*), are in phase with the line voltages, and so the corresponding vectors are drawn parallel to the line-voltage vectors.   The line currents are then represented by the sides of the triangle *lmn*, and are in phase with what we may consider the fictitious *Y* voltages *ob*, *oc*, *oa*.   Thus the current in a line wire is equal to $\sqrt{3}$ times the current in one of the armature windings.   If

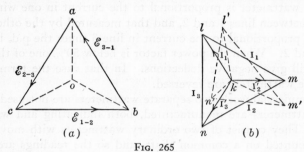

Fig. 265

the load is inductive and unbalanced, the currents may be represented by the broken lines in Fig. 265(*b*).

Power. — If $\mathscr{E}$ is the effective voltage between two line wires, and $I = \sqrt{3}I'$ the current in each line wire, the power in one winding is

$$p = \mathscr{E} I' \cos \phi = \mathscr{E} \frac{I}{\sqrt{3}} \cos \phi.$$

And in all three windings

$$P = \sqrt{3}\, \mathscr{E} I \cos \phi. \qquad (274.1)$$

275. Measurement of Power in a Three-Wire System. — It is evident from Figs. 260 and 264 that the generator load may be measured by using three wattmeters, one in each phase, the potential terminals of the wattmeters being connected between the neutral point and the mains, the current terminals in the respective mains, and the readings then added.   The power at the receiving end may be measured in the same way.   This obtains for *Y* connection.   For Δ connection the power may also be measured in each of the three windings separately, and then added.   In practice this is not done.   Two wattmeters are used.   This method is based upon the fact that any one of the three wires may be considered a return wire for the currents flowing in the other two.

Let us say that the wires are numbered 1, 2, and 3, and that number 2 is selected as the common return wire. Then the current terminals of one meter are connected in line number 1 and for the other meter in line number 3. The potential terminals of the first meter are connected from main 1 to main 2, and for the second meter from main 3 to main 2. The readings of the two meters are then added. This method gives correct results with unbalanced as well as with balanced load. It is evident that this is so, since the power measured with one wattmeter is proportional to the current in one wire times the p.d. between lines 1 and 2, and that measured by the other wattmeters is proportional to the current in line 3 times the p.d. between lines 3 and 2. When the power factor is below 50% one of the wattmeters will give negative deflections. In that case the terminals of one of the wattmeters are reversed.

In commercial work two separate wattmeters are not used. Polyphase wattmeters are manufactured, both indicating and watthour meters. They consist of two ordinary wattmeters with moving elements mounted on a common shaft, and so the readings are added automatically. In case of a return wire in the Y-connected system and an unbalanced load, two wattmeters will not give the correct power. Three wattmeters must then be used.

276. Transformers and Load Connections. — When transformers are used in polyphase transmission lines they may be connected either in Y or Δ independently of the generator system of connection. The primaries of the transformers are connected in either Y or Δ, and the secondaries are then connected in either Y or Δ. In the case of Δ connection one of the transformers may be omitted when the load is light. The other two transformers will then carry the load. This arrangement is known as the *open delta*. If three transformers are connected in Δ and one of them burns out the other two will carry the load, if not too great, until the burned out transformer can be replaced, thus maintaining the service. This is not true of Y-connected transformers.

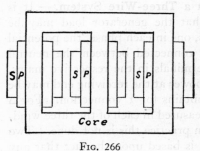

FIG. 266

277. Polyphase Transformers. — These transformers are made for both two-phase and three-phase systems. In polyphase transformers the core is continuous for all of the transformers of one set, i.e., two or three transformers are wound on cores which form a single set of stampings, as indicated in Fig. 266 for a three-phase, polyphase transformer. Polyphase transformers are cheaper, lighter, and more efficient than a corresponding number of single-phase transformers connected together to form a polyphase system.

PROBLEMS

1. The emf., as measured with an a.c. voltmeter, across a coil is 120 volts. The current, as measured with an a.c. ammeter, is 22 amperes. The ohmic resistance of the coil is 4 ohms, and the frequency of the supply is 60 cycles/sec. Calculate the inductance, the impedance, the inductive reactance, the active and wattless power, and the phase angle. Draw the vector diagram for p.d.'s. to scale.

Recalculate, using a frequency of 500 cycles/sec., the impressed emf., resistance, and inductance being as before.

2. A noninductive resistance R is connected in series with an inductance coil of L henrys and ohmic resistance R'. The impressed emf. is 120 volts. The emf. across the noninductive resistance measures 63.32 volts, and across the inductance coil 87 volts. The current measures 15.83 amperes. Calculate the phase angles, the resistances R and R', the inductance L, the active power in the inductance coil, the impedance, and the inductive reactance. The frequency is 60 cycles/sec. Draw the voltage vector diagram to scale.

Recalculate, using an impressed emf. of 120 volts and a frequency of 25 cycles/sec., the resistance and inductance being as before.

3. Two inductance coils are connected in series. One has an inductance of 0.05 henry and a resistance of 20 ohms, and the other has an inductance of 0.03 henry and a resistance of 50 ohms. The current measures 2 amperes. Calculate the overall p.d., the p.d. over each coil, and the phase angles. Calculate the active power expended in each coil and the total active power. The frequency is 60 cycles/sec. Draw the voltage vector diagram to scale.

Recalculate, using a frequency of 500 cycles/sec., all constants of the circuit being as before.

4. Two inductance coils are connected in parallel. The impressed emf. is 110 volts. R is 10 ohms and L is 0.015 henry for one coil, and for the other coil R' is 20 ohms and L' is 0.073 henry. The frequency is 60 cycles/sec. Calculate the currents and phase angles for the two branches, the total current and the equivalent phase angle. Calculate the equivalent resistance and equivalent inductance. Draw the voltage vector diagram and the current vector diagram to scale.

Recalculate, using an impressed p.d. of 110 volts and a frequency of 100 cycles/sec., the resistances and inductances being as before.

5. There are two inductance coils in parallel, and in series with the parallel circuit is an inductance coil. The branch coils constants are $R' = 10$ ohms and $L' = 0.015$ henry, and $R'' = 20$ ohms and $L'' = 0.073$ henry. The series coil has a resistance $R = 5$ ohms and an inductance $L = 0.05$ henry. The impressed p.d. over all is 120 volts. Calculate the

total current, the current in each branch, the phase angles, the equivalent inductances, and the equivalent resistance. The frequency is 60 cycles/sec. Draw the voltage and current vector diagrams to scale.

6. (a) A resistance of 10 ohms and a condenser of 50 mfs. are connected in series. The impressed p.d. across the combination is 110 volts, and the frequency is 60 cycles/sec. Calculate the current, the phase angle, the active power, the power factor, the impedance, the reactance, the p.d. across the resistance and across the condenser. Draw the voltage vector diagram to scale.

(b) Place in series with the resistance and capacitance of part (a) an inductance coil having an inductance of 0.073 henry and a resistance of 10 ohms. Let the p.d. be 110 volts and the frequency 60 cycles/sec. Calculate all values as in (a). Draw the voltage vector diagram to scale.

(c) Place the inductance coil of part (b) in parallel with the resistance and capacitance of part (a). Let the p.d. be 110 volts and the frequency 60 cycles/sec. Calculate all quantities, including the equivalent resistance and reactance. Draw the current and potential vector diagrams to scale.

7. A condenser of 50 mfs. and a resistance of 10 ohms are connected in parallel with a condenser of 200 mfs. and a resistance of 50 ohms. The impressed p.d. across the combination is 220 volts. Calculate the currents, the equivalent resistance and reactance, the active power, and the equivalent phase angle. Draw the current and voltage vector diagrams to scale. The frequency is 60 cycles/sec.

8. A generator operated at 220 volts supplies a.c. to a transmission line. The ohmic line p.d. is 8% of the generator voltage, and the inductive line p.d. is 10% of the generator voltage. If the load voltage is 193 volts, what is the power factor and the percentage voltage regulation of the line? If the resistance of the line measures 2 ohms, what is the current, the reactance of the line? If the frequency is 60 cycles/sec., what is the inductance of the line? Draw the vector diagram to scale. The load in this case is inductive. Calculate the reactance and resistance of the load.

If the load is noninductive what is the percentage regulation, other conditions remaining the same, except the generator voltage? Calculate the generator voltage.

9. The following data were obtained on a small, laboratory transformer: No-load voltages 114 and 12.2 volts. High voltage winding resistance 1.43 ohms. Low voltage winding resistance 0.035 ohm. On a short-circuit test, low resistance winding short-circuited, the primary p.d. was 3.7 volts and the current 0.75 ampere. When used as a step-down transformer, calculate the equivalent primary resistance and reactance. Calculate the percentage regulation when carrying a load of 200 watts at constant secondary voltage of 12.2 volts and power factor 0.7.

If the load is noninductive what is the percentage regulation, other conditions remaining the same?

10. An autotransformer has 200 turns. There are 120 turns between a and b, Fig. 253. When the line voltage is 2,200 volts, what is the load voltage between b and c? If the load is noninductive and equal to 4,400 watts, calculate I_1, I_2, and I, assuming no transformer losses.

11. Calculate the efficiency of a constant-potential transformer from the following data: A 5-kw. transformer has a no-load power consumption of 95 watts. The no-load primary and secondary p.ds. are 2,200 and 110 volts, used as a step-down transformer. The resistance of the primary winding

is 10 ohms and of the secondary 0.03 ohm. Calculate the efficiency at full, 0.5, and 0.2 load at constant secondary potential of 110 volts. The load power factor is 0.8.

12. A 55-ohm, noninductive resistance and a motor are connected in series across a 115-volt, 60-cycle line. The voltage across the resistance measures 66 volts, and across the motor 70 volts. (a) Calculate the current. (b) Calculate the phase angle for the motor and also for the combined load. (c) Calculate the total active power, and the active power used by the motor. Draw the voltage vector diagram to scale.

13. Each winding of a two-phase generator delivers 50 amperes at 440 volts to a three-wire transmission line. (a) What is the voltage between the outside wires and the common return wire? (b) What is the voltage between the outside wires? (c) What is the current in the common return wire? (d) What is the active power delivered to the receiving motor which has a lag angle of 25°?

14. 50 amperes at 440 volts are generated in each of the windings of a three-phase dynamo. The windings are Y connected to a transmission line. (a) What is the voltage between the mains? (b) What is the current in each main? (c) What is the active power delivered to a Y-connected motor having a phase lag angle of 25°?

15. Solve Problem 14 for a Δ-connected generator and a Δ-connected motor.

16. A transmission line has an ohmic resistance of 2 ohms and an inductance of 0.008 henry. The frequency is 60 cycles/sec. The load consists of a motor in parallel with a condenser. The terminal voltage, across motor and condenser, is 220 volts. The motor takes 10 amperes at a power factor of 0.8. The capacitance of the condenser is 30 mfs. Calculate (a) the current through the condenser and the line current. (b) The phase angle of the load. (c) The generator voltage. (d) The overall phase angle. (e) The % regulation of the line. (f) The load active power. (g) The generator active power. (h) The efficiency of the line.

What capacitance in parallel with the motor will cause the load phase angle to be zero? With this capacitance in parallel with the motor obtain answers to the foregoing questions.

17. As in Section 266, prove that when resistances and reactances are transferred from secondary to primary the relations are

$$R_1 = R_2 \left(\frac{N_1}{N_2}\right)^2,$$

and

$$x_1 = x_2 \left(\frac{N_1}{N_2}\right)^2,$$

where R_1 and x_1 are equivalent primary resistance and reactance respectively.

CHAPTER XX

COMPLEX QUANTITIES

278. Before 1797 algebraic expressions were used to represent magnitudes only. In 1797 Casper Wessel presented a memoir to the Royal Academy of Science and Letters of Denmark entitled, "On the Analytical Representation of Direction." This memoir laid the foundation for vector analysis, for the theory of functions of a complex variable, and for the Steinmetz method of handling alternating currents.

In this memoir Wessel introduced the $\sqrt{-1}$ as the sign of *perpendicularity*. He used the letter ϵ to indicate $\sqrt{-1}$. Both i and j are now used. We shall use j since i is used for currents. Wessel showed that a vector quantity may be represented both in magnitude and direction by an algebraic expression. He used j, not as a factor in the strict algebraic sense, but as an *operator* functioning to rotate a vector through an angle of 90°.

Before 1797 j was taken as a sign of the impossibility of a solution, just as at an earlier date a minus quantity was thought of as an impossibility. In the sense of being less than zero a negative quantity is unthinkable, but when used to indicate a magnitude relative to some fixed reference point it has a very definite meaning. Likewise, j has a very definite meaning when used as an operator which functions to rotate a vector through 90°, and it serves a very useful purpose.

279. j as an Operator. — Any vector quantity a may be represented by a line, thus ⟶, where the length of the line indicates magnitude and the arrow tip indicates sense. If now a be multiplied by -1, or rather operated upon by -1, we have $-a$, and the graphical representation is ⟵. Operating upon the vector a by -1 is equivalent therefore to rotating it through 180° in the positive or counterclockwise sense. Consequently, operating upon the vector a by j should be equivalent to rotating the vector through an angle of 90°, since $j^2 = -1$. Operating upon the vector a by j^3 rotates the vector through 270°, and by j^4 through 360°.   This is clearly shown in Fig. 267.

The horizontal axis, x axis, is called the *axis of reals*, and the vertical axis, y axis, is called the *axis of imaginaries*. It must be remembered, however, that vectors in or parallel to the axis of imaginaries are just as real as vectors in or parallel to the axis of reals.   All that ja means is that the vector a has been rotated in the positive sense through 90° from the positive x position. j is merely a symbol which tells us that this operation of rotation has been performed.

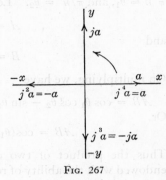

Fig. 267

280. Other Roots of −1 than the Square Root. — Since j, used as an operator, rotates a vector through an angle of 90°, it is to be expected that higher roots of −1, when used as operators, will, also, rotate a vector through some angle, but a smaller angle.   Thus, we

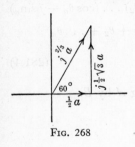

Fig. 268

should expect $\sqrt[3]{-1}$ to be endowed as an operator with the ability of rotating a vector through an angle of 60°, since three applications as an algebraic multiplier, is equivalent to multiplying by −1.   This may be represented as in Fig. 268.   The vector a has been rotated from the positive x position through an angle of 60°.   The *real* component is $a \cos 60° = (\frac{1}{2})a$, and the *imaginary* component is $a \sin 60° = \frac{1}{2}\sqrt{3}a$.   Thus, in the complex notation

$$\sqrt[3]{-1}\, a = j^{2/3}a = a \cos 60° + ja \sin 60° = c + jb. \qquad (280.1)$$

Likewise for the $\sqrt[4]{-1} = j^{2/4}$, when used as an operator, we have

$$j^{2/4}a = a \cos 45° + ja \sin 45° = c + jb. \qquad (280.2)$$

And for the $\sqrt[n]{-1} = j^{\frac{2}{n}}$, we have

$$j^{\frac{2}{n}}a = a \cos \frac{\pi}{n} + ja \sin \frac{\pi}{n} = c + jb. \qquad (280.3)$$

281. Products, Quotients, and Powers of $j^{\frac{2}{n}}$. — Let $j^{\frac{2}{n}} = A$, $j^{\frac{2}{n'}} = B$, $\pi/n = \theta_1$, and $\pi/n' = \theta_2$. Let us consider the two operators

$$A = \cos \theta_1 + j \sin \theta_1 \qquad (281.1)$$

and

$$B = \cos \theta_2 + i \sin \theta_2. \qquad (281.2)$$

On multiplying, we have

$$AB = \cos \theta_1 \cos \theta_2 - \sin \theta_1 \sin \theta_2 + j(\sin \theta_1 \cos \theta_2 + \cos \theta_1 \sin \theta_2).$$

Or

$$AB = \cos(\theta_1 + \theta_2) + j \sin(\theta_1 + \theta_2). \qquad (281.3)$$

Thus the product of two operators, A and B, is a new operator endowed with the ability of rotating the vector operated upon through an angle which is the algebraic sum of the rotations produced by the two operators when functioning separately.

Similarly, the product of any number of operators is a new operator which rotates the vector operated upon through an angle which is the sum of the individual rotations. Thus,

$$ABC, \ldots N = (\cos \theta_1 + j \sin \theta_1)(\cos \theta_2 + j \sin \theta_2) \ldots (\cos \theta_n + j \sin_n)$$

$$= \cos(\theta_1 + \theta_2 + \ldots \theta_n) + j \sin(\theta_1 + \theta_2 + \ldots \theta_n)$$

$$= \cos \sum_1^n \theta + j \sin \sum_1^n \theta. \qquad (281.4)$$

Let us next investigate the effect of dividing A by B.

$$\frac{A}{B} = \frac{\cos \theta_1 + j \sin \theta_1}{\cos \theta_2 + j \sin \theta_2}.$$

Multiply numerator and denominator by the *conjugate* of the denominator, i.e., by $\cos \theta_2 - j \sin \theta_2$, we have

$$A/B = \frac{(\cos \theta_1 \cos \theta_2 + \sin \theta_1 \sin \theta_2) + j(\sin \theta_1 \cos \theta_2 - \cos \theta_1 \sin \theta_2)}{\cos^2 \theta_2 + \sin^2 \theta_2}.$$

Or

$$A/B = \cos(\theta_1 - \theta_2) + j \sin(\theta_1 - \theta_2). \qquad (281.5)$$

Thus the quotient of two operators, A and B, is a new operator endowed with the ability of rotating the vector operated upon through an angle which is the difference of the rotations produced by the two operators when functioning separately.

The same result is obtained by multiplying the operator A by the conjugate of the operator B. Thus,

$$(\cos \theta_1 + j \sin \theta_1)(\cos \theta_2 - j \sin \theta_2) = \cos(\theta_1 - \theta_2) + j \sin(\theta_1 - \theta_2). \quad (281.6)$$

Thus, dividing an operator by an operator having any positive rotation is the same as multiplying it by an operator which has the same rotation in the reverse sense.

Reciprocal of an Operator. — Let us next examine the effect of taking the reciprocal of an operator. We have

$$\frac{1}{\cos \theta + j \sin \theta} = \frac{\cos \theta - j \sin \theta}{(\cos \theta + j \sin \theta)(\cos \theta - j \sin \theta)}$$

$$= \frac{\cos \theta - j \sin \theta}{\cos^2 \theta + \sin^2 \theta} = \cos \theta - j \sin \theta. \quad (281.7)$$

Therefore, taking the reciprocal of an operator which produces a positive rotation θ gives an operator which rotates the vector operated upon into the position $-\theta$. Likewise, the reciprocal of the conjugate of an operator gives an operator which, when acting upon a vector, rotates it into the position $+\theta$.

Powers of Operators. — In the case of two operators producing equal angular rotations, we have, when taking the product,

$$A^2 = \cos 2\theta + j \sin 2\theta = (\cos \theta + j \sin \theta)^2,$$

since

$$\cos 2\theta = \cos^2 \theta - \sin^2 \theta, \quad \text{and} \quad \sin 2\theta = 2 \sin \theta \cos \theta.$$

Or, in general

$$A^n = \cos n\theta + j \sin n\theta = (\cos \theta + j \sin \theta)^n \quad (281.8)$$

Since, as used here, $n\theta = \pi$ radians, we have

$$A^n = A^{\frac{\pi}{\theta}} = \cos \pi + j \sin \pi = -1. \quad (281.9)$$

And therefore,

$$A = \sqrt[n]{-1} = j^{\frac{2}{n}} = \cos \frac{\pi}{n} + j \sin \frac{\pi}{n}, \quad (281.10)$$

which is the same as equation (280.3).

Thus, $j^{\frac{2}{n}}$ is an operator which functions to rotate a vector operated upon through an angle π/n radians. In the applications of these operators the vector is rotated, through the angle indicated, from its initial position in the *complex plane*, which may or may not be the positive x position. The operator $(\cos \theta + j \sin \theta)$ rotates a vector through the angle θ in the positive sense from its initial position, and the operator $(\cos \theta - j \sin \theta)$ rotates the vector through the angle θ in the negative sense from its initial position.

Uniform Angular Rotation. — Let us say that we have a vector of constant magnitude which is rotating with constant angular velocity, $\omega = 2\pi f$ radians per second. Let the time $t = 0$ be when the vector is in the positive x position. At any subsequent time, t sec., the vector will be in the position ωt radians measured in the positive sense of rotation. Clearly, the operator which will function to effect this rotation is

$$j^{\frac{2}{\pi}\omega t} = j^{4ft} = \cos \omega t + j \sin \omega t. \qquad (281.11)$$

282. The Complex Form $a + jb$. — As we have seen the operator $\cos \theta + j \sin \theta$ rotates the vector operated upon through the angle θ in the positive sense from its initial position. Thus, the position of the vector $\bar{A}$ in the complex plane is given by

$$A(\cos \theta + j \sin \theta) = A \cos \theta + jA \sin \theta = a + jb, \quad (282.1)$$

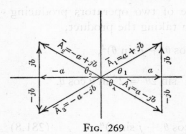

FIG. 269

where $a = A \cos \theta$ and $b = A \sin \theta$. To distinguish between vector and scalar quantities we will, as is customary, place a bar over the symbol, as $\bar{A}$, to indicate a vector quantity, and write the symbol without a bar to indicate a scalar quantity.

In Fig. 269 there are represented four vectors of equal magnitude but occupying different positions in the complex plane:

$$\bar{A}_1 = a + jb,$$
$$\bar{A}_2 = -a + jb,$$
$$\bar{A}_3 = -a - jb, \qquad (282.2)$$
$$\bar{A}_4 = a - jb.$$

The absolute value of the vector is always

$$A = \sqrt{a^2 + b^2}. \qquad (282.3)$$

The positions of the above vectors are given by $\theta_1 = \text{arc tan } b/a$, $\theta_2 = \text{arc tan } \dfrac{b}{-a}$, $\theta_3 = \text{arc tan } \dfrac{-b}{-a}$, $\theta_4 = \text{arc tan } -b/a$. The expression $a + jb$ is called a *complex number*.

In any equation involving complex numbers the algebraic sum of the real terms on one side of the equation is equal to the algebraic sum of the real terms on the other side of the equation. Also, the algebraic sum of the real parts of the imaginary terms on one side of the equation is equal to the algebraic sum of the real parts of the imaginary terms on the other side of the equation. Furthermore, as in (282.3), the square of the real part of a complex number plus the square of the real part of the imaginary term is equal to the square of the magnitude of the vector. j takes no part in obtaining the absolute value of a vector. It is merely an operator.

283. Application to Alternating Currents.

The expression for impedance is of the form $z = \sqrt{r^2 + x^2}$, where $x = L\omega$, $1/C\omega$, or $L\omega - 1/C\omega$ as the case may be. While impedance is not a vector quantity, it may be written in the complex form, thus $Z = r + jx$. Then, writing the equation $I = \dfrac{\mathscr{E}}{\sqrt{r^2 + x^2}}$ for absolute value, we have $\bar{I} = \dfrac{\bar{\mathscr{E}}}{r + jx}$ as the vector form of the equation. Therefore,

$$\bar{\mathscr{E}} = \bar{I}(r + jx) = r\bar{I} + jx\bar{I} = \mathscr{E} + j\mathscr{E}'. \qquad (283.1)$$

$r\bar{I} = \mathscr{E}$ is the voltage drop across the ohmic resistance and $jx\bar{I} = j\mathscr{E}'$ is the voltage drop across the reactance. j merely indicates that $x\bar{I}$ is in quadrature with $r\bar{I}$.

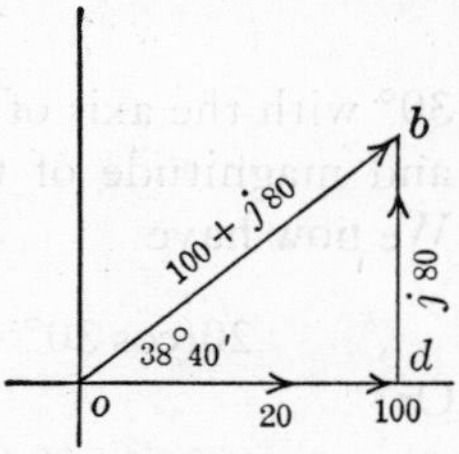

Example. — Let $r = 5$ ohms, $x = 4$ ohms ($L\omega = x$, if $f = 60$ cycles/sec, $L = 0.0106$ henry), and the current is 20 amperes.

Taking $\bar{I}$ as the axis of reference, i.e., as the axis of reals, we have for an inductive circuit

Fig. 270

$$\bar{\mathscr{E}} = 20(5 + j4) = 100 + j80.$$

Therefore

$$\mathscr{E} = \sqrt{100^2 + 80^2} = 128 \text{ volts.}$$

$\theta = $ arc tan $80/100 = 38°\,40'$.   The vector diagram is as shown in Fig. 270.

Instead of taking $\overline{I}$ as the axis of reals, let $\overline{\mathscr{E}}$ (unknown) be taken in the axis of reals.   We then have

$$20(\cos\theta + j\sin\theta) = \frac{\overline{\mathscr{E}}}{5 + j4} = \frac{\mathscr{E}(5 - j4)}{41}$$

Or

$$820\cos\theta + j820\sin\theta = 5\mathscr{E} - j4\mathscr{E}.$$ From which we have

$$820\sin\theta = -4\mathscr{E},$$

$$820\cos\theta = 5\mathscr{E},$$

and therefore, $\theta = $ arc tan $-4/5 = -(38°\,40')$, and $\mathscr{E} = 128$ volts, as before.   To obtain the complex form of $\overline{I}$, we have

$$I = \frac{128}{5 + j4} = \frac{128(5 - j4)}{41} = 15.6 - j12.48.$$

Hence the absolute value of $\overline{I}$ is $I = \sqrt{15.6^2 + 12.48^2} = 20$ amperes.

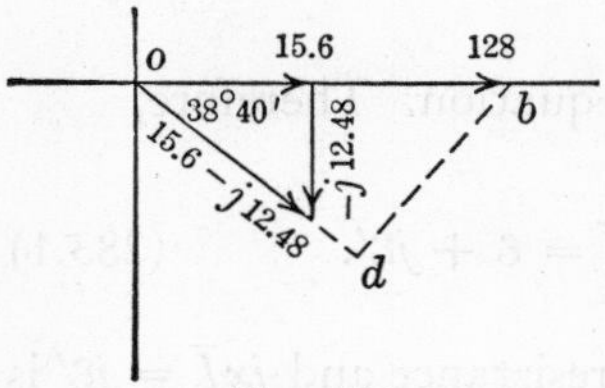

In this case the positions of the vectors in the complex plane are shown in Fig. 271.

FIG. 271

$\overline{I}$ is in the proper relation to $\overline{\mathscr{E}}$.   The vector diagram of Fig. 270 has been rotated in the negative sense through an angle of $77°\,20'$, but the absolute values are the same as before, as they should be.

As still another variation, let us say that the current vector makes an angle of $30°$ with the axis of reals, and let it be required to find the location and magnitude of the voltage vector.   Let the data be as before. We now have

$$20(\cos 30° + j\sin 30°)(5 + j4) = \mathscr{E}(\cos\theta + j\sin\theta).$$

Or

$$46.6 + j119.28 = \mathscr{E}\cos\theta + j\mathscr{E}\sin\theta.$$

And

$$\mathscr{E}\sin\theta = 119.28,$$

$$\mathscr{E}\cos\theta = 46.6.$$

Therefore, $\theta = $ arc tan $119.28/46.6 = 68°\ 40'$. The complex expression for $\mathscr{E}$ is $\overline{\mathscr{E}} = 46.6 + j\,119.28$, and therefore

$$\mathscr{E} = \sqrt{46.6^2 + 119.28^2} = 128 \text{ volts, as before.}$$

The complex expression for I is $\overline{I} = 17.32 + j\,10$, and therefore

$$I = \sqrt{17.32^2 + 10^2} = 20 \text{ amperes.}$$

The vectors in their proper relations in the complex plane are shown in Fig. 272. The triangle odb, Figs. 270, 271, and 272, represents the vector polygon for the potential drops, and therefore, is the same polygon as odb in Figs. 211 and 212. It is seen that the vectors may

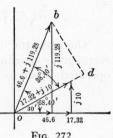

Fig. 272

take any position in the complex plane, but always they have the same positions relative to each other.

284. The Exponential Operator. $e^{\pm j\theta}$. — When, in the use of operators, the phase relationships between vectors are required the operator (cos $\theta \pm j$ sin θ) is convenient. The complex quantity $(a \pm j\,b)$ is a convenient form when adding, subtracting, multiplying, or dividing vector quantities in mixed equations. When multiplication and division of vectors alone are to be performed the exponential operator

$$e^{\pm j\theta}$$

is most convenient. To obtain the expression for $e^{j\theta}$, we use the well-known relations

$$e^{j\theta} = \cos\theta + j\sin\theta, \qquad (284.1)$$

$$e^{-j\theta} = \cos\theta - j\sin\theta. \qquad (284.2)$$

Therefore, since $n\theta = \pi$, we have, for counterclockwise rotation,

$$^{\frac{\pi}{\theta}}\!\sqrt{-1} = j^{\frac{2\theta}{\pi}} = e^{j\theta} = \cos\theta + j\sin\theta. \qquad (284.3), \text{ by } (281.10)$$

And for clockwise rotation,

$$^{-\frac{\pi}{\theta}}\!\sqrt{-1} = j^{-\frac{2\theta}{\pi}} = e^{-j\theta} = \cos\theta - j\sin\theta. \qquad (284.4)$$

If the rotation is to be a function of time, we have as operator, by putting $\theta = \omega t$,

$$\frac{\pi}{\omega t}\sqrt{-1} = j^{\frac{2\omega t}{\pi}} = e^{j\omega t} = \cos \omega t + j \sin \omega t, \qquad (284.5)$$

$$-\frac{\pi}{\omega t}\sqrt{-1} = j^{-\frac{2\omega t}{\pi}} = e^{-j\omega t} = \cos \omega t - j \sin \omega t. \qquad (284.6)$$

The operator $(\cos \theta \pm j \sin \theta)$ refers the vector operated upon to rectangular coordinates. The exponential operator refers the vector operated upon to polar coordinates. It is easy to show that the various forms the operator may take produce the same results when used as an operator.

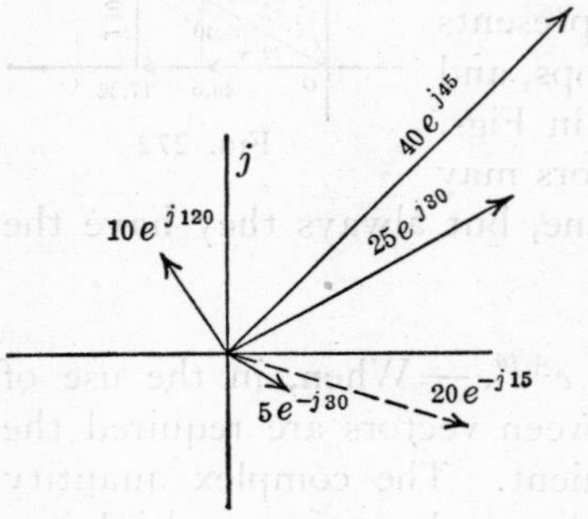

Fig. 273

Example. — Let it be required to obtain the result of dividing the product of two vectors, $\bar{A}_1$ and $\bar{A}_2$, by the product of two other vectors, $\bar{A}_3$ and $\bar{A}_4$. Let $A_1 = 25$, making an angle of 30° with the axis of reals, $A_2 = 40$, making an angle of 45° with the axis of reals, $A_3 = 5$, making an angle of −30° with the axis of reals, and $A_4 = 10$, making an angle of 120° with the axis of reals. We then have

$$\bar{A}_1 = 25 \,(\cos 30° \quad + j \sin 30°) \quad = 25e^{j30},$$

$$\bar{A}_2 = 40 \,(\cos 45° \quad + j \sin 45°) \quad = 40e^{j45},$$

$$\bar{A}_3 = 5 \,(\cos -30° + j \sin -30°) = 5e^{-j30},$$

$$\bar{A}_4 = 10 \,(\cos 120° \quad + j \sin 120°) \quad = 10e^{j120}.$$

Then

$$A = \frac{25 \times 40}{5 \times 10} \times \frac{e^{j30} \times e^{j45}}{e^{-j30} \times e^{j120}} = 20e^{j(30+45+30-120)}.$$

Or

$$20e^{-j15} = 20 \,(\cos 15 - j \sin 15) = 19.32 - j5.18,$$

and

$$A = \sqrt{19.32^2 + 5.18^2} = 20.$$

The vectors are shown in their proper phase relations in Fig. 273.

285. Further Consideration of $a + jb$. — a is called the *ordinary number* or *horizontal distance*. jb is called the *quadrature number* or *vertical distance*. j is the operator or *quadrature unit*.

Multiplication of $a + jb$ by j. Let $\bar{A}_1 = a + jb$. Then

$$\bar{A}_2 = (+a + jb)j = -b + ia,$$
$$\bar{A}_3 = (-b + ja)j = -a - jb,$$
$$\bar{A}_4 = (-a - jb)j = +b - ja,$$
$$\bar{A}_1 = \bar{A}_5 = (+b - ja)j = +a + jb.$$

Thus, multiplying a complex number by j rotates the vector through 90°, Fig. 274.

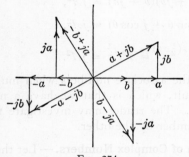

FIG. 274

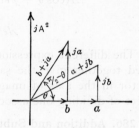

FIG. 275

Conjugate Numbers. — $a + jb$ and $a - jb$ are called *conjugate numbers*.

$$a + jb = A(\cos \theta + j \sin \theta) = Ae^{j\theta}, \quad \text{where } A = \sqrt{a^2 + b^2}.$$
$$a - jb = A(\cos \theta - j \sin \theta) = Ae^{-j\theta},$$
$$(a + jb)(a - jb) = a^2 + b^2 = A^2.$$

Also,

$$A(\cos \theta + j \sin \theta)A(\cos \theta - j \sin \theta) = A^2,$$

and

$$Ae^{j\theta} \times Ae^{-j\theta} = A^2.$$

Thus, the product of conjugate numbers is a vector equal to the (scalar value)^2 of one of them, which is located in the horizontal axis or axis of reals. It is left to the reader to investigate the effect of dividing $a + jb$ by $a - jb$.

Associate Numbers. — The complex numbers $a + jb$ and $b + ja$ are called *associate numbers*. Their positions are indicated in Fig. 275. Let us put them in the forms

$$a + jb = A(\cos \theta + j \sin \theta) = Ae^{j\theta},$$

$$b + ja = A\left(\cos\left(\frac{\pi}{2} - \theta\right) + j \sin\left(\frac{\pi}{2} - \theta\right)\right)$$

$$= A(\sin \theta + j \cos \theta) = Ae^{j\left(\frac{\pi}{2} - \theta\right)}.$$

Let us then form the products of these numbers.

$$(a + jb)(b + ja) = jA^2,$$

$$A(\cos \theta + j \sin \theta)A(\sin \theta + j \cos \theta) = jA^2,$$

$$Ae^{j\theta} \times Ae^{j\left(\frac{\pi}{2} - \theta\right)} = A^2 e^{j\frac{\pi}{2}} = jA^2.$$

The different expressions for the associate numbers when multiplied together give the same result, which is that we have a new vector in the axis of imaginaries. The reader may investigate the effect of dividing one associate number by the other.

286. Addition and Subtraction of Complex Numbers. — Let there be two vectors

$$\bar{A}_1 = a_1 + jb_1 \quad \text{and} \quad \bar{A}_2 = a_2 + jb_2,$$

as indicated in Fig. 276. When added, we have

$$\bar{A} = \bar{A}_1 + \bar{A}_2 = (a_1 + jb_1) + (a_2 + jb_2)$$

$$= (a_1 + a_2) + j(b_1 + b_2) = a + jb.$$

As will be seen, by comparing the mathematical expressions with Fig. 276, adding complex numbers is the same as geometric or vector addition.

Conversely.
$$\bar{A} - \bar{A}_1 = \bar{A}_2 = (a + jb) - (a_1 + jb_1)$$
$$= (a - a_1) + j(b - b_1) = a_2 + jb_2.$$

This is geometric or vector subtraction. Any number of vector quantities may be easily added or subtracted when represented as complex numbers. The absolute value of the vector $\overline{A}$, or the scalar value is $\sqrt{a^2 + b^2}$. The position of the vector A is given by

$$\theta = \text{arc tan } \frac{b}{a}$$

the quadrant in which the vector lies being determined by the signs attached to a and b in the complex number.

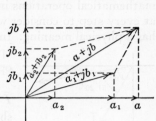

Fig. 276

Example. — Let there be a divided circuit consisting of two branches. The current in one branch is

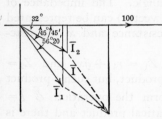

Fig. 277

$\overline{I}_1 = i_1 + ji_2$ and in the other branch $\overline{I}_2 = i_3 + ji_4$. Then the current in the main line is given by

$$\overline{I} = (i_1 + ji_2) + (i_3 + ji_4)$$
$$= (i_1 + i_3) + j(i_2 + i_4)$$
$$= i + ji'.$$

If the impedance of one branch is $Z_1 = 4 + j6$, and of the other branch is $Z_2 = 8 + j5$, and the impressed p.d. is 100 volts, we have

$$\overline{I}_1 = \frac{100}{4 + j6} = 7.69 - j11.53,$$

$$\overline{I}_2 = \frac{100}{8 + j5} = 9 - j5.61,$$

$$I_1 = \sqrt{7.69^2 + 11.53^2} = 13.86 \text{ amperes,}$$

$$I_2 = \sqrt{9^2 + 5.61^2} = 10.6 \text{ amperes,}$$

$$\overline{I} = (7.69 + 9) - j(11.53 + 5.61) = 16.69 - j17.14,$$

$$I = \sqrt{16.69^2 + 17.14^2} = 23.9 \text{ amperes,}$$

$$\theta_1 = \text{arc tan } -\frac{11.53}{7.69} = -(56° \ 20'),$$

$$\theta_2 = \text{arc tan } \frac{5.61}{9} = 32°,$$

$$\theta = \text{arc tan } \frac{17.14}{16.69} = 45° \ 45'.$$

The vectors are shown in their relative positions in Fig. 277.

287. Physical Interpretations of Mathematical Operations. — In mathematical operations involving physical quantities it is necessary at every step to consider whether or not the mathematical operation has a physical meaning. In the use of complex numbers, or any of the operators, it is imperative to inquire if the operations have physical interpretations.

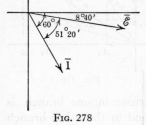

FIG. 278

Thus, in alternating currents the vector $\bar{I}$ can be represented by $\bar{I} = i_1 - ji_2$, as shown in Fig. 278. The voltage $\bar{\mathscr{E}}$ of the same frequency, may be represented by $\bar{\mathscr{E}} = \mathscr{E}_1 - j\,\mathscr{E}_2$. The angle between $\bar{\mathscr{E}}$ and $\bar{I}$ is the phase angle. The impedance of the circuit (not a vector) can be represented by $Z = r \pm jx$, where r is the ohmic resistance and x the reactance.

Now, if we have two impedances, $Z_1 = r_1 + jx_1$ and $Z_2 = r_2 - jx_2$, we can obtain the mathematical product, but such a product has no physical meaning. If we perform the operation $\bar{\mathscr{E}}\,\bar{I} = (i_1 + j\,i_2)(\mathscr{E}_1 + j\,\mathscr{E}_2)$, we have a mathematical product and there is some vector in the complex plane for which it stands. However, this product does not give the power in the circuit, since power has twice the frequency of either current or voltage, and hence, cannot be represented by a vector in the same vector diagram. This product, therefore, has no physical meaning. If we have a current $\bar{I} = i_1 + ji_2$ and an impedance $Z = r + jx$, the product is a voltage of the same frequency as the current, and so represents the actual voltage. Thus, in this case,

$$\bar{\mathscr{E}} = Z\bar{I} = (r + jx)(i_1 + ji_2) = (ri_1 - xi_2) + j(ri_2 + xi_1)$$

$$= \mathscr{E}_1 + j\mathscr{E}_2.$$

Example. — Let the current be 10 amperes and the angle it makes with the axis of reals, $-60°$. Required to find the voltage, the phase angle, and the angle $\bar{\mathscr{E}}$ makes with the axis of reals. We have

$$\bar{I} = 10(\cos - 60° + j \sin - 60°) = 5 - j8.66.$$

Let $Z = 4 + j5$. Then, $\bar{\mathscr{E}} = (5 - j8.66)(4 + j5) = 63.3 - j9.64.$

Therefore, $\mathscr{E} = \sqrt{63.3^2 + 9.64^2} = 64$ volts,

$\phi = $ arc tan $5/4 = 51° 20'$;

$$\theta = \text{arc tan } \frac{-9.64}{63.3} = - (8° 40').$$

The vectors are shown in Fig. 278.

PROBLEMS

1. Show that $j = e^{j\frac{\pi}{2}}$. That is, multiplying by j rotates the vector through $+ \frac{\pi}{2}$ radians.

Show, also, that $j^{-1} = e^{-j\frac{\pi}{2}}$. That is, dividing by j rotates the vector through $- \frac{\pi}{2}$ radians.

2. Show that, if n is an integar,
$$\sqrt[n]{j} = \cos \frac{\pi}{2} n + j \sin \frac{\pi}{2} n.$$

3. Find the value of j^j.

4. Find the vector represented by $(6 - j2)\left\{\dfrac{3 + j2}{4 - j5}\right\}$.

5. Show that
$$\sqrt{a + jb} = \pm \frac{1}{\sqrt{2}} \{(\sqrt{a^2 + b^2} + a)^{\frac{1}{2}} + j(\sqrt{a^2 + b^2} - a)^{\frac{1}{2}}\}.$$

6. Show that $\sqrt[n]{-1} = \cos \dfrac{(2m + 1)\pi}{n} + j \sin \dfrac{(2m + 1)\pi}{n}$, where m is any whole number, positive or negative, including zero.

7. Evaluate $\sqrt[j]{j}$.

See Revolving Vectors by G. W. Patterson.

CHAPTER XXI

COMPLEX QUANTITY METHOD IN ALTERNATING CURRENTS

288. Since alternating currents and voltages are essentially harmonic, their relations in networks of conductors, generators, motors, or transformers may be represented by vectors in a clock diagram. Hence, any problem in alternating currents may be solved in either one of two ways: (*a*) Graphically, by drawing the vectors in their proper relations one to another and measuring with a scale to obtain the desired results. (*b*) Trigonometrically, by setting up the trigonometric equations which express the conditions in vector diagrams and solving these equations to obtain the results. The trigonometric equations are often involved and the solutions are very tedious. This difficulty is lessened very markedly in many instances by the use of complex numbers. The solution of alternating current problems by the use of complex numbers does not constitute a distinct method; it is merely a systematic scheme for carrying out the trigonometric calculations.

The use of complex numbers in alternating current problems involves two distinct ideas: (*a*) The specification of vectors in a clock diagram by giving their components in the directions of chosen axes, the axis of reals and the axis of imaginaries. (*b*) The idea of using impedance and admittance as algebraic operators. Thus, currents and emfs. are vector quantities and are specified as follows:

$$\bar{I} = i_1 + ji_2,$$

$$\bar{\mathscr{E}} = \mathscr{E}_1 + j\mathscr{E}_2.$$

Impedance is of the same form, $Z = r \pm jx$, but it is in the nature of an operator and not a vector quantity. x is inductive reactance and $-x$ is capacitive reactance. The reference axes are conceived to rotate with $\bar{\mathscr{E}}$ and $\bar{I}$, so that $\bar{\mathscr{E}}$ and $\bar{I}$ are stationary with respect to the axes of reference, i.e., the phase relations do not change. The scalar values of $\bar{\mathscr{E}}$ and $\bar{I}$ are their effective values.

570

289. Impedance and Admittance. Ohm's Law. — Impedance, though not a vector quantity, may, nevertheless, be expressed as a complex quantity. The current $\bar{I}$ when multiplied by the impedance, $r \pm jx$, is the p.d. $\bar{\mathscr{E}}$, which is rotated relative to the current vector by this operation through the phase angle $\phi = $ arc tan x/r. Thus, if $\bar{I}$ is taken in the axis of reals, we have

$$\bar{\mathscr{E}} = (r + jx)\bar{I} = r\bar{I} + jx\bar{I} = Z\bar{I}. \tag{289.1}$$

This is Ohm's law in the complex form. $r\bar{I}$ is the potential drop in phase with the impressed emf., the active component, and $x\bar{I}$ is the inductive potential drop in quadrature with the active component of the emf., or wattless component. The scalar value of $\bar{\mathscr{E}}$ is

$$\mathscr{E} = \sqrt{(rI)^2 + (xI)^2}.$$

Thus, numerical magnitudes as well as phase relations are expressed

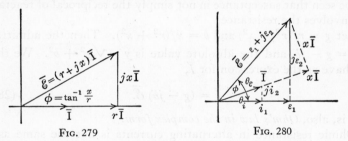

FIG. 279   FIG. 280

by Ohm's law in the complex form. These relations are shown in Fig. 279.

If $\bar{I}$ is not taken in the axis of reals, we have in general,

$$\bar{\mathscr{E}} = (r + jx)(i_1 + ji_2) = (ri_1 - xi_2) + j(ri_2 + xi_1)$$

$$= \mathscr{E}_1 + j\mathscr{E}_2. \tag{289.2}$$

The phase angle is, as always, $\phi = $ arc tan x/r. The angle that $\bar{I}$ makes with the axis of reals is $\theta_i = $ arc tan i_2/i_1, and the angle that $\bar{\mathscr{E}}$ makes with the axis of reals is $\theta_{\mathscr{E}} = $ arc tan $\mathscr{E}_2/\mathscr{E}_1$. The vectors are shown in their relative positions in Fig. 280.

Admittance. — If equation (289.1) is solved for $\bar{I}$, we have

$$\bar{I} = \frac{\bar{\mathscr{E}}}{r + jx}.$$

$r + jx$ is used here as a divisor. Multiplying numerator and denominator by the conjugate of the denominator, we have

$$\bar{I} = \frac{r - jx}{r^2 + x^2}\,\bar{\mathscr{E}} = \left\{\frac{r}{r^2 + x^2} - j\,\frac{x}{r^2 + x^2}\right\}\bar{\mathscr{E}}.$$

Thus,

$$\frac{r}{r^2 + x^2} - j\,\frac{x}{r^2 + x^2} = \frac{1}{r + jx},$$

and, since it is the reciprocal of the effective resistance or impedance of the circuit, it must be the effective conductance. It is called the *admittance* of the circuit, and is multiplied by $\bar{\mathscr{E}}$ to give $\bar{I}$.

The term $r/(r^2 + x^2)$ is called the *conductance* of the circuit. It will be seen that conductance is not the reciprocal of the resistance, but that it involves the reactance.

The term $x/(r^2 + x^2)$ is called the *susceptance* of the circuit. It will be seen that susceptance in not simply the reciprocal of reactance, but involves the resistance.

Let $g = r/(r^2 + x^2)$ and $b = x/(r^2 + x^2)$. Then the admittance is $Y = g - jb$, and the absolute value is $y = \sqrt{g^2 + b^2}$. We therefore have as the expression for $\bar{I}$,

$$\bar{I} = (g - jb)\,\bar{\mathscr{E}}. \tag{289.3}$$

This is, also, *Ohm's law in the complex form.*

Ohmic resistance in alternating currents is not the same as for direct currents, i.e., the measured resistance of a conductor for alternating currents is not the same as for direct currents, even though the temperature has not changed. In the case of a homogeneous isotropic conductor the current density is constant over the cross section of the conductor when a direct current flows in the conductor. If, however, an alternating current is flowing in the conductor the current density will not be constant over the cross section of the conductor. It will be greater at or near the surface than at the center. The current flowing in the conductor at or near the center will be surrounded by more magnetic flux than at or near the periphery. Therefore, the inductance, and hence the impedance, at or near the center will be greater than at or near the periphery. The impedance increases from the periphery to the center, and, consequently, the current density decreases from the periphery to the center. The impedance increases with the frequency, but more rapidly at the center than at the periphery. Thus, as the frequency increases the current is confined more and more to the surface layers of the conductor. This is the well-known *skin effect*. Since the effective cross section of the conductor decreases as the frequency increases, the ohmic resistance increases as the frequency increases. For this reason conductors used for high-frequent currents are hollow tubes or are made of finely stranded wires.

290. Capacitance in an Alternating Current Circuit. — In a circuit containing ohmic resistance and capacitance the potential drop across the resistance is rI and across the capacitance, $-I/C\omega = -x_1I$. If the potential drop across an inductance is positive (lagging current) the potential drop across a capacitance is negative (leading current). Thus, we have

$$\overline{\mathscr{E}} = r\overline{I} - \frac{j\overline{I}}{C\omega} = (r - jx_1)\overline{I}. \tag{290.1}$$

Steinmetz called x_1 *condensive reactance* or *condensance*. The complex quantity

$$Z = r - jx_1 \tag{290.2}$$

is a quantity which operates, when multiplied by the current, to rotate the emf. vector through the phase angle in the negative sense relative to the current vector. The phase angle is

$$\phi = \arctan \frac{x_1}{r}.$$

In general, when I is in the complex form, we have

$$\overline{\mathscr{E}} = (r - jx_1)(i_1 + ji_2) = (ri_1 + x_1i_2) + j(ri_2 - x_1i_1)$$

$$= \mathscr{E}_1 + j\mathscr{E}_2. \tag{290.3}$$

If in (290.1) we solve for $\overline{I}$, we have

$$\overline{I} = \frac{\overline{\mathscr{E}}}{r - jx_1} = \left\{ \frac{r}{r^2 + x_1{}^2} + j\frac{x_1}{r^2 + x_1{}^2} \right\} \overline{\mathscr{E}} = (g + jb)\,\overline{\mathscr{E}}. \tag{290.4}$$

In the most general case a circuit contains resistance, inductance, and capacitance. The complex expression for the impedance is then

$$Z = r + j(x - x_1). \tag{290.5}$$

The admittance is

$$Y = \frac{r}{r^2 + (x - x_1)^2} - j \frac{x - x_1}{r^2 + (x - x_1)^2} = g \pm jb. \quad (290.6)$$

The sign of the imaginary term will depend upon the relative magnitudes of x and x_1.

291. Kirchhoff's Laws in the Complex Form. — By expressing currents, voltages, and impedances as complex quantities Kirchhoff's laws are reestablished in their original form. In direct currents the quantities are all scalar, and the ordinary laws of algebra suffice for all solutions. In alternating current circuits, on the other hand, the quantities are vectors, expressible as complex numbers, and obey the laws of vector algebra. Therefore Ohm's law and Kirchhoff's laws are still true laws for the electric circuit, but the quantities involved are complex and used in the same manner as are real quantities in direct currents. Thus, Kirchhoff's laws may be stated as follows:

1. The sum of all the potential differences acting in a closed circuit is zero when expressed as complex quantities. That is, the sum of the components along the axis of reals, active components, is equal to zero, and the sum of the components along the axis of imaginaries, wattless components, is equal to zero.

2. The sum of all of the currents at a junction or distributing point is equal to zero when expressed in the complex form. That is, the sum of the components along the axis of reals, active components, is equal to zero, and the sum of the components along the axis of imaginaries, wattless components, is equal to zero.

To illustrate the first law, consider a simple circuit containing an impressed harmonic emf., a resistance, and an inductance. Then

$$\bar{\mathscr{E}} = Z\bar{I}, \quad \text{or} \quad \mathscr{E}_1 + j\mathscr{E}_2 = (r + jx)\bar{I}.$$

We then have

$$\mathscr{E}_1 - r\bar{I} = 0 \quad \text{and} \quad \mathscr{E}_2 - x\bar{I} = 0.$$

The vector representation is shown in Fig. 279.

To illustrate the second law, consider an alternating current which divides into two branches. Thus

$$\bar{I} = \bar{I}_1 + \bar{I}_2, \quad \text{or} \quad i_1 + ji_2 = (i_2 + ji_3) + (i_4 + ji_5).$$

Then

$$i_1 - (i_2 + i_4) = 0 \quad \text{and} \quad i_2 - (i_3 + i_5) = 0.$$

The vector representation is shown in Fig. 276, where the quantities stand for currents.

292. Impedances in Series. — Since the current is the same in all parts of a series circuit it will be taken as the basis of phase or the axis of reals in the statement of general equations. When the current is known this is the most convenient. In specific problems this is not always possible. Let us say that there are k impedances connected in series. We then have

$$\bar{\mathscr{E}}_0 = \bar{\mathscr{E}}_1 + \bar{\mathscr{E}}_2 + \ldots \bar{\mathscr{E}}_k = \sum_1^k \bar{\mathscr{E}} = \sum_1^k Z\bar{I}. \qquad (292.1)$$

$\bar{\mathscr{E}}_0 = \mathscr{E}_1 + j\mathscr{E}_2$ is the impressed emf.

$$\left.\begin{aligned}
\bar{\mathscr{E}}_1 &= (r_1 + jx_1)\bar{I}, \\
\bar{\mathscr{E}}_2 &= (r_2 + jx_2)\bar{I}, \\
&\cdots\cdots\cdots \\
\bar{\mathscr{E}}_k &= (r_k + jx_k)\bar{I}.
\end{aligned}\right\} \qquad (292.2)$$

Hence,

$$\bar{\mathscr{E}}_0 = \mathscr{E}_1 + j\mathscr{E}_2 = \sum_1^k \bar{\mathscr{E}} = \left\{\sum_1^k r + j\sum_1^k x\right\}\bar{I}, \qquad (292.3)$$

from which we obtain

$$\mathscr{E}_1 = I\sum_1^k r \quad \text{and} \quad \mathscr{E}_2 = I\sum_1^k x.$$

Thus, in series connection, the effective or equivalent resistance is equal to the scalar sum of the separate resistances, and the equivalent reactance is equal to the scalar sum of the separate reactances. x in the above expressions may be either positive or negative as the case may be.

The equivalent phase angle is

$$\phi = \text{arc tan } \frac{\sum_1^k x}{\sum_1^k r}.$$

The component phase angles are $\phi_1 = \text{arc tan } x_1/r_1, \ldots \phi_k = \text{arc tan } x_k/r_k$. When the current is taken as the basis of phase, and ϕ is positive, the current lags the emf. and inductance predominates in the circuit. If ϕ is negative the current leads the emf. and capacitance predominates in the circuit. When ϕ is positive, we have

$$\sum_{1}^{k} x = L\omega,$$

and when negative

$$\sum_{1}^{k} x = \frac{1}{C\omega}.$$

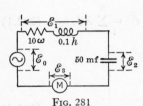

FIG. 281

L and C are the equivalent values for the entire circuit. When series resonance obtains

$$\sum_{1}^{k} x = 0.$$

Example. — Let there be a series circuit as shown in Fig. 281. M is a motor taking 6 amperes at a power factor of 0.8, which is to be maintained at a constant potential of 440 volts. The frequency is 60 cycles/sec. Calculate all of the unknown quantities.

Solution. $\qquad x = L\omega = 37.70$ ohms,

$$x_1 = -1/C\omega = -53.05 \text{ ohms},$$

$$\bar{\mathcal{E}}_0 = \bar{\mathcal{E}}_1 + \bar{\mathcal{E}}_2 + \bar{\mathcal{E}}_3.$$

Or

$$\bar{\mathcal{E}}_0 = (10 + j37.70)\bar{I} - j53.05\bar{I} + 440(\cos\phi_3 + j\sin\phi_3),$$

$$\phi_3 = 36° 52'.$$

Then

$$\bar{\mathcal{E}}_0 = \mathcal{E}_1 + j\mathcal{E}_2 = 10\bar{I} + j(37.70 - 53.05)\bar{I} + 352 + j264.$$

Hence

$$\bar{\mathcal{E}}_0 = \mathcal{E}_1 + j\mathcal{E}_2 = 412 + j171.9.$$

Therefore,

$$\mathcal{E}_0 = \sqrt{412^2 + 171.9^2} = 446.4 \text{ volts},$$

$$\bar{\mathcal{E}}_1 = 60 + j226.2,$$

and hence

$$\mathscr{E}_1 = \sqrt{60^2 + 226.2^2} = 234 \text{ volts,}$$

$$\mathscr{E}_2 = 318.3 \text{ volts,}$$

$$\phi_0 = \text{arc tan } 171.9/412 = 22° 39',$$

$$\phi_1 = \text{arc tan } 226.2/60 = 75° 9',$$

$$\phi_2 = \text{arc tan } -318.3/0 = -90°,$$

$$P_a \text{ (active power)} = \mathscr{E}_0 I \cos \phi_0 = 446.4 \times 6 \cos 22° 39'$$
$$= 2,472 \text{ watts,}$$

$$P_w \text{ (wattless power)} = \mathscr{E}_0 I \sin \phi_0 = 446.4 \times 6 \sin 22° 39'$$
$$= 1,031 \text{ watts.}$$

The vectors drawn to scale are shown in Fig. 282. It will be seen that the capacitance in the line has improved operating conditions. It is left to the reader to calculate the equivalent phase angle and the generator voltage when the condenser is removed.

293. Impedances in Parallel. — When solving problems involving parallel circuits, the first step is to find the equivalent resistance and reactance of each branch. The branches can then be handled as single impedances in parallel. The voltage across the parallel branches is constant. The resultant current, however, is the vector sum of the branch currents. The general expressions are as follows:

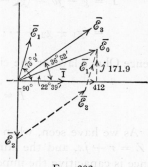

Fig. 282

$$\mathscr{E} = \text{constant,}$$

and therefore

$$\overline{\mathscr{E}} = Z_1 \overline{I}_1 = Z_2 \overline{I}_2 = \cdots Z_k \overline{I}_k, \tag{293.1}$$

$$\overline{I} = \overline{I}_1 + \overline{I}_2 + \cdots \overline{I}_k. \tag{293.2}$$

Therefore,

$$\overline{I} = \frac{\overline{\mathscr{E}}}{Z_1} + \frac{\overline{\mathscr{E}}}{Z_2} + \cdots \frac{\overline{\mathscr{E}}}{Z_k} = \overline{\mathscr{E}}\left(\frac{1}{Z_1} + \frac{1}{Z_2} + \cdots \frac{1}{Z_k}\right). \tag{293.3}$$

Hence the equivalent admittance of the circuit is

$$\frac{1}{Z} = \frac{1}{Z_1} + \frac{1}{Z_2} + \cdots \frac{1}{Z_k}. \tag{293.4}$$

Expressing this equation in the complex form, we have

$$\frac{1}{r + jx} = \frac{1}{r_1 + jx_1} + \frac{1}{r_2 + jx_2} + \cdots \frac{1}{r_k + jx_k}.$$

Rationalizing, we have

$$\frac{r}{r^2 + x^2} - j\frac{x}{r^2 + x^2} = \left(\frac{r_1}{r_1^2 + x_1^2} - j\frac{x_1}{r_1^2 + x_1^2}\right)$$

$$+ \left(\frac{r_2}{r_2^2 + x_2^2} - j\frac{x_2}{r_2^2 + x_2^2}\right) + \cdots \left(\frac{r_k}{r_k^2 + x_k^2} - j\frac{x_k}{r_k^2 + x_k^2}\right).$$

Therefore,

$$Y = g - jb = (g_1 - jb_1) + (g_2 - jb_2) + \cdots (g_k - jb_k)$$

$$= (g_1 + g_2 + \cdots g_k) - j(b_1 + b_2 + \cdots b_k) = \sum_1^k g - j \sum_1^k b.$$

Hence Ohm's law for the circuit in the complex form is

$$\bar{I} = \left(\sum_1^k g - j \sum_1^k b\right) \bar{\mathscr{E}}. \tag{293.5}$$

As we have seen, when the reactance is inductive the impedance is $Z = r + jx$, and the admittance is $Y = g - jb$. When the reactance is capacitive the impedance is $Z = r - jx$, and the admittance is $Y = g + jb$. Thus the signs of the imaginary terms in impedance and admittance are opposite. Further,

$$\bar{I} = (g - jb)\bar{\mathscr{E}} = Y\bar{\mathscr{E}}, \quad \text{and} \quad y = \sqrt{g^2 + b^2}$$

$$\tan \phi = \frac{b}{g}, \quad \cos \phi = \frac{\mathscr{E}g}{I} = \frac{\mathscr{E}g}{\mathscr{E}y} = \frac{g}{y}. \quad \sin \phi = \frac{b}{y}.$$

$$P_a = \mathscr{E}I \cos \phi = \frac{\mathscr{E}(\mathscr{E}y)\ g}{y} = \mathscr{E}^2 g \text{ watts.}$$

$$P_w = \mathscr{E}I \sin \phi = \frac{\mathscr{E}(\mathscr{E}y)\ b}{y} = \mathscr{E}^2 b \text{ watts.}$$

When calculating parallel circuits it is often necessary to determine the equivalent resistance and the equivalent reactance of the simple circuit which would replace the parallel circuit. The equivalent resistance r and reactance x may be found in terms of the equivalent conductance g and the equivalent susceptance b as follows, when the equivalent circuit is inductive:

$$Z = r + jx = \frac{1}{Y} = \frac{1}{g - jb} = \frac{g}{g^2 + b^2} + j\frac{b}{g^2 + b^2}.$$

Therefore,

$$r = \frac{g}{g^2 + b^2} \quad \text{and} \quad x = \frac{b}{g^2 + b^2} = L\omega.$$

When the circuit is capacitive, we have

$$Z = r - jx = \frac{1}{Y} = \frac{1}{g + jb} = \frac{g}{g^2 + b^2} - j\frac{b}{g^2 + b^2}.$$

Therefore,

$$r = \frac{g}{g^2 + b^2} \quad \text{and} \quad x = \frac{b}{g^2 + b^2} = \frac{1}{C\omega}.$$

Example. — An induction motor on a 200-volt, 60-cycle line takes a current of 50 amperes at a power factor of 0.80.

(*a*) Calculate the impedance and power.

(*b*) How will the impedance, total current, power, and power factor be affected by connecting a 200 mf. condenser in parallel with the motor?

(*c*) What capacitance will be required for parallel resonance? Then calculate the impedance, total current, power, and power factor.

Solution. — (*a*) Taking the line voltage as the axis of reals, we have

$$220 = Z50(\cos \phi - j \sin \phi) = Z50(0.8 - j0.6) = Z(40 - j30),$$

$$Z = \frac{220}{40 - j30} = \frac{220(40 + j30)}{2,500} = 3.52 + j2.64,$$

$$z = \sqrt{3.52^2 + 2.64^2} = 4.4 \text{ ohms},$$

$$\phi_L = \text{arc tan} \frac{30}{40} = 36° \, 52',$$

$$P_a = 220 \times 50 \times 0.8 = 8,800 \text{ watts},$$

$$P_w = 220 \times 50 \times 0.6 = 6,600 \text{ watts}.$$

The current vector is $\bar{I}_L = 40 - j30$, oa in Fig. 283, and lags behind the impressed emf. by 36° 52′.

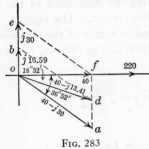

(b) 200 mfs. in parallel with motor.

$$x = \frac{10^6}{200 \times 120\pi} = 13.26 \text{ ohms},$$

$$220 = -j13.26\bar{I}_c, \quad \bar{I}_c = j\frac{220}{13.26} = j16.59,$$

$$I_c = 16.59 \text{ amperes},$$

FIG. 283

$$\bar{I}_L = 40 - j30, \text{ as before}.$$

Therefore,

$$\bar{I} = 40 - j30 + j16.59 = 40 - j13.41,$$

$$I = \sqrt{40^2 + 13.59^2} = 42.188 \text{ amperes},$$

$$\phi = \arctan -\frac{13.41}{40} = -(18° \, 32'),$$

$$\phi_c = \arctan \frac{16.59}{0} = 90°,$$

$$\phi_L = \arctan -\frac{30}{40} = -(36° \, 52'),$$

$$Z = \frac{220}{40 - j13.41} = 4.94 + j1.65,$$

$$z = \sqrt{4.94^2 + 1.65^2} = 5.2 \text{ ohms}.$$

$$P_a = 220 \times 42.188 \cos 18° \, 32' = 8{,}800 \text{ watts}.$$

$$P_w = 220 \times 42.188 \sin 18° \, 32' = 2{,}950 \text{ watts}.$$

The vectors are shown in Fig. 283. The current through the condenser is ob, and the total current is od. The active component of the current is 40 amperes, vector of, as before. The active power is unchanged, but the wattless power has been decreased. The total impedance has been increased, and therefore, the total current has been decreased.

(c) For resonance we have $\sum_{1}^{k} b = 0$. Therefore,

$$Y = \frac{1}{Z_1} + \frac{1}{Z_2} = \frac{1}{3.52 + j2.64} + \frac{1}{0 - jx_1} = \frac{3.52}{19.36} - j\frac{2.64}{19.36} + j\frac{1}{x_1}.$$

Hence

$$\frac{2.64}{19.36} = \frac{1}{x_1}.$$

Therefore,

$$x_1 = 7\tfrac{1}{3} \text{ ohms} = \frac{1}{C\omega}, \quad \text{and hence} \quad C = \frac{10^6}{7\tfrac{1}{3} \times 120\pi} = 361.7 \text{ mfs.}$$

$$Z = \frac{1}{Y} = \frac{19.36}{3.52} = 5.5 \text{ ohms}, \qquad I = \frac{220}{5.5} = 40 \text{ amperes},$$

$$\bar{I}_c = \frac{220}{-j7\tfrac{1}{3}} = j\frac{220}{7\tfrac{1}{3}}, \qquad\qquad I_c = \frac{220}{7\tfrac{1}{3}} = 30 \text{ amperes},$$

$$P_a = 220 \times 40 = 8,800 \text{ watts.} \quad P_w = 0.$$

The vectors are shown in Fig. 283. The current through the motor is vector *oa*, and through the condenser *oe*. The resultant current is *of*, which is now in phase with the impressed emf. The impedance has been increased and the total current decreased. The effect of the condenser is to decrease the wattless component of the current. The active component of the current remains unchanged.

294. Series-Parallel Circuits. — In series-parallel circuits no new problems enter. The circuit is first reduced to an equivalent series circuit by obtaining the equivalent resistance and reactance of the parallel branches. The admittance $(g - jb)$ for the parallel branches is first obtained, and then the equivalent impedance. Thus

$$Z = \frac{1}{g - jb} = \frac{g}{g^2 + b^2} + j\frac{b}{g^2 + b^2} = r + jx.$$

The impedances for the component parts of the circuit may then be added.

Suppose we have a circuit as shown in Fig. 284. For the parallel branches, we have

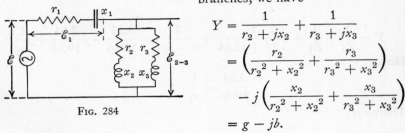

FIG. 284

$$Y = \frac{1}{r_2 + jx_2} + \frac{1}{r_3 + jx_3}$$

$$= \left(\frac{r_2}{r_2{}^2 + x_2{}^2} + \frac{r_3}{r_3{}^2 + x_3{}^2} \right)$$

$$- j \left(\frac{x_2}{r_2{}^2 + x_2{}^2} + \frac{x_3}{r_3{}^2 + x_3{}^2} \right)$$

$$= g - jb.$$

Then

$$Z_{2\text{-}3} = \frac{g}{g^2 + b^2} + j \frac{b}{g^2 + b^2} = r_{2\text{-}3} + jx_{2\text{-}3},$$

and the total impedance is

$$Z = (r_{2\text{-}3} + r_1) + j(x_{2\text{-}3} - x_1) = r \pm jx.$$

For the entire circuit $\bar{\mathscr{E}} = Z\bar{I}$. Also,

$$\bar{\mathscr{E}} = \bar{\mathscr{E}}_1 + \bar{\mathscr{E}}_{2\text{-}3}, \qquad \bar{\mathscr{E}}_1 = (r_1 - jx_1)\bar{I},$$

$$\bar{\mathscr{E}}_{2\text{-}3} = (r_2 + jx_2)\bar{I}_2 = (r_3 + jx_3)\bar{I}_3,$$

$$\bar{I} = \bar{I}_2 + \bar{I}_3, \qquad \phi_1 = \arctan \frac{x_1}{r_1}, \qquad \phi_2 = \arctan \frac{x_2}{r_2},$$

$$\phi_3 = \arctan \frac{x_3}{r_3}, \qquad \phi_{2\text{-}3} = \arctan \frac{x_{2\text{-}3}}{r_{2\text{-}3}}, \qquad \phi = \arctan \frac{x}{r},$$

295. Resonance. — The general equation for a series circuit is

$$\bar{\mathscr{E}} = \left(\sum_1^k r + j \sum_1^k x \right) \bar{I}.$$

In order that there may be resonance the phase angle must be zero; the current is in phase with the impressed emf., i.e.,

$$\phi = \arctan \frac{\sum\limits_1^k x}{\sum\limits_1^k r} = 0.$$

Therefore, in order that ϕ may be zero $\sum_1^k x$ must be zero. When this condition obtains, we have

$$\bar{\mathscr{E}} = \bar{I} \sum_1^k r.$$

The impedance is a minimum and the current a maximum at constant potential. The circuit as a whole behaves as though noninductive or noncapacitive, i.e., as though it contained ohmic resistance only. The voltage drops across the component parts of the circuit may be large, even larger than the impressed emf., and the component phase angles may be large. Series resonance is desirable for a power circuit, since the impressed voltage is a minimum for a given power transmission.

The general equation for a parallel circuit is

$$\bar{I} = \left(\sum_1^k g - j \sum_1^k b \right) \bar{\mathscr{E}}.$$

In the parallel circuit, as in the series circuit, the condition for resonance is zero phase angle. Therefore,

$$\phi = \arctan \frac{\sum_1^k b}{\sum_1^k g} = 0.$$

In order that this may obtain we must have $\sum_1^k b = 0$. With zero susceptance the admittance is a maximum and consists of conductance only. Then

$$\bar{I} = \bar{\mathscr{E}} \sum_1^k g.$$

With constant voltage the current is a minimum, since the impedance is a maximum. The impedance would be infinite were the resistance zero, and the current would then be zero. Though the line current may be small the branch currents may be very large if the resistance is small and reactance large. Also, the branch phase angles may be large, even though the equivalent phase angle is small or even zero. There can, however, be no excessive voltage across any branch, since the branch voltage cannot exceed the impressed voltage.

Parallel resonance is desirable on constant-potential circuits. It affords the minimum line current for a given power transmission.

Most power circuits are constant-potential circuits, and therefore, it is desirable to approximate the resonance condition at least. This permits, not only the transmission of the maximum power with the minimum current, but the minimum line loss (rI^2) and the minimum line drop. It also calls for the minimum generator capacity for a given power transmission. The capacity of an a.c. generator is given by the product of current times voltage and not by the active watts. The output is, therefore, a maximum at unity power factor. Hence it is desirable to keep the power factor of a commercial circuit as near unity as possible. With inductive load, which usually obtains, approximate resonance may be effected by paralleling the inductive load with capacitance.

296. Power in a Circuit. — In a d.c. circuit power is *always* generated (delivered) in one part of the circuit and used (absorbed) in another part of the circuit. Take the simple case of a battery or d.c. dynamo generating current to heat a soldering iron, say, of resistance *r*, or to run a motor. In the battery or dynamo there is a rise in potential *in the direction* of current (conventional) flow (current and emf. have the same sense) and power is delivered to the outside circuit. In a resistance or motor (load) there is a drop in potential *in the direction* of current flow (current flowing against a resistance) and there is absorption of power by the resistance or motor. Thus, in a d.c. circuit there is *never* any doubt as to where power is generated (delivered) and where power is used (absorbed). In all cases where there is a rise in potential in the direction of current flow power is generated, and where there is a drop in potential in the direction of current flow power is being used. If a d.c. dynamo is charging a storage battery, say, there is a rise in potential in the dynamo in the direction of current flow, and hence power is being generated in the dynamo. In the storage battery there is a drop in potential (current and potential have opposite signs), and hence power is being absorbed. If we adopt the convention of giving a positive sign to power terms represented by a rising potential in the direction of current flow, positive power means generated power. A negative sign would then represent power absorption.

In an a.c. circuit the conditions are, in general, quite different. It does not always occur that the current is in the direction of potential rise or potential drop during all parts of the cycle, owing to phase differences between current and voltage. Thus, if we focus our attention upon the dynamo, we will see that, in general, during a part of the cycle the current is in the direction of potential rise, i.e., current and voltage have the same sign, and power is delivered to the load or outside circuit. During the other part of the cycle the current is in opposition to the potential rise in the dynamo, i.e., current and voltage are in opposition. In this part of the cycle the current is doing work in flowing against the potential in the dynamo, and energy is being returned to the dynamo from the outside circuit. This occurs when the energy of the magnetic field of an inductance or the energy of the electrostatic field of a condenser is returned to the circuit. This point will be made clearer in the following sections.

297. Products of Current, Voltages, and Impedances. — The impedance of a circuit is

$$Z = r + jx = \sqrt{r^2 + x^2} \, (\cos \phi + j \sin \phi) = z \, e^{j\phi}. \quad (297.1)$$

Impedance is a complex quantity and not a revolving vector. The angle ϕ in (297.1) is a fixed angle. If the current and emf. vectors are conceived to rotate with constant angular speed ω relative to the fixed axes, the angle for the emf. vector at any instant is ωt, and for the current vector $(\omega t - \phi)$. Therefore, we may write with reference to fixed axes,

$$\left. \begin{array}{l} \text{Impedance} = z \, e^{j\phi}, \\ \text{Voltage} = \mathscr{E} \, e^{j\omega t}, \\ \text{Current} = I \, e^{j(\omega t - \phi)}. \end{array} \right\} \quad (297.2)$$

These equations satisfy the following conditions:

$$\bar{\mathscr{E}} = Z\bar{I} = z \, e^{j\phi} I^{j(\omega t - \phi)} = zI \, e^{j\omega t} = \mathscr{E} \, e^{j\omega t}, \quad (297.3)$$

$$\bar{I} = \frac{\bar{\mathscr{E}}}{Z} = \frac{\mathscr{E} \, e^{j\omega t}}{z \, e^{j\phi}} = I \, e^{j(\omega t - \phi)}, \quad (297.4)$$

$$Z = \frac{\bar{\mathscr{E}}}{\bar{I}} = \frac{\mathscr{E} \, e^{j\omega t}}{I \, e^{j(\omega t - \phi)}} = z \, e^{j\phi}. \quad (2975.)$$

On the other hand, the product of current times voltage gives

$$P = \mathscr{E} \, e^{j\omega t} I \, e^{j(\omega t - \phi)} = \mathscr{E} I \, e^{j(2\omega t - \phi)}. \quad (297.6)$$

Thus, power is represented by a revolving vector having twice the frequency of either $\bar{\mathscr{E}}$ or $\bar{I}$. In the same manner it may be shown that $Z\bar{I}^2$ or $\bar{\mathscr{E}}^2/Z$ give the same expression for power. Hence, any expression for power is a double-frequency function, and therefore, cannot be represented in the same vector diagram with current and voltage.

298. Power When Current and Voltage Are Harmonic and in Phase. — As we have seen

$$\mathscr{E} = \mathscr{E}_m \sin \omega t, \tag{298.1}$$

$$i = I_m \sin \omega t, \tag{298.2}$$

where the phase angle ϕ is zero. Therefore, we have, for instantaneous power,

$$p = \mathscr{E}i = \mathscr{E}_m I_m \sin^2 \omega t = \mathscr{E}_m I_m (\tfrac{1}{2} - \tfrac{1}{2} \cos 2\omega t), \tag{298.3}$$

and the effective power is

$$P = \frac{1}{T} \int_0^T \mathscr{E}i \, dt = \frac{1}{T} \int_0^T \frac{\mathscr{E}_m I_m}{2} \, dt - \frac{1}{2} \int_0^T \frac{\mathscr{E}_m I_m}{2} \cos 2\omega t \, dt$$

$$= \frac{\mathscr{E}_m I_m}{2} = \mathscr{E}I. \tag{298.4}$$

Thus, when $\phi = 0$, power is given by $\mathscr{E}I$, as in direct currents, where $\mathscr{E}$ is the effective emf. and I the effective current.

From (298.3), we have for instantaneous power

$$p = \frac{\mathscr{E}_m I_m}{2} - \frac{\mathscr{E}_m I_m}{2} \cos 2\omega t,$$

or

$$p = P - P \cos 2\omega t. \tag{298.5}$$

Equations (298.1), (298.2), and (298.5) are plotted in Fig. 285. It will be seen that the power curve is a harmonic curve of twice the frequency of either the current or voltage, and symmetrical with respect to an axis at a distance P above the common axis for the current and voltage. The amplitude of the power curve is the product of effective volts by effective amperes, or one half the product of their maximum values.

When the current and voltage are in phase the instantaneous values of the power are always positive (above the axis ox), since the corresponding values of current and voltage are always of the same sign. This means that for all parts of the cycle the source of energy

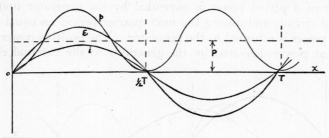

FIG. 285

(dynamo) is doing work upon the external circuit. The outside circuit absorbs energy during all parts of the cycle, and at no time returns energy to the dynamo.

299. Power When Current and Voltage Are Harmonic and in Quadrature. — This case is one that requires unnatural operating conditions, and therefore, is *never* strictly complied with. It is interesting, however, since it represents the limiting condition when there is only reactance in the circuit. The equations for $\mathcal{E}$ and i are now

$$\mathcal{E} = \mathcal{E}_m \sin \omega t, \tag{299.1}$$

$$i = I_m \sin\left(\omega t - \frac{\pi}{2}\right), \tag{299.2}$$

$$p = \mathcal{E}i = \mathcal{E}_m I_m \sin \omega t \left(\sin \omega t \cos \frac{\pi}{2} - \cos \omega t \sin \frac{\pi}{2}\right)$$

$$- \left(\frac{\mathcal{E}_m I_m}{2}\right) \sin 2\omega t. \tag{299.3}$$

The effective power for a complete period is

$$P = \frac{1}{T}\int_0^T \frac{\mathcal{E}_m I_m}{2} \sin 2\omega t \, dt = 0. \tag{299.4}$$

Thus, when the current and voltage differ in phase by $\pi/2$ the power over a complete period is zero. Equations (299.1), (299.2), and (299.4) are plotted in Fig. 286. The power is, as always, a double-frequency function of the time. Its amplitude is equal to the product of effective volts by effective amperes. Its axis coincides with the axis of symmetry of the current and voltage. This is because the active power is zero. The power loops above and below the common axis of symmetry are equal in area, which means that during one quarter of a period power is expended by the generator upon the external circuit, and during the next quarter period an equal quantity of power is returned to the generator. The positive power loops represent power delivered by the generator to the external circuit,

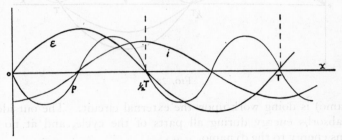

FIG. 286

and the negative power loops represent power returned to the generator. Thus, during two quarters of each cycle energy is delivered to the external circuit and during the other two quarter cycles energy is returned to the generator. When the current and voltage are in the same sense the power is positive and energy is being stored in the magnetic field of an inductance or the electrostatic field of a condenser. When the current and voltage are in opposition the stored energy is returned to the generator. The current is entirely wattless. There is an equal oscillation between stored or potential energy and active or kinetic energy. This case is analogous to the oscillations between potential and kinetic energy in a frictionless pendulum.

300. Power When Current and Voltage Are Harmonic and differ in Phase by an Angle between Zero and $\pi/2$. — This is the condition most commonly met with in practice. We have

$$\mathcal{E} = \mathcal{E}_m \sin \omega t, \qquad (300.1)$$

$$i = I_m \sin (\omega t - \phi). \qquad (300.2)$$

The instantaneous power is

$$p = \mathscr{E}i = \mathscr{E}_m I_m \sin \omega t \sin (\omega t - \phi)$$

$$= \frac{\mathscr{E}_m I_m}{2} \left\{ \cos \phi - \cos (2\omega t - \phi) \right\}. \qquad (300.3)$$

The effective power is

$$P = \frac{1}{T} \int_0^T \frac{\mathscr{E}_m I_m}{2} \cos \phi \, dt - \frac{1}{T} \int_0^T \frac{\mathscr{E}_m I_m}{2} \cos (2\omega t - \phi) \, dt$$

$$= \mathscr{E}I \cos \phi. \qquad (300.4)$$

From (300.3) we have

$$p = \mathscr{E}I \cos \phi - \mathscr{E}I \cos (2\omega t - \phi). \qquad (300.5)$$

Thus,

$$p = P - \mathscr{E}I \cos (2\omega t - \phi). \qquad (300.6)$$

Equations (300.1), (300.2), and (300.6) are plotted in Fig. 287. The power is a double-frequency function of the time. Its axis of

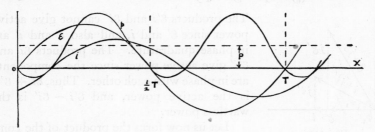

Fig. 287

symmetry lies above the common axis of symmetry of the current and voltage a distance $P = \mathscr{E}I \cos \phi$ (effective power). Its amplitude is $\mathscr{E}I$ (product of the effective amperes and effective volts). The positive loops above the axis ox represent energy delivered to the external circuit, and the negative loops below the axis of symmetry ox represent energy returned to the generator. When $\phi = 0$, the instantaneous power is

$$p = P - P \cos 2\omega t$$

and the effective power is $\mathscr{E}I$, as for noninductive load. When $\phi = \pi/2$, the instantaneous power is

$$p = \mathscr{E}I \sin 2\omega t,$$

and the average power is zero.

301. Power with Complex Quantities. — Let the current and voltage in the complex form be

$$\bar{I} = i + ji'. \tag{301.1}$$

$$\bar{\mathcal{E}} = \mathcal{E} + j\mathcal{E}'. \tag{301.2}$$

The vectors are shown in their relative positions in Fig. 288.

Let us obtain an expression for the active power as follows:

$$P_a = \mathcal{E}I \cos (\phi_2 - \phi_1) = \mathcal{E}I (\cos \phi_2 \cos \phi_1 + \sin \phi_1 \sin \phi_2)$$

$$= \mathcal{E}I \left(\frac{\mathcal{E}}{\mathcal{E}} \times \frac{i}{I} + \frac{\mathcal{E}'}{\mathcal{E}} \times \frac{i'}{I} \right) = \mathcal{E}i + \mathcal{E}'i'. \tag{301.3}$$

The wattless power is

$$P_w = \mathcal{E}I \sin (\phi_2 - \phi_1) = \mathcal{E}I (\sin \phi_2 \cos \phi_1 - \cos \phi_2 \sin \phi_1)$$

$$= \mathcal{E}I \left(\frac{\mathcal{E}'}{\mathcal{E}} \times \frac{i}{I} - \frac{\mathcal{E}}{\mathcal{E}} \times \frac{i'}{I} \right) = \mathcal{E}'i - \mathcal{E}i'. \tag{301.4}$$

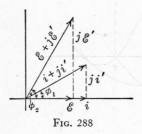

FIG. 288

The products $\mathcal{E}'i$ and $\mathcal{E}i'$ cannot give active power since $\mathcal{E}'$ and i, and also $\mathcal{E}$ and i' are in phase quadrature. The products $\mathcal{E}i$ and $\mathcal{E}'i'$ give active power since the components are in phase with each other. Thus, $\mathcal{E}i + \mathcal{E}'i'$ is the active power, and $\mathcal{E}'i - \mathcal{E}i'$ is the wattless power.

Let us now form the product of the complex expressions for $\bar{\mathcal{E}}$ and $\bar{I}$. We have

$$\bar{\mathcal{E}}\bar{I} = (\mathcal{E} + j\mathcal{E}')(i + ji') = (\mathcal{E}i - \mathcal{E}'i') + j(\mathcal{E}'i + \mathcal{E}i') \tag{301.5}$$

$\mathcal{E}i - \mathcal{E}'i'$ is not the active power, nor is $\mathcal{E}'i + \mathcal{E}i'$ the wattless power. Therefore, the product $\bar{\mathcal{E}}\bar{I}$ has no physical meaning, although true mathematically.

The product of the complex expressions for current and voltage may be made to yield correct results by the application of the following arbitrary rule: *Change the sign of the imaginary term in the lagging vector and then perform the multiplication in the usual manner.* Thus,

$$P = (\mathcal{E} + j\mathcal{E}')(i - ji') = (\mathcal{E}i + \mathcal{E}'i') + j(\mathcal{E}'i - \mathcal{E}i') = P_a + jP_w.$$

Example. — Let $\bar{\mathcal{E}} = 10 + j50$, and $\bar{I} = 3 + j4$. Then

$$P = (10 + j50)(3 - j4) = 230 + j110.$$

Thus, the active power is 230 watts and the wattless power is 110 watts. This may be checked by the usual expressions $\mathscr{E}I \cos \phi$ and $\mathscr{E}I \sin \phi$. Thus

$$P_a = 50.99 \times 5 \cos 25° 34' = 230 \text{ watts.}$$

$$P_w = 50.99 \times 5 \sin 25° 34' = 110 \text{ watts.}$$

It is left as an exercise for the reader to change the positions of the vectors so that I is the basis of phase, i.e., lies in the axis of reals, and recalculate.

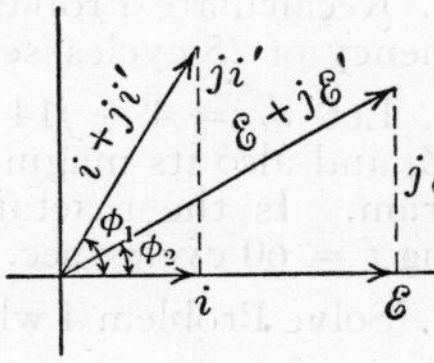

Let us next examine the case where the reactance is capacitive, and hence the current is leading the voltage. The vectors are shown in their relative positions in Fig. 289. The active power is

FIG. 289

$$P_a = \mathscr{E}I \cos (\phi_1 - \phi_2) = \mathscr{E}I(\cos \phi_1 \cos \phi_2 + \sin \phi_1 \sin \phi_2)$$

$$= \mathscr{E}I\left(\frac{i}{I} \times \frac{\mathscr{E}}{\mathscr{E}} + \frac{i'}{I} \times \frac{\mathscr{E}'}{\mathscr{E}}\right) = \mathscr{E}i + \mathscr{E}'i'. \tag{301.7}$$

The wattless power is

$$P_w = \mathscr{E}I \sin (\phi_1 - \phi_2) = \mathscr{E}I (\sin \phi_1 \cos \phi_2 - \cos \phi_1 \sin \phi_2)$$

$$= \mathscr{E}I\left(\frac{i'}{I} \times \frac{\mathscr{E}}{\mathscr{E}} - \frac{i}{I} \times \frac{\mathscr{E}'}{\mathscr{E}}\right) = \mathscr{E}i' - \mathscr{E}'i. \tag{301.8}$$

This same result is obtained if we form the product of the complex expressions for $\bar{\mathscr{E}}$ and $\bar{I}$ with the sign of the imaginary term in the lagging vector changed. Thus,

$$P = (i + ji')(\mathscr{E} - j\mathscr{E}') = (\mathscr{E}i + \mathscr{E}'i') + i(\mathscr{E}i' - \mathscr{E}'i)$$

$$= P_a + jP_w. \tag{301.9}$$

While the arbitrary rule for calculating power by the use of complex expressions yields correct results, it will be found that the calculations are simplified, as a rule, by using the ordinary expressions for power, i.e., $\mathscr{E}I \cos \phi$ and $\mathscr{E}I \sin \phi$.

References. — "Principles of Alternating Currents" by Ralph R. Lawrence, "Revolving Vectors" by George W. Patterson, "Alternating Current Phenomena" by Charles Proteus Steinmetz.

PROBLEMS

Solve all problems by use of complex quantities.

1. Let $Z = 3 + j4$ and $I = 3$ amperes. Take $\bar{I}$ in the axis of reals and obtain the complex expression for $\mathscr{E}$ and the magnitude of $\mathscr{E}$. What is the magnitude of the impedance? What is the phase angle? What is the inductance if $f = 60$ cycles/sec.? Draw the vector diagram.

2. Let $\bar{I}$ of the preceding Problem make an angle of $+20°$ with the axis of reals. Recalculate all quantities, obtaining the complex expressions and the magnitudes. Draw the vector diagram.

3. Recalculate Problem 1 using the same current and impedance, but a frequency of 25 cycles/sec. Draw the vector diagram.

4. Let $\mathscr{E} = 4 + j14$ and $\bar{I} = 2 + j3$. Obtain the complex expression for Z, and also its magnitude. What is the phase angle? Draw the vector diagram. Is the reactance inductive or capacitive? Calculate its value, taking $f = 60$ cycles/sec.

5. Solve Problem 4 when $\mathscr{E} = 14 - j4$ and $\bar{I} = 2 + j3$.

6. Let $\bar{I} = 2.8 + j1.2$ and $Z = 3 - j4$. Solve for $\mathscr{E}$ and $\mathscr{E}$. Draw the vector diagram. Obtain the complex expression for the admittance. Calculate the magnitudes of the impedance and admittance.

7. Calculate the power in Problem 6, first by the use of the usual expressions $P_a = \mathscr{E}I \cos \phi$ and $P_w = \mathscr{E}I \sin \phi$, and then by the use of complex quantities.

8. A 60-cycle generator supplies current to a motor over a line having a resistance of 3 ohms and an inductive reactance of 4 ohms. The induction motor has a power factor of 0.8 and draws 6 amperes. It is required to maintain a constant potential of 110 volts across the motor. Calculate the generator voltage, in complex form and in magnitude, the phase angle, the line drop, and the power, both active and wattless. Calculate the per cent regulation of the line and its efficiency. Draw the vector diagram.

What series capacitance will produce resonance for load and line? How will the quantities just calculated be affected by connecting in this capacitance? Draw the vector diagram for this case.

9. In a laboratory experiment two inductance coils were placed in parallel on a 120-volt, 60-cycle line. One coil had a resistance of 15 ohms and an inductance of 0.02655 henry. The other coil had a resistance of 10 ohms and an inductance of 0.159 henry. Calculate the total current, the component currents, the power in each branch, the total power, all phase angles, the impedance of each branch, and the equivalent impedance. Obtain the complex expressions and the magnitudes of the currents, voltage, impedances, and the power. Draw the vector diagram.

What series capacitance will produce resonance, the potential drop across condenser and the parallel circuit being 120 volts? Recalculate and draw the vector diagram.

What parallel capacitance will produce resonance? Recalculate and draw the vector diagram.

10. Two induction motors are being operated in parallel on a 220-volt, 25-cycle line. One motor takes a current of 50 amperes and has a power factor of 0.8. The other motor takes a current of 20 amperes and has a phase angle of 40°. Obtain the complex expression and the magnitude of the impedance for each motor. Obtain the admittance of each motor, the equiva-

lent admittance, and the equivalent impedance. Calculate the power consumed by each motor and the total power.

If 15, 440 watt 220 volt incandescent lamps are now placed in parallel with the motors, what is the equivalent impedance? The equivalent phase angle? The total current?

11. Consider the circuit shown in Fig. 284. $r_1 = 5$ ohms. x_1 is the reactance due to a 150 mf. condenser. r_2 and x_2 represent a motor drawing 6 amperes and having a power factor of 0.8. $r_3 = 10$ ohms, and x_3 is the reactance of an inductance of 0.06 henry. $\bar{\mathcal{E}}_{2-3}$ is maintained at 120 effective volts. The frequency is 60 cycles/sec.

Obtain the complex expression and the magnitudes of $\bar{\mathcal{E}}$ and $\mathcal{E}$, and also the angle each makes with the axis of reals. Obtain the complex expressions and magnitudes for the component currents and the total current, and the angle each makes with the axis of reals. Obtain the component impedance and the equivalent impedance. What is the equivalent phase angle for the entire load? Calculate the component powers and the total power.

What capacitance will give x_1 such a value as to produce resonance? How will the other quantities then be affected?

Suggestion. Take the vector for 120 volts as the axis of reals. Then all other vectors will fall in their proper positions relative to the 120-volt vector. Draw the complete vector diagram in each case.

12. A synchronous motor takes a current of 50 amperes, which leads the voltage by 60°. The potential is 440 volts.

(*a*) Calculate the power, both active and wattless, by the complex number method and check by the trigonometric method.

(*b*) Obtain the complex expression for the impedance, and its absolute value.

CHAPTER XXII

ALTERNATING CURRENT BRIDGES

302. Alternating current bridges are used extensively in measuring capacitance and inductance. In most laboratory manuals on this subject the working equations are derived by the differential-equations method. In many cases the derivations of the bridge equations are much simplified by the use of complex quantities. In this Chapter, therefore, a few of the important a.c. bridges for measuring capacitance and inductance will be discussed and the bridge equations will be derived by the complex-quantity method in order to show the process and to give further applications of complex numbers.

303. Condensers Subjected to Alternating Potentials. — As we have seen, a transient current flows in a line containing a condenser for only a brief interval of time when making or breaking the circuit when subjected to d.c. potential. In an a.c. line, however, a continuous a.c. current flows through a condenser when subjected to an a.c. potential. If the condenser is a perfect condenser, i.e., has no absorption, the current will lead the potential by 90°. There is no energy loss in the condenser. There are no absolutely perfect condensers. Air condensers, when well insulated, approach the perfect condenser most closely. In case the condenser has a solid or liquid dielectric there is more or less expenditure of energy in the dielectric on the continuous application of an alternating potential, as is evident from its rise in temperature. This was discussed in Section 52. If there is expenditure of energy in the dielectric, then there must be an active component of the power, and hence a power factor. The phase angle is something less than 90°. This is indicated in Fig. 290a. ϕ is the phase angle as ordinarily used in power calculations. Since ϕ is always large in any condenser, the angle θ is usually taken as a measure of the quality of a condenser and is called the *phase difference* or *phase defect* (sometimes called the phase angle of the condenser). A condenser having large absorption will have a large phase defect. The phase angle of a condenser is very sensitive to a change in frequency since the phase angle is a function of the frequency. The measured capacitance of a faulty condenser is also found to be influenced by the frequency.

Since there is a dissipation of energy in a faulty condenser, it may be represented as a perfect condenser in series with a resistance r_1, Fig. 290b. The resistance r_1 will be of such value as to dissipate the same amount of energy as the imperfect dielectric. An equivalent arrange-

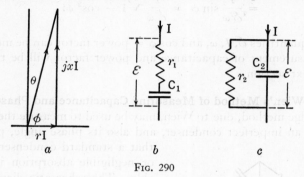

FIG. 290

ment may also be a perfect condenser in parallel with a resistance r_2, as shown in Fig. 290c.

Let us consider the series arrangement.

$$P_a = r_1 I^2, \quad \text{or} \quad r_1 = \frac{P_a}{I^2}. \qquad Z = r_1 - jx_1.$$

Therefore,

$$\tan \phi = \frac{x_1}{r_1} = \frac{1}{r_1 C \omega}.$$

Then

$$C = \frac{1}{r_1 \omega \tan \phi} = \frac{I^2}{P_a \omega \tan \phi} = \frac{I^2}{\mathcal{E} I \omega \cos \phi \tan \phi}$$

$$= \frac{I}{\mathcal{E} \omega \sin \phi} = \frac{I}{\mathcal{E} \omega \sqrt{1 - \cos^2 \phi}}. \qquad (303.1)$$

Let us consider the parallel arrangement.

$$P_a = \frac{\mathcal{E}^2}{r_2}, \quad \text{or} \quad r_2 = \frac{\mathcal{E}^2}{P_a}.$$

$$Y = \frac{1}{r_2 + j0} + \frac{1}{0 - jx} = \frac{1}{r_2} + j\frac{1}{x}.$$

Therefore,

$$\tan \phi = \frac{r_2}{x} = r_2 C \omega.$$

Then

$$C = \frac{\tan \phi}{r_2 \omega} = \frac{P_a \tan \phi}{\mathscr{E}^2 \omega} = \frac{\mathscr{E} I \cos \phi \tan \phi}{\mathscr{E}^2 \omega}$$

$$= \frac{I}{\mathscr{E} \omega} \sin \phi = \frac{I}{\mathscr{E} \omega} \sqrt{1 - \cos^2 \phi}. \tag{303.2}$$

The quantities $\mathscr{E}$, I, ω, and $\cos \phi =$ power factor can be measured. The measurement of capacitance and power factor will be taken up in the next section.

304. Wien's Method of Measuring Capacitance and Phase Angle.
— A bridge method, due to Wien, may be used to measure the capacitance of an imperfect condenser, and also its phase angle, provided

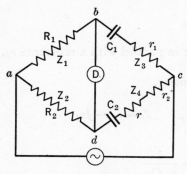

FIG. 291

that a standard condenser of zero or negligible absorption is available. The schematic diagram for the Wien bridge is shown in Fig. 291. The resistances R_1, R_2, r_1, and r_2 should be noninductive and noncapacitive. r_1 and r_2 should be finely-divided, variable resistances. r is the fictitious, series resistance of the condenser C_2 which is under test. C_1 is the standard, known capacitance. D is a detector, usually a telephone receiver. The a.c. power supply may be a microphone hummer or a Vreeland oscillator.

The resistances r_1 and r_2 are for the purpose of bringing about equality of phase in the currents in the upper and lower branches of the bridge. This is necessary, since, if one condenser has no absorption and the other has, the p.d. between b and c and between d and c cannot be equal in magnitude and phase at every instant of time. Thus, an exact balance of the bridge cannot be obtained. The sound in the telephone will decrease to a minimum for certain values of R_1 and R_2, but will never be zero.

The balance is effected as follows: Let r_1 and r_2 be zero. Then

R_1 and R_2 are adjusted until the sound in the telephone is a minimum. The balance is then improved by use of r_1 and r_2, and still further improved by readjusting R_1 and R_2. For perfect balance this process may be repeated. When the bridge is in balance the impedances in the four arms of the bridge bear the same relation to each other as do the resistances in a d.c. bridge. That is,

$$Z_1 Z_4 = Z_2 Z_3, \text{ where} \tag{304.1}$$

$Z_1 = R_1, \quad Z_2 = R_2, \quad Z_3 = r_1 - jx_1, \quad \text{and} \quad Z_4 = (r + r_2) - jx_2.$

Therefore,

$$R_1 \{ (r + r_2) - jx_2 \} = R_2 (r_1 - jx_1).$$

Equating reals, we have

$$r_1 R_2 = R_1 (r + r_2). \tag{304.2}$$

This is the d.c. balance. From this equation r may be obtained. Equating imaginaries, we have

$$x_2 R_1 = x_1 R_2.$$

But

$$x_2 = \frac{1}{C_2 \omega} \quad \text{and} \quad x_1 = \frac{1}{C_1 \omega}.$$

Therefore,

$$\frac{R_1}{R_2} = \frac{C_2}{C_1}. \tag{304.3}$$

This expresses the condition for phase equality. From the vector diagram, we obtain $\tan \theta = r C_2 \omega$. From equations (304.2) and (304.3) we obtain

$$\frac{C_2}{C_1} = \frac{r_1}{r + r_2}. \tag{304.4}$$

Multiplying numerator and denominator of the left-hand member of this equation by ω and clearing of fractions, we have

$$\tan \theta = C_2 r \omega = C_1 r_1 \omega - C_2 r_2 \omega. \tag{304.5}$$

This equation permits the calculation of θ and hence ϕ.

305. Modification of Wien's Bridge. Let us next consider the equivalent arrangement of an imperfect condenser as a resistance in parallel with a perfect condenser, Fig. 290c. The arrangement of the bridge is shown in Fig. 292. R is the fictitious, parallel resistance of the condenser.   Since the arm bc of the bridge contains both inductance and capacitance it may be made to behave as a pure resistance by proper adjustment of values. L is a variable, standard inductance.

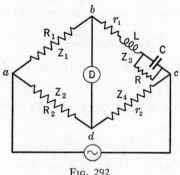

FIG. 292

It is convenient to take $R_1 = R_2$. The impedances are $Z_1 = R_1$, $Z_2 = R_2$,

$$Z_4 = r_2,$$

$$Z_3 = r_1 + jx_1 + \frac{1}{1/R + j1/x_2} = r_1 + jx_1 + \frac{1/R}{1/R^2 + 1/x_2{}^2} - j\frac{1/x_2}{1/R^2 + 1/x_2{}^2},$$

$$x_1 = L\omega, \quad \text{and} \quad x_2 = \frac{1}{C\omega}.$$

Substituting in equation (304.1), we have

$$R_1 r_2 = R_2 r_1 + jx_1 R_2 + \frac{R_2(1/R)}{1/R^2 + 1/x_2{}^2} - j\frac{R_2(1/x_2)}{1/R^2 + 1/x_2{}^2}.$$

Equating reals, we have

$$R_1 r_2 = R_2 r_1 + \frac{R_2(1/R)}{1/R^2 + C^2\omega^2}.$$

Since $R_1 = R_2$, this reduces to

$$r_2 = r_1 + \frac{R}{1 + C^2 R^2 \omega^2}. \tag{305.1}$$

Equating imaginaries, we have

$$x_1 = \frac{1/x_2}{1/R^2 + C^2\omega^2},$$

from which we obtain

$$L = \frac{CR^2}{1 + C^2R^2\omega^2}. \tag{305.2}$$

If L and ω are known, equations (305.1) and (305.2) permit the calculation of both C and R. If C is a perfect condenser and R is a known resistance placed in parallel with it, and ω is known, the bridge may be used to measure either L or C. If C is a fixed, standard condenser it will be seen from equation (305.2) that a balance may be effected by varying R and L. If both L and C are known standards, ω may be calculated, and hence the frequency of the power supply.

If only frequency is to be measured a more convenient arrangement is to omit the parallel resistance R and use a perfect, standard condenser. Either L or C must be variable. The equations are obtained as follows:

$$Z_1 = R_1, \ Z_2 = R_2, \ Z_4 = r_2, \ Z_3 = r_1 + j(x_1 - x_2),$$

$$x_1 = L\omega \quad \text{and} \quad x_2 = \frac{1}{C\omega}.$$

Substituting these values in equation (304.1), we have

$$R_1 r_2 = R_2 \{ r_1 + i(x_1 - x_2) \}.$$

Equating reals, we have

$$R_1 r_2 = R_2 r_1.$$

r_1 is the resistance of the inductance L plus any additional resistance in the arm bc. Equating imaginaries, we have

$$R_2(x_1 - x_2) = 0, \quad \text{or} \quad x_1 = x_2,$$

that is,

$$L\omega = \frac{1}{C\omega},$$

which reduces to

$$f = \frac{1}{2\pi\sqrt{LC}}. \tag{305.4}$$

306. Wien's Modification of Maxwell's Bridge. — Max Wien modified the original Maxwell bridge, which is used for comparing an unknown self inductance with a known self inductance, by using a.c. power instead of d.c. power. The arrangement of the bridge is

shown in Fig. 293. R_1, R_2, and r are noninductive resistances capable of variation. r_1 and r_2 are the resistances of the induction coils. The switch s_2 makes it possible to transfer r from arm bc to arm dc or vice

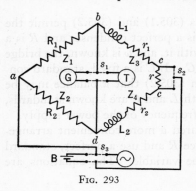

Fig. 293

versa, depending upon the values involved. In balancing the bridge it facilitates matters materially to obtain a d.c. balance with a galvanometer G and battery B, as with the ordinary Wheatstone bridge. Switches s_1 and s_3 make it possible to transfer easily from d.c. to a.c. The d.c. balance will determine in which arm of the bridge the resistance r belongs.

The impedances are: $Z_1 = R_1$, $Z_2 = R_2$, $Z_3 = r_1 + jx_1$, $Z_4 = (r + r_2) + jx_2$ (in case r is in the arm dc), $x_1 = L_1\omega$, and $x_2 = L_2\omega$. Substituting in (304.1), we have

$$R_1\{(r + r_2) + jx_2\} = R_2(r_1 + jx_1).$$

On equating reals, we have

$$R_1(r + r_2) = R_2 r_1, \qquad (306.1)$$

which is the d.c. balance. Equating imaginaries, we have

$$x_2 R_1 = x_1 R_2, \quad \text{or} \quad L_2 R_1 = L_1 R_2. \qquad (306.2)$$

Then

$$\frac{L_1}{L_2} = \frac{R_1}{R_2} = \frac{r_1}{r + r_2}. \qquad (306.3)$$

Since the final equation does not involve ω, the wave form of the impressed p.d. need not be a pure harmonic, nor need the frequency be known.

If the unknown inductance L_1, say, is much too large to be measured with any available standard inductance it will not be possible to obtain a balance. In such a case a common artifice is to connect a condenser having negligible absorption and of suitable value in series with the inductance L_1. This has the effect of an apparent inductance in the arm bc which is less than L_1.

Let x be the reactance of the condenser. Then the impedance of the arm bc is $Z_3 = r_1 + j(x_1 - x)$, and the complex equation is

$$R_1\{(r_2 + r) + jx_2\} = R_2\{r_1 + j(x_1 - x)\}.$$

Equating reals, we have

$$R_1(r_2 + r) = R_2 r_1. \tag{306.4}$$

Equating imaginaries, we have $x_2 R_1 = R_2(x_1 - x)$. Therefore,

$$L_1 = \frac{L_2 R_1}{R_2} + \frac{1}{C\omega^2}. \tag{306.5}$$

If $R_1 = R_2$,

$$L_1 = L_2 + \frac{1}{C\omega^2}. \tag{306.6}$$

If L_2 is too large the condenser is connected in arm dc. In this use of the bridge ω must be known.

307. The Anderson Bridge. The Anderson bridge is a modification of the original Maxwell bridge. The wiring diagram is shown in Fig. 294. As originally used the detector G was a d.c. galvanometer and the source of power was a battery. The d.c. balance was obtained as with the ordinary Wheatstone bridge. The variable-current balance was obtained by use of a make and break key. The Anderson bridge is now generally used with a.c. power and a vibration galvanometer or telephone as detector. This is one of the most important bridge methods since it

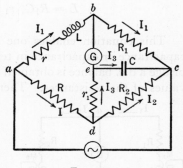

Fig. 294

is very accurate. It was used at the Bureau of Standards by E. Rosa and F. W. Grover in much of their very accurate measurements of inductance.

In the derivation of the bridge equations we will apply Kirchhoff's laws, using complex numbers. When the bridge is balanced, points b and e are at every instant of time at the same potential and phase, and so there is no current in arm be. From the loop $badeb$, we have

1. $(r + jL\omega)\bar{I}_1 = R\bar{I} + r_1\bar{I}_3.$

From loop $bceb$, we have

$$2. \quad R_1 \bar{I}_1 = -j\frac{1}{C\omega}\bar{I}_3.$$

From loop $decd$, we have

$$3. \quad r_1 \bar{I}_3 - j\frac{1}{C\omega}\bar{I}_3 = R_2 \bar{I}_2.$$

And at junction d,

$$4. \quad \bar{I} = \bar{I}_2 + \bar{I}_3.$$

The currents are all complex quantities, but need not be so expressed since they are to be eliminated. Eliminating the currents, there results

$$-j\frac{rR_2}{R_1 C\omega} + \frac{LR_2}{R_1 C} - r_1 R_2 = R_2 R + R r_1 - j\frac{R}{C\omega}. \quad (307.1)$$

Equating imaginaries, we have

$$rR_2 = RR_1. \quad (307.2)$$

This is the d.c. balance. Equating reals, we have

$$L = R_1 C \left\{ r_1 \left(1 + \frac{R}{R_2} \right) + R \right\}. \quad (307.3)$$

This equation enables one to calculate inductance in terms of capacitance or capacitance in terms of inductance. In balancing the bridge a d.c. balance is obtained first, which gives a line on the relative values of the resistances. Then the a.c. balance is obtained. This balance may necessitate some change in the d.c. balance.

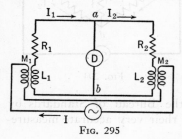

FIG. 295

308. A Mutual Inductance Bridge. A simple arrangement for measuring an unknown mutual inductance by comparing it with a known mutual inductance is indicated in Fig. 295. In order that points a and b may be maintained at the same potential and phase the currents in the coils L_1 and L_2 must be in the same sense. By applying Kirchhoff's law, we have

$$(R_1 + jL_1 \omega)\bar{I}_1 + jM_1 \omega \bar{I} = 0,$$

$$(R_2 + jL_2 \omega)\bar{I}_2 + jM_2 \omega \bar{I} = 0.$$

Any resistance there may be in the power circuit (primary) has no influence upon the balance. The terms $jM_1\omega\bar{I}$ and $jM_2\omega\bar{I}$ operate to induce emfs. in the loops of the network, the arrows indicating the inducing and induced currents being opposite. Since $\bar{I}_1 = \bar{I}_2$, we have by division

$$\frac{R_1 + jL_1\omega}{R_2 + jL_2\omega} = \frac{jM_1\omega}{jM_2\omega}.$$

Thus

$$jR_1M_2\omega - L_1M_2\omega^2 = jR_2M_1\omega - L_2M_1\omega^2.$$

Equating reals, we have

$$L_1M_2 = L_2M_1. \tag{308.1}$$

Equating imaginaries, we have

$$R_1M_2 = R_2M_1. \tag{308.2}$$

Thus,

$$\frac{L_1}{L_2} = \frac{M_1}{M_2} = \frac{R_1}{R_2}. \tag{308.3}$$

Both equations represent a.c. balances and hence the adjustments must be made simultaneously. As used the bridge consists of two fixed mutual inductances, one of which is known. A variable self inductance is placed in the arm which has the smallest self inductance. R_1 and R_2 are noninductive and include respectively the resistance of the corresponding coil. If the variable self inductance is calibrated, and either L_1 or L_2 is known, the other may be calculated.

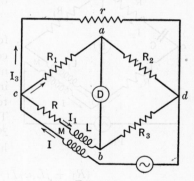

Fig. 296

309. Maxwell's Mutual Inductance Bridge. The network is shown in Fig. 296. Applying Kirchhoff's laws, we have

$$(R + jL\omega)\bar{I}_1 + jM\omega\bar{I} = R_1\bar{I}_2,$$
$$R_1\bar{I}_2 + R_2\bar{I}_2 = r\bar{I}_3,$$
$$R_2\bar{I}_2 = R_3\bar{I}_1,$$
$$\bar{I} = \bar{I}_1 + \bar{I}_2 + \bar{I}_3.$$

Eliminating the Is, there results

$$\frac{RR_2r}{R_3(R_1+R_2)} + j\left\{\frac{MRr\omega}{R_3(R_1+R_2)} + \frac{Mr\omega}{R_1+R_2} + M\omega\right\}$$

$$+ j\frac{LR_2r\omega}{R_3(R_1+R_2)} = \frac{R_1r}{R_1+R_2}.$$

Equating reals, we have

$$RR_2 = R_3R_1, \tag{309.1}$$

which is the d.c. balance.   Equating imaginaries, we have

$$M = -L\left\{\frac{R_2r}{R_2r + R_3r + R_3(R_1+R_2)}\right\}, \tag{309.2}$$

which is the a.c. balance.   The a.c. balance may be made by adjusting r, which does not affect the d.c. balance.   Equation (309.2) shows that L must be larger than M.   The negative sign means that the coupling is negative, i.e., the currents in the coupled coils are in opposition.

310. The Heydweiller Network for Mutual Inductance. This is a convenient method for measuring mutual inductance in terms of self inductance and resistance, or in terms of capacitance and resistance. The wiring diagram is shown in Fig. 297.   Applying Kirchhoff's laws, we have

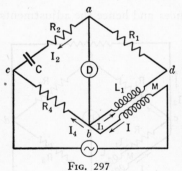

Fig. 297

$$(R_1 + jL_1\omega)\bar{I}_1 + jM\omega\bar{I} = 0,$$

$$\left(R_2 - j\left(\frac{1}{C\omega}\right)\right)\bar{I}_2 = R_4\bar{I}_4,$$

$$\bar{I} = \bar{I}_2 + \bar{I}_4.$$

Since no current flows through the detector D, $\bar{I}_1 = \bar{I}_2$.   Eliminating the currents, we have

$$R_1 + jL_1\omega + j\omega\left(M + \frac{MR_2}{R_4}\right) + \frac{M}{CR_4} = 0.$$

Equating reals, we have

$$M = -CR_1R_4. \tag{310.1}$$

Equating imaginaries, we have

$$M = -L\frac{R_4}{R_2 + R_4}. \tag{310.2}$$

The negative sign means that the mutual inductance must be connected for negative coupling. Both balances are a.c., and so must be made simultaneously, which occasions closer and closer adjustments until a balance obtains. This is effected most easily by adjusting R_1 and R_2 alternately, since each of these appears in only one of the equations. It is seen that L_1 must be greater than M. If necessary a separate self inductance may be placed in series with L_1 in order to effect a balance. If C is known, both L_1 and M may be calculated. If L_1 is known, C may be calculated.

311. The Heaviside Mutual Inductance Bridge. The wiring diagram for this bridge is shown in Fig. 298. This bridge is more sensitive than the Maxwell bridge, and it is not limited, as is the Maxwell bridge, by relative values of L_1 and M. Applying Kirchhoff's laws, we obtain the following equations:

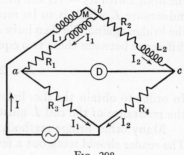

FIG. 298

$$\bar{I} = \bar{I}_1 + \bar{I}_2,$$

$$R_3\bar{I}_1 = R_4\bar{I}_2,$$

$$(R_2 + jL_2\omega)\bar{I}_2 = (R_1 + jL_1\omega)\bar{I}_1 + jM\omega\bar{I}.$$

Eliminating the currents, we have

$$R_2R_3 + j(L_2 - M)\omega R_3 = R_1R_4 + j(L_1 + M)\omega R_4.$$

Equating reals, we have the d.c. balance

$$R_2R_3 = R_1R_4. \tag{311.1}$$

Equating imaginaries, we have the a.c. balance

$$M = \frac{L_2R_3 - L_1R_4}{R_3 + R_4}. \tag{311.2}$$

For an equal-arm bridge, i.e., where $R_3 = R_4$ the value of M is given by

$$M = \tfrac{1}{2}(L_2 - L_1).$$ (311.3)

If $L_2 R_3 > L_1 R_4$, the coupling is positive (currents in the two coils have the same sense). If $L_2 R v < L_1 R$ the coupling is negative (currents in the two coils in opposition). The equal-arm bridge requires in general, an adjustable resistance in series with either L_1 or L_2 as the case may require.

The Heaviside bridge may be used to measure a self inductance in terms of mutual inductance alone. Thus, suppose M to be a variable calibrated mutual inductance standard, and L_1 and L_2 are fixed self inductances of about the same order of magnitude. First, balance the bridge with $R_3 = R_4$ and $M' = \tfrac{1}{2}(L_2 - L_1)$. Then, place the inductance L which is to be measured in series with L_2 and balance the bridge again. We then have $M'' = \tfrac{1}{2}(L_2 + L - L_1)$. Taking the difference between these two equations, we have

$$L = 2(M' - M'').$$ (311.4)

In order to obtain the d.c. balance an amount of resistance equal to the resistance of the coil L must be inserted in the arm ab.

Many other bridge methods will be found in the following books. The reader should work out a few of these bridge networks (not given in this book) by the use of complex quantities.

Vigoureux, P. and Webb, C. E.: Principles of Electric and Magnetic Measurements, New York, Prentice-Hall, 1936
Smythe, W. R. and Michels, W. C.: Advanced Electrical Measurements, New York, D. Van Nostrand Co., Inc., 1932
Terry, E. M.: Advanced Laboratory Practice in Electricity and Magnetism, 3rd ed., McGraw-Hill Book Co., Inc., 1936
Hague, B.: Alternating Current Bridge Methods, London, Sir Isaac Pitman and Sons, Ltd., 1923

312. A.C. Circuit Differential Equations. The mathematical development in Chapters XX and XXI when applied to a.c. circuit problems effects simple solutions in many cases. As an example, let us again solve the general differential equation which was solved in Section 245. The equation to be solved is

$$L \frac{d^2 i}{dt^2} + R \frac{di}{dt} + \frac{i}{C} = \frac{d\mathcal{E}}{dt}.$$ (312.1)

In this equation both i and ε are complex quantities. That is

$$i = I (\cos \omega t + j \sin \omega t) = I e^{j\omega t}$$

and

$$\varepsilon = \mathscr{E} (\cos \omega t + j \sin \omega t) = \mathscr{E} e^{j\omega t}.$$

Let us use the expressions

$$i = I e^{j\omega t} \quad \text{and} \quad \varepsilon = \mathscr{E} e^{j\omega t}.$$

Substituting in equation (312.1), we have

$$L \frac{d^2}{dt^2} (I e^{j\omega t}) + R \frac{d}{dt} (I e^{j\omega t}) + \frac{I}{C} e^{j\omega t} = \frac{d}{dt} (\mathscr{E} e^{j\omega t})$$

or

$$\left(-L\omega^2 + jR\omega + \frac{1}{C} \right) I e^{j\omega t} = j\omega \mathscr{E} e^{j\omega t},$$

whence

$$\left\{ R + j \left(L\omega - \frac{1}{C\omega} \right) \right\} I = \mathscr{E}. \tag{312.2}$$

Hence

$$I = \frac{\mathscr{E}}{R + j \left(L\omega - \frac{1}{C\omega} \right)} = \frac{\mathscr{E}}{Z}. \tag{312.3}$$

The denominator of this expression is the *complex impedance*, and is

$$Z = z e^{j\phi}.$$

Therefore, by (297.2), we have

$$i = \frac{\mathscr{E} e^{j\omega t}}{Z} = \frac{\mathscr{E}}{z} \frac{e^{j\omega t}}{e^{j\phi}} = \frac{\mathscr{E}}{z} e^{j(\omega t - \phi)}, \tag{312.4}$$

where the absolute value of Z is

$$z = \sqrt{R^2 + \left(L\omega - \frac{1}{C\omega} \right)^2},$$

and

$$\phi = \arctan \frac{L\omega - 1/C\omega}{R}.$$

In the trigonometric form, which is most familiar, equation (312.4) is

$$i = I \sin (\omega t - \phi) \;\; = \frac{\mathscr{E}}{z} \sin (\omega t - \phi)$$

$$\varepsilon = \mathscr{E} \sin \omega t.$$

This is the same solution that was obtained in Section 245. It is a much simpler and shorter solution than the former. Any a.c. circuit differential equation may be solved by this method. Solutions of the other a.c. differential equations of Chapter XX are left as an exercise.

CHAPTER XXIII

ELECTRIC OSCILLATIONS AND ELECTRIC WAVES ON WIRES

313. Hertz's Experiment. — In the year 1879 Helmholtz set the following question for one of the prizes of the Berlin Academy: "Whether the polarization and depolarization of an insulator should produce in its neighborhood the same electromagnetic effect as a galvanic current in a conductor." Among the men who had studied under Helmholtz was Heinrich R. Hertz. Hertz obtained his doctor's degree *summa cum laude* in 1880, and was professor of physics in the Polytechnic School at Karlsruhe from 1885 to 1889. It was during this period that he obtained an answer to the question propounded by Helmholtz, and also showed that electromagnetic waves travel with the speed predicted by Maxwell's theoretical analysis.

As we have seen in Section 234, when a circuit containing capacitance, inductance, and resistance is left to itself, with the condenser charged, electric oscillations are set up in the circuit if the resistance is below a certain critical value. In 1853 Lord Kelvin predicted from mathematical deductions that the discharge of a Leyden jar would, under the conditions found mathematically, be oscillatory. In 1857 Fedderson examined the spark produced by the discharge of a Leyden jar and found that it was oscillatory as predicted by theory. The discovery of the oscillatory character of the electric spark, under these conditions, is attributed also to Joseph Henry. According to the electromagnetic theory such electric oscillations should send out trains of electromagnetic waves of the same frequency as the frequency of the oscillator and of wavelength given by the equation $c = f\lambda$, where c is the speed of light. In 1887 and 1888 Hertz proved the existence of such waves from the discharge of a Leyden jar.

According to the prevalent views in the early part of the nineteenth century, electric and magnetic disturbances were conceived to be propagated with infinite velocity, that is, instantaneously. If there is a charge q at b there is an intensity at P equal to q/d_1^2, Fig. 299. If now q changes its position abruptly from b to c the intensity at P changes to q/d_2^2 with no time lag, according to the older theory.

According to electromagnetic theory, beginning about 1845, there should be a time interval between the change in position of q and the change in intensity at P, the time interval being the time required for a wave traveling with the speed of light c to travel from b to P. Further, the sudden change in the position of q develops at P a magnetic intensity simultaneously with the change in electric intensity at P. In fact, the change in electric intensity, together with the

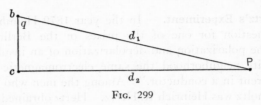

FIG. 299

attendant magnetic intensity, should be propagated from b to P with the speed c. This is the electromagnetic wave. Now, a change in the position of q cannot be made by mechanical means with sufficiently great acceleration to produce at P a measurable effect. Hertz obtained the requisite acceleration, and hence measurable electromagnetic waves, by means of the discharge of a pair of charged plates, called a "vibrator."

One form of vibrator used by Hertz consisted of a pair of brass plates aa' each 40 cms. square to which were attached two short rods

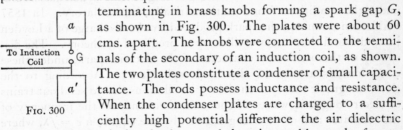

FIG. 300

terminating in brass knobs forming a spark gap G, as shown in Fig. 300. The plates were about 60 cms. apart. The knobs were connected to the terminals of the secondary of an induction coil, as shown. The two plates constitute a condenser of small capacitance. The rods possess inductance and resistance. When the condenser plates are charged to a sufficiently high potential difference the air dielectric separating the knobs breaks down and there is a sudden rush of negative electrons across the gap G to the positive plate. The hot gases in the air gap constitute a conductor of comparatively low resistance and the current surges back and forth with very high frequency. The current is strongly damped and quickly dies away to a point where the spark is quenched, owing to the dissipation of energy as ri^2t heat and radiation. The whole process is over with before the next break of the primary circuit by the interrupter. The dissipation of energy by radiation is large in this case since this is a so-called open-circuit type of oscillator. The whole process is repeated at each break of the primary circuit. Thus, successive groups of high-frequency, damped oscillatory currents surge back and forth across the gap. The number of complete cycles in a given group is not large, about 4 to 10 in the Hertz oscillator. The period is not quite constant owing to the changing resistance in the gap as the gases cool down. The period of the Hertz oscillator was about $1.4 (10)^{-8}$ second, corresponding to a wavelength of 420 cms. or 4.2 m., the velocity of propagation being taken as $3(10)^{10}$ cms./sec. In order that the oscillator may function properly the knobs must be highly polished so that the discharge will start suddenly.

314. Measurement of Wavelength. — In order to measure the wavelength Hertz reflected the waves from a large rectangular slab of zinc, and so produced stationary waves. Any conducting medium acts as a reflector of electromagnetic waves. The Kennelly-Heaviside reflecting layers in the earth's upper atmosphere are conspicuous examples. As a detector for the purpose of locating the antinodal points he used a resonator (syntonator) consisting of a wire bent into a circle, the ends terminating in small brass knobs. The length of the air gap separating the knobs was regulated by a micrometer screw. The diameter of the circle was adjusted until the free natural period of the resonator was the same as the period of the oscillator. The antinodal points were the points where the maximum length of spark was obtained with the resonator, i.e., the points where the induced emf. in the resonator is a maximum. Parenthetically, it may be stated that the photoelectric effect was first observed by Hertz in these experiments, as was shown in Chapter X. He found that when the spark gap of the resonator was illuminated by the spark of the oscillator a longer spark was obtainable with the resonator, thus indicating that the air gap was rendered a better conductor than when not illuminated.

It was found that the orientation of the plane of the resonator is important, since the waves emitted by the oscillator are plane polarized. Suppose the waves to be propagated along the x axis and the rods of the oscillator to be coincident with the z axis, Fig. 301. Then the electric vector Z is parallel to the z axis and the magnetic vector β is parallel to the y axis. If the plane of the resonator is parallel to the xz plane or to the yz plane, as shown in positions 1 and 2, it will respond, i.e., when the gap is parallel to the electric vector. This is because the electric vector causes the electrons to move thus building up a p.d. across the gap. Or in these positions the magnetic field links with the loop of the resonator, and as the magnetic field varies rapidly it builds up a p.d. across the gap of the resonator which causes a spark to form. If the plane of the resonator is the xy plane, position 3, the gap is normal to the electric vector, and its plane is parallel to the magnetic vector, and therefore it will not respond. By means of this arrangement Hertz showed that electromagnetic waves

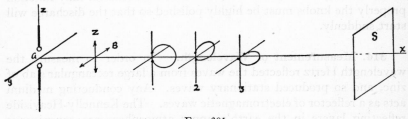

FIG. 301

are propagated through space with the velocity of light in accordance with Maxwell's theory. Having measured the wavelength from the distance between points of resonance and determining the frequency of the oscillator, the velocity of propagation is calculated by use of the equation $c = f\lambda$.

The interpretation of the experiment as here indicated is not quite accurate, as was pointed out by Sarasin and De la Rive. The Hertz oscillator, shown in Fig. 300, is of the so-called open circuit type, and therefore the oscillations are strongly damped owing to copious radiation. This means that in a single discharge or wave group there are not enough complete waves to enable the oscillator to establish stationary waves. The wave group will, however, by impact so to speak, set up oscillations in the detector, which, being of the closed type and hence not strongly damped, will continue to oscillate for a long enough time to establish stationary waves of its own if the distance from the detector to the reflector is an odd number of quarter wavelengths. Thus, the frequency of the stationary waves coincides with that of the resonator rather than that of the oscillator. If, however, the detector is brought into resonance with the oscillator the stationary waves will have the same frequency as both detector and oscillator, and the effect will be as found by Hertz.

315. Reflection, Refraction, and Polarization. — In order to study reflection, refraction, and polarization effects two metal, cylindrical, parabolic reflectors are required, as shown in Fig. 302. The axis of the oscillator o, consisting of two brass rods, is made to coincide with the principal focal axis of one of the reflectors, 1 say. The beam that is reflected from this mirror therefore consists of parallel rays. The detector d is made to coincide with the principal focal axis of the other reflector 2, which brings to a focus the plane polarized waves reflected from mirror 1. If these two reflectors are placed so as to

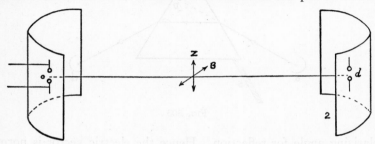

Fig. 302

face each other with focal axes parallel, as shown, the detector responds most vigorously. In this position the electric vector Z is parallel to the focal axes of the mirrors, i.e., normal to the plane of polarization as used in optics. If the detector is turned about the axis joining the detector and oscillator the strength of the response gradually weakens until when detector and oscillator are normal to each other the response ceases altogether. Thus the waves are plane polarized.

Professor Trouton has repeated many of the ordinary optical experiments using electromagnetic waves from an oscillator of the Hertz type. He found that electromagnetic waves from an oscillator are reflected as are light waves, the angle of incidence being equal to the angle of reflection. If a large prism of pitch or paraffine is arranged, as shown in Fig. 303, with the oscillator at o the detector does not respond until in a position such as d. In this position it responds as for direct radiation. A prism of pitch with refracting angle $A = 30°$, when placed as shown, gave an angle of minimum deviation $D = 22°$. Using the ordinary formula from optics the index of refraction is found to be 1.69. S is a metal screen used to shield the detector from direct radiation.

Electromagnetic waves were reflected from a large slab of paraffine. It was found that reflection takes place at all angles of incidence provided the electric vector Z is perpendicular to the plane of incidence, but when the electric vector is in the plane of incidence there is some angle for which copious reflection does not occur. This angle is the

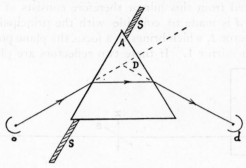

FIG. 303

polarizing angle for reflection. Hence the electric vector is normal to the plane of polarization as used in optics.

The plane of polarization may be shown in still another way. If equally spaced wires are stretched on a wooden frame, forming a kind of diffraction grating, and, if this grating is placed between the oscillator and detector, as shown in Fig. 304, the detector fails to respond when the wires are parallel to the electric vector Z as shown. If, however, the wire grating is rotated about the x axis the detector

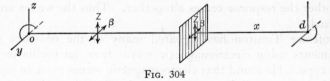

FIG. 304

will at first give weak signals with gradually increasing strength until the wires are normal to the electric vector, when signals of maximum strength are received. In the position shown where the wires are parallel to the electric vector a part of the energy of the advancing wave is absorbed, since currents are set up in the wires, and the remainder of the energy is reflected as from a metal sheet. Therefore, the wire grating behaves as a Nicol's prism. If two wire gratings are used, one behind the other, along the x axis and the one nearer to the oscillator is in the position for maximum transmission, i.e., wires normal to the vector Z, the other grating blocks the waves when its wires are normal to those of the first grating. This corresponds to the case of crossed Nicols or polaroids in optics.

316. Other Types of Oscillators. — Many other types of oscillators have been used since Hertz performed his classic experiments. Of these, perhaps the Lodge oscillator is best known and so constructed as to emphasize fundamental principles. Sir Oliver Lodge arranged two circuits as shown in Fig. 305. Each circuit contained a Leyden jar, a rectangle of wire forming the external circuit, and a spark gap. Thus each circuit contains capacitance and inductance in series, since the circuit outside the jar possesses inductance. One of the Leyden jar circuits, A say, was the oscillator. The other Leyden jar circuit B

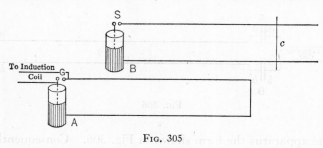

FIG. 305

was the resonator or detector. The circuit B had two parallel wires cross connected by a sliding conductor c. The oscillator A may be charged by an electrostatic generator or an induction coil, the connections being made as indicated. When the spark gap G in circuit A breaks down, and oscillations are set up, electromagnetic waves travel outward and sweep over resonator B. If B has the same natural frequency as A, oscillations will be set up in B and a minute spark will bridge the gap S between the inner and outer coats of the Leyden jar. Circuit B is brought into resonance with circuit A by moving the slider c until sparking occurs at S.

Lodge also obtained oscillations in a single metallic sphere. Another similar metallic sphere a few yards distant served as a detector. Minute sparks were obtained from this sphere when a conductor was arranged so as to form contacts connecting the two ends of a diameter, the points of contact being determined by the relative positions of the two spheres. In this case the oscillations take place from pole to pole of the emitting sphere, and like oscillations are set up in the resonating sphere. J. J. Thomson has shown that the wavelength of the radiation emitted by a sphere is 1.4 times the diameter of the sphere. The spheres used by Lodge were 5 cms. in diameter. Therefore, the emitted radiation had a wavelength of 7 cms. and a frequency of $4.28(10)^9$ cycles per second.

317. Electromagnetic Waves on Parallel Wires. — Let a pair of long, parallel wires, $a'a''$ and $b'b''$, be connected to the plates of two condensers, A and B, as shown in Fig. 306. Let the other two plates, a and b, be connected through a spark gap G as shown. When connected to the secondary of an induction coil, as indicated, the spark gap G and condenser plates a and b constitute a Hertz oscillator. E. Lecher made a very careful study of sustained waves on wires and

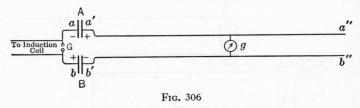

Fig. 306

gave the apparatus the form shown in Fig. 306. Consequently, any similar system, no matter what the manner of excitation may be, is called a Lecher parallel wire system. When the spark gap G breaks down high-frequency oscillations are set up in the circuit aGb, and electric waves travel out along the wires $a'a''$ and $b'b''$ as the condenser plates a' and b' are charged alternately positive and negative. The electric waves are reflected from the far ends of the wires, and, on combining with the direct waves, produce stationary waves. These waves are primarily waves in the conduction electrons within the wires. However, as the electrons are accelerated with the forward motion of the electronic wave, an electromagnetic wave between and surrounding the wires appears simultaneously, and the electromagnetic wave travels along the wires, being directed by them, at the same speed as the electronic wave within the wires. The speed of this wave motion is very nearly the speed of light in free space. Therefore, in order to obtain stationary waves on wires of a length that may be strung up in a laboratory room the frequency must be very high.

We must distinguish between two types of nodal and antinodal points in the stationary waves produced, current and potential, related as shown in Fig. 307. The current nodal points are separated from the potential nodal points by a quarter wavelength, the distance between successive nodal points in either case being a half wavelength, as in all stationary waves. The potential antinodal points may be located by connecting across the wires some potential indicator, such as a neon tube or a thermogalvanometer g, Fig. 306. At the potential nodes there is no action, but when potential antinodal points are connected the neon tube glows or the galvanometer is deflected. Maximum illumination or maximum deflection of the galvanometer

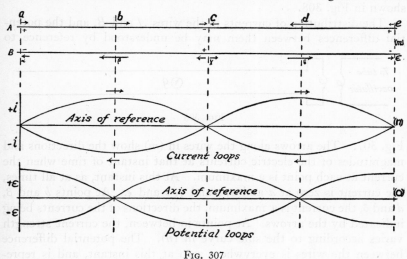

Fig. 307

locates an antinodal point. As the distance between two successive antinodal points is a half wavelength, the speed of propagation is given by the familiar wave equation $s = f\lambda$. λ is measured directly, and if either f or s can be determined the other quantity may be calculated. Lecher wires have been used quite extensively in measuring the frequency of oscillation by assuming s to be the speed of light in free space. However, s is not quite equal to the speed of light in free space as it is affected by the resistance, capacitance, and inductance of the wires. Also, the nodal and antinodal points are not quite equally spaced along the wires. Thus there is an element of uncertainty in such frequency measurements.

If the Lecher wires are open at the far end the open end is a potential antinode but a current node. If the far ends of the wires are bridged by a low-resistance conductor there is a potential node at the ends but a current antinode. The potential nodes and antinodes correspond to the nodes and antinodes in stationary sound waves, e.g., in a Kundt tube or an organ pipe. The stationary waves on Lecher wires are most pronounced and accurate when the lengths of the wires are such as to resonate with the oscillator. In the modern use of Lecher wires the oscillator is usually a tube oscillator. In this manner of use the input end of the parallel-wire system is bridged by a single loop of wire and coupled inductively with the oscillator as shown in Fig. 308.

The distribution of currents in the wires A and B, and the potential differences between them may be understood by reference to

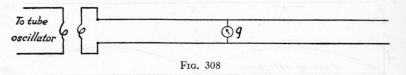

FIG. 308

Fig. 307. The arrows along the wires in (m) show the directions and magnitudes of the electric currents at that instant of time when the current at each point is a maximum. At this instant, as at all times, the current is zero at a and α, c and γ, e and ϵ. At points b and β, d and δ, the current is a maximum, the directions of the currents being indicated by the arrows. At points in between, the current strength varies according to the sine curve in (n). The potential difference between the wires is everywhere zero at this instant, and is represented by the axis of reference in (o). Since the current everywhere has reached its maximum value, the magnetic field surrounding the wires is a maximum, and so distributed as to have maximum intensity at the antinodal points and zero at the nodal points. Since the difference of potential between the wires is everywhere zero, there is no electric field. Thus at this instant the field is wholly magnetic.

During the next quarter period the currents in both wires everywhere decreases and becomes zero at every point at the end of the quarter period, and is represented by the axis of reference in (n). But at the end of the quarter period negative charge has accumulated at α and ϵ, and positive charge at γ on wire B. On wire A positive charge has accumulated at a and e, and negative charge at c. Thus there is a maximum difference of potential between points a and α, c and γ, e and ϵ, the polarity being shown by $+$ and $-$ signs in (m). The difference of potential between these points is distributed according to the sine curves in (o). Since the difference of potential between the wires has reached its maximum value at every point the electric field between the wires is a maximum, and so distributed as to have maximum value between the points a and α, c and γ, e and ϵ, and zero value between points b and β, d and δ. At points between, the electric intensity is distributed as the difference of potential is distributed. Since at this instant the current is everywhere zero, there is no magnetic field. The field is wholly electric. At the end of the next quarter period the currents everywhere are reversed in direction and have reached their maximum values. At this instant the potential difference between the wires is everywhere zero. The magnetic field has reached its maximum value in the reverse sense. There is no electric field between the wires. Thus, the process goes on in cyclic order as long as the excitation is maintained.

This is a sort of pulsating effect between the magnetic field and the electric field, one being a maximum when the other is zero. The currents in the segments between nodal points surge first in one direction and then in the reverse direction, which is also a sort of pulsating effect. It will be seen that the electromagnetic waves considered here are not of the same type as the Maxwellian electromagnetic waves, since they are composite, consisting of direct and reflected waves, and always associated with the electronic waves in the wires, and hence influenced by them. These waves are never wholly detached from the wires as are the electromagnetic waves from a Hertz oscillator or the antenna of a broadcasting station.

318. Speed of Propagation of Electromagnetic Waves on Wires — Elementary Treatment. — Fig. 309 represents what is called a

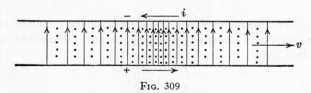

Fig. 309

"rectangular wave pulse" traveling along a pair of wires with a speed s. The fine, vertical lines represent the electric lines of flux, and the dots represent the lines of magnetic flux which are normal to the electric lines. A sectional view of such a field is shown in Fig. 139. The electric and magnetic lines of flux move in a direction normal to themselves with a speed s, which is the electromagnetic wave disturbance. We may think of the moving magnetic field as inducing, and thereby sustaining, the electric field, which is the induced emf. Conversely, the moving electric field may be thought of as inducing, and thereby sustaining, the magnetic field, which is the induced mmf. Thus, *an electromagnetic wave consists of a magnetic field of force and an electric field of force moving along together, in a direction normal to each, and mutually sustaining each other.* The relative directions of magnetic flux, electric flux, and wave velocity may be remembered by holding the middle finger, the forefinger, and the thumb of the right hand mutually at right angles to each other. Let the direction in which the middle finger points indicate the direction of magnetic flux, the direction in which the forefinger points indicate the direction of electric flux, then the thumb will point in the direction of wave propagation.

We may derive an expression for the speed of propagation of these waves, s cms./sec., in a simple manner, which, however, is not strictly accurate since it neglects factors which affect the speed. Let H be the intensity of the magnetic field and E' the intensity of the electric field, both in cgsm. units. Let d cms. be the distance between the wires. The lateral motion of the magnetic field induces an emf. $\mathcal{E}'$ between the wires of value given by

$$\mathcal{E}' = \frac{d\phi}{dt}, \quad \text{or} \quad \mathcal{E}' = Hds. \tag{318.1}$$

The electric field intensity between the wires is $\mathcal{E}'/d$, or

$$E' = Hs \quad \text{cgsm. potential difference per cm.} \tag{318.2}$$

In an electromagnetic wave the electric energy density is equal to the magnetic energy density at every instant. Therefore, we may write for free space

$$\frac{H^2}{8\pi} = \frac{E^2}{8\pi},$$

where E is in cgse. units. To change E to cgsm. units, we have $cE = E'$, where c is the ratio between the two systems of units, which has been shown to be essentially equal to the speed of light in free space. Then

$$\frac{H^2}{8\pi} = \frac{E'^2}{c^2 8\pi}.$$ (318.3)

And by (318.2)

$$\frac{H^2}{8\pi} = \frac{H^2 s^2}{c^2 8\pi}.$$ (318.4)

Hence $s = c$, which is the speed of light in free space. Thus, neglecting resistance, capacitance, and inductance of the line the waves travel along the wires with the speed of light in free space.

If the medium between and surrounding the wires is not free space, we have

$$E' = \mu Hs, \quad \text{and hence} \quad E = \frac{\mu Hs}{v}.$$

Therefore,

$$\frac{\mu H^2}{8\pi} = \frac{\epsilon E^2}{8\pi} = \frac{\epsilon(\mu Hs)^2}{c^2 8\pi}.$$ (318.5)

Hence

$$s = \frac{c}{\sqrt{\epsilon\mu}}.$$ (318.6)

In equation (318.6) μ is in cgsm. units and ϵ in cgse. units. The line capacitance, inductance, and resistance have been neglected.

The capacitance and inductance of the line may be taken account of in the following manner: Let L' be the line inductance per cm. of length and i' the current (out in one wire, return in the other). Since by definition, L' is the flux linked with the circuit in the cgsm. system when unit current flows, $L'i'$ is the flux when a current i' flows. If the lateral speed of the flux is s cms./sec., then $1/s$ seconds is the time required for all of the flux between the wires of a cm. in length to travel forward 1 cm. and to cross a line drawn from wire to wire. Therefore, since $\mathcal{E}' = L'(di'/dt)$, we have

$$\mathcal{E}' = \frac{L'i'}{1/s} = L'i's.$$ (318.7)

Let C' be the capacitance of the two wires in cgsm. units per cm. of length. The magnetic energy per cm. of length of line is $\frac{1}{2}L'i'^2$ ergs, and the electric energy per cm. of length if line is $\frac{1}{2}C'\mathcal{E}'^2$. Since in an electromagnetic wave the energy is equally divided at every instant of time between the two fields, we have

$$L'i'^2 = C'\mathcal{E}'^2. \tag{318.8}$$

On combining this equation with (318.7), there results

$$s = \frac{1}{\sqrt{L'C'}}. \tag{318.9}$$

Thus the speed of propagation depends upon the capacitance and inductance per cm. of length of line.

In order to calculate the speed s by equation (318.9) it will be necessary to obtain expressions for the capacitance and inductance per cm. of length of line. This we have already done in the special case of concentric cylindrical conductors, as for a submarine cable. For the inductance we obtained

$$L' = 2\mu \log_e \left(\frac{b}{a}\right) \text{ cgsm. units. Equation (176.2).}$$

And for the capacitance

$$C' = \frac{\epsilon'}{2 \log_e b/a} \text{ cgsm. units. Equation (26.4).}$$

From these two equations we obtain $L'C' = \epsilon'\mu$ and (318.9) becomes

$$s = \frac{1}{\sqrt{\epsilon'\mu}}. \tag{318.10}$$

This is the expression for the speed of light c in free space where ϵ' is in cgsm. measure. Thus, in this special case, the electromagnetic wave travels along the wires with the speed of light, since $\mu = 1$ for free space, and $\epsilon' = 1/c^2$.

319. Differential Equation for Waves along Wires. — It will be interesting and instructive to solve the last problem of the preceding Section by the differential-equations method. When an electromagnetic wave is traveling along a transmission line the current is varying from point to point, and hence the electrons are being accelerated. Let us consider a long, straight wire coaxially within a cylindrical tube, as above. An elementary length of the cable has both capacitance and inductance. The charge on each elementary condenser of which the cable is made up is constantly changing, i.e., the current flowing into an element is not in general equal to the current flowing out at the same instant.

Let the length of the element of cable be dx, and the rate of variation of current with distance along the cable be $\partial i'/\partial x$. If i' is the current entering the element, the current leaving is $i' + (\partial i'/\partial x)dx$. The difference between the current entering and leaving the element is

$$\frac{\partial i'}{\partial x}\, dx. \tag{319.1}$$

Let $\mathcal{E}'$ be the difference of potential between the inner and outer conductors of the cable at the element considered, and C' the capacitance per cm. of length of cable. Then the charge on the element is $C'\mathcal{E}'dx$. The rate of change of charge with time is

$$C'\frac{\partial \mathcal{E}'}{\partial t}\, dx, \tag{319.2}$$

which is the change in the current in the element, and hence equal to (319.1). Therefore, we have

$$\frac{\partial i'}{\partial x} = C'\frac{\partial \mathcal{E}'}{\partial t}. \tag{319.3}$$

Another differential equation may be obtained in terms of the inductance and resistance of the cable as follows: Let L' be the inductance per unit length of cable. Then the difference of potential over the element of cable will be

$$L'\frac{\partial i'}{\partial t}\, dx + r'i'\, dx. \tag{319.4}$$

The p.d. between the ends of the element will be $(\partial \mathcal{E}'/\partial x)dx$. Therefore

$$\frac{\partial \mathcal{E}'}{\partial x}\, dx = L'\frac{\partial i'}{\partial t}\, dx + r'i'\, dx. \tag{319.5}$$

If $\mathcal{E}'$ is varying rapidly, as in the transmission of voice or music over a transmission cable, $r'i'\, dx$ will be small in comparison with the other terms and therefore may be neglected without sensible error. Then

$$\frac{\partial \mathcal{E}'}{\partial x} = L'\frac{\partial i'}{\partial t}. \tag{319.6}$$

Differentiating (319.3) with respect to t, we have

$$\frac{\partial^2 i'}{\partial x \partial t} = C' \frac{\partial^2 \mathcal{E}'}{\partial t^2}. \tag{319.7}$$

Differentiating (319.6) with respect to x, we have

$$\frac{\partial^2 \mathcal{E}'}{\partial x^2} = L' \frac{\partial^2 i'}{\partial x \partial t}. \tag{319.8}$$

Combining (319.7) and (319.8), there results

$$\frac{\partial^2 \mathcal{E}'}{\partial t^2} = \frac{1}{L'C'} \frac{\partial^2 \mathcal{E}'}{\partial x^2}. \tag{319.9}$$

Or, setting $s^2 = 1/L'C'$,

$$\frac{\partial^2 \mathcal{E}'}{\partial t^2} - s^2 \frac{\partial^2 \mathcal{E}'}{\partial x^2} = 0. \tag{319.10}$$

This is the differential equation of a wave motion traveling with a speed s. The solution for the propagation in the positive x direction is

$$\mathcal{E}' = f(x - st)^1. \tag{319.11}$$

The speed of the wave is

$$s = \frac{1}{\sqrt{L'C'}}. \tag{319.12}$$

If the impressed potential is harmonic and of the form $\mathcal{E}' = \mathcal{E}' \sin \omega t$, the wave equation is given by

$$\mathcal{E}' = \mathcal{E}' \sin \frac{2\pi}{T} \left(t - \frac{x}{s} \right). \tag{319.13}$$

Thus a potential wave travels along the line with a velocity s, and hence the electromagnetic wave has the same speed. An equation in i' similar to (319.10) may also be derived.

320. Practical Applications. — All of the early-type oscillators were of the spark variety which produced groups of damped waves, and therefore lasted only a brief interval of time. With the advent of the three-electrode thermionic vacuum tube or triode, undamped, sustained oscillations were possible, and therefore constant amplitude waves. However, because of the internal capacitance of the tube

---

[1] For method of solution see any textbook on differential equations.

itself and the unavoidable distributed capacitance and inductance outside the tube, there is a certain lower wavelength limit with any particular tube beyond which we cannot go with the tube oscillator.

The sustained oscillations produced by tube generators provide an improved means of studying the free oscillations in circuits containing distributed inductance and capacitance, such as single or parallel wires and solenoids. Interest in this subject has been rejuvenated in recent years because of the development of short-wave triode generators. One of the problems in connection with the use of short-wave generators is to devise some means whereby the frequency of the generator may be accurately measured. A method that has been used frequently for the measurement of such frequencies consists in determining the antinodal distance for stationary waves on parallel conductors, or Lecher wires. This mode of measurement is based upon the assumption that the relation $c = f\lambda$ holds accurately for electromagnetic waves along Lecher wires. However, this method of measurement is attended with some difficulties and uncertainties. For instance, the speed s depends to some extent upon the resistance of the conductors, and therefore it is not accurately equal to the speed of light in free space. Reflections from surrounding objects, such as the ground, floor or walls of a room, interfere with the waves upon the wires and this interference is of indeterminate amount. There is also an end correction to be made for the length of the wires where the wires are the shortest possible corresponding to the fundamental wavelength.

In 1898 Abraham[1] calculated the free period of electric oscillations of a long, narrow metallic ellipsoid of revolution when electrically excited. He found to a good approximation the relation $\lambda = 2l$, where λ is the wavelength and l is the length of the ellipsoid or conductor. Undoubtedly a rectilinear conductor of circular cross section cannot differ greatly from an elongated ellipsoid of revolution, as Abraham concluded. In 1902 Macdonald,[2] by theoretical reasoning quite different from that used by Abraham, derived the relation $\lambda = 2.53l$. The discrepancy between these two results is so great that implicit reliance cannot be placed upon wave measurements based upon the free oscillations of linear conductors. Since 1902 many papers have been published for the purpose of clearing up this discrepancy, but with unsatisfactory results. In 1928 this whole

[1] Abraham, Ann. der Phys. 66, p. 435, 1898.
[2] Macdonald's Electric Waves, pp. 111–112.

subject was studied by C. R. Englund [1] for the purpose of obtaining a wave meter for short electromagnetic waves. The wavelengths were measured upon a pair of Lecher wires of large diameter (No. 8 B & S gauge) and a satisfactory wave meter was found to be a quarter-wavelength Lecher frame with an end correction. Englund found that reflections from floor and walls of the laboratory introduced such a large error that it could not be neglected, and so the apparatus was taken out-of-doors and mounted well above the ground. The end correction as given by Englund's formula for a quarter wave pair of rods is:

$$\lambda = 4(l + 3.1) \text{ cms.}$$

where l is the length of the parallel-rod systems, or Lecher frame. This Lecher frame consisted of a pair of straight, parallel copper tubes 1.27 cms. in diameter and spaced 10.1 cms. from center to center. The end effect seems to be due to the open end, and undoubtedly changes with spacing, but is constant with any given spacing. The wave along the wires behaves as though it were reflected from a point a little beyond the ends of the wires. In this study the wave along the wires was assumed to be that of light in free space, or rather air.

For an extended discussion of this subject the reader is referred to the original papers.

321. Velocity of Electric Waves on Open-Wire Line. — It will be a matter of some interest now to determine the speed of an electric wave on a two-wire, open line where the distance d between the wires is large compared with the radius of the wires. The capacitance per unit length of loop line is given very approximately by

$$C' = \frac{\epsilon'}{4 \log_e d/a}, \qquad (325.1)$$

since $v^2 C' = C$, and $v^2 \epsilon' = \epsilon$.

The inductance L' per unit length of loop line for high-frequency current, assuming no loading, is given by

$$L' = 4\mu \log_e \left(\frac{d}{a}\right). \qquad (325.2)$$

---

[1] Englund, Reprint B-340, Bell Tel. Lab.
[2] Calculations of Alternating Current Problems by Louis Cohen.

Multiplying (325.1) by (325.2), we have $L'C' = \epsilon'\mu$, and by equation (318.10), we obtain

$$s = \frac{1}{\sqrt{\epsilon'\mu}} = \frac{1}{\sqrt{L'C'}} = c.$$

Thus the speed of electric waves on open, two-wire, resistanceless lines is very nearly that of light in free space, i.e., where capacitance and inductance can be expressed in the manner here indicated. However, capacitance and inductance, in general, affect the speed of propagation and produce distortion as well as attenuation. These effects have limited the use of telephone and telegraph lines, and therefore much research has been carried on in an effort to correct the defects. The methods that have been adopted to correct such defects come under the name of *loading*. Loading has been guided by elaborate mathematical analyses, which, however, are beyond the scope of this book; but the general problems and methods that have been used in loading lines may be considered with profit.

322. Loading Lines.—In the case of actual lines used for telephone work and radio hookups the velocity of the electric waves is not quite equal to the velocity of light in free space. Besides the different frequencies prevailing in the human voice and music do not travel with the same speed when translated into electric waves on wires. Capacitance usually predominates in telegraph and telephone lines, and this brings about distortion. Resistance is the chief factor in producing attenuation. Modifying the characteristics of a line so as to approximate ideal conditions is called loading.

Some twenty years ago Oliver Heaviside made the suggestion that the transmission power of a telephone line could be improved by increasing the inductance of the line, as this would reduce attenuation and distortion. Since this first suggestion mathematical physicists and practical telephonists have been working constantly on this problem with the result that great improvements have been made in the transmitting power of both telephone and telegraph lines. This is very important in connection with national radio hookups.

Many schemes were brought forward for increasing the inductance of the line, but with very little practical success until Pupin proposed to locate inductances in the line in equispaced loading coils. The improvement in transmitting power has been brought about by carrying out one of two methods of loading, viz., by " increasing the inductance of the line by uniform loading and increasing it by loading coils at intervals." " Uniform loading consists in wrapping or enclosing the copper conductor in iron wire in such a manner that the magnetic flux produced around it by the telephonic current is increased, with a corresponding increase in the effective inductance, with more or less reduction in the distortion of the wave form produced by the line."

There are three types of lines used in practice, each attended with its own problems, viz., aerial or overhead lines, underground cables, and submarine cables.   The improved transmitting power of overhead lines has been brought about solely through the use of loading coils or inductances placed in the line at equispaced intervals.   Overhead lines are not adapted to uniform loading owing to the fact that the increased weight of the line makes the cost of construction and maintenance of the line prohibitive.

The two essential qualities requisite in wire telephony, as well as in radio telephony, is *loudness* and *clearness*.   The loss of loudness or volume is due to attenuation, but the loss of clearness is due to the differences in attenuation and wave speed of the various frequencies which go to make up speech.   In the case of aerial lines the loss in volume is due chiefly to the resistance of the line, and, insofar as this is the case, it cannot be improved very much by the introduction of inductance coils which add resistance to the line.   It is only the attenuation which is due to distributed capacitance that can be reduced by adding inductance.   Experience, however, goes to show that aerial lines are improved by loading coils.   These coils are low-resistance, closed, laminated, iron-circuit choking coils placed directly in the line at intervals of 8, 10, or 12 miles.   As an example of loading we may cite the New York-San Francisco line, which is the longest aerial loaded telephone line in the world.   This line was completed in 1916, and is 3,400 miles in length.   It consists of a pair of copper circuits, each of No. 8 wires carried on wooden poles.   The line is loaded with coils each having an inductance of 0.25 henry spaced 8 miles apart.   The unloaded line has a resistance of 4.14 ohms and an inductance of 0.0034 henry per loop mile, and the capacitance between the two wires of each circuit is 0.0091 mf. per loop mile. When loaded with inductance coils every 8 miles, each having an effective resistance of 6.5 ohms, the average effective resistance is about 5 ohms per loop mile, and the average inductance is about 0.0365 henry per loop mile.   Direct speech transmission between

New York and San Francisco however is impossible, even with loading. To make speech possible for this distance devices which are called *repeaters* are introduced at intervals in the line, which function to amplify the attenuated current when too weak to be effective. The repeaters now used are generally of the thermionic or three-electrode tube type. They are in principle amplifiers such as are used in radio work.

With underground and submarine cables the predominant cause of attenuation is line capacitance. Attenuation due to this cause can be greatly remedied by adding inductance to the line, since inductance and capacitance have opposite effects so far as reactance is concerned.

323. Under-ground Telephone Cables. — Under-ground cables are adapted to both uniform and spaced loading. The impedance coils used in spaced loading are enclosed in water-tight iron cases housed in water-tight chambers placed at regular intervals along the line. This method of loading is used extensively in England. In the English system the coils are spaced 2.5 miles apart. They are toroidal in form having a closed iron magnetic circuit. The effective resistance of each coil at a frequency of 1,000 cycles/second varies from 3.5 to 15 ohms, and the inductance varies from 0.06 to 0.25 henry. Each coil is wound in two equal parts, one winding being inserted in the lead and the other in the return circuit. In the United States there is an under-ground, loaded telephone cable between Boston and Washington, D. C., by way of New York and Philadelphia, which is 475 miles in length. It is a multiple cable of No. 10 copper wire, and the loading coils are spaced from 1 to 4 miles. The effect of loading in all telephone lines has been to reduce attenuation and distortion, and thus to increase the practical commercial speaking distance, without the aid of repeaters, from two to three times the distance attainable without loading, the wire gauge number being the same in each case.

324. Under-water Telephone Cables. — In the case of under-water cables uniform loading has been used, but the mechanical difficulties encountered in spaced loading have been overcome and such loading is now used. Uniform loading has two disadvantages as compared with spaced loading. Uniform loaded cables are more expensive to manufacture. Where iron wire is used to wrap the cable it is difficult to calculate with any degree of certainty the attenuation factor because of the impossibility of determining in advance the permeability of the iron wire wrapping, the effect on its permeability of laying and aging, and the change in effective resistance of the cable due to hysteresis and eddy currents developed in the iron-wire envelope.

In uniform loading the copper core is insulated and then wrapped with several layers of fine wire. This is then insulated with either gutta percha or paper. If paper is used a continuous lead sheath is placed over the paper to keep it dry, and outside of this the usual protecting layer of jute or hemp, and then the protecting steel armor.

There is usually a great discrepancy between the calculated attenuation constant and that obtained by actual measurement in the case of uniform loaded cables. Thus, for a certain cable, the core of which has an envelope of three layers of iron wire, the measured attenuation constant was 0.0296, whereas the calculated value was 0.0197. The cost of uniform loading is about double that of spaced loading. For these reasons attention has been directed toward overcoming the mechanical difficulties attendant upon the manufacture and laying of spaced loaded cables. This has finally been accomplished and there are now a number of such cables in operation. There is a spaced loaded cable across the English Channel between England and France and another between England and Belgium. A spaced loaded cable was later laid across the Irish Channel. This cable is 64 nautical miles in length, and is the longest spaced loaded cable in actual service. The spaced loading of under-water cables is accomplished by placing small inductance coils inside the protective sheathing of the cable. This, of course, causes an enlargement at the point which makes it difficult to manufacture and lay.

It was stated above that hysteresis and eddy-current losses in the loading iron have the effect of increasing the effective resistance of the cable. This is true also where spaced loading is used. Of late the Western Electric Company has developed an iron core which has the desired magnetic properties but small eddy-current loss. This type of core is called a " dust core," and it is made as follows: " Electrolytically deposited iron is ground up into a very fine powder and the grains are coated with zinc by shaking them up with zinc dust. The powdered iron is then mixed with shellac, and, under heat and pressure of 100 to 150 tons to the square inch, it is pressed into flat, circular rings, which can be piled one on the other so as to make any size core required." Such a core has a permeability that is about half that of solid iron under the same conditions. The electric conductivity, however, is only one 80,000th that of solid iron, and so the eddy-current loss is reduced to a negligible quantity.

For very long under-water telephone cables spaced loading is not considered feasible. Accordingly, when the Key West-Havana telephone cable was laid, which is 105 nautical miles in length, uniform loading was used. This cable has a single stranded copper core insulated with gutta percha. The copper core itself, before being insulated, was wrapped with fine iron wire 0.008 inch in diameter and 120 turns to the inch in one layer. Over the gutta percha is wound a spiral of thin copper tape to provide a return circuit. This cable is then insulated and armored in the usual manner.

It is interesting to note that in the Key West-Havana cable the Heaviside requirement for a distortionless cable, is far from being fulfilled. In order to fulfill this requirement the inductance should be increased twentyfold. This cannot be done with iron wire because of the low permeability of iron for the small magnetizing fields produced by currents of telephonic magnitude. A ferromagnetic substance having a high permeability at low magnetizing field strength is required. Such a substance has been found in the nickel-iron alloy permalloy. Permalloy is remarkably susceptible to magnetization. Also, it has remarkably small hysteresis loss as compared with iron under the same conditions. We have, therefore, in permalloy a substance ideally adapted to loading of telephone and telegraph cables.

Permalloy when used for cable loading is made in the form of a very thin narrow tape. This tape is then wound spirally in close turns over the conductor of the cable. In this manner the conductor is given an inductance per mile for alternating currents of telephonic frequency and magnitude greatly in excess of that obtainable with iron wire wrappings. In the case of permalloy loaded submarine telegraph cables the signal speed is increased. This does not mean that electric waves travel faster in loaded cables than in unloaded cables, but that the signals can be fed into the loaded cables at a higher rate without blurring at the receiving end than with an unloaded cable, and the more perfect the loading the greater is the obtainable speed of transmission. Thus the practical commercial carrying capacity of a cable has been greatly increased by permalloy loading. Some long permalloy loaded submarine cables have been laid and are now in use. Others undoubtedly will be laid in the near future. Thus science has achieved another marked triumph.

The requirements for telephone transmission and code transmission over a cable are quite different. In telephone transmission of speech there are two requirements: The volume must not be reduced too much through attenuation. The attenuation and wave speed for different frequencies must be the same so as not to impair the quality of the transmitted speech. In telegraphic transmission electric impulses are transmitted, and these impulses must be sharply differentiated one from the other, i.e., the dots and dashes must build up quickly and cut off quickly at the receiving end. In the case of an unloaded cable the signal builds up gradually and cuts off gradually. Thus, time is required between signals. Iron wire loading improves the sharpness of the signal and so increases the speed of transmission. Permalloy loading increases the sharpness of the signal very much more and so very greatly increases the transmission speed, and hence the commercial value of the cable.

CHAPTER XXIV

THE ELECTROMAGNETIC FIELD

325. We have had occasion many times to speak of electric and magnetic fields of force, of the fact that a moving electric field engenders a magnetic field of force, and that a varying magnetic field of force develops an electric intensity. During most of the nineteenth century these fields were conceived to be strains in a postulated ether, which, though imponderable, was supposed to be capable of sustaining stresses and strains as are ponderable elastic bodies. However, with the advent of the electron theory, the quantum theory, and the theory of relativity this postulated universal ether has vanished from physics, but many of the developments built upon the ether concept have survived and have value.

With the names of Coulomb, Ampère, Weber, Gauss, Kirchhoff, Helmholtz and others is associated the development of the mathematics of electrodynamics. The forces between current, charges, and magnets were expressed in terms of the entities themselves. There was no attempt in these mathematical developments to express the means by which electric and magnetic forces act through space. The developments were based upon the action-at-a-distance theory. To Faraday action-at-a-distance was repugnant. He thought of electrodynamic action through space as due to stresses in a strained universal ether brought about by the presence of charges of electricity and magnets, and he represented the lines of strain by lines of electric displacement and magnetic induction. Though entirely fanciful, this pictorial representation of electric and magnetic fields of force has survived down to the present time, even though a universal ether plays no part in modern physics.

In the early theories there was no suggestion that electric and magnetic effects were propagated through space with a finite speed. However, in a letter to Weber in 1845, Gauss mentioned that he had himself attempted in 1835 to deduce the fundamental laws of electrodynamics from a consideration of the propagation of electric and magnetic effects with a finite speed of propagation, but had not published his results because he had failed to fully achieve what he con-

633

sidered the real task. In 1857 Kirchhoff noticed that the ratio between the cgse. and cgsm. units is the same as the speed of light in free space. In 1858 B. Riemann wrote a paper (published in 1867) in which he assumed a finite speed of propagation of electromagnetic effects, and deduced that this speed must be equal to the ratio between the two systems of units, and hence to the speed of light. In 1867 L. Lorenz of Copenhagen extended the work of Newmann, and was led independently of Maxwell to a conception of light as an electromagnetic phenomenon. From his work Lorenz drew the conclusion that if light is electromagnetic in nature there is no further need for the hypothesis of an ether. This conclusion was the antithesis of Maxwell's conclusion, for Maxwell arrived at the same result by giving a physical reality to the ether. Practically all of the theory for the propagation of electromagnetic disturbances with a finite speed was worked out independently of Maxwell, but this work has been lost sight of in the glare of Maxwell's achievements.

Maxwell was undoubtedly impressed by this previous work, and especially by Poisson's theory of magnetic polarization (1824), Faraday's suggestion that dielectrics might likewise be polarized under electric stresses (1837), and the more extended elaboration of dielectric polarization by Lord Kelvin in 1845 and by Mossotti in 1847. He was impressed also by Faraday's conception of lines of electric and magnetic force, and Kelvin's analogies of electric and magnetic fields with flow of heat, elastic deformation, and fluid motion. Maxwell diverted his attention from currents, electric charges, and magnets and conceived all observed effects to be due to conditions existing in a mechanical medium, the ether, which he conceived to be capable of polarization as were magnets and dielectrics. This conception of the polarizability of a universal space-filling medium led him to the conception of displacement currents in free space and to the finite speed of propagation of electromagnetic disturbances. He arrived at the same goal as had his predecessors but by a different route. The conception of displacement currents in a postulated polarizable ether is unique in Maxwell's theory. This view however is incompatible with the modern electron theory, because electric charges and hence polarization is restricted to ponderable media.[1]

---

[1] For a complete critical evaluation of Maxwell's work, as well as all other authors in this field, see Electromagnetic — A Discussion of Fundamentals by Alfred O'Rahilly, Longmans, Green and Co.

As an introduction to the development of Maxwell's theory, we can perhaps do no better than to quote from Hertz, whose experiments led to the universal acceptance of Maxwell's theory, although Hertz "declined to commit himself to any proof or any theory." When asked "What Is Maxwell's Theory?" he made the following reply:

> To the question "What Is Maxwell's Theory?" I know of no shorter or more definite answer than the following: Maxwell's theory is Maxwell's system of equations. Every theory which leads to the same system of equations and therefore comprises the same possible phenomena, I would consider as being a form or special case of Maxwell's theory. . . . Maxwell arrived at them by starting with the idea of action-at-a-distance and attributed to the ether the properties of a highly polarisable dielectric medium. We can also arrive at them in other ways. But in no way can a direct proof of these equations be deduced from experience. It appears most logical therefore to regard them independently of the way in which they have been arrived at, to consider them as hypothetical assumptions, and to let their probability depend upon the very large number of natural laws they embrace. If we take up this point of view, we can dispense with a number of auxiliary ideas which render the understanding of Maxwell's theory more difficult, partly for no other reason than that they really possess no meaning if we finally exclude the notion of direct action-at-a-distance.

Maxwell's electromagnetic theory of light did not receive ready acceptance. It was thought that to reduce optics to a mere branch of electromagnetics was fanciful if not bizarre. Maxwell had few contemporaneous followers in this field. Helmholtz and Rowland were practically the only physicists who used Maxwell's theory in their university lectures. While Oliver Heaviside advocated the theory, Lord Kelvin openly claimed not to understand it and insisted that it was a backward step when they already had a perfectly good elastic-solid theory of light.

Before taking up Maxwell's equations we will consider some fundamental formulas.

326. Some Fundamental Formulas. — In the development of the science of electricity through the years two systems of electric units have evolved and taken their places in the science. One system of units, the electrostatic system, is built upon Coulomb's law

$$F = \frac{qq'}{\epsilon d^2}.$$

This equation defines the cgse. charge, and since $i = dq/dt$, it defines the cgse. current. We have defined in Section 4 cgse. flux density D and intensity E, the relation between them being $D = \epsilon E$. When unit charge is carried from one point to another against the field and one erg of work is done the potential difference between the two points is unit potential difference. Since current and potential difference are thus defined, unit resistance follows immediately by Ohm's law. With current and potential difference defined, capacitance is defined from the general relation $Q = CV$. And finally self inductance is defined from the relation

$$\varepsilon = - L \frac{di}{dt}.$$

Thus a whole system of cgse. units has been built up starting with unit charge as defined by Coulomb's law.

Another system of units, the magnetic (cgsm.) system, is based upon Coulomb's law for magnetic poles, i.e.,

$$F = \frac{mm'}{\mu d^2},$$

where m and m' are hypothetical, point poles. In this system of units, the current i' is first defined. The current i' is defined in terms of Ampère's law (91.1), which is

$$dH = \frac{i' \sin \theta \, dl}{r^2},$$

as that current which, when flowing in a circle of 1 cm. radius, develops at its center a magnetic intensity of 2π oersteds. The quantity q' then follows from the relation

$$q' = \int i' dt.$$

The flux density B and magnetic intensity H are defined in terms of the unit pole, and the relation (59.1) $B = \mu H$ follows. The other units are defined from these units in the same manner as in the cgse. system of units.

The absolute practical system of units is based upon the cgsm. system of units according to the ratios given in Section 18.

327. Ratio between the Two Systems of Units. Weber's Constant. — Weber first determined this ratio, which was before Maxwell

developed his electromagnetic theory of radiation. If a given current is measured in cgse. units and then in cgsm. units the ratio v between the numerics expressing the currents is very closely the velocity of light in free space. Thus,

$$v = \frac{i}{i'} = \frac{\text{current expressed in cgse. units}}{\text{current expressed in cgsm. units}} = \frac{q}{q'}. \quad (327.1)$$

Unprimed letters stand for cgse. units and primed letters stand for cgsm. units.

328. Maxwell's Displacement Currents. — Thus far in our study we have recognized three kinds of electric currents: (1) Conduction currents, as in metallic conductors, in which the current is thought of as a flow of conduction electrons between the atoms and molecules composing the lattice structure of the conductor. (2) Convection currents, as in an electrolytic conductor or a gas, in which the electric charges constituting the current are carried by ions, both positive and negative. (3) Polarization currents, as in an actual material dielectric. This is a transient current consisting of a displacement of the electric constituents of the atoms of a dielectric as they are polarized under the influence of an electric field. All of these currents are accompanied by a magnetic field of force. We have now to consider a fourth kind of current which Maxwell denominated a *displacement current*. We may arrive at a conception of a displacement current by the following consideration: Let us arrange a circuit as shown in Fig. 310. Assume the space between the plates of the condenser C to be a perfect vacuum. a_1 and a_2 are milliammeters. If the contact point p be moved along the potentiometer wire bc there will be a flow of electrons to the plate n of the condenser and a flow of electrons away from the plate m of like magnitude as the potential difference across the plates increases. The milliammeters a_1 and a_2 will register identical currents. If, after the contact point p reaches c, it were to be moved back to b a current in the reverse direction would be set up, both meters indicating identical currents. Thus the circuit behaves on varying potential as though a current were flowing through the condenser, which is of the same value as the current in the conductors leading to and from the plates, and this is true in spite of the fact that free space separates the plates.

Maxwell conceived all circuits to be closed circuits, i.e., the circuit shown in Fig. 310 is a closed circuit even though it contains a condenser. In light of the electron theory we may say, as electrons accumulate on plate n an electric field of force is established between the plates and increases at the same rate as the electronic charge increases. This increasing electric field reaches across the free space

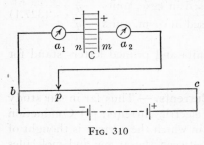

separating the plates and causes an equal flow of electrons away from plate m, which means that plate m takes a positive charge equal in magnitude to the negative charge on plate n. Maxwell thought that an electric field between the plates of a vacuum condenser produces polarization in an ether, and, therefore, represents a real displacement current, as in ponderable dielectrics. He did not distinguish between two conditions.

Fig. 310

We have derived the equation (46.2), which is

$$\mathbf{i} = \frac{1}{4\pi} \frac{dD}{dt} = \frac{1}{4\pi} \frac{dE}{dt} + \frac{dP}{dt}. \tag{328.1}$$

In this equation $\frac{dP}{dt}$ is a real displacement current in a material dielectric. It represents the rate at which actual electric charge crosses each sq. cm. of the dielectric. $\frac{1}{4\pi} \frac{dE}{dt}$ is due merely to a varying electric field intensity which has, so far as the creation of a magnetic field is concerned, the same effect as a convection current or a conduction current. When no material dielectric is present, $\frac{dP}{dt} = 0$ and $\frac{1}{4\pi} \frac{dE}{dt}$ is all that remains. Maxwell did not distinguish between the two terms as he thought that the ether was capable of polarization as is a ponderable dielectric. The term displacement current as applied to a vacuum is misleading as there is no displacement of electricity, only a varying electric field accompanied by a magnetic field as is a conduction or convection current. However, there is experimental evidence that the term $\frac{1}{4\pi} \frac{dE}{dt}$ develops a magnetic field. In 1929 Van Cauwenberghe placed an iron ring between the plates of an air condenser with its plane parallel to the plates of the condenser. When an alternating potential was applied to the plates of the condenser magnetic flux was induced in the iron ring. A coil of wire wound on the ring permitted the measurement of the magnetic flux because of the emf. induced in the coil. The flux was found to have the value which it would have if a conduction current were to flow through it given by equation (46.2).

329. When $dP/dt = 0$, equation (328.1) may be interpreted in this wise: If in free space an electric field intensity is changing at the rate of dE/dt the effect of such a variation is the same as if a current of density $\mathbf{i}$, given by $\dfrac{1}{4\pi}\dfrac{dE}{dt}$, were actually flowing through the same space in the direction in which E is changing.

As a further interpretation of (328.1) $\mathbf{i} = \dfrac{1}{4\pi}\dfrac{dD}{dt} = \dfrac{\epsilon}{4\pi}\dfrac{dE}{dt}$, we may consider that whenever an electric field varies anywhere in space, due originally to a change in the positions of electric charges or their concentration somewhere at some previous time, there is an equivalent current given by $\dfrac{\epsilon}{4\pi}\dfrac{dE}{dt}$. And further, if E has any direction whatsoever relative to arbitrarily chosen axes, we may resolve it into components in the directions of the axes. Let the components of E be X, Y, and Z. Then the components of dE/dt are

$$\frac{\partial X}{\partial t}, \ \frac{\partial Y}{\partial t}, \ \text{and} \ \frac{\partial Z}{dt}.$$

Thus the components of the current density $\mathbf{i}$ are

$$\mathbf{i}_x = \frac{\epsilon}{4\pi}\frac{\partial X}{\partial t},$$

$$\mathbf{i}_y = \frac{\epsilon}{4\pi}\frac{\partial Y}{\partial t}, \qquad (329.2)$$

$$\mathbf{i}_z = \frac{\epsilon}{4\pi}\frac{\partial Z}{\partial t}.$$

It has been pointed out that a displacement current may have two aspects. If an actual material dielectric is present the dielectric will become polarized internally, and while the polarization is in progress electric charges are in motion within the atoms of the dielectric, thus constituting an actual transient current of electricity, which we here denominate a *polarization current*. There is another aspect, and for our present purpose more important. Maxwell lived and worked at a time when an elastic ether was believed to permeate all space, and the atoms and molecules of material media were conceived to be embedded in the ether as in a matrix and to be capable of reacting with and upon it. Maxwell advanced the concept that a circuit containing a vacuum condenser in which a transient current is flowing is a complete circuit, that the circuit is completed across the free space between the plates by a polarization of the ether, and that during the time this displacement in the ether is in progress the effect is the same as though a conduction current were flowing. This part of the current between the plates of a condenser is here called a *displacement current*, although Maxwell was not always careful to separate the two aspects of this type of current. Of course, the displacement current is always present whenever an electric intensity is varying whether there are electric charges nearby or not, whereas the polarization current exists in a dielectric while being subjected to a varying electric intensity. Since we are now primarily concerned with varying electric fields in space we shall use the term displacement current to include both terms of equation (328.1), i.e., $1/4\pi \ (dE/dt)$ and (dP/dt).

330. Maxwell's First Set of Equations for the Electromagnetic Field. — Let us consider an electric current or its equivalent flowing in a direction making any angles whatsoever with arbitrarily selected

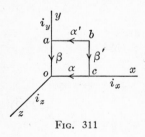

FIG. 311

axes. The current will have components in the directions of the axes, Fig. 311. Consider an elementary rectangle *abcoa* in the xy plane whose sides are dx and dy. Let the *current density* in the neighborhood of o be $\mathbf{i}'$ units per sq. cm. Its z component is then $\mathbf{i}'_z$, and the current flowing in the positive z direction through the rectangle *abcoa* is

$$d\mathbf{i}'_z = \mathbf{i}'_z \, dx \, dy.$$

Let the magnetic intensity H, which accompanies the current, have components along the sides of the rectangle *abcoa* of values α, α', β, and β', directed as indicated in Fig. 311.

In general, α will differ from α' and β will differ from β'. If α varies with y, let the variation be represented by a curve as in Fig. 312. We then have

$$\alpha' = \alpha + d\alpha.$$

Also

$$d\alpha = \tan \theta \, dy = \frac{\partial \alpha}{\partial y} \, dy.$$

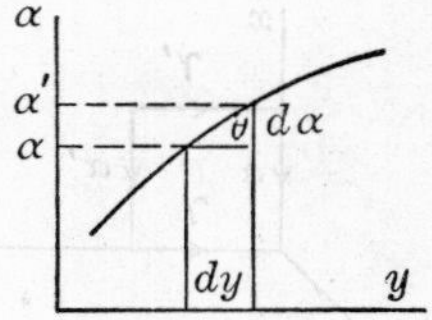

Hence,

$$\alpha' = \alpha + \frac{\partial \alpha}{\partial y} \, dy.$$

Fig. 312

We therefore have, likewise

$$\beta' = \beta + \frac{\partial \beta}{\partial x} \, dx.$$

The work done in moving a unit positive magnetic pole once around this rectangle in the counterclockwise sense is

$$dW = \alpha dx + \beta' \, dy - \alpha' \, dx - \beta \, dy. \tag{330.1}$$

Substituting from the above equations, we have for this work

$$dW = \alpha \, dx - \left(\alpha + \frac{\partial \alpha}{\partial y} \, dy \right) dx + \left(\beta + \frac{\partial \beta}{\partial x} \, dx \right) dy - \beta \, dy.$$

Or

$$dW = \left(\frac{\partial \beta}{\partial x} - \frac{\partial \alpha}{\partial y} \right) dx \, dy. \tag{330.2}$$

But by equation (160.1) this work is also

$$dW = 4\pi di'_z = 4\pi i'_z \, dx \, dy.$$

These two expressions for the work must have the same value. We therefore have

$$4\pi i'_z \, dx \, dy = \left(\frac{\partial \beta}{\partial x} - \frac{\partial \alpha}{\partial y} \right) dx \, dy.$$

Or

$$4\pi i'_z = \frac{\partial \beta}{\partial x} - \frac{\partial \alpha}{\partial y}. \tag{330.3}$$

In equation (330.3) the current is measured in cgsm. units. The current may be expressed in cgse. units by making use of relation (327.1). We then have

$$\frac{4\pi}{v} i_z = \frac{\partial \beta}{\partial x} - \frac{\partial \alpha}{\partial y}. \tag{330.4}$$

In order to obtain an expression for i'_y we rotate the axes of Fig. 311 in the positive direction into the position shown in Fig. 313.

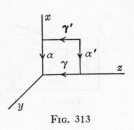

FIG. 313

Then, proceeding as before, we have for the work done in moving a unit positive pole once around the rectangle in the positive direction

$$dW = \left(\frac{\partial \alpha}{\partial z} - \frac{\partial \gamma}{\partial x}\right) dx\, dz.$$

Then

$$4\pi i'_y = \frac{\partial \alpha}{\partial z} - \frac{\partial \gamma}{\partial x} \tag{330.5}$$

Then, changing the current to cgse. units, we have

$$\frac{4\pi}{v} i_y = \frac{\partial \alpha}{\partial z} - \frac{\partial \gamma}{\partial x}. \tag{330.6}$$

To obtain the expression for i'_x we rotate the axes again in the positive direction so that the x axis occupies the position of the y axis, and proceed as before. We then have the following set of equations:

$$\frac{4\pi}{v} i_x = \frac{\partial \gamma}{\partial y} - \frac{\partial \beta}{\partial z}$$

$$\frac{4\pi}{v} i_y = \frac{\partial \alpha}{\partial z} - \frac{\partial \gamma}{\partial x} \tag{330.7}$$

$$\frac{4\pi}{v} i_z = \frac{\partial \beta}{\partial x} - \frac{\partial \alpha}{\partial y}$$

Equations (330.7) state in terms of differentials a well-known elementary fact. Take, for example, the first equation. If a current of density i_x flows in a long, straight conductor in the x direction the left-hand side of the equation is the work done in carrying a unit pole once around one sq. cm. The right-hand side of the equation is expressed in terms of the magnetic intensity, which depends upon y and z but not upon x, as it is normal to x. If we let $dy = dz = 1$ cm., it may be seen that the right-hand side of the equation is, also, the work done in carrying a unit magnetic pole once around a sq. cm. through which a current i_x is flowing.

Combining equations (329.2) and (330.7), we obtain finally

$$\frac{\epsilon}{v}\frac{\partial X}{\partial t} = \frac{\partial \gamma}{\partial y} - \frac{\partial \beta}{\partial z}$$

$$\frac{\epsilon}{v}\frac{\partial Y}{\partial t} = \frac{\partial \alpha}{\partial z} - \frac{\partial \gamma}{\partial x} \qquad (330.8)$$

$$\frac{\epsilon}{v}\frac{\partial Z}{\partial t} = \frac{\partial \beta}{\partial x} - \frac{\partial \alpha}{\partial y}.$$

Equations (330.8) constitute the first set of Maxwell's differential equations for the electromagnetic field. They express the time rate of change of the electric field intensity in terms of the space rate of change of the magnetic field intensity.

These equations state in the language of mathematics some very elementary concepts pertaining to the electric current and the electric and magnetic fields of force which accompany it. Let us consider a long, straight conductor nm, Fig. 314, in which a current (conventional) is flowing in the direction n to m. Such a current-bearing conductor is surrounded by a concentric magnetic field of force, as was

Fig. 314

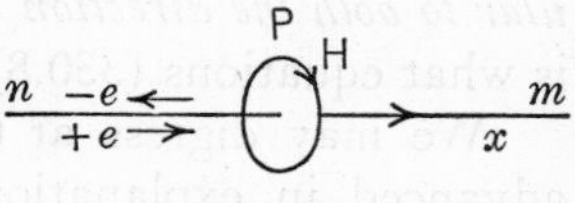

first shown by Oersted. When no current was flowing in the conductor there was no magnetic field of force about it, although electric charges were present in the conductor. We may, therefore, conclude that the magnetic field has been created in some way by the electric current through the agency of its electric field. We now regard a current of electricity as a flow of electrons in a direction reverse to that of the conventional current. However, a flow of negative charge in the direction m to n is electrically equivalent to a flow of positive charge in the direction n to m, since motion is purely relative. We may, therefore, use for the purpose of explanation a positive charge moving to the right, which may be taken as the positive x direction. The magnetic field, as experiments show, is concentric with the axis of the conductor and normal thereto. We may depict it as a family of concentric rings, one of which is shown in Fig. 314. The direction of the magnetic intensity relative to the direction of flow of positive charge is given by the right-hand rule, as is represented in the Figure. The magnetic intensity at any point P, say, must be the resultant effect of all of the moving charges throughout the length and extent of the conductor. That is, if $+e$ were moving alone, as indicated, it would contribute its share to the magnetic effect at P irrespective of the motions of other charges. Now the *only way*, so far as is known, that the charge $+e$ can produce a magnetic effect at a distant point P is through the agency of its electric field. While $+e$ is stationary relative to the conductor, or rather the negative charges in the conductor, there is an electric field at P but no magnetic field. However, when $+e$ moves to the right there is developed at P a magnetic field. Therefore, we may conclude that the development of a magnetic field about a current is due to the time rate of change of the electric field associated with the moving charges which constitute the current; in reality negative charges moving to the left relative to the fixed positive nuclear charges. Thus, *a varying electric field develops a magnetic field.* As is shown in the Figure the direction of the resultant magnetic intensity is normal to the direction of motion of the perpendicular component of the electric intensity. That is, *an electric field moving normal to itself develops a magnetic field which is perpendicular to both the direction of motion and sense of the electric field.* This is what equations (330.8) mean.

We may digress at this point to present a theory that has been advanced in explanation of the development of a magnetic field through the agency of electric fields. It may be pointed out to begin with that an electrically neutral conductor (or any substance), from which radiate equal electric fields of opposite signs, will exhibit no magnetic effects while in motion as a whole relative to other bodies. This fact suggests that while there is no net relative motion between the positive and negative charges in the conductor there is no magnetic field at any point P, although the electric fields associated with the positive and negative charges within the conductor are present and moving with it. One field is evidently the antithesis of the other, and being equal in intensity if the conductor is electrically neutral, they annul one another. Thus, when there is no relative motion between the positive and negative electric fields there is no magnetic effect at any point within or without the conductor.

We now regard the electric field associated with a proton to be an integral part of the proton, and the electric field associated with an electron to be an integral part of the electron; each proton or electron, together with its associated field, being an independent entity; i.e., the quantum of electricity ($+$ or $-$) includes the associated field. These electric quanta are of two kinds, positive and negative, the one being the antithesis of the other, so that if there is a coterminous overlapping the electric field vanishes. It is not considered that the electric field associated with a positive charge terminates on an equal negative charge, the field being thus shared by the two kinds of electric charges. The two kinds of electric fields are evidently distinct and independent, but inherently different in nature. Now when the conduction electrons within a conductor have a net motion relative to the fixed positive atomic nuclei, there is a relative motion between the positive and negative electric fields at all points within and external to the conductor. Therefore, it is concluded that the development of a magnetic field around a conductor when bearing a current of electricity is due to the relative motion between the positive and negative electric fields; the shearing that takes place between the positive and negative fields in some mysterious way creates a magnetic field. This is an *electromagnetic effect*; magnetism has no independent existence. Thus, *wherever a positive electric field moves relative to a negative electric field there is developed at the same time a magnetic field, the intensity of the magnetic field being proportional to the rate of shear between the two fields, and the direction of the magnetic field being normal to the direction of shear.* However, this explanation, though plausible, in no way reveals the ultimate nature of either an electric or magnetic field; it merely states the conditions necessary for the genesis of a magnetic field.

331. Maxwell's Second Set of Electromagnetic Equations. — As we have just seen, a varying electric field (a shift of a positive field relative to a negative field) develops a magnetic field, i.e., moving electric charges of one kind relative to the other kind develop a magnetic field. Conversely, a varying magnetic field, due to a moving

Fig. 315

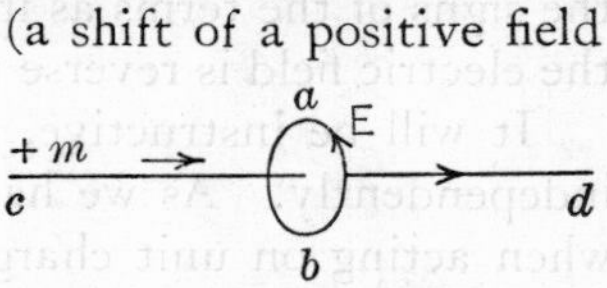

magnetic pole, say, should develop an electric field. This is exactly what is observed. If, as shown in Fig. 315, there is a circular conductor about the line *cd* along which a magnetic pole $+m$ is moving to the right there will be developed an electric field of intensity E which will urge a plus charge in the conductor in the direction indicated, or a negative charge in the reverse direction. The negative charges (conduction electrons) being free to move do so, thus developing an electric current. The positive charges are fixed in position in the conductor and cannot move. The $\oint E dl$ is called an induced emf. Of course, the electric field E developed by the varying magnetic field will exist whether or not there is a conductor present in which a current may be set up. It is only the component of the magnetic field normal to the line cd that is effective in developing an electric field. Thus, *a magnetic field moving normal to itself develops an electric field which is normal to both the direction of motion of the magnetic field and the field itself.* The electric field is constant if the rate of change of the magnetic field is constant, and varies in intensity if the rate of change of the magnetic field varies, and in like manner. This is the induced electric field which was discovered by Faraday and Henry.

The phenomenon represented by Fig. 314 is expressed in mathematical form in equations (330.8). An exactly similar set of equations may be derived for the phenomenon illustrated by Fig. 315. The left-hand members express the time rate of change of the magnetic field and the right-hand members express the space rate of change of the electric field. These equations may be written down immediately from equations (330.8) by replacing the components of the electric intensity X, Y, and Z on the left-hand side by the corresponding components of the magnetic intensity α, β, and γ, and on the right-hand side replacing the components of the magnetic intensity by the corresponding components of the electric intensity, and replacing the dielectric coefficient ϵ by the permeability μ, since these coefficients occupy corresponding positions in Coulomb's law. It is necessary to change the signs of the terms as it is seen from Fig. 315 that the direction of the electric field is reverse to that of the magnetic field in Fig. 314.

It will be instructive, however, to develop this set of equations independently. As we have seen, the electric intensity in Fig. 315, when acting on unit charge through a distance, is equivalent to an emf. This is an induced emf. and is given by

$$\mathcal{E}' = -\frac{d\phi}{dt}, \tag{331.1}$$

where ϕ is in maxwells. $\mathcal{E}'$ may be changed to cgse. units by the following relation

$$v = \frac{\mathcal{E}'}{\mathcal{E}} = \frac{\text{emf. in cgsm. units}}{\text{emf. in cgse. units}}.$$

Hence $\mathcal{E}' = v\mathcal{E}$. Introducing this relation in equation (331.1), we have

$$\mathcal{E} = -\frac{1}{v}\frac{d\phi}{dt}. \tag{331.2}$$

Referring to Fig. 316, we see that the flux ϕ through the elementary rectangle *ocbao* is $\mu\gamma\,dx\,dy$. Then

$$\mathcal{E} = -\frac{1}{v}\frac{\partial(\mu\gamma)}{\partial t}\,dx\,dy. \tag{331.3}$$

Also, in a manner analogous to the former case, we have

$$X' = X + \frac{\partial X}{\partial y}\,dy \quad \text{and} \quad Y' = Y + \frac{\partial Y}{\partial x}\,dx.$$

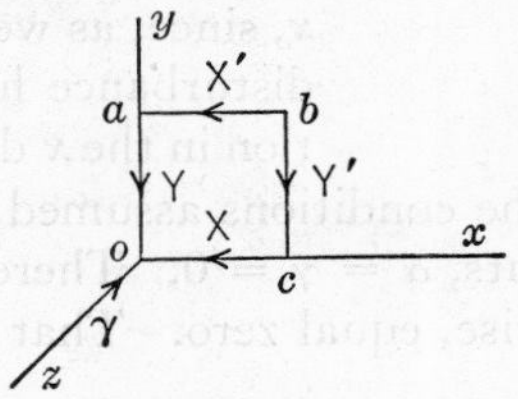

FIG. 316

Remembering that the emf. in any closed circuit is the work done in carrying unit charge once around the circuit, we have for the total emf. the work done in carrying unit charge once around the rectangle *ocbao*, which is

$$X\,dx - \left(X + \frac{\partial X}{\partial y}\,dy\right)dx + \left(Y + \frac{\partial Y}{\partial x}\,dx\right)dy - Y\,dy = \left(\frac{\partial Y}{\partial x} - \frac{\partial X}{\partial y}\right)dx\,dy.$$

This is equivalent to the emf. given by equation (331.3), Therefore,

$$-\frac{\mu}{v}\frac{\partial\gamma}{\partial t} = \frac{\partial Y}{\partial x} - \frac{\partial X}{\partial y}.$$

In exactly the same manner we obtain the other equations. Therefore,

$$-\frac{\mu}{v}\frac{\partial\alpha}{\partial t} = \frac{\partial Z}{\partial y} - \frac{\partial Y}{\partial z},$$

$$-\frac{\mu}{v}\frac{\partial\beta}{\partial t} = \frac{\partial X}{\partial z} - \frac{\partial Z}{\partial x}, \tag{331.4}$$

$$-\frac{\mu}{v}\frac{\partial\gamma}{\partial t} = \frac{\partial Y}{\partial x} - \frac{\partial X}{\partial y}.$$

332. The Electromagnetic Wave. — We may derive the wave equation from the differential equations (330.8) and (331.4) in the following manner: Let us consider a very extensive conducting sheet coincident with the xy plane, theoretically an infinite sheet. Imagine a uniformly distributed current flowing in this sheet in the positive z direction. At some point P, Fig. 317, there is a magnetic field of

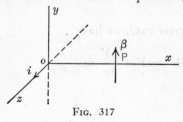

intensity and direction indicated by the vector β. Now if the current i in the sheet is varying at the rate $\partial i/\partial t$ the magnetic intensity will vary at the rate $\partial \beta/\partial t$. $\partial \beta/\partial t$ will vary with x, since, as we shall see, the magnetic disturbance has a speed of propagation in the x direction.

Fig. 317

Now, since under the conditions assumed, the magnetic intensity has no x or z components, $\alpha = \gamma = 0$. Therefore, all the derivatives of α and γ must, likewise, equal zero. That is

$$\frac{\partial \alpha}{\partial t} = \frac{\partial \alpha}{\partial y} = \frac{\partial \alpha}{\partial z} = 0 \quad \text{and} \quad \frac{\partial \gamma}{\partial t} = \frac{\partial \gamma}{\partial y} = \frac{\partial \gamma}{\partial x} = 0.$$

The magnetic and electric intensities will not vary with either y or z because of the infinite extent of the current sheet, and because the same occurrence takes place simultaneously at all points in the plane parallel to the yz plane which passes through P. Therefore,

$$\frac{\partial \beta}{\partial z} = 0, \quad \text{and also} \quad \frac{\partial Z}{\partial y} = \frac{\partial Y}{\partial z} = \frac{\partial X}{\partial z} = \frac{\partial X}{\partial y} = 0.$$

The two sets of differential equations then reduce to

$$\frac{\epsilon}{v} \frac{\partial Z}{\partial t} = \frac{\partial \beta}{\partial x}, \tag{332.1}$$

and

$$\frac{\mu}{v} \frac{\partial \beta}{\partial t} = \frac{\partial Z}{\partial x}. \tag{332.2}$$

Now differentiate (332.1) with respect to x, and (332.2) with respect to t, and there results

$$\frac{\epsilon}{v} \frac{\partial^2 Z}{\partial t \partial x} = \frac{\partial^2 \beta}{\partial x^2} \quad \text{and} \quad \frac{\mu}{v} \frac{\partial^2 \beta}{\partial t^2} = \frac{\partial^2 Z}{\partial x \partial t}.$$

On combining these equations, we have

$$\frac{\partial^2 \beta}{\partial t^2} = \frac{v^2}{\epsilon \mu} \frac{\partial^2 \beta}{\partial x^2}. \tag{332.3}$$

Next differentiate (332.1) with respect to t and (332.2) with respect to x, and there results

$$\frac{\epsilon}{v} \frac{\partial^2 Z}{\partial t^2} = \frac{\partial^2 \beta}{\partial x \partial t} \quad \text{and} \quad \frac{\mu}{v} \frac{\partial^2 \beta}{\partial x \partial t} = \frac{\partial^2 Z}{\partial x^2}.$$

On combining these equations, we have

$$\frac{\partial^2 Z}{\partial t^2} = \frac{v^2}{\epsilon \mu} \frac{\partial^2 Z}{\partial x^2}. \tag{332.4}$$

Equations (332.3) and (332.4) are partial differential equations of the same type, and therefore it will suffice to solve only one of them. For convenience let us set

$$\frac{v^2}{\epsilon \mu} = c^2.$$

We then have

$$\frac{\partial^2 \beta}{\partial t^2} - c^2 \frac{\partial^2 \beta}{\partial x} = 0. \tag{332.5}$$

To solve this equation, we put

$$\beta = f(x + mt).$$

On differentiating,

$$\frac{\partial^2 \beta}{\partial t^2} = m^2 f''(x + mt) \quad \text{and} \quad \frac{\partial^2 \beta}{\partial x^2} = f''(x + mt). \tag{332.6}$$

On substituting (332.6) in (332.5), we have

$$m^2 f''(x + mt) - c^2 f''(x + mt) = 0.$$

The auxiliary equation is

$$m^2 - c^2 = 0, \quad \text{or} \quad m = \pm c.$$

Hence the complete solution of the differential equation is

$$\beta = f_1(x + ct) + f_2(x - ct), \tag{332.7}$$

where f_1 and f_2 are arbitrary functions. Equation (332.7) represents a wave disturbance traveling in both directions parallel to the x axis. Taking the wave traveling in the positive direction only, we have

$$\beta = f_2(x - ct).^1 \qquad (332.8)$$

That equation (332.8) represents a wave motion propagated in the positive x direction may be seen from the following consideration: As an example of a wave motion, let us say that $y = f(x - ut)$, where y is a displacement normal to the x axis and u is a velocity. At time $t = 0$ the disturbance, represented by point P_1 on the solid curve,

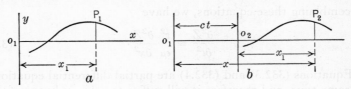

FIG. 318

Fig. 318a, is at a distance x, say, from the fixed origin o_1. We may then write

$$y = f(x_1). \qquad (332.9)$$

At a time t later the disturbance is at P_2, say, having traveled a distance ut. We may think of the curve and origin moving together to the right with a velocity u. At a later time t the origin will be at o_2 and the curve indicated by point P_2. The equation of the curve in Fig. 318b with respect to o_2, the moving origin, is still $y = f(x_1)$. If however x is the distance of P_2 from the fixed origin o_1, we have $x_1 = x - ut$. Substituting in (332.9), we have

$$y = f(x - ut),$$

which is the equation of the curve referred to the fixed origin o_1.

Returning now to the equation (332.8), β is a magnetic intensity which varies according to some function f. However, at any point P in space β will vary in the same manner as the current varies in the yz plane, since it is created by the current, though not simultaneously. If there is no damping β will have the same maximum and minimum values at all distances x from the fixed origin. If the current in the yz plane is varying harmonically according to the equation

$$i = I \sin \omega t,$$

[1] See Cohen's Differential Equations, p. 239, Section 88.

then at any point P in space distant x from the origin, β will also vary harmonically with the same frequency. This is the most common as well as the most important form of the function f. Therefore, the variations of β at any point P will be harmonic and of the form

$$\beta = \beta_0 \sin \omega t = \beta_0 \sin \left(\frac{2\pi}{T}\right) t, \qquad (332.10)$$

where β_0 is the maximum value of β, and therefore the amplitude. Because of the velocity of the wave motion, whatever changes take plate at o will take place at P distant x from the origin at some time t later. With o as origin, $oP = x$, the time for the disturbance to travel the distance x is x/c. If we subtract the time interval x/c from t in equation (332.10), there results

$$\beta = \beta_0 \sin \frac{2\pi}{T} \left(t - \frac{x}{c}\right). \qquad (332.11)$$

This is the equation of a plane-polarized wave traveling in the positive x direction with a speed c. To analyze this equation further

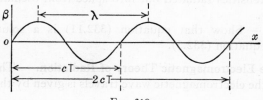

FIG. 319

we may take x constant and permit t to vary. We then have a harmonic variation of β at any point P distant x from o. If we keep t constant and permit x to vary we obtain the familiar sine curve, Fig. 319. We might view this as an instantaneous glimpse of the wave throughout its entire extent. Starting with $x = 0$, we see that the values of β are the same at points $x = 0$, $x = cT$, $x = 2cT$, $x = 3cT$, etc. The distance between these points is denominated a wavelength λ; it is the distance between successive points where the magnetic intensity has attained the same value. A well-known relation in wave motion is $cT = \lambda$. Introducing this relation in equation (332.11), we have the alternate form of the wave equation

$$\beta = \beta_0 \sin 2\pi \left(\frac{t}{T} - \frac{x}{\lambda}\right). \qquad (332.12)$$

The differential equation (332.4) for the electric intensity, when solved, leads to equations similar to (332.11) and (332.12). Thus,

$$Z = Z_0 \sin \frac{2\pi}{T}\left(t - \frac{x}{c}\right),$$

$$Z = Z_0 \sin 2\pi\left(\frac{t}{T} - \frac{x}{\lambda}\right).$$

(332.13)

We have here, also, a plane-polarized wave traveling in the positive x direction with the speed c. It has the same frequency and wavelength as the magnetic wave, and is always in phase with it, but the

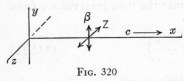

Fig. 320

electric and magnetic vectors are mutually perpendicular. These conditions are shown schematically in Fig. 320. Thus, two mutually perpendicular and dependent plane-polarized waves constitute the electromagnetic wave. Electromagnetic waves are waves of electric and magnetic intensities radiated out into space from oscillating charges of electricity.

Problem. — Show that equation (332.11) is a solution of the differential equation (332.5).

333. The Electromagnetic Theory of Radiation. — The velocity c with which the electromagnetic wave travels is given by the relation

$$c = \frac{v}{\sqrt{\epsilon\mu}} \quad {}^1$$

(333.1)

Thus, if this represents a true law of nature, the velocity of an electromagnetic disturbance is known for any medium from the measured values of ϵ and μ, and the ratio v between the cgse. and cgsm. units. Now in free space $\epsilon = 1$ and $\mu = 1$, when these coefficients are measured in cgse. and cgsm. units respectively as they are in (333.1). Thus, in free space $c = v$, the ratio between the two systems of units. When

[1] If ϵ' and μ are in cgsm. units, we have $v = q/q'$, or $q = vq'$

$$F = \frac{q^2}{\epsilon d^2} = \frac{v^2 q'^2}{\epsilon d^2} = \frac{q'^2}{\epsilon/v^2} d^2 = \frac{q'}{\epsilon' d^2}.$$

Thus

$$c = \frac{v}{\sqrt{\epsilon\mu}} = \frac{v}{\sqrt{v^2\epsilon'\mu}} = \frac{1}{\sqrt{\epsilon'\mu}}$$

which is the form sometimes given.

an electric quantity is measured in both systems of units and the ratio between their numerics is taken it comes out equal to c or some power of c. Thus, the numerical value of the capacitance of a given condenser, when expressed in cgse. units, is c^2 times its value when expressed in cgsm. units. $c = v$ has been measured many times by purely electric methods. The following Table gives some of the most important determinations.

v	Observer	v	Observer
$x\ 10^{10}$		$x\ 10^{10}$	
2.963	J. J. Thomson (1883)	3.009	Pellat (1891)
2.982	Rowland (1889)	2.993	Abraham (1892)
3.000	Rosa (1889)	3.001	Hurmuzescu (1896)
2.997	Thomson & Searle (1890)	2.997	Perot & Fabry
2.9971	Rosa & Dorsey (1907)		

From Houston's "A Treatise on Light," p. 389.

Numerous measurements of the velocity of light in free space have been made. Some of the most important values are given in the following Table:

c	Observer
$x\ 10^{10}$	
2.92	Roemer (1676)
3.13	Fizeau (1862)
2.986	Foucault (1862)
3.004	Cornu (1874)
2.999	Michelson (1879)
2.998	" (1882)
2.99796	" (1926)
2.99774	" (1935)

Richtmyer's "Introduction to Modern Physics," p. 112, 2nd ed.

The electromagnetic theory of light removed some of the difficulties met with in the older theory of light, which viewed light as a vibratory motion in a material elastic solid called the ether. This was a purely mechanical process. According to the electromagnetic theory of light, a light wave is a vibratory disturbance consisting of electric and magnetic intensities. This substituted something that was more tenuous for the elastic solid ether, and so overcame some of the inherent difficulties associated with the conception of a medium filling all space which has the properties of an elastic solid. However, this conception brings us no nearer to an understanding of the ultimate nature of light, since electric and magnetic intensities, though quite real, are beyond our sense perceptions and are revealed to us only by indirect means. The identification of electromagnetic waves as light waves having their origin in accelerated charges of electricity led inevitably to the electric nature of matter itself. Since electric and magnetic fields are continuous, the wave front must be continuous, and therefore there must be a continuous distribution of energy over the wave front, and a continuous flow of energy, which does not accord with the events that have led to the *quantum theory* of light, such as an explanation of line spectra or the photoelectric effect.

In setting up the conditions out of which to derive a plane wave motion in the x direction we assumed an infinite current sheet coincident with the yz plane. The conditions will be fulfilled equally well if we assume a current in a straight wire coincident with the x axis. The only difference met with is that, instead of plane waves, we will have cylindrical waves traveling out radially from the wire. This is approximately the condition actually met with in oscillating electric circuits, as, for example, the vertical wire in the antenna system of a broadcasting station.

As we have seen, an oscillating electric circuit is obtained when we have a circuit consisting of capacitance and inductance, if the resistance of the circuit is below a certain critical value, the frequency of vibration being given by

$$ f = \frac{1}{2\pi \sqrt{LC}}. $$

Now, as C and L decrease in value, the frequency increases and the wavelength decreases. We may imagine the capacitance and inductance to shrink to very small values, that is, to tiny condensers and tiny inductances, in fact to a very short rod or a very small closed circuit in which the electric oscillations are taking place. The character of the oscillation has not changed except in frequency; electromagnetic waves are still being radiated. Let us imagine an oscillating circuit to shrink still more until there is but a single electron executing oscillations of some kind within an atom of matter. In this case C and L will be exceedingly small and consequently the frequency will be exceedingly high. This single electron, according to the electromagnetic theory, will radiate energy in the form of electromagnetic waves, with, of course, extremely high frequencies as compared with the waves emitted by even the shortest wave radio transmitter. *Whenever an electric charge is accelerated it must, accordnig to the electromagnetic theory, radiate energy.* This means that all of the planetary electrons within an atom must be steadily and constantly radiating energy, if we accept the Bohr conception of the atom. If this were so the planetary electrons would steadily lose their store of energy relative to the nucleus, and would approach closer and closer to the nucleus, emitting waves of higher and higher frequencies, until eventually they would merge with the nucleus, their store of energy having been exhausted. This is what would happen if we adopted the conception of a purely mechanical atom. However, we have abundant evidence to show that this is not the case. For example, the fixed lines in the spectrum of any element indisputably proves that the vibration frequencies do not change. This discrepancy between the requirements of the electromagnetic theory, or any purely wave theory of radiation, and the experimental facts, together with other evidence looking toward a quantum theory of radiation, led Bohr to fabricate an atom model in which the planetary electrons occupy non-radiating orbits or energy levels, emitting radiant energy only when changing abruptly from one orbit or energy level to another orbit or energy level closer to the nucleus. On the other hand, atoms absorb energy when an electron is forced to move abruptly from a lower to a higher energy level. Furthermore, the frequency of the emitted radiation is not the orbital frequency of the electron in the atom, according to Bohr's calculations. However artificial this Bohr scheme of radiation may seem to be it nevertheless has one redeeming feature; it has been very successful in the field of spectroscopy. In the light of modern physics the classic mechanical atom is vanishing in the presence of a nebulous and misty haze of theorizing, leaving it with little semblance of form or structure and a great uncertainty as to what it really is.

334. Concluding Remarks. — This Chapter has been devoted to an exposition of a theory which ranked as the outstanding achievement of the nineteenth century in theoretical physics. It has had signal success in related fields. In the domain of optics it has been adapted to the explanation of refraction, dispersion, and polarization. It has been helpful in explaining reflection, the Zeeman effect, the optical properties of metals, and the rotation of the plane of polarization by a magnetic field (Faraday effect). An extensive discussion of the electromagnetic theory and its applications is quite beyond the scope of this book. The reader, if interested, will find complete explanations and developments of this theory in numerous advanced treatises.

In the light of modern physics there are two grave defects in the electromagnetic theory. First, the theory demands that an accelerated charge of electricity emit electromagnetic waves; that it radiate energy. This point has been amplified in earlier chapters. As we have seen the electromagnetic theory fails completely in explaining some occurrences, such as line spectra and the photoelectric effect; in fact it fails in all cases of absorption and emission of radiant energy. Second, the emission of radiant energy must be continuous over the wave front; there are no holes in the wave front, not even of infinitesimal dimensions, nor are there regions or points of energy concentration; the energy is absolutely uniformly and continuously distributed over the wave front. The wave is composed of electric and magnetic intensities (vector quantities), which are without form or structure. A line of force is merely a convenient artifice which was conceived by Faraday for the purpose of visualization, and used by Maxwell as akin to reality; it gives us a simple geometric picture which has been useful in rendering our concepts concrete, and nothing more. Since a continuous wave theory has failed to explain the emission and absorption of radiant energy, twentieth century physicists have turned to a quantum theory of radiation, but the problem is not yet completely solved.

CHAPTER XXV

THERMIONIC ELECTRON TUBES AND THEIR USE

335. In preceding chapters we have described briefly the researches of two eminent scientists, Maxwell and Hertz. Their achievements were in pure science (science for its own sake), and yet it is true that the discovery of electromagnetic waves led to a gigantic industry, the industry of radio in all of its varied forms and applications. However, Hertz did not anticipate the utilitarian possibilities of electromagnetic waves. It was not until two years after his death (Jan. 1, 1894) that Marconi made the first application for a radio patent. The chief interest of the scientific world at the time was the disposal of a great scientific controversy which centered around the electromagnetic theory of light, a theory which in effect annexed to electricity the entire domain of light and radiant energy as then understood. There was little in the current literature of prophecy as to utility. However, at that time Sir William Crookes had sufficient vision to penetrate the future. In an article in the Fortnightly Review for February 1892 he made a remarkably accurate forecast of impending events, for he says, all that is required from a utilitarian standpoint is "simpler and more certain means of generating electric rays of any desired wavelength," . . . "more delicate receivers which will respond to wavelengths between certain definite limits and be silent to all others, . . . "means of darting the sheafs of rays in any desired direction." "The rays could be concentrated with more or less exactness upon the receiver." "The correspondents must attune their instruments to a definite wavelength." "This is no mere dream of a visionary philosopher." "All the requisites needed to bring it within the grasp of daily life are well within the possibilities of discovery, and are so reasonable and so clearly in the path of researches which are now being actively prosecuted in every capital of Europe that we may any day expect to hear that they have emerged from the realms of speculation into those of sober fact." How accurate the prognostication. Marconi was the first to grasp its significance, in part at least.   He had the initiative, resourcefulness, and determination to make Hertzian waves useful.   Professor A. Righi at Bologna, Italy, was one of the most active workers who established the analogy between electromagnetic waves and light waves. One day Marconi asked Professor Righi how he could increase the distance at which electromagnetic waves might be detected.   Righi replied, "Make your oscillators longer."   Following this clue, Marconi made notable progress.   In 1899 he was able to bridge the English channel.   In 1901 the world was startled and amazed when it was learned that wireless signals had been transmitted and detected across the Atlantic ocean.   But before the world could reap the full benefits of electromagnetic waves other discoveries had to be made, and so the era of electronics followed close upon the researches of Hertz and Marconi.

There are three main developments which have made radio communication possible: The development of the electromagnetic theory by Maxwell and others, the experimental realization of electromagnetic waves by Hertz in 1888, and the development of the radio tube. The development of the radio tube began with Edison's discovery in 1885, "Edison effect" (Section 146), and culminated in the invention of the grid tube by De Forest in 1907.   Of course, there have been many variations introduced into radio tubes, and tube circuits, but the filament, grid, and plate are the essentials of any radio tube.   In Chapter X we developed the fundamental theory of thermionic emission.   In this Chapter we shall describe typical practical applications of thermionic emission, together with related phenomena.

336. The Two-Element Vacuum-Tube Rectifier.

— It will be seen from a consideration of thermionic emission, which was treated in Chapter X, that an evacuated tube with a hot filament (cathode) and cold plate (anode) will develop an electronic current i_p from filament to plate, and that the current i_p will vary as the potential between filament and plate varies, the temperature of the filament being sufficiently high to insure a copious supply of electrons.   The electronic current will be from filament to plate within the tube, and thence through the external circuit in the direction indicated by arrow tips in Fig. 321.   If we impress an alternating potential across such a tube it will be seen that as long as the plate is positive relative to the filament a current i_p will flow, but that when the plate becomes negative relative to the filament no current will flow, owing to a combination of

negative space charge surrounding the filament and a retarding potential between filament and plate.   It is apparent, therefore, that such
an arrangement will operate to rectify (i.e., give only a direct current)
an alternating current impressed upon the vacuum tube.   This property of the two-element vacuum tube was first recognized by J. J.
Thomson and J. A. Fleming.   In 1905 Fleming applied this principle
in rectifying alternating
currents and obtained his
valve patent, so called because a vacuum tube when
so operated acts as a thermionic valve.   A common
form of a two-element vac-

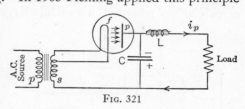

FIG. 321

uum tube, designed as a rectifier tube, is sold in the United States
under the trade name *kenotron*.

It is apparent that the hookup shown in Fig. 321 rectifies only one
half of the alternating-current wave, the other half being entirely
suppressed.   Thus the load current is a pulsating unidirectional current, or a sinusoidal current with the negative loops removed.   It is
customary to attempt to reduce this irregularity in the load current
and to smooth out the half-cycle surges by accumulating the charge
on a condenser C of large capacitance, in parallel with the load,
coupled with a series inductance L which functions to oppose rapid
changes in the load current.   The higher the frequency of the alternating current supply the less serious will be the irregularities or
ripples in the rectified current.

Rectification of both halves of the current wave may be obtained
by using two two-element vacuum tubes, the circuit arrangement
being as shown in Fig. 322.   In this hookup the tubes take turns each
half cycle in delivering current to the load.   This arrangement
requires a transformer having a secondary with a center tap as shown.
Therefore, the peak load voltage is one half the secondary peak voltage, less the potential drop in the tubes and circuit.   It will be seen
by tracing the electronic current i_p that it flows through the load
always in the same direction.   The load current is smoothed out by
the use of low-resistance chokes and condensers as in any tube rectifier.   Another method for obtaining full-wave rectification is shown
in Fig. 323.   This layout requires a transformer without a center tap
and four tubes connected as shown.   The load peak voltage is the
secondary peak voltage less the potential drop in the tubes and circuit.

It will be seen that the load current i_p is always in the same direction through the load. The diagram makes clear the operation and no further explanation is required.

High-vacuum thermionic tubes which operate with a pure electronic discharge are satisfactory for the rectification of small currents at high potentials, but tubes that will carry more than a fraction of an ampere at low potentials are unduly large and too expensive for practical use. For low-potential

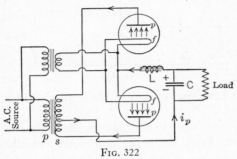

FIG. 322

currents, as for use in charging storage batteries, the General Electric Company has developed a gas-filled tube at a pressure of eight to ten cms. of mercury. The circuit is essentially as shown in Fig. 321, the device being known as the Tungar rectifier. An inert gas, such as argon, is used in the tube. When the potential between filament and plate exceeds the ionizing potential of the gas ionization ensues. The positive ions serve to neutralize the negative space charge about the filament, and consequently the tube will operate on a much lower plate voltage than a high-vacuum tube. The positive ions also aid materially in carrying charge through the tube, and consequently the current is markedly increased. Gas-filled tubes may be used in the layouts illustrated in Figs. 322 and 323, thus permitting operation at lower voltages with increased current output. Many rectifier two-element tube circuits have been devised for stepping the d.c. voltage up much higher than

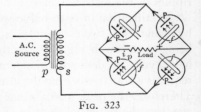

FIG. 323

the source. Such rectifiers are used as "B battery eliminators" for radio receiving sets, amplifiers, and broadcasting transmitters. They are also used in operating X-ray tubes, and in many other ways. There has also been developed a three-phase full-wave tube rectifier. In a three-phase system the potential waves are spaced 120° apart, and therefore full-wave rectification results in a smoother d.c. current.

337. The Mercury-Arc Rectifier. — The mercury-arc rectifier depends for its operation upon the valve action of certain conductors. The arrangement is as shown in Fig. 324. A large evacuated bulb B has sealed in it four electrodes. Two of these, a and a', are anodes. c is the common cathode, and a'' is a starting electrode. The terminals c and a'' are pools of mercury. When the mercury vapor in bulb B is ionized electrons move from the cathode c to anode a or a' as the case may be. The anodes a and a' are usually iron, but graphite may also be used. When the mercury vapor in the bulb becomes ionized electron can flow from the mercury to the iron anode a or a', but they cannot leave the iron and flow to the mercury. Thus iron acts as an electronic valve, permitting flow of electrons in but one direction. In order to start the rectifier an extra mercury terminal a'' is provided. The switch S is closed and the bulb is slightly tipped so as to permit the mercury to flow over from c to a'', thus completing the circuit through a protective resistance R. When the bulb is returned to its fixed position the mercury contact between terminals c and a'' is broken and a momentary arc is formed which is sufficient to ionize the mercury vapor in the bulb and so set the rectifier into action. As soon as the bulb is warmed up the switch S is opened. There are other starting devices, but in any starting device the essential operation is to ionize the mercury vapor. If an alternating voltage is applied to the transformer T, each iron anode acts in turn each half cycle and hence the current through the bulb and load is in one direction only. This will be a pulsating unidirectional current. The d.c. current may be smoothed out by a filter system such as is used in kenotron rectifiers.

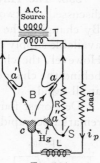

FIG. 324

So long as current flows through the bulb the mercury vapor is kept ionized, but if the current ceases for a fraction of a second the ionization vanishes and the rectifier ceases to operate. Since the potential of the transformer passes through zero once each cycle, the current also passes through zero each cycle, and therefore the rectifier would cease to function unless some provision is made to prolong the current of one half cycle until the next begins. In order to obviate this contingency an inductance coil L (sustaining coil) of low ohmic resistance is placed in series with the load. This reactance causes the current to lag the transformer potential with the result that some current is still flowing when the other terminal, a or a' as the case may be, becomes an anode. Thus ionization is maintained and the rectifier continues in operation. The mercury-arc rectifier here described is a single-phase rectifier. Polyphase rectifiers are also made.

Mercury-arc rectifiers are now made for heavy loads as well as for light loads. They are used wherever a motor-generator might be used for industry, mining, and railway service. They are made in capacities as high as 500 kw. at 600 volts. Of course the transformer used with a rectifier must be designed to give the proper secondary potential. The potential drop in a single-phase mercury-arc rectifier is about 14 volts when in operation. The overall efficiency is from 80% to 90%, with a lagging power factor in the neighborhood of 0.9.

338. The Three-Element Thermionic Tube. — In Section 336 we discussed the two-element thermionic tube, and its use as a rectifier. By changing the temperature of the filament, thereby changing the available supply of electrons, it is possible to vary the plate current i_p. However, the change in temperature of the filament lags somewhat behind the change in current and therefore the variations in i_p are not at all rapid.

De Forest found that the plate current i_p may be controlled with remarkable rapidity and fidelity by inserting between the filament and plate, a third electrode in the form of a fine grid or screen (grid) through which the electrons must pass as they move from filament to plate. A hookup for testing purpose is shown in Fig. 325. If the grid g is given a negative potential by means of the battery C it tends to retard the flow of electrons to the plate, and thus decreases the plate current i_p. If the grid is given a positive potential it tends to accelerate the flow of electrons and thus increases the plate current. Thus the grid either increases or counteracts the space charge and so controls the plate current i_p. The response of change in plate current to change in grid potential is exceedingly rapid, essentially instantaneous. The time for an electron to travel from filament to plate may be calculated by the equations

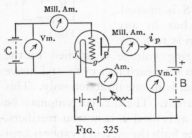

FIG. 325

$$\mathcal{E}e = \tfrac{1}{2}mv^2 \quad \text{and} \quad s = \tfrac{1}{2}vt.$$

For tubes of ordinary dimensions t is of the order of 10^{-8} sec. Thus, the response is essentially instantaneous since the electrons are devoid of sensible inertia.

This method of controlling the plate current has the advantage that a small amount of energy may be used to control a much larger amount of energy. If the grid is negative with respect to the filament no electrons flow to it from the filament and the only energy drawn from the C battery is the very small amount required to charge the filament-grid condenser. If the grid is positive with respect to the filament a few electrons flow to it and a small amount of energy is drawn from the C battery, the amount decreasing with the fineness of the grid mesh. The B battery is usually of high potential, and, therefore, the plate current will have a relatively large amount of energy associated with it. Thus, by the expenditure of a small amount of energy in the grid circuit, a large amount of energy in the plate circuit may be controlled, i.e., the tube acts as an *amplifier*.

The operation of the three-element thermionic tube may be explained best by a consideration of the "static characteristic" curve shown in Fig. 326. This curve shows the relationship between the grid potential and plate current. Suppose the grid potential is zero.

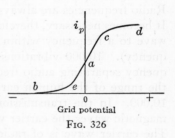

Grid potential

Fig. 326

The plate current will then be represented by the point a on the static characteristic curve. Now give the grid a negative potential, and, step by step, increase the negative potential; the curve aeb will be obtained. It will be noticed that the curve undergoes a rather rapid change, in the region e, as it approaches the grid-potential axis. This is important in the operation of the tube, as will be seen. Starting at zero grid potential and, step by step, increase the positive potential on the grid; the curve acd is obtained. The flat part of the curve cd is due to the fact that, with a given filament temperature, there is a limited supply of electrons, and, consequently, when the full supply is used any further increase in grid potential fails to increase the plate current; all available electrons are drawn to the plate. It will be noticed that the part of the static characteristic eac is practically a straight line. This is important in some uses of the tube. This curve was obtained by keeping the plate potential and filament current constant. If the filament temperature is maintained con-

stant and the plate potential changed by steps, curves such as shown
in Fig. 327 are obtained.   Since the fila-

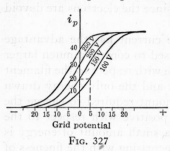

FIG. 327

ment temperature is constant the maximum supply of electrons is constant, and
hence the saturation plate current has
the same value for all potentials.   Increasing the plate potential has the
effect of shifting the static characteristic curve to the left.   An increase in
filament temperature would have the
effect of shifting the curves up.

339. Thermionic Tube Detector using C Battery. — In radio
communication the transmitted electromagnetic wave is always of
very high frequency (radio frequency), and is called a "carrier wave."
Radio frequencies are always far beyond the range of the human ear.
It becomes necessary, therefore, to change the frequency of the carrier
wave to a frequency within the range of the human ear (audio frequency).   10,000 vibrations per second is usually taken as the frequency separating audio frequencies and radio frequencies, although
the range of the human ear is generally in excess of a frequency of
10,000.   In the transmission of speech, music, or code by electromagnetic waves the carrier wave is "modulated" at the transmitter.
The carrier wave is of radio frequency and of constant amplitude,
when not modulated.   Modulation of the carrier wave at the transmitter consists in changing its amplitude so that it may follow the
vibrations (audio frequency) of the human voice, for example, if
speech is being broadcast.   The audio-frequency wave, which is
a wave corresponding to the variations of the human voice, is
superposed upon the radio-frequency carrier wave, or the audio-
frequency wave is the envelope of the variations in the carrier wave
which have been brought about by modulation at the transmitter.
It becomes necessary, therefore, to change this audio-frequency wave
into a wave such that the variations are essentially in one direction,
and then translate it into sound waves that may be picked up by the
human ear.   This is called detection, and any device that accomplishes
detection is called a *detector*.   The three-element thermionic tube is
the most sensitive detector, and practically the only detector now
used, and consequently the only one which we shall describe.
    A simple hook-up for detection when a single tube is used in con-

junction with a C battery is shown in Fig. 328*a*. The modulated
carrier wave is picked up by the antenna system, i.e., modulated high-
frequency currents are set up in the antenna system. The antenna
system is coupled with the receiver by an air-core transformer, L_3L_1,
or the transformer may be an autotransformer. The condenser C_3
is for the purpose of tuning the antenna system to the frequency of the
transmitter, although this is usually not necessary. The circuit L_1C_1
is the tuning circuit. This circuit has a natural frequency given by
the equation

$$f = \frac{1}{2\pi\sqrt{L_1C_1}}$$

This will be radio frequency. Tuning consists in varying C_1, and
possibly L_1 also, until the frequency of the circuit L_1C_1 is the same as
that of the modulated carrier wave being received. There will then be
the maximum current in the circuit L_1C_1, and the peak of the resonant
current curve will be sharp if the ohmic resistance in the circuit is

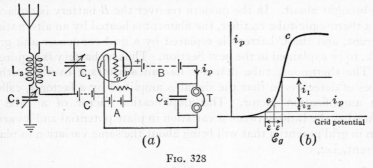

FIG. 328

small. When the circuit L_1C_1 is oscillating the potential of the grid g
will be caused to vary with the same frequency, and the amplitudes of
the variations of the grid potential will correspond to the variations
of the current in the circuit L_1C_1, which variations have been brought
about by modulation. Thus the plate current i_p will be caused to
vary in the same manner, and a varying current will flow through the
telephone receiver or loud speaker, as the case may be. Now the telephone or speaker cannot follow the radio-frequency variations, nor
could the ear detect them were it possible to devise a mechanical system which would respond to radio frequencies. However, the telephone or speaker will follow the audio-frequency variations of the
modulated current i_p. The current i_p is a direct current which is

caused to vary, increasing and decreasing in cadence with the modulations superposed upon the carrier wave.

It is possible by means of the C battery to adjust the grid potential $\mathscr{E}_g$ to such a value that, when no oscillations are being received, the operating point of the tube is either at e or c on the static characteristic curve, Fig. 326. The point e is usually used, as i_p is less at that point and there is less energy drawn from the B battery. It will be seen by reference to Fig. 327 that the B battery also may be adjusted to bring the operating point of the tube to either e or c. Let us say that the operating point of the tube is e, and that modulated oscillations are being received by the antenna. The grid potential will vary about the mean value $\mathscr{E}_g$, producing at every cycle equal and opposite variations of value e, say, Fig. 328b. It will be seen that the resulting variations in i_p are not equal, but that the increase i_1 is much larger than the decrease i_2. Thus symmetrical variations of the grid potential bring about asymmetrical variations of the plate current, as a result of which deflections of the telephone or loud speaker diaphragm are brought about. In the modern receiver the B battery is replaced by a thermionic-tube rectifier, the filament is heated by an alternating current, and the C battery is replaced by a grid condenser and grid leak, to be explained in the next Section. Thus no battery is required.

The thermionic tube detector has an advantage over all other types of detectors in that the signal is amplified by a factor k, called the amplification factor. The amplification factor of a tube is defined as the ratio between a variation in plate potential and a variation in grid potential that will bring about the same variation in plate current, i.e.,

$$k = \frac{d\mathscr{E}_p}{d\mathscr{E}_g}.$$

This may be made clear by reference to Fig. 327. Suppose the plate potential to be 100 volts and the grid potential zero. If the grid potential is increased to $+5$ volts the plate current is increased by 10 milliamperes. This same increase in plate current may be brought about by 50 volts increase in plate potential. Thus $k = 50/5 = 10$. It is obvious that the amplification factor depends upon the fineness of the grid mesh and its position relative to the filament. If the grid mesh is coarse a certain change in grid potential is not as effective in controlling the space current in the tube as if the mesh were finer. If the grid is close to the filament it is more effective in controlling the space current than when farther away, since the grid potential then acts upon the electrons before they have gained an appreciable speed. The amplification factor commonly runs from 5 to 20, although amplification factors up to 100 have been obtained.

340. Radio-frequency Amplification and Detection. — In Fig. 329

is shown schematically the wiring diagram of a receiving set having two stages of radio-frequency amplification followed by a detector tube which employs a grid condenser and grid resistance (grid leak) instead of a C battery.   The plate potentials of the amplifier tubes A_1 and A_2 must be such as to bring the operating points of the tubes at a point, such as a, Fig. 326, on the straight part of the static characteristic curve.   For such a point equal positive and negative variations

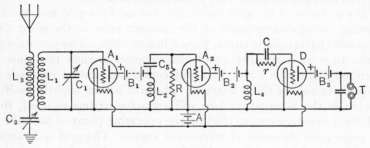

FIG. 329

in the grid potential will bring about equal increases and decreases in the plate current i_p.   The coupling between tubes in the layout shown is inductive.   The inductance coils L_2 and L_4 could as well be large resistances or air-core transformers.   We would then have either resistance coupling or transformer coupling.   If in Fig. 329 the coupling inductance coils L_2 and L_4 were each shunted by a variable condenser, C_2 and C_4, and the circuits L_2C_2 and L_4C_4 were then tuned to the frequency of the wave being received, these circuits would offer an infinite impedance and amplification would be a maximum.   The inductance coils L_2 and L_4 should have low ohmic resistance, thus permitting lower plate potentials than would obtain were the ohmic resistance larger.

Let us say that the antenna system is excited by a modulated carrier wave of some radio frequency f.   The circuit L_1C_1 is tuned to the same frequency.   This impresses upon the grid of the first amplifier tube A_1 a modulated potential of the same frequency.   This in turn causes pulsations of the plate current i_p, thus generating in the coil L_2 induced counter emfs. These emfs. will be amplified reproductions of the input emfs. These amplified emfs. are then impressed upon the second amplifier tube A_2, are again amplified and then impressed upon the detector tube D. The resistance R is for the purpose of completing the d.c. circuit between grid and filament. The condenser C_5 will pass alternating currents but not direct currents. If k is the amplification factor of each of the tubes A_1 and A_2, the signal impressed upon the detector tube is k^2 times as intense as the input signal. One advantage of using radio-frequency amplification before detection is that a detector tube acts best when the signals are of comparatively large amplitude, while rectification is very poor if the received oscillations are of very small amplitude.

The purpose of the grid condenser shunted by a grid resistance is to bring the operating point of the detector tube at the point e on the static characteristic curve, Figs. 326 and 328b. The performance of the tube as a rectifier and hence detector is then the same as described in Section 339. The grid connection should be made to the positive side of the A battery. The grid is then slightly positive relative to the filament, and so will attract electrons to itself, thus making it negative and so shifting the operating point of the tube to the point e on the static characteristic curve. The grid resistance r serves to permit the grid negative charge to escape, and thus prevents building up a negative grid potential sufficient to block the tube, i.e., reduce i_p to zero. The grid resistance r should be of such a value as to permit the electrons to escape fast enough so that the tube will not block, and with sufficient rapidity so that the escape takes place between groups of oscillations, thus permitting the tube to follow the audio-frequency variations. This adjustment is made by trial. For tubes now in use the grid condenser is about 0.00025 mf. and the grid resistance r is from 2 to 5 megohms. If still further amplification is required there may be one or two stages of audio-frequency amplification following the detector tube. For audio-frequency amplification the inductance coupling coils, or transformers, have iron cores.

Amplifiers as such are constructed in the same manner as here described in connection with a receiving set. Such amplifiers have extensive use in experimental work, and in telephone lines. The batteries shown in the drawings are merely schematic, and for the purpose of indicating a potential difference. In all commercial amplifiers and receivers the B battery potential is obtained by means of a tube rectifier and the filament is heated by an alternating current, or the cathode is heated indirectly by an alternating current.

341. The Regenerative Receiver.

As a prelude to a discussion of tube oscillators we shall consider the regenerative receiver, since it exhibits the fundamentals of regenerative oscillatory circuits. The wiring diagram is shown in Fig. 330. This circuit is essentially the same as the circuit shown in Fig. 328a, except that the plate circuit is inductively coupled with the grid circuit by means of the air-core transformer L_2L_3. This permits energy to be fed back from the plate circuit to the oscillatory circuit $L_1L_2C_1$, thereby strengthening the current oscillations and the amplitudes of the grid-potential variations, which in turn are passed on to the plate circuit. Thus the sound in the telephone or speaker is markedly louder. The coupling

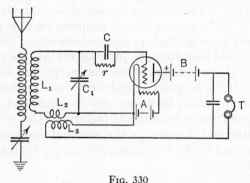

FIG. 330

coil L_3 must be so connected as to act with the electric oscillations in circuit $L_1L_2C_1$ and not against them. The degree of regeneration can be controlled by the closeness of coupling. In a receiving set this scheme for increasing the loudness of the signal is called regenerative amplification, since it produces the same effect as an amplifier.

However, at a certain critical closeness of coupling between coils L_2 and L_3 this receiver becomes an oscillator, and then emits electromagnetic waves at the same time that it receives them, or it may continue to emit electromagnetic radiation after all incoming waves have ceased. In order to understand this phase of its operation let us say that damped waves are being picked up by the antenna system, e.g., code signals from a spark transmitter. Each group of damped waves received by the antenna sets up oscillatory currents of the same frequency in the tuning circuit $L_1L_2C_1$, and of the same damping characteristics. This produces an alternating difference of potential on the grid, between filament and plate, of the same frequency and damping characteristics, thus causing the steady plate current to pulsate in like manner. The pulsations in the plate current have the same frequency and damping characteristics as the current in the tuning circuit $L_1L_2C_1$. The effect is to superpose on the normally constant plate current an alternating current. This alternating current flowing through coil L_3 induces an alternating emf. in coil L_2 of the same frequency. Since this induced emf. is in phase with the oscillatory current in the tuning circuit $L_1L_2C_1$, the current is strengthened and its degree of damping is decreased, since the dissipation of energy, which is the cause of damping, is partially compensated by energy received from the B battery through the coupling transformer L_2L_3. If the coupling is made closer damping is still further decreased. At a certain critical coupling there is no damping, and oscillations, once started, persist indefinitely. This will occur when the energy fed back from the plate circuit into the tuned oscillatory circuit $L_1L_2C_1$ just compensates the energy lost due to heating and radiation. If the coupling is made still closer the oscillatory current in the circuit $L_1L_2C_1$ increases until the feed-back energy compensates the losses due to heating and radiation. This is then a regenerative oscillator and it portrays the essential features of all tube oscillators, the feed back of synchronized energy from the plate circuit to the grid circuit.

342. The Radio Transmitter. — In Fig. 331 is shown the wiring diagram of a radio transmitter consisting of an oscillator tube O, a modulator tube M, and an amplifier tube A. The oscillatory circuit here shown is known as the Hartley circuit. The plate circuit of the oscillator tube O is coupled with the oscillatory circuit L_1C_1 through the condenser C, thus affording a means of transmitting energy from the plate circuit to the grid circuit and so causing sustained oscillations. The coil L_1 is inductively coupled with the antenna system. When the oscillator is in operation a constant-amplitude radio-frequency current flows in the circuit L_1C_1 of frequency

$$f = \frac{1}{2\pi\sqrt{L_1C_1}}.$$

This sets up an alternating current of the same frequency in the antenna circuit, and a carrier wave of constant amplitude is emitted into space by the antenna. This is the condition when there is no modulation of the oscillatory current in the circuit L_1C_1.

The method of modulation, illustrated schematically in Fig. 331, is known as the Heising modulation system. The operation of the circuit is as follows: The oscillator tube O generates undamped oscillations in the antenna circuit. If speech, say, is impressed upon the telephone transmitter or microphone m, varying audio-frequency currents are induced in the secondary of the iron-core transformer T_1, the current variations being in cadence with the sound variations received by the microphone. This causes the potential of the grid of the amplifier tube A to vary in like manner, and an amplified variation of the plate

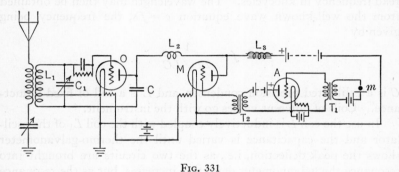

FIG. 331

current of tube A induces a current of like variations in the secondary of the iron-core transformer T_2, which acts upon the grid of the modulator tube M. Thus the plate current in the modulator tube M is caused to vary in the same manner, and these variations are superposed upon the plate current of the oscillator tube O, and so bring about variations of like kind in the constant-amplitude radio-frequency current in the circuit L_1C_1. And so the carrier wave emitted by the antenna is caused to vary in amplitude in cadence with the sound waves that impinge upon the diaphragm of the microphone. This is modulation. The choke coil L_3 serves to maintain a constant current in the plate circuit of the modulator tube M and also to block any high-frequency currents. The choke coil L_2, which is only a few turns of wire of low ohmic resistance, prevents radio-frequency currents generated by the oscillator tube O from flowing through the modulator tube M, thus isolating it from the radio-frequency circuit.

343. Frequency Measurements. The Wavemeter. — Measurement of frequency is very important in many phases of radio work. It is especially important in operating a broadcasting station, since to prevent interference, the Government requires each station to broadcast on an assigned frequency within prescribed limits. A meter

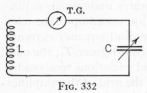

FIG. 332

designed to measure frequency or wavelength is called a wavemeter. The wiring diagram of a wavemeter is shown in Fig. 332. It is merely a series circuit containing inductance L, capacitance C, small ohmic resistance, and a thermo-galvanometer T.G. The instrument is calibrated to read frequency in kilocycles. The wavelength may then be obtained from the well-known wave equation $c = f\lambda$, the frequency being given by

$$f = \frac{1}{2\pi\sqrt{LC}}.$$

C is a calibrated precision condenser, and L is a coil of fixed inductance. Coils of different values go with the instrument.

In use the coil L is inductively coupled with the coil L_1 of the oscillator and the capacitance is varied until the thermo-galvanometer shows the peak deflection, i.e., as the two circuits are brought into resonance the galvanometer deflection increases, but as the resonance point is passed the deflection decreases. The coupling should be such as to give about a half scale deflection. The frequency is then read from the scale on the instrument.

In adjusting the frequency of a broadcast transmitter, as for instance the one shown in Fig. 331, the oscillatory circuit L_1C_1 is brought into resonance with the wavemeter, which is set on the assigned frequency. This is done by varying C_1. The antenna circuit must then be brought into resonance with the circuit L_1C_1. This is accomplished by means of the variable condenser in the antenna circuit. There is a thermo-ammeter in the antenna circuit, not shown. When resonance obtains the antenna thermo-ammeter shows a peak deflection.

The frequency of a transmitter is now usually controlled automatically by use of a crystal oscillator, which is so connected in the circuit as to influence the frequency and keep it constant within limits if set near the assigned frequency. This is putting the piezoelectric effect to practical use. The piezoelectric effect will be taken up in the next Section.

344. Piezoelectric Effect. — In general, when an anisotropic dielectric, having an asymmetrical atomic structure, is mechanically strained charges of electricity of opposite signs appear at different points on the crystal, i.e., it becomes electrically polarized. The axis of polarization and the magnitudes of the charges depend upon the kind of crystal, the manner and magnitude of strain, and upon the direction of the impressed force producing the strain relative to the optic axis of the crystal. Conversely, when such a crystal is subjected to an electric field there is set up, in addition to the electrostrictive effect, other strains which are usually much larger. This type of strain is known as the *piezoelectric effect*. Electric polarization resulting from strain is known as the *direct piezoelectric effect*, whereas, strain resulting from an impressed electric field, is known as the *converse piezoelectric effect*. In both cases, the relation between cause and effect can be represented by the relation

$$q = KF,$$

where q is the electric charge, F the impressed force, and K a constant of proportionality, known as the *piezoelectric constant*. The mechanical force in the piezoelectric effect, resulting from an impressed electric field, is directly proportional to the impressed electric field intensity E, whereas, in the electrostrictive effect, the force is proportional to E^2. This difference serves to separate the two effects.

The piezoelectric effect was first investigated by P. and J. Curie in 1880. They investigated the piezoelectric properties of crystals, discovered both the direct and converse effects, and obtained the above equation. Since these pioneer investigations, this subject has been studied extensively both from the theoretical and practical standpoint. Various uses have been made of piezoelectric crystals, such as for pressure gauges, loud speakers, and sound transmitters for under-water signals. The piezoelectric effect has been used for the measurement of pressure due to the ignition of gasoline in a cylinder and the ignition of powder in a gun. In the latter case a number of thin quartz plates are placed in a housing in the breech block of the gun. When the gun is fired a plunger is driven against the plates, thereby developing an electric potential difference which is amplified by a tube amplifier, and the rise and fall of pressure of the exploding gas is recorded upon a film. This method was devised by G. F. Hull during the World War at the Aberdeen proving grounds, and later improved and standardized by R. H. Kent, head of the Instrument Section of the proving grounds. Cady was the first to discover that quartz crystals can be used as resonators, and as such may serve as frequency standards. Later he discovered that quartz crystals can be used to hold the frequency of a vacuum-tube oscillator constant. He developed several circuits for such crystal-controlled oscillators. It is in this capacity that the piezoelectric effect finds its greatest use. A chance discovery in 1880 found little practical use until another discovery ushered in the broadcasting industry with its multiplicity of transmitters, thus making it imperative that the Government restrict the variations in frequency to rather narrow prescribed limits. It was then that the quartz crystal stabilizer found its place in the industrial world, and now all broadcast transmitters are crystal controlled.

There are a number of asymmetrical crystals, such as quartz, tourmaline, and Rochelle salts that exhibit the piezoelectric property to a marked degree. All of them are doubly refracting and possess an asymmetrical atomic structure. It is to be expected that crystals possessing the same optical and structural properties would exhibit the piezoelectric effect. This seems to be true quite generally, for something like 20 out of 32 such crystals which have been investigated show some piezoelectric effect. Of the three most commonly known piezoelectric crystals (quartz, tourmaline, and Rochelle salts) quartz has the greatest commercial value. Rochelle salts, though exhibiting the piezoelectric effect many times stronger than any other crystal, is too fragile to be reliable as a commercial product. Tourmaline is too rare and expensive to be used commercially. Therefore, quartz is the only crystal, thus far discovered, which is sufficiently available and robust to satisfy the severe demands required in the commercial world.

Quartz (SiO_2) is obtained in Brazil, Madagascar, and the United States. Quartz for commercial purposes must be free from flaws, intergrowths, and optical twinning. The quartz crystal is hexagonal, and when complete has a hexagonal pyramid at each end, Fig. 333. The optic axis is any line parallel to the line z connecting the two apices of the complete crystal. The electric axes are of two types: One is any line parallel to the line x connecting opposite corners of the hexagonal sides of the crystal, and the other is parallel to any line y drawn normal to the flat faces of the sides of the crystal (also called mechanical axis). Thus there are three x electric axes, three y electric axes, and one optic axis. The optic axis is normal to any electric axis, Fig. 334. One method of cutting a quartz crystal for a frequency regulator is to cut a slab from the original crystal, the cut being normal to the optic axis (Curie or x cut). Then from this slab a slice is cut as shown in Fig. 335. Thus, the slice that is used in this method of cutting has faces parallel to the three axes, x, y, and z. It is found that when a crystal is cut as described there are three frequencies to which it will respond strongly. One frequency corresponds to the x dimension, one to the y dimension, and the other lies between these two, and is called the coupling frequency. In any case the frequency depends upon the dimensions of the cut, increasing as the dimensions increase. In rectangular cuts, as here described, the frequency per mm. of the x dimension (within certain limits) varies from 2,898.5 kilocycles per second to 2,867.6 kilocycles per second, while for the y dimension the frequency per mm. varies from 2,727.3 kilocycles per second to 2,564.1 kilocycles per second. The wavelength of the radiation from a crystal-controlled transmitter is obtained from the well-known wave equation $c = f\lambda$, where $c = 3 (10)^8$ meters per second, λ = wavelength in meters, and f = frequency in cycles per second. There are other methods of cutting crystals, the frequency depending upon the method of cutting. The rectangular cut,

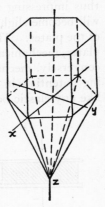

FIG. 333

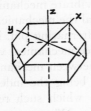

FIG. 334

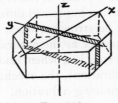

FIG. 335

however, is cheaper to make, and the finished crystal is more robust than in most other methods of cutting. A crystal cut normal to the y axis is called a y cut.

When a crystal is used as a standard of frequency it is mounted between two metal plates, constituting a condenser, in which the crystal is the dielectric, Fig. 336. The plates are pressed gently against the two faces of the crystal. Now, if the plates are pressed together, squeezing the crystal slightly, the crystal will develop a positive charge on one face and a negative charge on the other, i.e., a difference of potential will be developed between the plates. Conversely, if the plates are connected to the two terminals of a battery, thus impressing a difference of potential between them, the crystal will become slightly flattened or bulged depending upon the polarity of the plates. Thus, if an alternating potential is impressed upon the plates, mechanical vibrations of the same frequency will be set up, or, conversely, mechanical vibrations of the plates will develop alternating potentials in the crystal of the same frequency. Now a crystal, like any elastic body, has a natural frequency of vibration which will

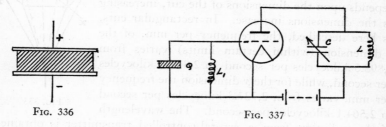

FIG. 336   FIG. 337

depend upon its dimensions and temperature. Thus, if a crystal is struck, and thereby set into free vibrations, an alternating difference of potential will appear between its two faces which will have a frequency equal to that of the free natural period of mechanical vibration of the crystal. If the crystal is made to vibrate mechanically by an alternating impressed difference of potential the mechanical vibrations will be strongest when the impressed alternating p.d. is of the same frequency as the natural frequency of free mechanical vibration of the crystal, i.e., when resonance obtains between mechanical and electric vibrations, the mechanical vibration being the independent and determining vibration. One hookup in which such reciprocal vibrations may be arranged is illustrated in Fig. 337.

In the circuit shown, the crystal condenser Q is connected between the grid and the filament of a three-element electron tube. A difference of potential between the plates of the condenser Q will result. By inserting in the plate circuit a closed, oscillatory circuit LC strong oscillations will be set up when the circuit LC is tuned to the same frequency as that of the free mechanical vibrations of the crystal Q.

The operation of the circuit is somewhat as follows: There is an internal grid-to-plate capacitance of the tube, which, when coupled with the external circuit as arranged, sets up a slight alternating p.d. In the grid-to-filament circuit this alternating p.d. impresses an alternating p.d. upon the crystal condenser Q, and, since an alternating p.d. impressed upon the crystal will set up alternating variations in the crystal, thereby developing alternating variations of potential in the crystal itself, it can be seen that the alternating p.d. in the circuit will be augmented and sustained when the electric frequency of the circuit is the same as the free mechanical frequency of the crystal, the mechanical frequency of the crystal being the fixed and controlling frequency. A choke coil L_1 of large impedance is connected from grid to filament, because otherwise the grid would be insulated from the filament.

With most methods of cutting crystals, the frequency changes with change of temperature, and therefore, in such cases, if the crystal is to serve as a constant frequency standard, its temperature must be maintained constant. There are several methods employed in practice to effect this end. The temperature coefficient of quartz crystals (obtained at the Naval Research Laboratory) is a frequency change of 25 parts in a million per degree C. for the x dimension, and a frequency change of 50 parts in a million per degree C. for the y dimension. However, it is possible to cut a crystal, with proper orientation relative to the axes of the crystals, so that its temperature coefficient is zero or near zero.

For a complete index to the literature of electrostriction, piezoelectricity, and pyroelectricity, see an article by W. G. Cady in the Proc. of the Institute of Radio Engineers, Vol. 18, No. 7, p. 1259 ff, 1930, or, by the same author, International Critical Tables, Vol. VI, p. 212.

REFERENCES

Starling, S. G.: Electricity and Magnetism, New York, Longmans, Green and Co., 1927

Richtmyer, F. K.: Introduction to Modern Physics, New York, McGraw-Hill Book Co., Inc., 1934.

Fleming, J. A.: The Propagation of Electric Currents in Telephone and Telegraph Conductors, London, Constable and Co., Ltd., 1927.

Pierce, G. W.: Electric Oscillations and Electric Waves, New York, McGraw-Hill Book Co., Inc., 1920.

American Telephone and Telegraph Co.: New York Principles of Electricity applied to Telephone and Telegraph Work.

Glazebrook, Sir Richard: A Dictionary of Applied Physics, Vol. III, New York, The Macmillan Co., 1922.

Page and Adams: Principles of Electricity, New York, D. Van Nostrand Co., Inc., 1931.

Hertz, H.: Electric Waves, Tr. by D. E. Jones, New York, The Macmillan Co., 1893.

Wulf, Theodor: Modern Physics, A General Survey of Its Principles, Tr. by C. J. Smith, London, Methuen and Co., Ltd., 1930.

Thomson, J. J.: Elements of the Mathematical Theory of Electricity and Magnetism, New York, The Macmillan Co., 1921.

Thomson, J. J.: Recent Researches in Electricity and Magnetism, New York, The Macmillan Co., 1893.

Zeleny, Anthony: Elements of Electricity, New York, McGraw-Hill Book Co., Inc., 1930.

Campbell, N. R.: Modern Electrical Theory, New York, G. P. Putnam's Sons, 1907.

Gibson, C. R.: Modern Conceptions of Electricity, London, Seeley, Service and Co., Ltd., 1928.

Whittaker, E. T.: A History of the Theories of Aether and Electricity, New York, Longmans, Green and Co., 1910.

Zworykin, V. K. and Wilson, E. D.: Photocells and their Applications, New York, John Wiley and Sons, Inc., 1930.

Whitehead, J. B.: Lectures on Dielectric Theory and Insulation, New York, McGraw-Hill Book Co., Inc., 1927.

Harnwell, G. P.: Principles of Electricity and Electromagnetism, New York, McGraw-Hill Book Co., Inc., 1938.

Hoag, J. B.: Electron and Nuclear Physics, 2nd ed., New York, D. Van Nostrand Co., Inc., 1938.

Crowther, J. A.: Ions, Electrons, and Ionizing Radiations, 7th ed., New York, Longmans, Green and Co., 1939.

Harnwell, G. P. and Livingood, J. J.: Experimental Atomic Physics, New York, McGraw-Hill Book Co., Inc., 1933.

Hirst, A. W.: Electricity and Magnetism, New York, Prentice-Hall, Inc., 1937.

Ramsay, A. S.: Electricity and Magnetism. An Introduction to the Mathematical Theory, Cambridge, Eng., The University Press, 1937.

Hull, G. F.: An Elementary Survey of Modern Physics, New York, The Macmillan Co., 1936.

Members of the Physics Staff, Univ. of Pittsburgh: An Outline of Atomic Physics, New York, John Wiley and Sons, Inc., 1937.

Eldridge, J. A.: The Physical Basis of Things, New York, McGraw-Hill Book Co., Inc., 1934.

Laws, F. A.: Electrical Measurements, New York, McGraw-Hill Book Co., Inc., 1917.

Lawrence, R. R.: Principles of Alternating Currents, New York, McGraw-Hill Book Co., Inc., 1922.

Jeans, J. H.: The Mathematical Theory of Electricity and Magnetism, Cambridge, Eng., The University Press, 1911.

Berthoud, Alfred, Tr. by Eden and Cedar Paul: The New Theories of Matter and the Atom, New York, The Macmillan Co., 1924.

Franklin, W. S.: Electric Waves, New York, The Macmillan Co., 1909.

Thomson, J. J., and G. P.: Conduction of Electricity Through Gases, Vols. I, II, Cambridge, Eng., The University Press, 1928.

Shoenberg, D.: Superconductivity, New York, The Macmillan Co., 1939.

McClung, R. K.: Conduction of Electricity Through Gases and Radioactivity, Philadelphia, P. Blakiston's Sons Co., 1909.

Kraus, C. A.: The Properties of Electrically Conducting Systems, New York, The Chemical Catalog Co., Inc., 1922.

Gemant, Andreas: Liquid Dielectrics, New York, John Wiley and Sons, Inc., 1933.

Smith, A. W.: Electrical Measurements in Theory and Application, New York, McGraw-Hill Book Co., Inc., 1934.

Northrup, E. F.: Methods of Measuring Electrical Resistance, New York, McGraw-Hill Book Co., Inc., 1912.

Hund, A.: High-Frequency Measurements, New York, McGraw-Hill Book Co., Inc., 1933.

Farmer, F. M.: Electrical Measurements in Practice, New York, McGraw-Hill Book Co., Inc., 1917.

Campbell, A. and Childs, E. C.: The Measurement of Inductance, Capacitance, and Frequency, New York, D. Van Nostrand Co., Inc., 1935.

Rhodes, W. G.: An Elementary Treatise on Alternating Currents, New York, Longmans, Green and Co., 1902.

Jolley, L. B. W.: Alternating Current Rectification, New York, John Wiley and Sons, Inc., 1927.

Bedell, F. and Crehore, A. C.: Alternating Currents, New York, McGraw-Hill Book Co., Inc., 1911.

van der Bijl, H. J.: The Thermionic Vacuum Tube, New York, McGraw-Hill Book Co., Inc., 1920.

Richardson, O. W.: The Emission of Electricity from Hot Bodies, New York, Longmans, Green and Co., 1916.

Prince, D. C. and Vogdes, F. B.: Principles of Mercury Arc Rectifiers and their Circuits, New York, McGraw-Hill Book Co., Inc., 1927.

Darrow, K. K.: Introduction to Contemporary Physics, New York, D. Van Nostrand Co., Inc., 1926.

Thomson, J. J.: Rays of Positive Electricity, New York, Longmans, Green and Co., 1913.

Millikan, R. A.: Electrons (+ and −), Protons, Photons, Neutrons, and Cosmic Rays, Chicago, The University of Chicago Press, 1935.

Debye, P.: Polar Molecules, New York, Chemical Catalog Co., Inc., 1929.

Compton, A. H.: X-Rays and Electrons, New York, D. Van Nostrand Co., Inc., 1926.

Thomson, J. J.: The Corpuscular Theory of Matter, London, Archibald Constable and Co., Ltd., 1907.

Stine, W. M.: The Contributions of H. F. E. Lenz to Electromagnetism, Philadelphia, The Acron Press, 1923.

O'Rahilly, A.: Electromagnetism. A Discussion of Fundamentals, New York, Longmans, Green and Co., 1938.

Foster and Porter: Elementary Treatise on Electricity and Magnetism, New York, Longmans, Green and Co., 1908.

Maxwell, James Clerk: A Treatise on Electricity and Magnetism, Vols. I, II, Oxford, Eng., The Clarendon Press, 1873.

Hughes, A. L. and DuBridge, L. A.: Photoelectric Phenomena, New York, McGraw-Hill Book Co., Inc., 1932.

De Broglie, Maurice: X-Rays, Tr. by J. R. Clarke, London, Methuen and Co., Ltd., 1925.

Rutherford, E.: Radioactive Substances and their Radiations, Cambridge, Eng., The University Press, 1913.

Pidduck, F. B.: A Treatise on Electricity, Cambridge, Eng., The University Press, 1925.

Karapetoff, V.: Experimental Electrical Engineering, Vols. I, II, New York, John Wiley and Sons, 1913.

Karapetoff, V.: The Magnetic Circuit, New York, McGraw-Hill Book Co., Inc., 1911.

Karapetoff, V.: The Electric Circuit, New York, McGraw-Hill Book Co., Inc., 1912.

Loeb, L. B.: Fundamentals of Electricity and Magnetism, New York, John Wiley and Sons, Inc., 1938.

Gilbert, N. E.: Electricity and Magnetism, New York, The Macmillan Co., 1932.

Richardson, O. W.: The Electron Theory of Matter, Cambridge, Eng., The University Press, 1916.

Richardson, S. S.: Magnetism and Electricity, London, Blackie and Sons, Ltd., 1908.

Stoner, E. C.: Magnetism and Atomic Structure, New York, E. P. Dutton and Co., 1926.

Barnett, S. J.: Elements of Electromagnetic Theory, New York, The Macmillan Co., 1903.

Ewing, J. A.: Magnetic Induction in Iron and other Metals, 3rd ed., London, "The Electronics" Printing and Publishing Co., 1900.

Fleming, J. A. and Contributors: Physics of the Earth—VIII. Terrestrial Magnetism and Electricity, New York, McGraw-Hill Book Co., Inc., 1939.

Spooner, T.: Properties and Testing of Magnetic Materials, New York, McGraw-Hill Book Co., Inc., 1927.

Jauncey, G. E. M.: Modern Physics, New York, D. Van Nostrand Co., Inc. Second Edition, 1937.

Jauncey, G. E. M. and Langsdorf, A. S.: M. K. S. Units and Dimensions, and a Proposed M. K. O. S. System, New York. The Macmillan Co., 1940.

INDEX